Principles of ATOMIC SPECTRA

WILEY SERIES IN PURE AND APPLIED SPECTROSCOPY

ADVISORY EDITOR: Harry C. Allen, Jr., Bureau of Mines,
The Department of the Interior

Principles of Atomic Spectra, Bruce W. Shore and Donald H. Menzel

Techniques of Vacuum Ultraviolet Spectroscopy, James A. R. Samson

Magnetic Resonance Spectroscopy, Harry G. Hecht

Flame Spectroscopy, R. Mavrodineanu and H. Boiteux

Chemical Infrared Spectroscopy, Volume I: *Techniques*, W. J. Potts, Jr.

Molecular Vib-Rotors, Harry C. Allen, Jr., and Paul C. Cross

Theory and Applications of Ultraviolet Spectroscopy, H. H. Jaffe and Milton Orchin

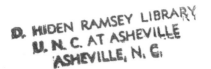

Principles of
ATOMIC SPECTRA

BRUCE W. SHORE and DONALD H. MENZEL

Harvard College Observatory

JOHN WILEY AND SONS, INC., New York • London • Sydney

Library of Congress Catalog Card Number: 67-27275
Printed in the United States of America

Preface

This book is an extension of lecture notes for an introductory course in atomic spectra, taught first by Menzel and later by Shore. Our audience ranged from undergraduates who had only a cursory knowledge of atomic physics to graduate students who had studied elementary wave mechanics. Some of our students, who were carrying out astrophysical research, sought a practical introduction to the nomenclature, the notation, and the physical interpretation of atomic spectra. Other students were motivated by their interest in the theory of atomic structure—the calculation of energy levels and transition probabilities.

We kept this varied audience in mind as we wrote and have attempted to provide a self-contained introduction to the basic principles of atomic structure and atomic spectra, including the tools of Racah algebra, without requiring a prior introduction to quantum mechanics.

We have organized the text into three parts. The first part, Chapters 1 and 2, states the basic observations of atomic spectra—the empirical foundation for quantum theory—and draws on these observations to develop a heuristic model of atoms (the Bohr–Sommerfeld vector model of atomic structure). Although quantum theory has superseded the "old quantum mechanics," which originally provided the foundation for this model, spectroscopists retain both the nomenclature and the intuitive picture of the model. We believe that its proved usefulness warrants a relatively long discussion in a book on atomic structure.

The second part, Chapters 3 to 6, provides the theoretical foundation of quantum theory, first through wave mechanics and then through the more abstract formulation of Dirac and von Neumann. Because our primary goal is the description of atomic structure, we have pointed out those aspects of quantum theory that have direct application to this subject.

In particular we have stressed the quantum theory of angular momentum with its attendant coupling and recoupling of angular momenta, tensor operators, and the computational techniques that are often referred to as Racah algebra.

In the final part, Chapters 7 to 11, we re-examine and extend the heuristic atomic model of the first part by using the mathematical tools developed in the second. Here we examine the meaning of coupling schemes and parentage and show how to calculate matrix elements in various angular-momentum schemes. We develop the elementary theory of photons as quantized electromagnetic fields—multipole fields in particular—and show how to calculate transition strengths. Finally, we discuss the perturbing effects of static fields.

We have deliberately limited the scope of our book to a discussion of what might be called the "independent-particle model" of the atom. This model, the successor to the Bohr–Sommerfeld vector model, has a counterpart in the shell model for the structure of atomic nuclei. A wealth of organized data supporting this atomic model appears in the recent article "Atomic Spectra" by B. Edlén, in Volume 27 of the *Handbuch der Physik* (Springer-Verlag, Berlin, 1964). We have not attempted a comparable discussion of empirical evidence here but have focused our attention instead on the theory required for the study of spectroscopic data.

We have omitted several topics which, although commanding wide current interest, are treated in detail elsewhere. For discussion of the Hartree–Fock–Slater methods of determining self-consistent radial wavefunctions we refer the reader to the recent two-volume exposition *Quantum Theory of Atomic Structure* by J. C. Slater (McGraw-Hill, New York, 1960). The specific problems of hydrogen and helium are extensively discussed by H. A. Bethe and E. E. Salpeter in *Quantum Mechanics of One- and Two-Electron Atoms* (Academic Press, New York, 1957). The definitive treatise on collision processes is the third edition of *The Theory of Atomic Collisions* by N. F. Mott and H. S. W. Massey (Oxford University Press, New York, 1965). For practical discussions covering a wide range of atomic phenomena we recommend *Quantum Theory* by A. M. Davydov (Addison-Wesley, Reading, Massachusetts, 1965) or the second edition of *Quantum Mechanics, Non-Relativistic Theory* by L. D. Landau and E. M. Lifshitz (Addison-Wesley, Reading, Massachusetts, 1965). The text *The Theory of Atomic Structure* by E. U. Condon and G. H. Shortley will undoubtedly remain the classic reference on atomic structure for another generation. The student will find that book rewarding reading once he has mastered the elements of quantum theory.

We hope our book will prove useful as a text for a junior–senior level course on atomic structure and as a reference work for those concerned with the interpretation of atomic spectra or the calculation of energy levels and transition strengths.

We are indebted to Mr. Jack Tech for his criticism and his numerous suggestions for improving our presentation. We are grateful to the Air Force for financial support through contracts AF 19(604)-4962 and AF 19(628)-3322 and (for B.W.S.) to the National Aeronautics and Space Administration for support through grant NsG-438 and contract NASw-184.

Bruce W. Shore
Donald H. Menzel

Cambridge, Massachusetts
September 1967

Contents

List of Tables

Principles of ATOMIC SPECTRA

1. The Nature of Atomic Spectra

1.1 BASIC PRINCIPLES OF SPECTROSCOPY

As the nature of atoms became clear during the nineteenth century, evidence grew that these basic units themselves had distinctive structures. Principally, this evidence came from *spectroscopy*—that is, the observation and interpretation of the light emitted and absorbed by collections of atoms. More recently other observations, particularly of the scattering of atomic particles, have provided further details. However, spectroscopy remains the foremost tool for investigating atomic structure.

Spectroscopy may be said to date from Isaac Newton's observation [1] that a prism refracts blue light more than red light. By examining the spectrum of colors produced by a prism from white sunlight, Newton reasoned that the prism was dispersing the white light into its constituent colors.

We now know that the visible-light spectrum forms a small part of a broader spectrum of electromagnetic radiation and that the white light analyzed by Newton is a superposition of monochromatic waves. The *wavelength* λ and *frequency* ν (in units of cycles per second or hertz, Hz) of a monochromatic wave are related by the condition

$$\nu\lambda = v, \tag{1.1}$$

where v is the *phase velocity* in the propagation medium. In a vacuum electromagnetic waves travel with the phase velocity [2]

$$c = 2.997925 \times 10^{10} \text{ cm sec}^{-1},$$

whereas in some other medium the waves propagate with the velocity

$$v = \frac{c}{n}, \tag{1.2}$$

where n is the *index of refraction* for the particular medium. The frequency of a wave remains unchanged as it propagates through various media. Thus for a vacuum (1.1) reads

$$\nu\lambda_{\text{vac}} = c \tag{1.3a}$$

(the subscript "vac" is often omitted), whereas for air it becomes

$$\nu\lambda_{\text{air}} = \frac{c}{n_{\text{air}}}. \tag{1.3b}$$

Wavelengths in the visible portion of the spectrum are customarily expressed in angstrom units, honoring the Swedish spectroscopist Anders J. Ångström, whose meticulous measurements [3] provided the first precise wavelength standards; the angstrom is abbreviated as Å (sometimes, for typographical simplicity, as A):

$$1\ \text{Å} = 10^{-8}\ \text{cm} = 10^{-10}\ \text{m} = 10^{-1}\ \text{nm}$$

(the unit nm = nanometer = 10^{-9} meter is also used). In the astronomical literature, wavelengths in angstroms are often written following the symbol λ:

$$\lambda 5000 = 5000\ \text{Å} = 5000\ \text{angstroms.}$$

Infrared wavelengths longer than 10,000 Å are often expressed in microns (abbreviated μ) or millimicrons ($\text{m}\mu$):

$$1\ \mu = 10^{-4}\ \text{cm} = 10^{4}\ \text{Å} = 10^{3}\ \text{nm},$$
$$1\ \text{m}\mu = 10^{-7}\ \text{cm} = 10\ \text{Å} = 1\ \text{nm}.$$

Wavelengths shorter than 1 Å (x-rays) are usually given in Manne Siegbahn's *X-Unit* [4], originally intended to be 1 mÅ. Siegbahn defined the X-Unit in terms of the lattice spacing of calcite. The conversion factor

$$1\ \text{XU} = 1.00202 \times 10^{-10}\ \text{cm}$$

is often used, although there is presently some dispute [2] as to the best way to define the X-Unit in order to connect properly the many tabulated x-ray lines with lines in the visible spectrum.

In contrast to the precision (about two parts in 10^9) with which wavelengths and frequencies can be measured the sensation of color is quite subjective (cf. the masterly treatise by von Helmholtz [5]). Although there are no universally accepted definitions of monochromatic colors, Table 1.1 typifies the working definitions found in the literature.

The frequency of a light wave has greater physical significance than its wavelength, since the frequency of a wave remains unchanged as the wave passes through various media. Therefore wavelength measurements must

Table 1.1 The Color Spectrum

Color	Wavelength Range (Å)	Energy (eV)
Ultraviolet	<3850	>3.22
Visible		
Violet	3850–4240	3.22–2.92
Blue	4240–4910	2.92–2.52
Green	4910–5750	2.52–2.16
Yellow	5750–5850	2.16–2.12
Orange	5850–6470	2.12–1.92
Red	6470–7800	1.92–1.58
Infrared	>7800	<1.58

For later reference, column 3 expresses the frequency in energy units: 1 eV = 8066 cm^{-1}.

be converted into frequency units for analysis. We often find it convenient to deal with *angular frequency* ω (in units of radians per second):

$$\omega \equiv \frac{\nu}{2\pi} = \frac{c}{2\pi\lambda_{vac}}. \tag{1.4}$$

Since measurements of c, the velocity of light, improve with time, spectroscopists customarily deal with *wavenumbers* (the number of waves per centimeter) rather than with frequencies. The wavenumber, $\tilde{\nu}$ (also denoted by σ in some works on spectroscopy), is defined by:

$$\tilde{\nu} = \frac{\nu}{c} = \frac{2\pi\omega}{c} = \frac{1}{\lambda_{vac}} = \frac{1}{n_{air}\lambda_{air}}; \tag{1.5}$$

that is, the wavenumber is the reciprocal of the vacuum wavelength. To find the wavenumber for a wavelength measured in air, one may refer to a standard table of wavenumbers. At present the most extensive tables are those by Coleman, Bozman, and Meggers [6] based on an empirical formula derived by Bengt Edlén [7]:

$$n_{air} = 1 + 6432.8 \times 10^{-8} + \frac{2949810}{146 \times 10^8 - \tilde{\nu}^2} + \frac{25540}{41 \times 10^8 - \tilde{\nu}^2}. \tag{1.6}$$

Edlén's formula fits the observations within one part in 10^8 over the interval 2000–7000 Å. Here, as elsewhere in the literature, wavenumbers are expressed in units of reciprocal centimeters (cm^{-1}). These units are also called *kaysers* (K) in honor of spectroscopist Heinrich Kayser, whose tables

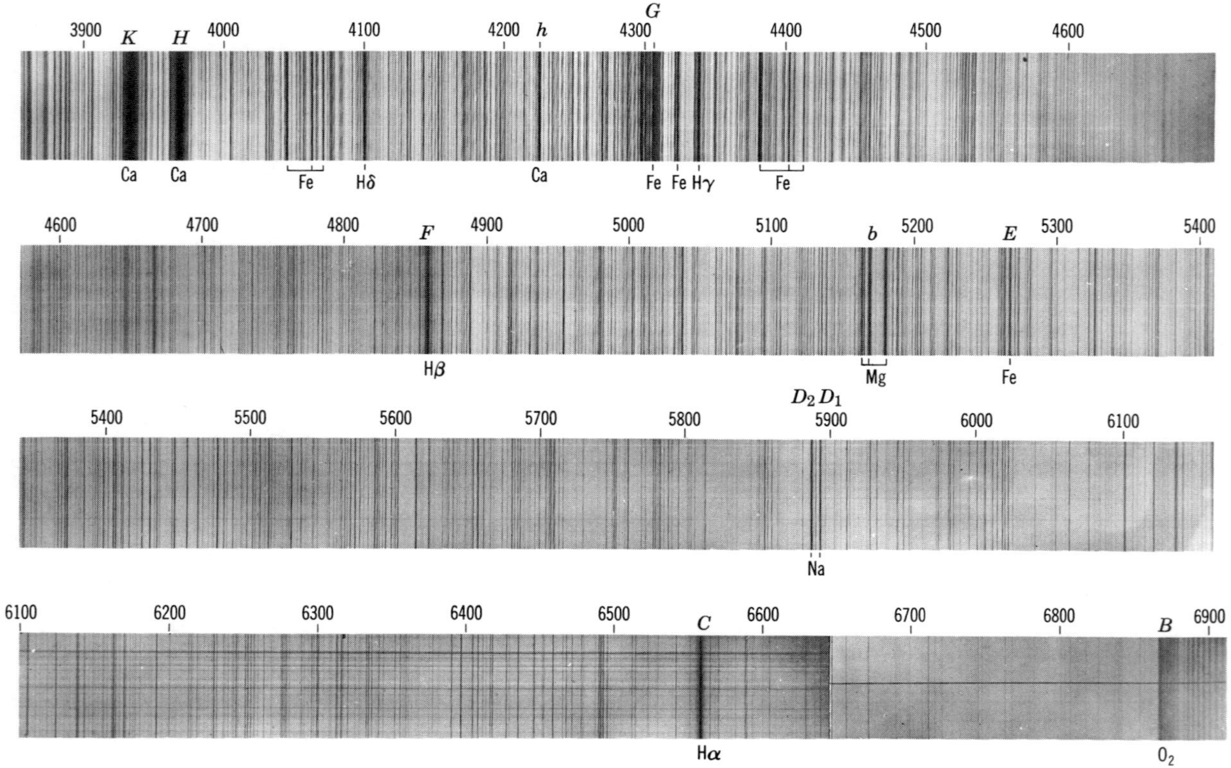

Fig. 1.1 The solar spectrum. Wavelengths in angstroms and Fraunhofer designations appear above spectrum; symbols below spectrum indicate element responsible for a particular line. (Courtesy Mt. Wilson Observatory.)

[8] provided for many years the most accurate conversion from wavelengths to wavenumbers:

$$1 \text{ K} \equiv 1 \text{ cm}^{-1} \equiv 10^2 \text{ m}^{-1}.$$

After Newton, the next great advance in spectroscopy began when Joseph Fraunhofer in 1814 observed [9] numerous dark lines interrupting the continuum of color in the solar spectrum (these were noticed earlier, but not appreciated, by W. H. Wollaston [10] in 1802). Fraunhofer recorded some 600 such lines, now generally known as *Fraunhofer lines*, and he labeled the strongest lines alphabetically, as shown in Fig. 1.1. Soon other workers found such dark lines, and similar bright lines, in the spectra of stars and laboratory flames and sparks.

The lines in a spectrum are produced in the following way. A spectrograph disperses light focused on its narrow entrance slit and forms, in its focal plane, an image of this slit. Images in different wavelengths occur at different points along the focal plane. A spectrogram is essentially a succession of images of the entrance slit. (Because of diffraction, the images are not absolutely sharp. Furthermore, a grating spectrograph will produce overlapping spectra from various orders in the diffraction pattern.) Thus, if a particular wavelength is missing in the incident radiation, the image of a narrow slit will appear as a dark line in the spectrogram. If a wavelength is enhanced the image of the slit will appear as a bright line on the spectrogram.

Gustav Kirchhoff and Robert Bunsen did much to establish spectrum analysis as a science, and their expositions [11] helped popularize the new science in the late nineteenth century. Illuminating accounts of this early work appear in the account by Meggers and Tech [12], in the book by Sawyer [13], and in the eleventh edition of the *Encyclopedia Brittanica* [14].

The major principles of practical spectroscopy, as observed by nineteenth century spectroscopists, may be summarized as follows:

1. When heated to incandescence, monatomic gases emit a spectrum of distinct bright *emission lines;* polyatomic gases produce bands of closely spaced lines; and solids (or very dense gases) produce a continuum of emission.

2. A cool gas absorbs from light those same frequencies it emits when heated; a continuous spectrum, viewed through a cool gas, exhibits *absorption lines* or *absorption bands.*

3. The positions (i.e., wavelengths) of spectral lines uniquely characterize the atoms or molecules that produce them. The intensity of the lines grows as the concentration of atoms increases.

Principle 3 underlies the applications of spectroscopy to chemical analysis: each atomic or molecular substance in a source reveals its presence by its characteristic spectrum. Various books provide useful tabulations of spectral lines for identifying unknown lines in a spectrogram. Bibliography 1 lists some of the more common of these reference books.

Comparisons of relative frequencies and wavelengths are the most precise physical measurements that can be made today. Thus a spectral line can provide a standard of length that is superior to the standard meter bar. Recognizing this fact, international scientific unions have adopted a suitable spectral line as a standard. In 1907 the red line of cadmium at 6438 Å was adopted as the primary standard. Subsequently the green 5460 Å line of mercury was widely advocated for a wavelength standard because of the ease with which it can be observed. More recently, the General Conference on Weights and Measures, meeting in 1960, adopted the orange line of krypton at 6058 Å (specifically the $2p_{10}$–$5d_5$ line of the isotope Kr^{86}, to use the accepted notation of Paschen) as the international standard of length. Its wavelength in vacuum is defined as

$$\lambda_{\text{vac}} = 6057.802106 \text{ Å},$$

so that

$$1 \text{ meter} = 1{,}650{,}763.73 \text{ wavelengths of } Kr^{86}\ (2p_{10}\text{–}5d_5).$$

The definition of wavelength standards has been reviewed by C. V. Jackson [15]; more recent discussions, with lists of secondary standards, appear in the triennial *Transactions of the International Astronomical Union* (*Commission 14*).

Although the coarsest features of a spectrum — the number and positions of spectral lines — are characteristic of the particular species of source atoms, finer details of the spectrum reflect the physical conditions in the source. We should therefore add a fourth principle of practical spectroscopy:

4. Intensities and shapes of spectral lines vary with the temperature pressure, and chemical composition of the source.

Spectroscopy, as a research tool, offers a means for ascertaining conditions in light sources. The disciplines of astrophysics and plasma physics depend on such details of spectral observations to reveal conditions in stellar atmospheres and laboratory plasmas. However, our attention will be directed toward the insight that spectroscopy can provide into the structure of the atoms themselves. For details of experimental work, the reader should consult Bibliography 2.

REFERENCES

[1] I. Newton, *Opticks* (1730), 4th ed.; reprinted by Dover, New York (1952).
[2] E. R. Cohen and J. W. M. Du Mond, in *Proceedings of the Second International Conference on Nuclidic Masses and Related Constants*, p. 152, Springer-Verlag, Vienna (1964); *Natl. Bur. Stds. Tech. News Bull.* **47,** 175 (October 1963).
[3] A. J. Ångström, *Ann. chim. phys.* **17,** 518 (1869); *Recherches sur le spectre soleil; Spectre normal du soleil*, W. Schultz, Upsala (1868), F. Dümmier, Berlin (1869).
[4] M. Siegbahn, *Spectroscopie der Röntgenstralen*, Springer-Verlag, Berlin (1931), 2nd ed.
[5] H. von Helmholtz, *Treatise on Physiological Optics*, English translation of 3rd German ed. (1909), reprinted by Dover, New York (1962).
[6] C. D. Coleman, W. R. Bozman, and W. F. Meggers, *Table of Wavenumbers*, NBS Monograph 3 (1960), Vol. I: 2000 to 7000 Å; Vol. II: 7000 to 1000 Å.
[7] B. Edlén, *J. Opt. Soc. Am.* **43,** 339 (1953).
[8] H. Kayser, *Tabelle der Schwingungszahlen*, S. Hirzel, Leipzig (1925); corrections in *Phys. Rev.* **48,** 98 (1935).
[9] J. Fraunhofer, *Ann. d. Physik.* **56,** 264 (1817); cf. H. Shapley, *A Sourcebook in Astronomy*, McGraw-Hill, New York (1925), p. 196.
[10] W. H. Wollaston, *Phil. Trans.* **92,** 365 (1802).
[11] R. Bunsen and G. R. Kirchhoff, *Ann. d. Phys. u. Chem.* **110,** 160 (1860); **113,** 337 (1861); Phil. Mag. **22,** 329 and 498 (1861); *Ann. Chem. et Phys.* **54,** 257 [1862].
[12] W. F. Meggers and J. L. Tech, *J. Opt. Soc. Am.* **50,** 1035 (1960).
[13] R. A. Sawyer, *Experimental Spectroscopy*, Dover, New York (1963), 3rd ed.
[14] A. Schuster, Spectroscopy, in *Encyclopaedia Brittanica*, 11th edition, **25,** 619 (1910).
[15] C. V. Jackson, *Rept. Progr. Phys.* **1,** 118 and 121 (1934).

1.2 THE SPECTRUM OF HYDROGEN

The spectrum of atomic hydrogen exhibits a remarkably simple pattern of lines. Historically, this simplicity provided the foundation for our present understanding of atomic structure. Figure 1.2 shows the visible portion of the hydrogen spectrum. This spectrum consists of a sequence of lines, called a *series*, whose spacing and intensity decrease regularly toward the violet. The *Balmer series* starts with the red Fraunhofer C line at 6562.8 Å followed by the blue Fraunhofer F line at 4861.3 Å, and progresses toward

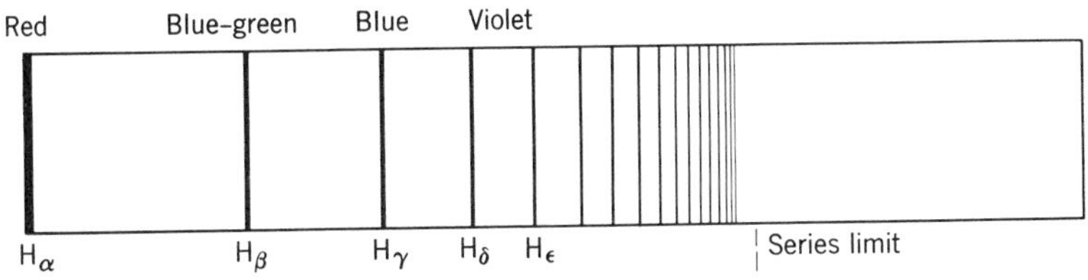

Fig. 1.2 The visible spectrum of hydrogen, showing Balmer series.

a limit in the violet at 3646 Å. In modern notation, these lines carry the designations of Hα, Hβ, Hγ, ... The *Lyman series*, a similar series of lines (discovered by Theodore Lyman in 1906 [1]), is observed in the ultraviolet beginning at 1215.67 Å and converging to a limit at 912 Å. The members of this series are known as Ly α, Ly β, . . . (read "Lyman alpha," "Lyman beta," etc.). Further series are observed in the infrared: the *Paschen series* (found by Frederic Paschen in 1908 [2]), the *Brackett series* (first seen by Frederick Brackett in 1923 [3]), the *Pfund series* (reported by Hermann Pfund in 1924 [4]), and the *Humphreys series* (discovered by Curtis Humphreys in 1953 [5]). Table 1.2 gives the wavelengths of these series.

Table 1.2 Wavelengths of Hydrogen Lines

n_2	Lyman ($n_1 = 1$)		Balmer ($n_1 = 2$)		Paschen ($n_1 = 3$)	Brackett ($n_1 = 4$)	Pfund ($n_1 = 5$)	Humphreys ($n_1 = 6$)
2	(Ly α)	1215.67						
3	(Ly β)	1025.72	(H α)	6562.80				
4	(Ly 4)	972.537	(H β)	4861.32	18751.0			
5	(Ly 5)	949.743	(H γ)	4340.46	12818.1	40512.0		
6	(Ly 6)	937.803	(H δ)	4101.73	10938.1	26252.0	74578	
7	(Ly 7)	930.748	(H ϵ)	3970.07	10049.4	21655.0	46525	123680
8	(Ly 8)	926.226	(H 8)	3889.05	9545.98	19445.6	37395	75005
9	(Ly 9)	923.150	(H 9)	3835.38	9229.02	18174.1	32961	59066
10	(Ly 10)	920.963	(H 10)	3797.90	9014.91	17362.1	30384	51273
11	(Ly 11)	919.352	(H 11)	2770.63	8862.79	16806.5	28722	46712
12	(Ly 12)	918.129	(H 12)	3750.15	8750.47	16407.2	27575	43753
∞		911.5		3646.0	8203.6	14584	22788	32814

W. L. Wiese, M. W. Smith, and B. M. Glennon, *Atomic Transition Probabilities Volume I Hydrogen Through Neon*, National Standard Reference Data Series, Natl. Bur. Stds. NSRDS-NBS 4 (1966).

Despite the simple appearance of the hydrogen spectrum, spectroscopists struggled vainly to account for the pattern. Then in 1885 the Swiss high-school teacher Joseph Balmer [6] discovered a formula capable of predicting the wavelengths of all the lines in what became the Balmer series:

$$\lambda \text{ (angstroms)} = 3645.6 \frac{n^2}{n^2 - 4}, \qquad n = 3, 4, 5, \ldots . \tag{2.1}$$

Subsequently, Johannes Rydberg [7] found that Balmer's formula was a special case of the more general formula

$$\tilde{\nu} = R_H \left[\frac{1}{(n_1)^2} - \frac{1}{(n_2)^2} \right], \tag{2.2}$$

where n_1 and n_2 are positive integers ($n_2 > n_1$) and

$$R_H = 109677.581 \text{ cm}^{-1}$$

is the *Rydberg constant* for hydrogen. To obtain Balmer's formula set $n_1 = 2$.

With the aid of (2.2) we can classify the spectral lines of hydrogen into the array in Table 1.2, taken from the useful NSRDS-NBS monograph [8]. For high members of the Lyman and Balmer series, it is customary to use number designations rather than continue the Greek letters. The number denotes the value of n_2; thus Ly α is Ly 2 and H α is H 3.

Table 1.3 Hydrogen Radio Lines

Designation	n_1	n_2	Frequency (Mhz)	Reference
90α	90	91	8872.6	(a, b)
104α	104	105	5762.9	(a, b)
109α	109	110	5008.9	(c)
156α	156	157	1715.676	(d)
158α	158	159	1651.544	(d)
166α	166	167	1424.736	(e)

[a] Z. V. D. Dravskikh and A. F. Dravskikh, *Astron. Zirk.* **282,** 2 (1964).
Z. V. D. Dravskikh, A. F. Dravskikh, and V. A. Kolbasov, unpublished, quoted in ref. (c).
[b] R. L. Sorochenko and E. V. Borodzich, unpublished, quoted in ref. (c).
[c] B. Hoglund and P. G. Mezger, *Science* **150,** 339 (1965).
[d] A. E. Lilley, D. H. Menzel, H. Penfield, and B. Zuckerman, *Nature* **209,** 468 (1966).
[e] P. Palmer and B. Zuckerman, *Nature* **209,** 1118 (1966).

Radio astronomers, following up a suggestion by N. S. Kardashev [9], have now found additional lines at radio frequencies. The frequencies of these lines are also governed by (2.2), which may be written

$$\nu = \text{Ry}_H \left[\frac{1}{(n_1)^2} - \frac{1}{(n_2)^2} \right] \tag{2.3}$$

in terms of the *Rydberg frequency* for hydrogen,

$$\text{Ry}_H = cR_H = 3.28805 \times 10^{15} \text{ Hz}.$$

Table 1.3 lists the radio lines of hydrogen observed at present. To label these and other such radio lines, Palmer and Zuckerman proposed [10] a modification of the optical notation. Each line is denoted by the value of n_1, with a Greek suffix to indicate the value of n_2, according to the scheme

$$\begin{array}{lcccc} n_2 = & n_1 + 1 & n_1 + 2 & n_1 + 3 & \cdots \\ \text{suffix} = & \alpha & \beta & \gamma & \cdots . \end{array}$$

Thus in this notation Lyman α is 1α, Hβ is 2β, etc.

As we progress along a series, the subsequent lines appear broader and fainter and their spacing decreases until finally it becomes impossible to distinguish the individual lines. In practice, we derive the *series limit* from formula (2.2) by setting $n_2 = \infty$. The number of series members that can be observed depends on the conditions of the source. For the Balmer series typical laboratory spectra may show H 12, whereas H 33 appears in the solar chromospheric spectrum. In some stars the series may be seen as far as H 40.

Equation 2.2 correctly predicts all known series of hydrogen lines. Higher-resolution spectrograms, however, show these lines as closely spaced pairs of lines or *doublets*. The Hα (6563 Å) doublets are separated by 0.33 cm^{-1} [or 0.33 $cm^{-1} \times (6563\ \text{Å})^2 = 0.13$ Å]. Other hydrogen lines show smaller separation.

Actually the fine structure of the hydrogen lines is more complicated than even a high-resolution spectrogram indicates. The hydrogen atoms of ordinary light sources have random thermal velocities, and the consequent *Doppler broadening* ordinarily masks the more minute details of the hydrogen fine structure (see section 1.6B for details). For further discussion, consult the texts by Series [11], Kuhn [12], or Candler [13].

REFERENCES

[1] T. Lyman, *Astrophys. J.* **23,** 181 (1906).
[2] F. Paschen, *Ann. Physik.* (*Leipzig*) **27,** 537 (1908)
[3] F. S. Brackett, *Astrophys. J.* **56,** 154 (1922).
[4] A. H. Pfund, *J. Opt. Soc. Am.* **9,** 193 (1924).
[5] C. J. Humphreys, *J. Res. Natl. Bur. Stds.* **50,** 1 (1953).
[6] J. J. Balmer, *Ann. Phys. Chem.* **25,** 80 (1885).
[7] J. R. Rydberg, *Astrophys. J.* **4,** 91 (1996); *Kgl. Svenska Akad. Handl.* **23** (1889).
[8] W. L. Wiese, M. W. Smith, and B. M. Glennon, *Atomic Transition Probabilities Volume I. Hydrogen Through Neon,* National Standard Reference Data Series, Natl. Bur. Stds. NSRDS-NBS 4 (1966).
[9] N. S. Kardashev, *Soviet Astron.-AJ* **3,** 813 (1959).
[10] P. Palmer and B. Zuckerman, *Nature* **209,** 1118 (1966).
[11] G. W. Series, *Spectrum of Atomic Hydrogen,* Oxford University Press, New York (1957).
[12] H. G. Kuhn, *Atomic Spectra,* Academic, New York (1960), Chap. 3.
[13] C. Candler, *Atomic Spectra and the Vector Model,* Van Nostrand, Princeton, New Jersey (1964), Chap. 3.

1.3 SPECTRAL SERIES

As reliable light sources and wavelength standards became available in the second half of the nineteenth century, spectroscopists began to note regularities in the spacing of spectral lines. In the 1870's George Liveing and James Dewar discovered [1] that the spectral lines of neutral aluminum, sodium, potassium, thallium, and zinc, could be grouped into distinct series analogous to those of hydrogen. Subsequent studies have disclosed series in the spectra of nearly all elements.

A. Monovalent Atoms

The simplest series seen in spectra of neutral atoms, apart from those in hydrogen, occur in the spectra of alkali metals: lithium (Li), sodium (Na), potassium (K), rubidium (Rb), cesium (Cs), and francium (Fr). These elements from the first column of the periodic chart share many chemical properties, a similarity attributed to the presence of a single *valence* (or chemically active) electron. As one can see from the examples in Fig. 1.3, the alkalis share many spectroscopic characteristics as well.

A typical alkali spectrum consists of three distinct series. The strongest lines, those that persist even in low-temperature flames, form what J. R. Rydberg called [2] the *principal series*. Except for the first member of the series, all these lines have wavelengths in the ultraviolet. Rydberg classified the remaining visible lines into the *sharp series* and *diffuse series*, both converging to a common limit. As Rydberg's nomenclature suggests, he distinguished these two so-called *subordinate series* by the appearance of their member lines: lines of the diffuse series looked broad or hazy on one or both sides of the line, whereas lines of the sharp series seemed narrower and more sharply defined. Additional subordinate series occur in the infrared region. The next major series was long ago christened the *fundamental series*, a misnomer that persists to the present.

Guided by an assumed analogy with acoustical vibrations, spectroscopists vainly sought to explain spectral series as harmonic overtones of basic frequencies. Then, shortly after Balmer's striking success with hydrogen, Rydberg found a formula governing the location of the lines observed by Liveing and Dewar. Rydberg's formula [2] for the lines of a particular series was

$$\tilde{\nu}_n = \tilde{\nu}_\infty - \frac{R_A}{(n - \Delta)^2}, \tag{3.1}$$

where $\tilde{\nu}_\infty$ is the *series limit*, R_A is now called the *Rydberg constant* for ele-

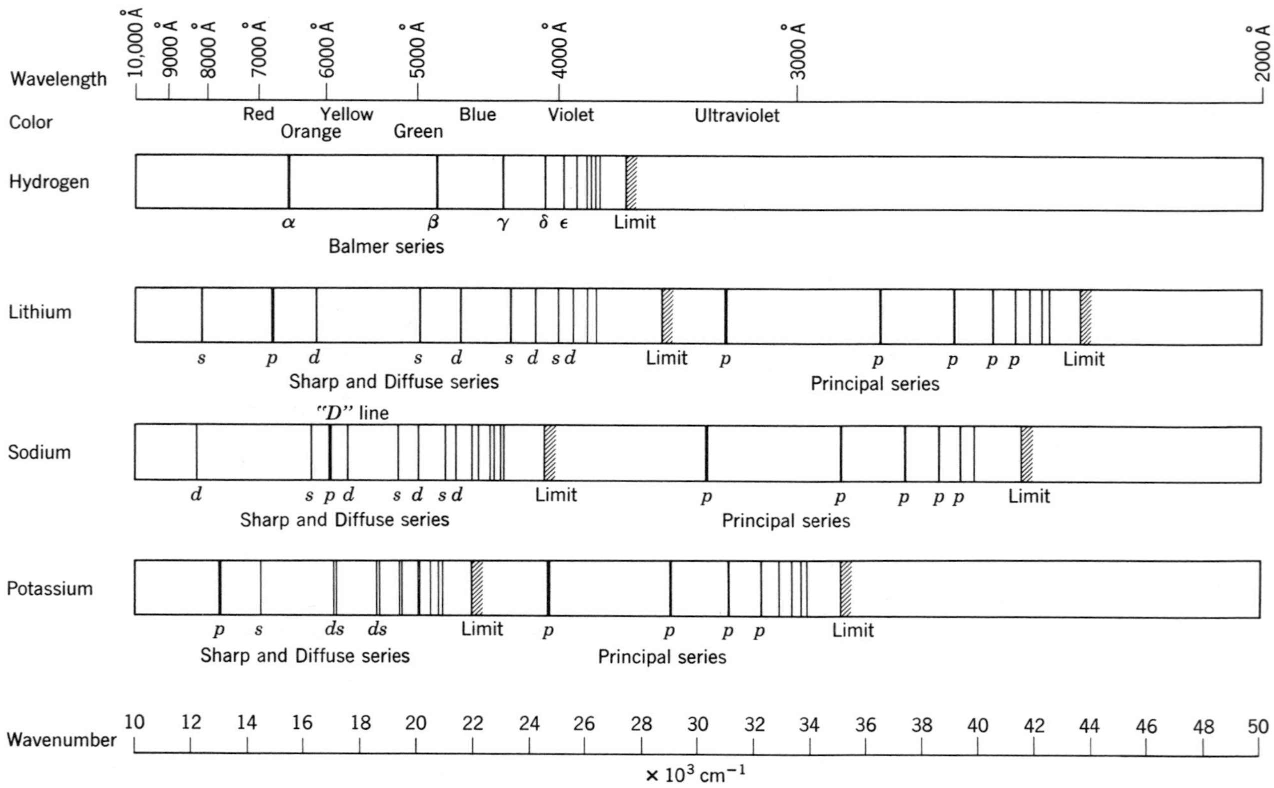

Fig. 1.3 Representation of alkali spectra, showing principal, sharp, and diffuse series. [After H. Kayser, *Handbuch der Spectroscopie*, S. Hirzel, Berlin (1920), vol. 2.]

ment A, n is an integer (the *principal quantum number*) and Δ is now known as the *quantum defect.*

The Rydberg constant varies slightly from element to element and therefore the symbol R usually carries a chemical symbol as a subscript: R_H for hydrogen, R_{He} for helium, etc. (The variation attributable to finite nuclear mass is discussed in Section 2.4.)

In treating the spectrum of a given element, Rydberg used one value of Δ for all lines in the principal series, another value for the lines in the sharp series, and a third value for the diffuse series. Later he obtained better results by permitting Δ to vary slightly with n as well. The most useful expression for Δ, derived by W. Ritz [3], involves two parameters, a and b, the *Ritz Formula:*

$$\Delta = a + \frac{b}{n^2}. \tag{3.2}$$

The sharp and the diffuse series have a common series limit, whereas the principal series has a series limit higher than this common limit. By writing the series limit as

$$\tilde{\nu}_\infty = \frac{R_A}{(n_1 - \Delta_1)^2} \tag{3.3}$$

we can rewrite Rydberg's formula as

$$\tilde{\nu} = R_A \left[\frac{1}{(n_1 - \Delta_1)^2} - \frac{1}{(n_2 - \Delta_2)^2} \right], \tag{3.4}$$

and thereby emphasize the resemblance to the formula for hydrogen.

Careful examination of an alkali spectrum reveals that the lines consist of closely spaced pairs, called *doublets.* To be precise, only the sharp and the principal series consist of simple pairs; the members of the diffuse series have an additional faint *satellite line* toward the red (this satellite causes the diffuse appearance). The spacing between pairs of lines, known as the *fine-structure* splitting, becomes steadily more pronounced with increasing atomic size. In the principal series the splitting diminishes toward the series limit, whereas in the sharp and the diffuse series the wavenumber separation of the doublets remains constant along the series (*Hartley's law* [4]).

Further description of the alkali spectra will be found in the books by Kuhn [5] and Candler [6].

B. Divalent Atoms

Next in complexity beyond the alkalis come the elements of the second column of the periodic system: beryllium (Be), magnesium (Mg), calcium

(Ca), strontium (Sr), barium (Ba), and radium (Ra). The chemical similarity of these *alkaline earths* results from the presence of two valence electrons.

The visible spectrum of a typical alkaline earth contains more lines than an alkali spectrum, but the lines still appear in converging series. With good resolution, one can distinguish two distinct *systems* of lines: a system of closely spaced *triplets*, and a system of *singlets*. Each system has a principal series (the strongest, most persistent lines), a sharp series (fainter, sharp lines), a diffuse series (marked by faint satellites), and a fundamental series (also with faint satellites). Like the alkali spectra, the fine structure becomes more pronounced in the heavier elements of the group.

The spectrum of neutral helium, an atom with two electrons, resembles that of the divalent elements, although the fine structure is too small to be seen on an ordinary spectrogram. At one time it was thought that neutral helium existed in two forms. The singlet system was attributed to *parahelium* (or *parhelium*), while the triplet system was attributed to *orthohelium*.

C. Ions

So far our discussion has concerned only the spectra of neutral atoms—spectra produced by flames and direct-current arcs. At higher temperatures of the light source additional emission lines appear. At sufficiently high temperatures, as achieved in spark discharges, many of the atoms lose one electron. Such ions then emit a distinct spectrum that is characteristic of the singly ionized atom. Early workers called this the *spark spectrum* or *enhanced spectrum* of an element and referred to the spectrum of the neutral atom as the *arc spectrum*. Modern spectroscopic notation indicates the *spectrum* of a given stage of ionization by a Roman numeral after the element symbol:

I neutral atom,
II singly charged ion,
III doubly charged ion, etc.;

that is, Na I denotes the *spectrum* of neutral sodium, Na IV denotes the *spectrum* of the Na^{3+} ion. (The Na^{3+} ion is referred to as Na III by chemists, who use Roman numerals to denote the *oxidation state* of a species.)

The simplest ionic spectrum, He II, arises from singly ionized helium. Neutral helium has two electrons, and removal of one electron renders the atom hydrogenic in character. The lines of He II follow the pattern predicted by formula (2.2) but with one significant change: the Rydberg constant R_A must be replaced by $4R_A$. The helium lines thus obey the formula

$$\tilde{\nu} = 4R_{\text{He}}\left[\frac{1}{(n_1)^2} - \frac{1}{(n_2)^2}\right]. \tag{3.5}$$

For example, the series with $n_1 = 4$ is given by

$$\tilde{\nu} = R_{He}\left[\frac{1}{4} - \frac{1}{(n_2/2)^2}\right]. \tag{3.6}$$

By comparison, the Balmer series of hydrogen, for which $n_1 = 2$, follows the formula

$$\tilde{\nu} = R_H\left[\frac{1}{4} - \frac{1}{(n)^2}\right].$$

The helium line $n_2 = 6$, $n_1 = 4$ nearly coincides with the H α line of hydrogen (i.e., the Balmer line $n_2 = 3$, $n_1 = 2$). Because the Rydberg constant for helium, R_{He}, differs slightly from the Rydberg constant for hydrogen, R_H, the helium line lies about 1.6 Å to the violet of the hydrogen line. Higher members of the helium series are displaced by smaller amounts.

The lines for which n_2 is an odd integer have no hydrogen counterpart; they lie between successive members of the Balmer series. E. C. Pickering [7] was the first to observe this helium series (in the spectrum of the hot star ζ Puppis), and it still generally bears the name of *Pickering series*. Pickering incorrectly ascribed the spectrum to hydrogen, using half-integers $\frac{3}{2}$, $\frac{5}{2}$, etc., for n_2 in the Balmer formula. In 1913 Niels Bohr showed [8] that the Pickering series originated in singly ionized helium.

Other series for ionized helium have also been observed. That for $n_1 = 1$ lies in the extreme ultraviolet, its first member at about 303 Å. Members of the *Fowler series* [9] with $n_2 = 2$ nearly coincide with the Lyman series of hydrogen. The first member of the series for $n_1 = 3$, the transition $4 \rightarrow 3$, gives rise to a line at 4686 Å, a prominent line in the spectra of stars and gaseous nebulae of high excitation. It is also conspicuous in the spectrum of the solar corona.

Hydrogenic series are not confined to hydrogen and singly ionized helium; other elements, deprived of all but one electron, also produce such series. The wavelengths are governed by Rydberg's formula but with the Rydberg constant R_A replaced by Z^2R_A, where Z is the atomic number:

$$\tilde{\nu} = Z^2R_A\left[\frac{1}{(n_1)^2} - \frac{1}{(n_2)^2}\right]. \tag{3.7}$$

For example, this formula applies to

	H I	He II	Li III	Be IV	B V	C VI	N VII	...
$Z =$	1	2	3	4	5	6	7	....

Similarly, the spectra of alkali-like ions, such as Be II, B III, C IV, . . . or Mg II, Al III, . . . , have the appearance of an alkali spectrum: a system of doublet lines, arranged in sharp, principal, and diffuse series. The lines follow the pattern predicted by Rydberg's formula, but with the substitution of $(Z - N + 1)^2 R$ for $Z^2 R$, where N is the number of electrons remaining in the atom. The modified formula is

$$\tilde{\nu} = \zeta^2 R_A \left[\frac{1}{(n_1 - \Delta_1)^2} - \frac{1}{(n_2 - \Delta_2)^2} \right], \tag{3.8}$$

$$\zeta = (Z - N + 1).$$

The preceding summary of spectral observations illustrates a general principle:

> The number of valence electrons determines the qualitative character of a spectrum (e.g., number and type of series), whereas the net atomic charge affects quantitative details (e.g., wavelengths of lines in series).

D. Complex Atoms

As we proceed to elements in the middle of the periodic chart—atoms with several valence electrons—the visible spectra become more complex, and the groupings of lines into series become less pronounced. (For example, the visible spectrum of iron comprises more than 4000 lines.) Regularities of a different sort appear, first discovered in the spectrum of manganese by Miguel Catalán [10] and in the spectrum of molybdenum by Carl Kiess [11]. The lines are grouped in patterns called *multiplets*, resembling the doublets of sodium or triplets of helium.

Yet even with complex spectra, it is always possible to express the wavenumber of any spectral line as the difference of two numbers, a generalization of formula (3.3). The Rydberg–Ritz *combination principle* [12] expresses this observation:

> The wavenumber of any spectral line is the difference of two numbers T_2 and T_1, called *spectroscopic terms* (or *term values*):
>
> $$\tilde{\nu} = T_2 - T_1.$$

The combination principle permits us to describe the numerous lines of a spectrum as resulting from transitions between a smaller number of spectroscopic terms. Each term gives rise to several spectral lines, through combinations with other terms. However, not all possible combinations correspond to observed spectral lines (see Section 1.5).

The references in Bibliography 3 provide more detailed descriptions of atomic spectra.

REFERENCES

[1] G. D. Liveing and J. Dewar, *Proc Roy. Soc. (London)* **29,** 398 (1879); *Phil. Trans. Roy. Soc.* **174,** 187 (1883).
[2] J. R. Rydberg, *Kgl. Svenska Akad. Handl.* **23** (1889); *Astrophys. J.* **4,** 91 (1906).
[3] W. Ritz, *Ann. d. Physik* **12,** 264 (1903); *Phys. Z.* **9,** 521 (1908).
[4] W. N. Hartley, *J. Chem. Soc.* **43,** 390 (1883).
[5] H. G. Kuhn, *Atomic Spectra,* Academic, New York (1960).
[6] C. Candler, *Atomic Spectra and the Vector Model,* Van Nostrand, Princeton, New Jersey (1964).
[7] E. C. Pickering, *Astrophys. J.* **4,** 369 (1896); **5,** 92 (1897).
[8] N. Bohr, *Phil. Mag.* **26,** 1 (1913).
[9] A. Fowler, *Monthly Notices, Roy. Astron. Soc.* **73,** 62 (1912).
[10] M. A. Catalán, *Trans. Roy. Soc. (London)* **A223,** 127 (1922).
[11] C. C. Kiess, *Nat. Bur. Stds. Sci. Papers* **474,** 113 (1923).
[12] W. Ritz, *Astrophys. J.* **28,** 237 (1908).

1.4 X-RAY SPECTRA

Although x-rays form simply an extension of the visible electromagnetic spectrum to very short wavelengths (roughly 1 to 100 Å), special techniques are required to disperse, focus, and detect these wavelengths [1]–[5]. Thus they remained unknown until Wilhelm Röntgen's studies [6] of electron beams (then called *cathode rays*) disclosed a penetrating radiation, generated whenever energetic electrons struck a target. Röntgen dubbed this new unknown radiation *x-rays* (the name *Röntgen rays* was also used for many years) and found immediate medical application of their ability to penetrate flesh and bone.

Like visible light, a monochromatic beam of x-rays suffers an exponential drop in intensity I as it passes a small distance d through matter:

$$I = I_0 e^{-\mu d}. \tag{4.1}$$

Since the *linear absorption coefficient* μ decreases monotonically with frequency (apart from abrupt increases at "absorption edges"), the *penetrating power* or *hardness* of an x-ray beam is generally a measure of frequency. High-frequency x-rays are generally "harder" than x-rays of low frequency.

The x-rays generated by the impact of energetic electrons comprise a spectrum of emission lines overlying a continuum. The emission continuum originates in the deceleration of the bombarding electrons as they collide with target atoms—so-called *bremsstrahlung*. The shape of this continuum depends on the kinetic energy of the electrons as they strike the target. In turn, this energy is equal to the potential energy $E = eV$ gained by an electron (of charge e) moving through a potential difference V (in volts).

Although the continuum x-rays are distributed over a range of frequencies, none has frequencies exceeding

$$\nu_{\text{max}} = 2.43 \times 10^{14} E = \frac{E}{h}, \tag{4.2}$$

where ν is expressed in hertz (1 Hz = 1 cycle per second) and E is expressed in electron volts. That is, the kinetic energy of the electrons, eV, sets an upper limit to the radiation frequency:

$$h\nu_{\text{max}} = eV. \tag{4.3}$$

C. G. Barkla [7] in 1908 was the first to discover x-ray emission lines. In his studies with various target elements, Barkla noted two discrete components of the radiation, distinguished by their penetrating ability. The "harder" component Barkla called "K radiation," the "softer" component he called "L radiation." Additional components discovered at longer wavelengths became "M radiation," "N radiation," etc. William Bragg, applying his crystal spectrometer [8], found these radiations to be groups of emission lines characteristic of the target element. Emission x-ray lines therefore became known as *characteristic lines.*

H. G. J. Moseley carried out [9] a systematic study of the emission lines produced by various target elements and discovered a smooth variation of frequency with atomic number Z (Fig. 1.4). Moseley's plot of square root

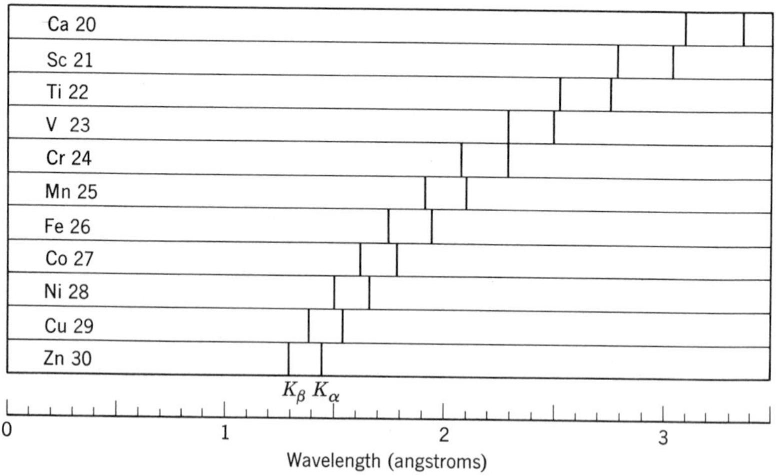

Fig. 1.4 Variation of characteristic x-ray wavelength with atomic number, as observed by Moseley [*Phil. Mag.* **26,** 1024 (1913); redrawn here after H. E. White, *Introduction to Atomic Spectra,* McGraw-Hill, New York (1934)].

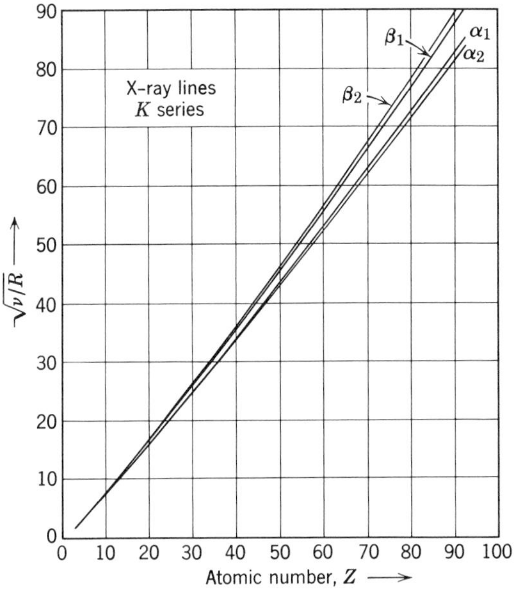

(a)

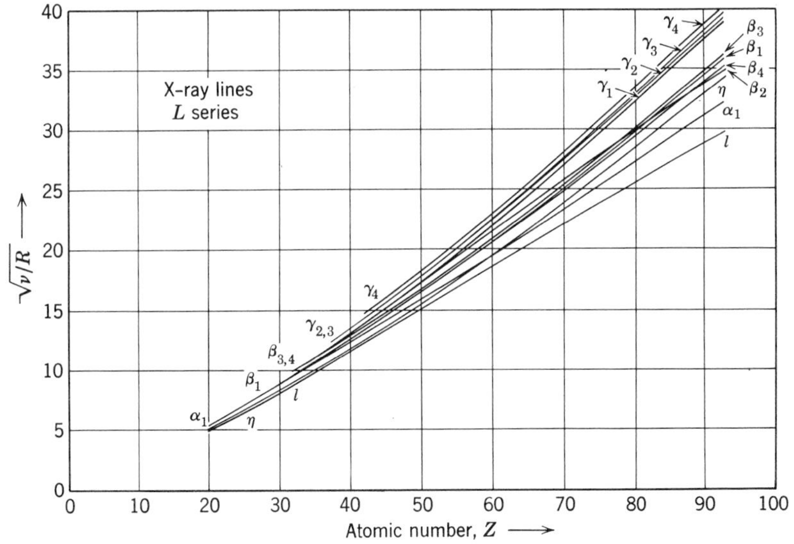

(b)

Fig. 1.5 Moseley diagram for *K*-series (*a*) and *L*-series (*b*). [From H. E. White, *Introduction to Atomic Spectra*, McGraw-Hill, New York (1934).]

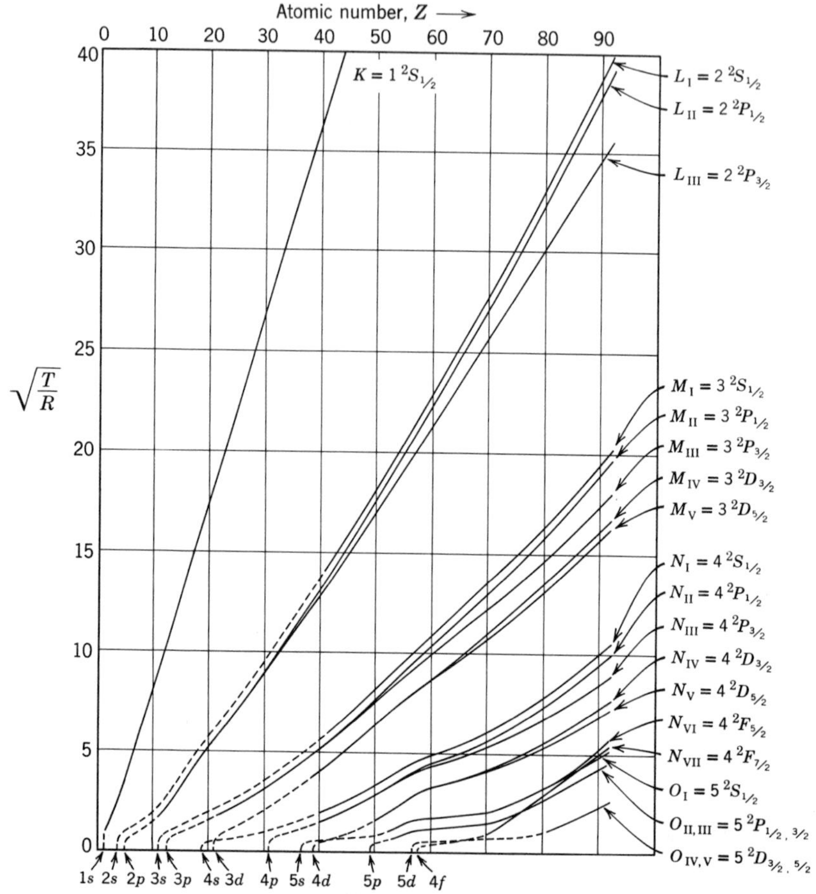

Fig. 1.6 Bohr-Coster diagram of x-ray term values. [After N. Bohr and D. Coster, *Z. Phys.* **12,** 342 (1923), and H. E. White, *Introduction to Atomic Spectra*, McGraw-Hill, New York (1934).]

of frequency against Z (the *Moseley diagram* of Fig. 1.5) provided the first definitive method for assigning atomic numbers to the elements: *the square roots of characteristic frequencies vary approximately linearly with atomic number* (*Moseley's law*).

In contrast to the optical properties of elements, the x-ray spectra vary smoothly from one element to the next. There is no trace of the periodicity that distinguishes one chemical family from another.

Following the combination principle, we can write the wavenumber of any characteristic x-ray as the difference of two *x-ray term values:*

$$\tilde{\nu} = T_2 - T_1. \tag{4.4}$$

The x-ray term values are given, approximately, by the formula

$$T = \frac{R(Z - \sigma)^2}{n^2}, \tag{4.5}$$

where Z is the atomic number, σ is a *screening parameter*, and n is the principal quantum number. Evidence for this formula may be found in a *Bohr–Coster diagram* [10]—a plot of $\sqrt{T/R}$ versus atomic number, as shown in Fig. 1.6. To the extent that term values follow (4.5), the diagram should be a plot of

$$\left(\frac{T}{R}\right)^{1/2} = \frac{Z - \sigma}{n}. \tag{4.6}$$

In examining the diagram, we immediately note a term value with unit slope ($n = 1$), three term values with slope $\frac{1}{2}$ ($n = 2$), five with slope $\frac{1}{3}$ ($n = 3$), etc. The letter designations K, M, N, . . . , introduced to distinguish x-ray *lines*, have become associated with particular *term values*. The conventional notation is

principal quantum number:	1	2	3	4	5
term designation:	K	L	M	N	O

From Fig. 1.6 we see that as many as $2n - 1$ terms may occur for a given principal quantum number n. These terms are conventionally designated by Roman-numeral subscripts, as

$$\begin{array}{cccccc} & \mathrm{L_I} & \mathrm{L_{II}} & \mathrm{L_{III}} & & \\ \mathrm{M_I} & \mathrm{M_{II}} & \mathrm{M_{III}} & \mathrm{M_{IV}} & \mathrm{M_V}, & \text{etc.} \end{array}$$

X-ray lines are often designated by a complicated notation requiring Greek subscripts that in turn are subscripted. For example, the *line* $K\alpha_1$ involves the *terms* K and L_{III}; the *line* $K\alpha_2$ involves the *terms* K and L_{II}. (When unresolved, the two lines form K_α.) Table 1.4 shows a notation proposed by M. Siegbahn [1], with Greek letters assigned according to decreasing intensity. Other authors use variants of this notation. For later reference, Column 1 gives an alternative label for the x-ray term, using the quantum numbers n, l, j.

The separation between adjacent x-ray terms of the same principal quantum number is often referred to as an *x-ray doublet*. Intervals that stay nearly constant with increasing Z (such as L_I–L_{II}, M_I–M_{II}, or M_{III}–M_{IV}, which, in quantum-number notation, have the same n and j, but different l)

Table 1.4 X-ray Nomenclature

		K lines	*L* lines		
		K	L_{I}	L_{II}	L_{III}
$1s_{1/2}$	K				
$2s_{1/2}$	L_{I}				
$2p_{1/2}$	L_{II}	α_2			
$2p_{3/2}$	L_{III}	α_1			
$3s_{1/2}$	M_{I}			η	l
$3p_{1/2}$	M_{II}	β_1	β_4		
$3p_{3/2}$	M_{III}		β_3		
$3d_{3/2}$	M_{IV}		β_{10}	β_1	α_2
$3d_{5/2}$	M_{V}		β_9		α_1
$4s_{1/2}$	N_{I}			γ_5	β_6
$4p_{1/2}$	N_{II}	β_2	γ_2		
$4p_{3/2}$	N_{III}		γ_3		
$4d_{3/2}$	N_{IV}			γ_1	β_{15}
$4d_{5/2}$	N_{V}				β_2
$4f_{5/2}$	N_{VI}				
$4f_{7/2}$	N_{VII}				
$5s_{1/2}$	O_{I}			γ_8	β_7
$5p_{1/2}$	O_{II}		γ_4		
$5p_{3/2}$	O_{III}				
$5d_{3/2}$	O_{IV}			γ_6	
$5d_{5/2}$	O_{V}				β_5

are known as *screening doublets* or *irregular doublets*. These doublets were found by Hertz [11]. Intervals that increase with Z (such as L_{II}–L_{III}, M_{II}–M_{III}, or M_{IV}–M_V, which have the same n and l, but different j) are known as *spin doublets*, *regular doublets*, or *relativity doublets*. These were found by Sommerfeld.

Further discussion of x-ray phenomena appears in the specialized texts [1]–[5] or in references on atomic physics [12]–[15].

REFERENCES

[1] M. Siegbahn, *Spectroscopy of X-Rays*, Oxford University Press, Oxford, England (1925); *Spectroscopie der Röntgenstrahlen*, Springer-Verlag, Berlin (1931), 2nd ed.
[2] A. H. Compton and S. K. Allison, *X-Rays in Theory and Experiment*, Van Nostrand, Princeton, New Jersey (1935).
[3] G. L. Clark, *Applied X-Rays*, McGraw-Hill, New York (1955).
[4] A. E. Sandström, *Handbuch der Physik* **30**, 78 (1957).
[5] G. L. Clark, *Encyclopedia of X-Rays and Gamma Rays*, Reinhold, New York (1963).
[6] W. K. Röntgen, *Sitzungsberichte der Wurzburger Physicalischen–Medicinischen Gesellschaft*, December (1895); March (1896); *The Electrician* **36**, 415 (1896); **36**, 850 (1897); *Ann. d. Phys. Chem.* **64** (1898) [A translation appears in M. H. Shamos, *Great Experiments in Physics*, Holt, New York (1959), p. 200, and in W. F. Magie, *A Source Book in Physics*, McGraw-Hill, New York (1935), p. 600].
[7] C. G. Barkla, *Phil. Mag.* **16**, 550 (1908); **22**, 396 (1911); **23**, 987 (1911); *Proc. Camb. Phil. Soc.* **15**, 257 (1909).
[8] W. L. Bragg, *Proc. Camb. Phil. Soc.* **17**, 43 (1912); *Nature* **90**, 410 (1912); **91**, 477 (1913); W. H. and W. L. Bragg, *Proc. Roy. Soc.* (*London*) **88**, 428 (1913).
[9] H. G. J. Moseley, *Phil. Mag.* **26**, 1024 (1913); **27**, 703 (1914).
[10] N. Bohr and D. Coster, *Z. Physik* **12**, 342 (1923).
[11] G. Hertz, *Z. Physik* **3**, 19 (1920).
[12] L. Pauling and S. Goudsmit, *Structure of Line Spectra*, McGraw-Hill, New York (1930), Chap. X.
[13] O. Oldenberg, *Introduction to Atomic Physics*, McGraw-Hill, New York (1954), 2nd ed.
[14] F. K. Richtmyer, E. H. Kennard, and T. Lauritsen, *Introduction to Modern Physics*, McGraw-Hill, New York (1955), 5th ed., Chap. 8.
[15] H. G. Kuhn, *Atomic Spectra*, Academic, New York (1961), Chap. IV. C.

1.5 GROTRIAN DIAGRAMS

A. Energy Levels

The explanation for the combination principle, which provides the foundation for all spectroscopy and atomic theory, begins with the work of Max Planck [1] on the radiation from incandescent solids. Such radiation is an approximation to the radiation from a *black body*, an object that is black or absorbent to all frequencies. Planck found from thermodynamic considerations that the radiation behaved as if it were emitted and absorbed in discrete units or *quanta*, rather than continuously. According to Planck, the energy E of a radiation quantum (a *photon*), is proportional to the frequency:

$$E = h\nu = hc\tilde{\nu} = \hbar\omega. \tag{5.1}$$

In the Planck formula (5.3) *Planck's constant* h has the value 6.6253×10^{-27} erg-sec; $\hbar$ is $h/2\pi = 1.05450 \times 10^{-27}$ erg-sec.

Further proof of the corpuscular nature of light came from Albert Einstein's explanation [2] of the photoelectric effect. An alkali metal, irradiated with ultraviolet light, emits free electrons from the metal surface. The electron current increases in proportion to the light intensity, but the kinetic energy of individual electrons (i.e., the voltage) depends only upon the light frequency. Einstein explained this experimental result in terms of Planck's quanta of radiation: each emitted electron has absorbed a photon with energy $E = \hbar\omega$. The observed electrons have this energy $\hbar\omega$ less an amount φ, the *work function* of the particular metal, needed to overcome the attractive forces that keep the electron in the metal.

Guided by these clues to the nature of radiation, Niels Bohr [3] was able to suggest an explanation for the combination principle. (Moreover, he was able to derive Balmer's formula and explain the numerical value of Rydberg's constant, as we shall note in Section 2.4A.) Bohr proposed two postulates, slightly paraphrased here:

1. Atoms (and ions) exist in discrete, stationary states with energies E_1, E_2, ...

2. Atoms absorb and emit energy only in transitions between two stationary states: $\hbar\omega = E_2 - E_1$, etc.

The first hypothesis indicates a similarity between atoms and vibrating strings or membranes, for which only discrete modes of vibration occur. (This analogy provides impetus for the wave mechanics in Chapter 3.) The second hypothesis is simply a statement of energy conservation: the energy carried off by radiation is equal to the energy lost by the atom.

Bohr's hypotheses provide the following explanation for spectral lines: in a spectral source an atom receives energy from its surroundings, either by absorbing radiation or by colliding with energetic electrons, and the energy of the atom increases from the normal *ground level* to one of many possible *excited levels*. From this excited state of high internal energy the atom returns to its normal *ground state* of lowest internal energy by emitting the internal energy as radiation. The return may cascade through several intermediate energy levels, each step producing radiation. The atom may also transmit its excitation energy to surrounding free electrons under appropriate conditions. We may observe either the energy absorbed by an atom, as in absorption spectra or electron scattering experiments, or we may record the emitted energy, as in emission spectra.

An energy-level diagram provides a useful way to visualize the energy structure of an atom. Following Wolfgang Grotrian, we mark off a vertical scale of energies (or of wavenumbers) and draw short horizontal lines to mark the positions of the energy levels. The ground level lies near the bottom of the diagram, and the remaining (excited) levels are ranked by energy above this level. Each spectral line is represented by a vertical line joining two energy levels. The difference of the two energies, expressed in reciprocal centimeters, is the wavenumber of the spectral line, according to the combination principle.

It has become common practice to express *excitation energies* relative to the ground level E_0; that is, we assign the arbitrary zero-point of the energy scale such that

$$E_0 = 0. \tag{5.2}$$

All states of the atom then have positive energies. The tabulations in *Atomic Energy Levels* [4] follow this convention. An alternative convention is frequently used for hydrogen: the ionization limit E_{lim} is defined as the zero point:

$$E_{\text{lim}} = 0. \tag{5.3}$$

With this convention, energies of the discrete excited states are negative numbers, whereas positive energies occur only when the atom is ionized.

With the convention of (5.1), we define the *absolute term value* T_n, expressed in reciprocal centimeters, as the separation of the relative energy E_n, expressed in reciprocal centimeters, from the first ionization limit:

$$T_n = (E_{\text{lim}} - E_n)/(hc). \tag{5.4}$$

(Here we neglect the fact that a term value usually corresponds to several closely spaced energy levels—the *fine structure*. This point is discussed below.) For example, hydrogen or a hydrogenic ion has the absolute term values

$$T_n = R_A \frac{Z^2}{n^2}, \tag{5.5}$$

whereas an alkali atom has the terms

$$T_n = R_A \frac{\zeta^2}{(n - \Delta)^2}, \tag{5.6}$$

with ζ equal to the net atomic charge less 1.

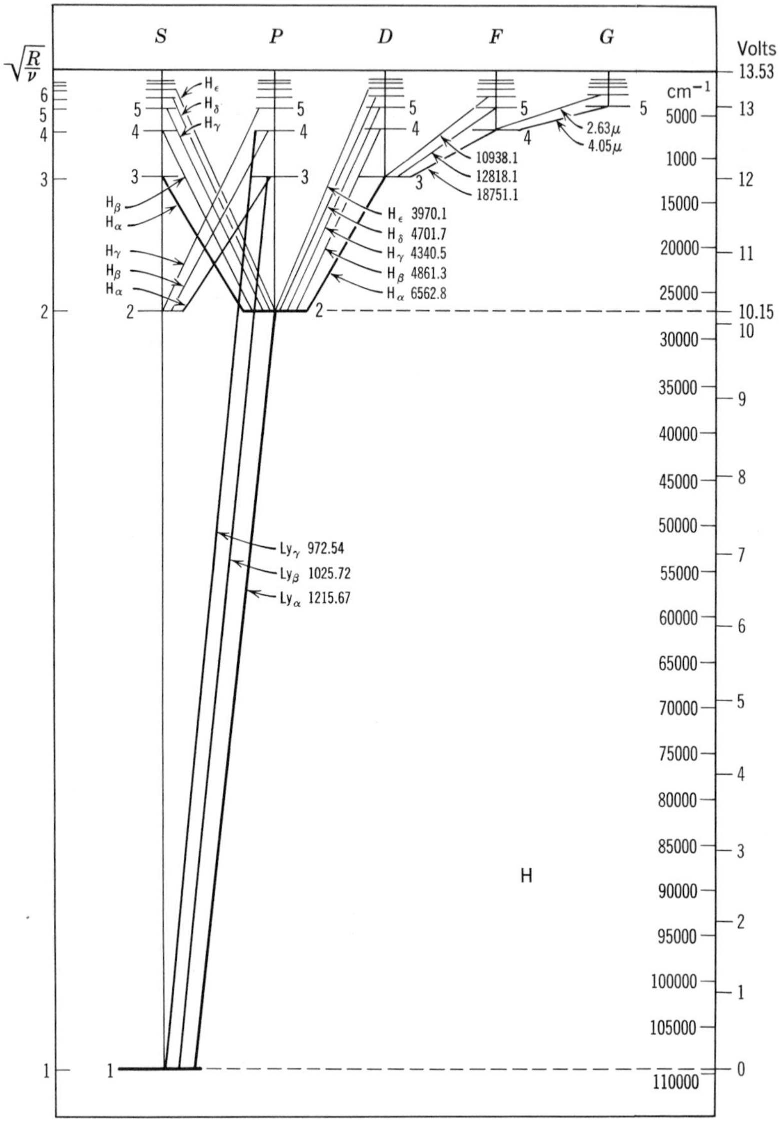

Fig. 1.7 Grotrian diagram for hydrogen (from Grotrian [1]).

B. Quantum Numbers

Figures 1.7 through 1.10 show *Grotrian diagrams* for typical simple atoms. Several, though by no means all, of the observed spectral lines are marked. The levels have been arranged in a two-dimensional array. The second dimension permits us to arrange into one column a series of energy levels having certain common properties (such as quantum defect). Let us see how this classification may be made.

To begin, the entire collection of levels of a given atom or ion can usually be classed into one or more *systems* of levels, distinguished by their *multiplicity:* hydrogen has a system of doublets; helium and neutral divalent elements have a system of singlets and a system of triplets; more complex atoms may have systems of doublets, quartets, . . . or systems of singlets, triplets, quintets, ... In any given stage of ionization an atom has systems of either even multiplicity or odd multiplicity.

The multiplicity nomenclature is the following:

1.	Singlet	2.	Doublet
3.	Triplet	4.	Quartet
5.	Quintet	6.	Sextet
7.	Septet	8.	Octet
9.	Nonet	10.	Dectet.

The multiplicity label provides an example of a *quantum number:* simply an integer, or half-odd-integer used as a distinguishing label on an energy level.

Within each system, the term values may be ranked according to the value of the integer n, the *principal quantum number*, that appears in expressions (5.5) or (5.6). With increasing n, the energy levels grow more closely spaced. The convergence of energy levels toward a limit as $n \longrightarrow \infty$ is reflected in the converging appearance of a spectral-line series.

It might be argued that observations of line series fix only the value of the *effective quantum number* n^*,

$$n^* = n - \Delta,$$

and that, by suitably adjusting the quantum defect Δ, one could choose n at will. Early classifications of energy levels often assigned the value $n = 1$ to the ground level of every atom, and these labels will be found in many diagrams drawn prior to 1940. As we point out in the following chapters, however, n cannot be assigned so arbitrarily. Evidence from x-ray spectra, from the spectra of adjacent elements in the periodic table, and from term diagrams of other members of an *isoelectronic sequence* (ions with varying

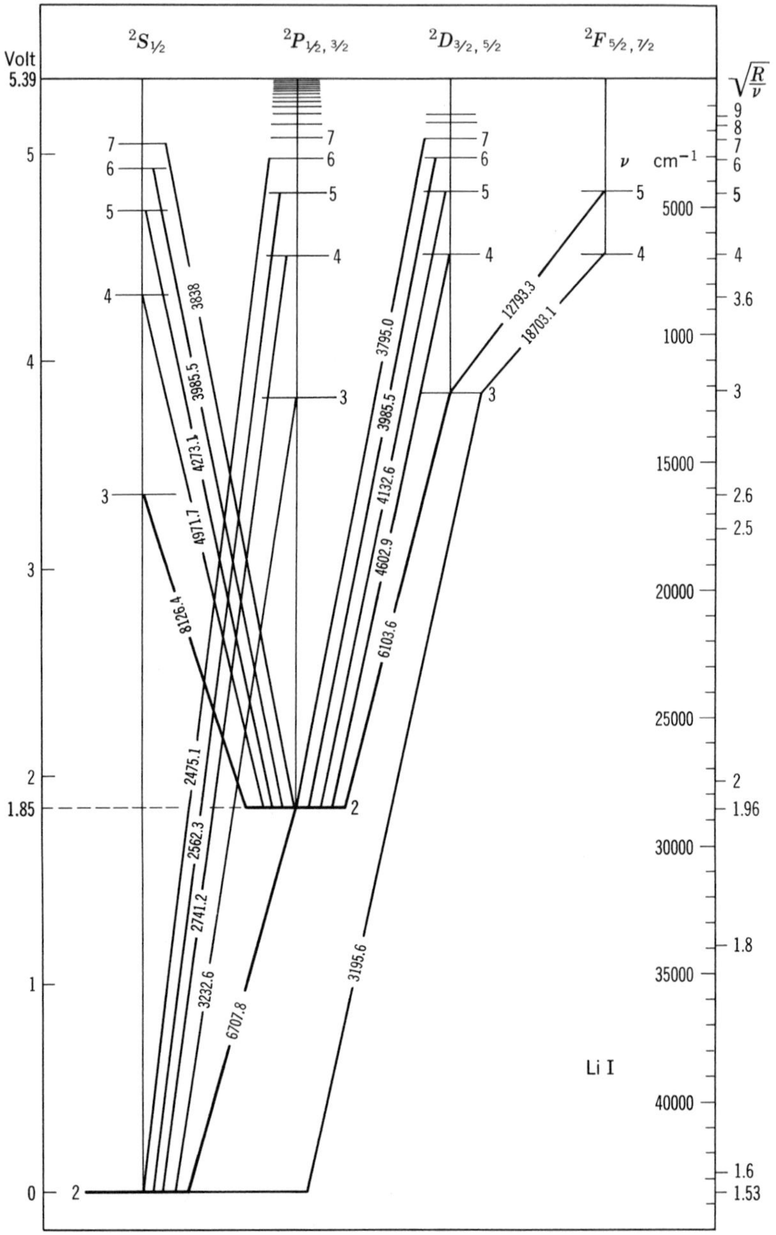

Fig. 1.8 Grotrian diagram for lithium, Li I (from Grotrian [1]).

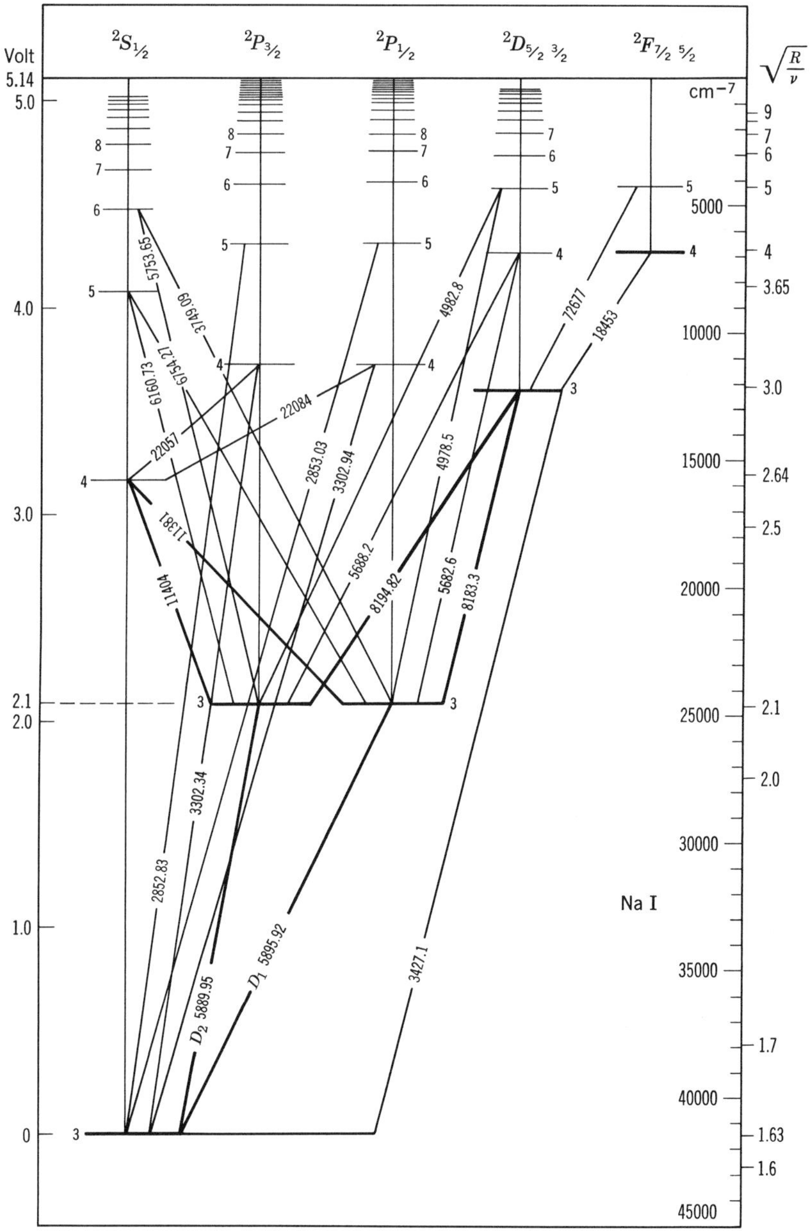

Fig. 1.9 Grotrian diagram for sodium, Na I (from Grotrian [1]).

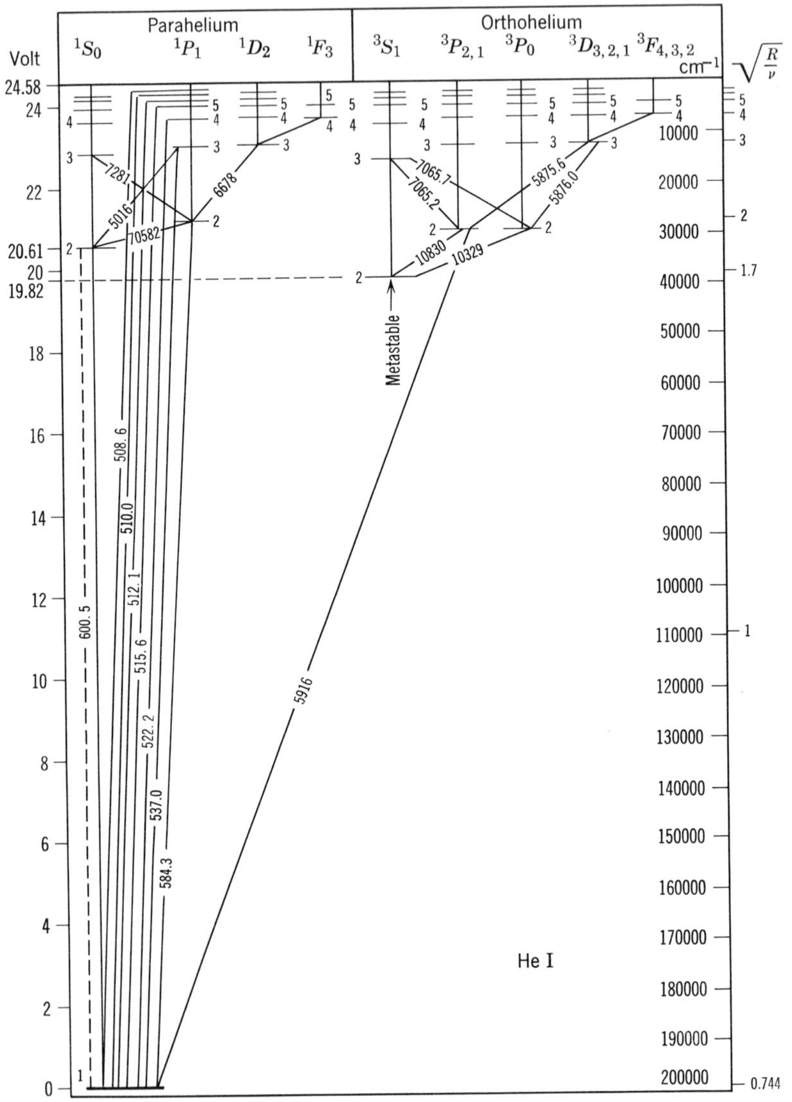

Fig. 1.10 Grotrian diagram for helium, He I (from Grotrian [1]).

net charge but a fixed number of electrons, such as Li, Be^+, and B^{2+}) all bears on the assignment of the principal quantum number.

We may further subdivide a system of spectroscopic terms into classes distinguished by their quantum defect and by their ability to provide observed transitions. This classification introduces a third label, the quantum number L, which conventionally takes integral values $L = 0, 1, 2, \ldots$. (For monovalent atoms, L is often denoted l and referred to as the *azimuthal quantum number* or the *orbital angular momentum.*) We may for the moment consider L as merely an additional index to use in the classification of the energy levels in a Grotrian diagram. We shall later interpret L as an angular momentum. The label L is assigned such that spectral series seen in emission spectra originate in the following transitions:

$L = 0$ to $L = 1$:	sharp series,
$L = 1$ to $L = 0$:	principal series,
$L = 2$ to $L = 1$:	diffuse series,
$L = 3$ to $L = 2$:	fundamental series.

Spectroscopists [5] introduced a shorthand notation, based originally on this series nomenclature, using letters to designate terms associated with a given value of L:

L:	0	1	2	3	4	5	6	7	8	9	10	11	$\cdots$
letter:	S	P	D	F	G	H	I	K	L	M	N	O	$\cdots$.

(Lower-case letters are often used for monovalent atoms.) Note that the letter J is omitted. In labeling a particular spectroscopic term, we denote the multiplicity as a left superscript to the letter, labeling terms ^2S, ^2P, etc. A more complete label may carry the value of the principal quantum number as well: 1^2S, 2^2P, etc.

A *spectroscopic term* generally consists of several closely spaced *energy levels.* A doublet P term constitutes two levels; a triplet D term constitutes three levels. (The number of levels comprising a term will be found in Table 2.2; the number of levels does not always equal the multiplicity.) For neutral light elements the energy separation between the levels of a term (the *fine-structure* or *term splitting*) is quite small, but it grows more pronounced with increasing atomic size. Sommerfeld introduced [6] an index J, which he called the *inner quantum number*, to distinguish the levels of a spectroscopic term. (The symbol j is often used for monovalent atoms.) J takes either integral values (for odd multiplicity) or half-integral values (for even multiplicity); the precise assignment of J is discussed in section 2.6. The J value appears as a right subscript in spectroscopic notation [5]. For example, the two levels of the doublet P term are denoted by $^2P_{1/2}$ and $^2P_{3/2}$.

It is not always possible to assign a value of multiplicity or L to a term, particularly terms of complex atoms, and other schemes of labeling terms

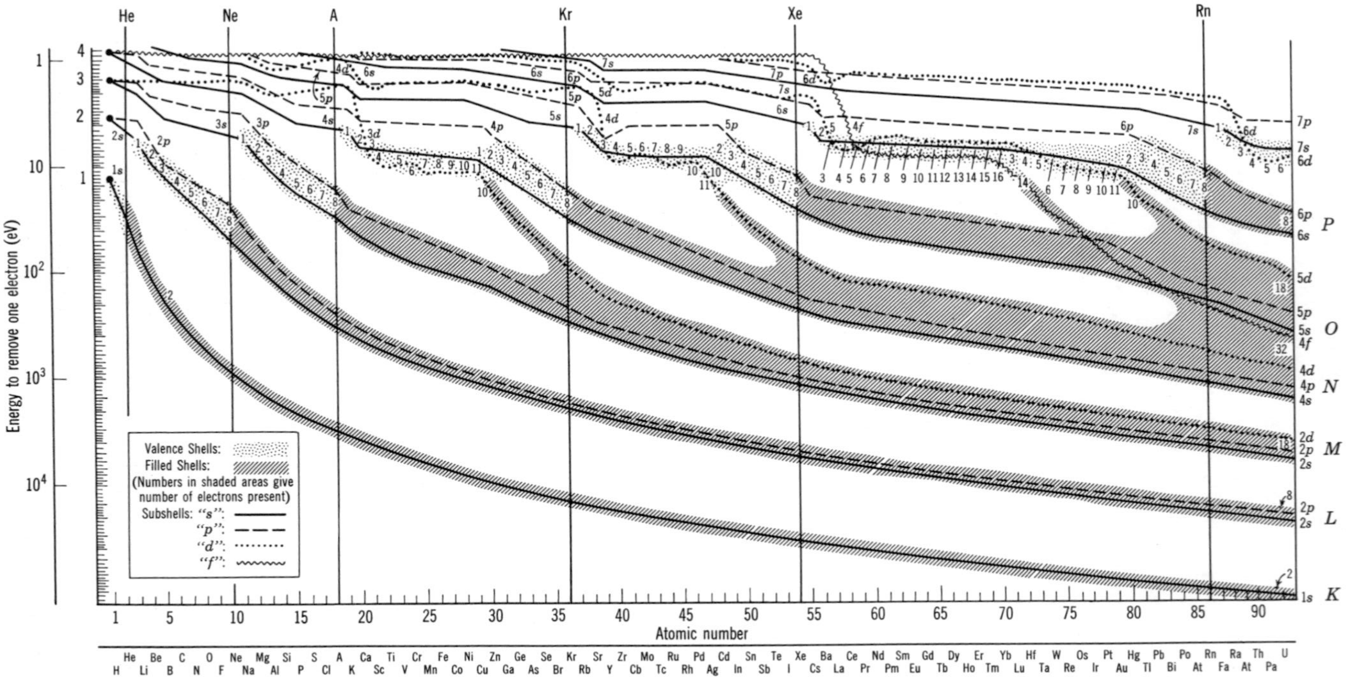

Fig. 1.11 Energy structure of the elements, showing filled shells (cross hatching) and partly filled valence shells (dotted). [From D. DeVault, *J. Chem. Ed.* **21**, 530 (1944).]

are often used. We shall discuss the assignment of quantum numbers in Chapter 9.

X-ray terms may also be displayed on a Grotrian diagram. Like the optical term values, these are best displayed with the lower term values placed higher on the diagram. (Many references plot excitation energies rather than term values. Such a convention inverts the ordering of x-ray term values.) For clarity it is best to use a logarithmic scale, as de Vault has done [7] in Fig. 1.11. X-ray terms are shown shaded in this diagram. Although Fig. 1.11 oversimplifies the structure of optical term values, it shows clearly the connection between optical term values and x-ray term values and it illustrates evidence that bears on the assignment of principal quantum numbers.

At present, the standard tabulations of energy levels are those published by the National Bureau of Standards [4]; these supersede the older tabulation by Bacher and Goudsmit [8]. The Bureau of Standards is issuing a series of monographs, the *National Data* series, which will provide data on each element. Grotrian diagrams can be found in references [9] through [15].

C. Selection Rules

Once we have classified the observed spectral lines into a Grotrian diagram, we can make several important observations. First, very few transitions take place between terms from two different systems (e.g., between a triplet and a singlet term). The *intersystem lines* that do occur usually connect the lowest terms of two systems. Neutral helium offers a good example. The triplet system has no connection with the singlet system. apart from the transition between 2^3P and 1^1S, which gives a line at 591.6 Å, This observation provides our first example of an empirical *selection rule* governing transitions: *multiplicity does not change.*

We observe a second selection rule when we note that the quantum number L *very rarely changes by more than unity:* we observe $S \rightarrow P$ and $P \rightarrow D$ transitions, but $S \rightarrow F$ transitions are quite rare. In the spectra of hydrogen and the alkalis L nearly always changes by exactly unity (e.g., $S \rightarrow S$ or $P \rightarrow P$ transitions are not observed), but in the spectra of more complex atoms, transitions may occur between terms having the same L values.

Soon after the discovery of multiplet structure in complex spectra, spectroscopists found that the terms of a given atom could be separated into two classes, which they distinguished by an attribute called *parity*. Transitions within a class were seldom observed. Only transitions between classes occurred. By assigning one class *even parity*, the other class *odd parity*,

Otto Laporte [16] expressed these combining properties as a selection rule (*Laporte's rule*): *parity changes in a transition*. Terms having odd parity conventionally carry a superscript 0 on the symbol.

These selection rules apply to most spectral lines, particularly in the spectra of light elements, but exceptions do occur. Early spectroscopists called these exceptions *forbidden lines*—a misleading name because many prominent spectral lines are in fact "forbidden" by these rules. Customarily, forbidden lines are indicated by a square bracket around the symbol for the spectrum of the atom or ion, as [Mg II]. Transitions that do satisfy the selection rules are called *allowed*.

Not all possible "allowed" lines will be seen in any given spectrum. The intensity of a spectral line is the product of two factors: an intrinsic atomic *transition strength* (which we discuss in Chapter 10) and the number of atoms that exist in a state capable of emitting or absorbing the radiation in question. As we shall see in Chapter 10, the selection rules are simply statements that the intrinsic transition strength is very small for certain transitions (the forbidden transitions). If the atoms are excited by thermal processes (as in an arc), the relative population of levels with excitation energies E_i and E_j is given by the *Boltzmann distribution* appropriate to temperature T:

$$\frac{N_i}{N_j} = \frac{\varpi_i}{\varpi_j} e^{-(Ei-Ej)/kT}, \tag{5.7}$$

where ϖ_i and ϖ_j denote the statistical weights ($2J_i + 1$ and $2J_j + 1$) and $k = 1.38054 \times 10^{-16}$ erg/deg is Boltzmann's constant. At low temperatures only the lowest lying levels have appreciable populations, and we observe only those emission lines that originate at these energy levels. A given absorption line $\hbar\omega = E_i - E_j$ will be seen only if an appreciable number of atoms are excited to level E_j so that they can absorb the radiation in passing to the level E_i of higher excitation.

If the atoms are excited by an electron beam, the electron energy must exceed the excitation energy E_i before the emission lines originating from that energy level become observable.

The larger the transition strengths, the quicker an atom will radiate away a quantum of energy. It may happen that by collisional excitation or radiative cascade an atom will arrive at an energy level whose radiative decay must proceed through a transition of small strength. The atom may then remain in this *metastable level* for an exceptionally long time if it is isolated from collisions. As an example, the lowest triplet level of neutral helium, the 2^3S_0, can decay only to the 1^1S_0 (the only energy level below the 2^3S_0), a decay that violates several selection rules. Atoms can remain in the metastable 2^3S_0 level for several days unless collisions intervene.

For reference, Table 1.5 provides the wavelengths and quantum-number designations for a number of noteworthy spectral lines.

Table 1.5 Some Noteworthy Spectral Lines

Color	Wavelength	Label	Source
Infrared	10830	. . .	He I (2^3S–2^3P°)
Red	7595 (band)	Fraunhofer A	O_2 molecule
Red	6867 (band)	Fraunhofer B	O_2 molecule
Red	6562.80	$H\alpha$ or Fraunhofer C	Hydrogen ($3d$–$2p$)
Orange	6057.80211	(standard of length)	Kr^{86} I ($2p_{10}$–$5d_5$) (Paschen notation)
Yellow	5895.92	Fraunhofer D_1	Na I resonance ($3p\ ^2P_{1/2}{}^{\circ}$–$3s\ ^2S_{1/2}$)
	5889.95	D_2	($3p\ ^2P_{3/2}{}^{\circ}$–$3s\ ^2S_{1/2}$)
Yellow	5876 (blend)	Fraunhofer D_3 (stellar spectra)	He I ($3d\ ^3D$–$2p\ ^3P^{\circ}$)
Green	5577.35	Auroral line	[O I] ($2p^4\ ^1D_2$–$2p^4\ ^1S_0$)
Green	5302.86	Coronal line	[Fe XIV] ($3p\ ^2P_{1/2}$–$3p\ ^2P_{3/2}{}^{\circ}$)
Green	5270.36	Fraunhofer E	Fe I ($z\ ^5D_1{}^{\circ}$–$a\ ^5F_2$)
Green	5250.21	(Solar magnetograph)	Fe I ($z\ ^7D_1{}^{\circ}$–$a\ ^5D_0$)
Green	5183.62	Fraunhofer b_1	Mg I ($4s\ ^3S_1$–$3p\ ^3P_2{}^{\circ}$)
	5172.70	b_2	($4s\ ^3S_1$–$3p\ ^3P_1{}^{\circ}$)
	5167.34	b_3	($4s\ ^3S_1$–$3p\ ^3P_0{}^{\circ}$)
Blue	4861.32	$H\beta$ or Fraunhofer F	H ($4d$–$2p$)
Blue	4340.46	$H\gamma$	H ($5d$–$2p$)
Violet	4303.94	Fraunhofer G	CH molecule
Violet	4226.73	—	Ca I resonance ($4p\ ^1P_1{}^{\circ}$–$4s\ ^1S_0$)
Violet	3968.47	Fraunhofer H	Ca II resonance ($4p\ ^2P_{1/2}{}^{\circ}$–$4s\ ^2S_{1/2}$)
Violet	3933.67	Fraunhofer K	Ca II ($4p\ ^2P_{3/2}{}^{\circ}$–$4s\ ^2S_{1/2}$)
Ultraviolet	1215.67	Lyman α	H resonance ($2p$–$1s$)
Far ultraviolet	584.34	—	He I resonance ($2\ ^1P_1{}^{\circ}$–$1\ ^1S_0$)

What does a term diagram imply about the structure of an atom? Conversely, how can we predict a term diagram and its attendant spectrum? These are the central questions of atomic spectroscopy, for which the present book provides at least partial answers.

REFERENCES

[1] M. Planck, *Ann. Physik* **31,** 758 (1910); **37,** 642 (1912); *Verhandl. Deut. Phys. Ges.* (1911) p. 138.
[2] A. Einstein, *Ann. Physik* **17,** 132 (1905); **20,** 199 (1906); **22,** 180 (1907).

[3] N. Bohr, *Phil. Mag.* **26**, 1 (1913); *Kgl. Danske Videnskab. Selskab Skrifter, Nat. Math. Afd.* **4**, 1 (1918).
[4] C. E. Moore, *Atomic Energy Levels*, Nat. Bur. Stds. Circ. 467, Vol. I (1946); Vol. II (1952); Vol. III (1958).
[5] H. N. Russell, A. G. Shenstone, and L. A. Turner, *Phys. Rev.* **33**, 900 (1929).
[6] A. Sommerfeld, *Ann. Physik* **70**, 32 (1923).
[7] D. de Vault, *J. Chem. Ed.* **21**, 530 (1944).
[8] R. F. Bacher and S. Goudsmit, *Atomic Energy States*, McGraw-Hill, New York (1932).
[9] W. Grotrian, *Graphische Darstellungen der Spectren*, Springer, Berlin (1928).
[10] H. E. White, *Introduction to Atomic Spectra*, McGraw-Hill, New York (1934).
[11] G. Herzberg, *Atomic Spectra and Atomic Structure*, Van Nostrand, Princeton, New Jersey (1937), reprinted by Dover, New York (1944).
[12] P. W. Merrill, *Lines of the Chemical Elements in Astronomical Spectroscopy*, Carnegie Institution of Washington, Publication 610, Washington, D.C. (1956).
[13] H. G. Kuhn, *Atomic Spectra*, Academic, New York (1961).
[14] *American Institute of Physics Handbook*, McGraw-Hill, New York (1963), 2nd ed.
[15] C. Candler, *Atomic Spectra and the Vector Model*, Van Nostrand, Princeton, New Jersey (1964).
[16] O. Laporte, *Z. Physik* **23**, 135 (1924).

1.6 PROFILES OF SPECTRAL LINES

Although we have argued that the existence of discrete spectral lines implies discrete energy levels, purely monochromatic spectral lines do not exist. Rather, a variation of light intensity spreads over a finite frequency (or wavelength) interval. We define the spectral-line *profile* $I(\omega)\,d\omega$ as the fraction of the recorded intensity that appears in the angular-frequency interval between ω and $\omega + d\omega$:

$$\int_{-\infty}^{\infty} I(\omega)\,d\omega = 1. \tag{6.1}$$

Many factors contribute to the observed broadening of spectral lines. The following sections mention several of them; fuller details will be found in texts on astrophysics (e.g., Unsold [1], Ambartsumian [2], and Aller [3]) and plasma physics (e.g., Griem [4], and Cooper [5]).

A. Spectrograph Resolution

A spectrograph employs a prism or diffraction grating to disperse the light from a narrow entrance slit. Suitably disposed lenses form an image of this slit on a detector (a photographic plate or photoelectric device). Because the image is a diffraction pattern, the spectrograph suffers inherent limitations in resolving abrupt changes of intensity over small wavelength intervals. The ability to separate two images is determined by the resolving power of the spectrograph. The theoretical resolving power of a prism spectrograph

$$r = w \frac{dn}{d\lambda}$$

depends on the width of the prism w and on the change of the refractive index n with wavelength. The theoretical resolving power of a grating spectrograph is determined by the number of lines on the grating, N_{lines}, and on the order of the spectrum, N_{order}:

$$r = N_{\text{lines}} N_{\text{order}}.$$

If the resolving power is r, one can distinguish two spectral lines at λ and $\lambda + \Delta\lambda$ (or $\bar{\nu}$ and $\bar{\nu} + d\bar{\nu}$):

$$r = \frac{\lambda}{\Delta\lambda} = \frac{\bar{\nu}}{\Delta\bar{\nu}}.$$

For example, a typical grating 15 cm long, with 6000 lines per cm, used in the third order ($N_{\text{order}} = 3$), has a theoretical resolving power of

$$r = 15 \times 6000 \times 3 = 270{,}000.$$

Such resolving power will permit us to distinguish lines separated by 0.02 Å at 5000 Å.

B. Thermal Motions

A stationary observer, viewing an atom that moves with velocity v at an angle θ to his line of sight, will record a frequency [6, 7]

$$\omega = \omega_0 \frac{1 - v/c \cos\theta}{[1 - (v/c)^2]^{1/2}} \simeq \omega_0 \left(1 - \frac{v}{c} \cos\theta\right) \tag{6.2}$$

if the atom radiates the frequency ω_0 in its own frame of reference. The *Doppler shift* resulting from this motion is

$$\frac{\Delta\omega}{\omega_0} \equiv \frac{\omega - \omega_0}{\omega_0} = \frac{v}{c} \cos\theta, \tag{6.3a}$$

or, in wavelength units,

$$\frac{\Delta\lambda}{\lambda_0} \equiv \frac{\lambda - \lambda_0}{\lambda_0} = \frac{v}{c} \cos\theta. \tag{6.3b}$$

Atoms comprising a source of radiation have random thermal motions, and consequently they display a variety of Doppler shifts. In thermal equilibrium, a *Maxwellian distribution* gives the fraction dN/N of atoms whose x component of velocity lies between v_x and $v_x + dv_x$:

$$\frac{dN}{N} = \frac{e^{-(v_x/u)^2}}{\sqrt{\pi}} \frac{dv_x}{u}. \tag{6.4}$$

Here $u/\sqrt{2}$ is the root-mean-square velocity for particles of mass M at temperature T,

$$u \equiv \left(\frac{2kT}{M}\right)^{1/2} = 1.28 \times 10^{-4} \frac{\text{cm}}{\text{sec}} \left(\frac{T\,(^\circ\text{K})}{M\,(\text{amu})}\right)^{1/2}, \tag{6.5}$$

and $k = 1.38054 \times 10^{-16}$ erg/°K is Boltzmann's constant. If we introduce the *Doppler widths* $\Delta\omega_D$ and $\Delta\lambda_D$,

$$\frac{\Delta\omega_D}{\omega_0} = \frac{\Delta\lambda_D}{\lambda_0} = \frac{u}{c} = \left(\frac{2kT}{Mc^2}\right)^{1/2} = 4.28 \times 10^{-6} \left(\frac{T\,(^\circ\text{K})}{M\,(\text{amu})}\right)^{1/2}, \tag{6.6}$$

and note, from (6.3), that $d(\Delta\omega) = d\omega$ and $d(\Delta\lambda) = d\lambda$, we obtain the relative distribution of Doppler shifts:

$$\frac{dN}{N} = \frac{e^{-(\Delta\omega/\Delta\omega_D)^2}}{\sqrt{\pi}} \frac{d\omega}{\Delta\omega_D} = \frac{e^{-(\Delta\lambda/\Delta\lambda_0)^2}}{\sqrt{\pi}} \frac{d\lambda}{\Delta\lambda_D}. \tag{6.7}$$

Thus the random thermal motions produce a *Gaussian profile* (see Fig. 1.2),

$$I(\omega) = \frac{e^{-(\Delta\omega/\Delta\omega_D)^2}}{\Delta\omega_D\sqrt{\pi}}, \tag{6.8}$$

centered on the unshifted frequency ω_0. The width of this distribution at the frequencies where $I(\omega)$ falls to half the central intensity $I(\omega_0)$ (the *half-width*) is

$$\begin{aligned}\text{Doppler half width} &= 2\sqrt{\ln 2}\,\Delta\omega_D \\ &= 2\omega_0 \left(\frac{2kT\ln 2}{Mc^2}\right)^{1/2} \\ &= 7.16 \times 10^{-7}\omega_0 \left(\frac{T}{M}\right)^{1/2}.\end{aligned} \tag{6.9}$$

The reasoning leading to (6.7) was first given by Lord Rayleigh [8] in 1889. Thermal broadening is most pronounced for light atoms (particularly hydrogen) and high temperatures; the Hα line (6563 Å) has a Doppler width of 0.6 Å at 400°K. Note that the area under the curve $I(\omega)$ is unity, as required by (6.1).

C. Fourier Analysis

Strictly monochromatic radiation—an absolutely sharp spectral line—requires an infinite wave train of constant amplitude. Thus any deviation from a purely sinusoidal wave, through intensity changes, phase changes, or termination of the wave, requires a superposition of waves of many frequencies. The distribution of these frequencies produces a spectral line with finite width.

The actual frequency distribution of the radiation follows from analysis of the wave train into harmonic components—*Fourier analysis*. We write the amplitude of disturbance, $f(t)$, as a superposition of many monochromatic wave trains of different frequencies:

$$f(t) = \frac{1}{\sqrt{2\pi}} \int_{-\infty}^{\infty} d\omega\, e^{i\omega t} F(\omega). \tag{6.10}$$

The *Fourier components* $F(\omega)$ specify the weight of each monochromatic wave; the square of $F(\omega)$ gives the spectral intensities:

$$I(\omega)\, d\omega = |F(\omega)|^2\, d\omega. \tag{6.11}$$

Conversely, knowledge of $f(t)$ permits us to calculate $F(\omega)$ from the *Fourier transform:*

$$F(\omega) = \frac{1}{\sqrt{2\pi}} \int_{-\infty}^{\infty} d\omega\, e^{i\omega t} f(t). \tag{6.12}$$

The following paragraphs illustrate these principles with two examples—simplified models of the radiation process. Further details of Fourier analysis will be found in the texts by Bracewell [9] and Franklin [10].

D. Finite Lifetime

An atom cannot continue to radiate indefinitely without being resupplied with energy from an external source; eventually the intensity must diminish as the atom exhausts its supply of energy. This diminution of intensity (or amplitude) means that even if the atom continues to radiate at a fixed frequency ω_0, the observed wave train of light is not monochromatic. Suppose, for example, a disturbance $f(t)$ oscillates at fixed frequency ω_0 but that the amplitude of $f(t)$ falls exponentially with time, starting at $t = 0$:

$$\begin{aligned} t < 0:&\quad f(t) = 0 \\ t \geq 0:&\quad f(t) = e^{i\omega_0 t} e^{-\gamma t} \sqrt{2\gamma}. \end{aligned} \tag{6.13}$$

The factor $\sqrt{2\gamma}$ has been inserted so that $f(t)$ will satisfy the equation

$$\int_{-\infty}^{\infty} dt\ |f(t)|^2 = 2\gamma \int_0^{\infty} e^{-2\gamma t}\, dt = 1.$$

The disturbance specified by (6.13) has the Fourier components

$$F(\omega) = \left(\frac{\gamma}{\pi}\right)^{1/2} \int_0^{\infty} dt\ e^{-i\omega t} e^{i\omega_0 t} e^{-\gamma t}$$

$$= \left(\frac{\gamma}{\pi}\right)^{1/2} \frac{(-i)}{\omega_0 - \omega + i\gamma}\,. \tag{6.14}$$

Thus the spectrum of light intensity emitted in exponential decay has a *Lorentz profile:*

$$I(\omega) = |F(\omega)|^2 = \frac{\gamma}{\pi} \frac{1}{(\omega_0 - \omega)^2 + \gamma^2}\,. \tag{6.15}$$

$\Gamma = 2\gamma$ is known as the Lorentz *width* or as the *damping factor;* the profile width is Γ at half-maximum intensity. γ is the "half half-width."

E. Collisions

As an atom moves it encounters other atoms, ions, or free electrons. Most encounters transfer no energy to or from a radiating atom, and serve only to alter the phase or plane of polarization of the radiation. Brief collisions (*impacts*) break the train of radiation into a sequence of smaller sinusoidal wavetrains. Between impacts the atom radiates at a fixed frequency ω_0 with constant amplitude. Figure 1.12 illustrates this simple model.

A wave train of frequency ω_0 starting at $t = 0$ and persisting until an abrupt termination at $t = \tau$ has the Fourier components,

$$F_\tau(\omega) = \frac{1}{\sqrt{2\pi}} \int_0^{\tau} dt\ e^{-i\omega t} e^{i\omega_0 t} = \frac{e^{i(\omega_0 - \omega)\tau} - 1}{i(\omega_0 - \omega)\sqrt{2\pi}}\,, \tag{6.16}$$

and thus produces the intensity

$$|F_\tau(\omega)|^2 = \frac{\sin^2 [(\omega_0 - \omega)\tau/2]}{2\pi[(\omega_0 - \omega)/2]^2}\,. \tag{6.17}$$

Because interruptions occur at random, we must weight each value of

Fig. 1.12 Interruption of sinusoidal wavetrain (schematic).

$|F_\tau|^2$ by the probability $P(\tau)\,d\tau$ that no collision occurs in the interval τ and then that one collision occurs in the interval $\tau + d\tau$, and so on. For independent random collisions, occurring at the rate γ per second, $P(\tau)\,d\tau$ is given by the *Poisson distribution* of random arrivals:

$$P(\tau)\,d\tau = \gamma e^{-\gamma\tau}\,d\tau. \tag{6.18}$$

This simple interruption process then produces the line profile

$$\begin{aligned} I(\omega) &= \int_0^\infty d\tau\, P(\tau)\gamma\,|F_\tau(\omega)|^2 \\ &= \frac{\gamma^2}{2\pi}\int_0^\infty d\tau\, e^{-\gamma\tau}\,\frac{\sin^2(\omega_0 - \omega/2)\tau}{(\omega_0 - \omega/2)^2} \\ &= \frac{\gamma}{\pi}\,\frac{1}{(\omega_0 - \omega)^2 + \gamma^2}\,. \end{aligned} \tag{6.19}$$

Again we find a Lorentz profile. The width γ is here the collision frequency. We can estimate γ from knowledge of the density of radiating atoms ρ, the mean velocity $\bar{v}$ of electrons causing collisions, and the effective area of the atom (the effective collision cross section $\bar{\sigma}$) [5]:

$$\gamma = \rho\overline{v\sigma}. \tag{6.20}$$

F. Voigt Profile

As we have now noted, influences that shorten the radiation wave train may be expected to produce a Lorentz profile (6.14), whereas thermal motions produce a Gaussian or Doppler profile (6.7). In many light sources, particularly the atmospheres of stars, both effects are important. Figure 1.13 shows the two basic profiles for a given common central intensity. The Lorentz profile extends to greater frequencies from the line center ω_0, whereas the Gaussian profile clusters near the line center. The combined profile appears Lorentzian in the *wings* (far from line center) and Gaussian near the *core* (near line center). The product of (6.7) and (6.14) is

$$I(\omega) = \int d(\Delta\omega)\left[\frac{e^{-(\Delta\omega/\Delta\omega_D)^2}}{\Delta\omega_D\sqrt{\pi}}\right]\cdot\left[\frac{\gamma}{(\omega_0 - \omega - \Delta\omega)^2 + \gamma^2}\right]. \tag{6.21}$$

With the substitutions

$$y = \frac{\Delta\omega}{\Delta\omega_D}, \qquad b = \frac{\omega - \omega_0}{\Delta\omega_D}, \qquad a = \frac{\gamma}{\Delta\omega_D}, \tag{6.22}$$

(6.21) becomes

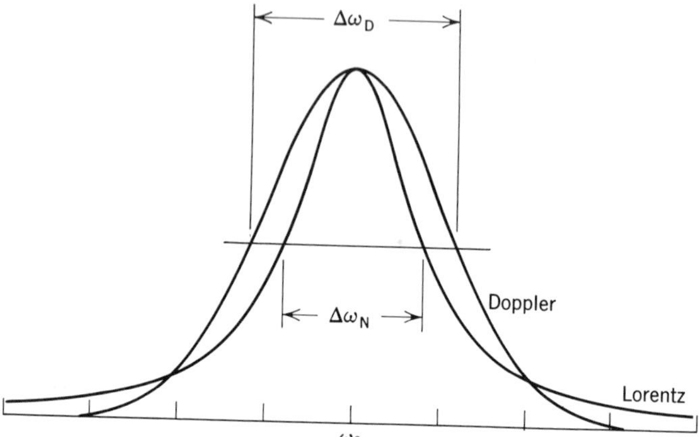

Fig. 1.13 Comparison of Lorentz and Gaussian profiles. Both curves have the same value at maximum, and both enclose unit area. The widths of the curves at half-maximum are shown as $\Delta\omega_D$ (for the Doppler profile) and as $\Delta\omega_N$ (for the Lorentz profile).

$$I(\omega) = \frac{\sqrt{\pi}}{\Delta\omega_D} \phi(a, b), \tag{6.23}$$

where $\phi(a, b)$ is the *Voigt function* [12–18]:

$$\phi(a, b) = \frac{a}{\pi} \int_{-\infty}^{\infty} dy \frac{e^{-y^2}}{(y - b)^2 + a^2}. \tag{6.24}$$

Numerous tables of $\phi(a, b)$ exist [15]–[18].

G. Atomic Properties

Spectral lines often comprise several closely spaced and unresolved components. These components may arise from hyperfine splitting (Section 2.9) or from fine structure. They may also be a manifestation of electric or magnetic fields acting to shift and separate the energy levels (Section 2.7). Such fields are often randomly distributed. The observed profile is then an average of the various line components, weighted by the appropriate probability [5].

H. Source Thickness

We can observe the radiation from a given atom only if our sample is sufficiently thin. As sample thickness grows, the radiation suffers more numerous collisions before it emerges from the sample. Increasing sample thickness tends to lessen the contrast between a spectral line and the adjacent continuum of background radiation. Ultimately, as the source becomes infinitely thick, the emergent radiation will have the appearance of blackbody radiation appropriate to the source temperature. Details of line profiles then disappear. The problem of predicting line profiles from sources of finite thickness is discussed in modern treatises on astrophysics or radiative transfer [1–3, 5].

REFERENCES

[1] A. Unsold, *Physik der Sternatmosphären*, Springer, Berlin (1955), 2nd ed.
[2] V. Ambartsumian (ed.), *Theoretical Astrophysics*, Pergamon, New York (1958).
[3] L. H. Aller, *Astrophysics: The Atmospheres of the Sun and Stars*, Ronald, New York (1963), 2nd ed.
[4] H. Griem, *Plasma Spectroscopy*, McGraw-Hill, New York (1964).
[5] J. W. Cooper, Plasma Spectroscopy, *Repts. Progr. Phys.* **29,** 35 (1966).
[6] P. G. Bergmann, *Introduction to the Theory of Relativity*, Prentice-Hall, Englewood Cliffs, New Jersey (1942).
[7] W. Pauli, *Theory of Relativity*, Pergamon, New York (1958).
[8] J. W. Strutt (Baron Rayleigh), *Phil. Mag.* **27,** 298 (1889).
[9] R. Bracewell, *The Fourier Transform and its Application*, McGraw-Hill, New York (1965).
[10] P. Franklin, *Introduction to Fourier Methods*, Dover, New York (1949).
[11] W. Feller, *An Introduction to Probability Theory and its Applications*, Wiley, New York (1957), Vol. 1, 2nd ed., Chap. XVII.
[12] W. Voigt, *Münch. Ber.* (1912), p. 603.
[13] A. C. G. Mitchell and M. W. Zemansky, *Resonance Radiation and Excited Atoms*, Cambridge University Press, Cambridge, England (1934), Sec. III.2.
[14] D. W. Posener, *Austral. J. Phys.* **12,** 184 (1959).
[15] B. D. Fried and S. D. Conte, *The Plasma Dispersion Function*, Academic, New York (1961).
[16] G. D. Finn and D. Mugglestone, *Monographs Nottingham Roy. Astron. Soc.* **129,** 221 (1965).
[17] D. G. Hummer, *Mem. Roy. Astron. Soc.* **70,** 1 (1905).
[18] B. H. Armstrong, *J. Quant. Spectrosc. Radiat. Transfer* **7,** 61 (1967).

2. The Nature of Atoms

2.1 KEPLERIAN MOTION

To interpret, in terms of basic atomic structure, the energy levels deduced from spectral information, we need some notion of how these internal energies arise. That is, we need a model of the atom.

The first clues to the structure of atoms appeared during the last years of the nineteenth century, when the electron was established as a universal constituent of matter. The theory of moving corpuscles of charge, as developed by H. A. Lorentz [1] and others, accounted for many of the electrical and optical properties of matter, and it seemed likely that such charges, when bound into atoms, were responsible for atomic spectra. For many years, however, no one proposed a theory that could account even qualitatively for the nature of observed spectra.

Then in 1911 experiments by Hans Geiger and Ernest Marsden [2] led Ernest Rutherford to propose [3] that the positive charge associated with an atom was concentrated in a very small region of the atom, and that this small atomic *nucleus* carried almost the entire mass of the atom. Guided by these experiments, Niels Bohr [4], in 1913, pictured the atom as a minute, dense, positively charged nucleus surrounded by an entourage of circling, negatively charged electrons. Bohr proposed that the atom was governed by the same laws of motion as our solar system, with the Coulomb attraction between electrons and nucleus replacing the gravitational attraction between planets and sun.

Through the work of Bohr and Arnold Sommerfeld [5], this simple model explained a large body of facts, and provided a convenient picture of atoms. Although the more abstract approaches of wave mechanics and quantum mechanics have now supplanted the earlier methods of Bohr and Sommerfeld, many of their results emerge from the more modern theories.

In this chapter, we examine this semiclassical theory of the atom both to appreciate its successes and to note some shortcomings. Bibliography 4 lists sources of further discussion.

The simplest realistic model of the most elementary atom, hydrogen, consists of a very light electron (mass m) revolving around a heavy nucleus (mass $= 1836m$). To a first approximation the nucleus remains stationary, and we can replace it by a fixed center of attraction. Thus we consider the motion of a point particle about a fixed center of force. We assume the atom to be isolated and free from external forces. The motion of the electron is then governed by two conservation equations. First, the total energy E, comprising potential (Coulomb) energy $-e^2/r$ plus kinetic energy $mv^2/2$, remains constant with time. In terms of components v_r and $v_\perp$ of radial and tangential velocity we have:

$$\begin{aligned} E = \text{constant} &= -\frac{e^2}{r} + \frac{m}{2}(v_r^2 + v_\perp^2) \\ &= -\frac{e^2}{r} + \frac{m\dot{r}^2}{2} + \frac{mr^2}{2}\dot{\phi}^2, \end{aligned} \tag{1.1}$$

where $\dot{r}$ and $\dot{\phi}$ stand for dr/dt and $d\phi/dt$, respectively. Because no torques act on the circling particle, the magnitude of the angular momentum p_ϕ is also constant:

$$p_\phi \equiv mv_\perp r \equiv mr^2\dot{\phi} = \text{constant}. \tag{1.2}$$

These two equations describe motion of a particle in a conic-section orbit as we will now see. First write r in terms of $dr/d\phi$, using (1.2) to eliminate $\dot{\phi}$:

$$\dot{r} \equiv \frac{dr}{dt} = \frac{dr}{d\phi} \cdot \frac{d\phi}{dt} = \frac{dr}{d\phi} \cdot \frac{p_\phi}{mr^2}. \tag{1.3}$$

Then use (1.2) again to eliminate $\dot{\phi}$ from (1.1):

$$E = -\frac{e^2}{r} + \frac{m}{2}\left(\frac{dr}{d\phi}\frac{p_\phi}{mr^2}\right)^2 + \frac{mr^2}{2}\left(\frac{p_\phi}{mr^2}\right)^2. \tag{1.4}$$

Next change variables, $r = 1/u$:

$$\frac{dr}{d\phi} = \frac{d}{d\phi} \cdot \frac{1}{u} = \frac{-1}{u^2}\frac{du}{d\phi},$$

$$E = -ue^2 + \frac{p_\phi^2}{2m}\left(\frac{du}{d\phi}\right)^2 + \frac{p_\phi^2 u^2}{2m}. \tag{1.5}$$

Solving for $du/d\phi$, we obtain the differential equation for the orbit:

$$\left(\frac{du}{d\phi}\right)^2 = \left(\frac{2mE}{p_\phi^2}\right) + \left(\frac{2me^2}{p_\phi^2}\right)u - u^2. \tag{1.6}$$

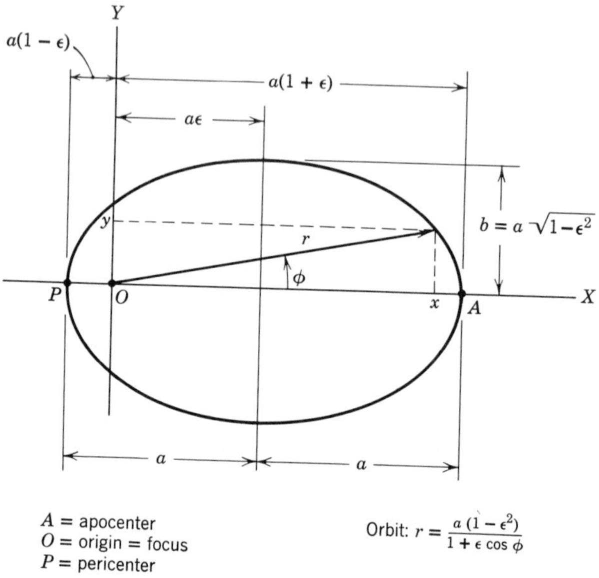

Fig. 2.1 Elements of an ellipse.

The equation for an ellipse in terms of the semimajor axis a and eccentricity ε is (see Fig. 2.1) [6], [7]:

$$r = \frac{a(1 - \varepsilon^2)}{1 + \varepsilon \cos \phi}, \tag{1.7}$$

so that, for an ellipse,

$$\frac{1}{r} = u = \frac{1}{a(1 - \varepsilon^2)} + \frac{\varepsilon \cos \phi}{a(1 - \varepsilon^2)}. \tag{1.8}$$

Differentiation gives the following equations:

$$\frac{du}{d\phi} = \frac{-\varepsilon \sin \phi}{a(1 - \varepsilon^2)}, \tag{1.9}$$

$$\left(\frac{du}{d\phi}\right)^2 = \frac{\varepsilon^2 \sin^2 \phi}{a^2(1 - \varepsilon^2)^2} = \frac{\varepsilon^2 - \varepsilon^2 \cos^2 \phi}{a^2(1 - \varepsilon^2)^2}. \tag{1.10}$$

Substitution of $\varepsilon^2 \cos^2 \phi$ from (1.8) into (1.10) gives

$$\left(\frac{du}{d\phi}\right)^2 = \frac{\varepsilon^2}{a^2(1 - \varepsilon^2)^2} - \left[u - \frac{1}{a(1 - \varepsilon^2)}\right]^2$$

$$= \left[\frac{\varepsilon^2 - 1}{a^2(1 - \varepsilon^2)^2}\right] + \left[\frac{2}{a(1 - \varepsilon^2)}\right] u - u^2. \tag{1.11}$$

On comparing the differential equation for an ellipse (1.11), with the equation of motion (1.6), we see they have the same form (i.e., the same dependence on u). We conclude, therefore, that the particle follows an elliptical path, with the nucleus at one focus. If we equate the coefficients of (1.6) with those of (1.11), we obtain the following relationship of the energy and angular momentum to the semimajor axis and eccentricity:

$$\frac{2mE}{p_\phi^2} = -\frac{1}{a^2(1-\varepsilon^2)}, \tag{1.12}$$

$$\frac{2me^2}{p_\phi^2} = \frac{2}{a(1-\varepsilon^2)}. \tag{1.13}$$

These equations give:

$$E = -\frac{e^2}{2a}, \tag{1.14}$$

$$p_\phi^2 = me^2a(1-\varepsilon^2) = -\frac{me^4(1-\varepsilon^2)}{2E}; \tag{1.15}$$

that is, the *energy depends only upon the semimajor axis* a, *not upon the eccentricity*. Note that the total energy E is negative, since a is positive by definition.

The special case of circular motion corresponds to the limit of an ellipse with eccentricity zero (a circle). The center of the circle coincides with the center of force. Denote the angular momentum for circular motion by p_{circ}. Then (1.15) gives:

$$p_\phi^2\,(\varepsilon = 0) \equiv p_{\text{circ}}^2 = me^2a. \tag{1.16}$$

Since motion in an elliptical orbit requires $0 \leq \varepsilon < 1$, the angular momentum in an orbit of fixed energy (fixed a) must be less than p_{circ}. Then from (1.15),

$$me^2a\varepsilon^2 = p_{\text{circ}}^2 - p_\phi^2,$$

or, according to (1.16),

$$\varepsilon^2 = 1 - \frac{(p_\phi)^2}{(p_{\text{circ}})^2}. \tag{1.17}$$

Thus we see that the *eccentricity measures the deviation of* p_ϕ^2 *from the maximum value* p_{circ}^2.

Although (1.14) and (1.16) imply that the circular radius a fixes both the energy and the maximum angular momentum, we can invert the argument and say that p_{circ} fixes the size of the orbit and the energy:

$$a = \frac{(p_{\text{circ}})^2}{me^2}, \tag{1.18}$$

$$E = -\frac{me^4}{2(p_{\text{circ}})^2}. \qquad (1.19)$$

With earth satellites, where a and ε are found from the observed elements of motion, (1.14) for $E(a)$ gives the energy. We can observe the orbit of an artificial satellite, but not the path of an electron within an atom. Consequently, (1.19) for $E(p_{\text{circ}})$ provides a more appropriate expression for the electron energy.

Motion along a hyperbolic path obeys the equation

$$r = \frac{a(\varepsilon^2 - 1)}{1 - \varepsilon \cos \phi}. \qquad (1.20)$$

An analysis analogous to (1.8) through (1.13) shows that, for hyperbolic motion,

$$E = +\frac{e^2}{2a}, \qquad (1.21)$$

$$p_\phi^{\,2} = \frac{me^4}{2E}(\varepsilon^2 - 1), \qquad (1.22)$$

where $\varepsilon > 1$. The angular momentum now has no upper bound for a given energy. Hence it is no longer possible to determine E from the maximum angular momentum. E is now a *positive* quantity. In the limit $\varepsilon \to 1$ the path is a parabola and the total energy is zero: the parabolic orbit provides the reference energy from which these hydrogen energies are reckoned. With this convention, a particle with *negative* total energy is *bound* to the center of attraction; that is, the elliptical orbit confines the particle to finite separations at all times. In contrast, a particle with *positive* energy will move in *unbound* hyperbolic orbit, and moves away indefinitely from the center of attraction. The parabolic orbit (the orbit with *zero* total energy), provides the classical dividing line between bound and unbound motion. (We may, of course, define the zero point of energy to be the lowest-lying bound energy, as is customary when tabulating or depicting energy levels. Such a convention adds a constant motion to all energies, but does not affect our conclusions about the motion.)

Whether the orbit is elliptic or hyperbolic, we can write (1.2) in an alternative form in terms of the area dA swept out in an infinitesimal time dt:

$$p_\phi = mr^2 \frac{d\phi}{dt} = 2m \frac{dA}{dt}; \qquad (1.23)$$

that is,

$$\frac{dA}{dt} = \text{constant} = \frac{p_\phi}{2m}. \qquad (1.24)$$

Thus the conservation of angular momentum is a statement of *Kepler's second law: the radius vector sweeps out equal areas in equal time intervals.* For periodic motion, (1.24) integrates to give

$$\frac{\text{area}}{\text{period}} = \frac{p_\phi}{2m}. \tag{1.25}$$

Thus the period τ is

$$\tau = \text{area} \times \frac{2m}{p_\phi} = \pi ab \frac{2m}{p_\phi}. \tag{1.26}$$

However, since the semiminor axis b is $a\sqrt{1 - \varepsilon^2}$, and according to (1.17) p_ϕ is $p_{\text{circ}}\sqrt{1 - \varepsilon^2}$, we find the period is independent of the eccentricity. In fact, we obtain *Kepler's third law:*

$$\tau^2 = \left(\frac{4\pi^2 m}{e^2}\right) a^3, \tag{1.27}$$

the square of the period is proportional to the cube of the mean radius. For our purposes it is more convenient to write the period in terms of energy and angular momentum. Equation 1.27 can be written as

$$\tau = 2\pi \frac{a}{e^2} p_{\text{circ}} = \frac{\pi p_{\text{circ}}}{(-E)} = 2\pi \frac{(p_{\text{circ}})^3}{me^4}. \tag{1.28}$$

This equality holds for any elliptical orbit.

More detailed discussions of Keplerian motion will be found in texts on celestial mechanics [8] or mechanics [6, 9] (Appendix B of Evans [7] is also useful). Shapley's source book [10] contains a translation of Kepler's laws as Kepler stated them.

REFERENCES

[1] H. A. Lorentz, *The Theory of Electrons*, Teubner, Leipzig (1909, 1916) [reprinted by Dover, New York (1952)].
[2] E. Rutherford, *Phil. Mag.* **21,** 669 (1911).
[3] H. Geiger and E. Marsden, *Proc. Roy. Soc. (London)* **82,** 495 (1909); *Phil. Mag.* **25,** 605 (1913).
[4] N. Bohr, *Phil. Mag.* **26,** 1, 476, and 857 (1913).
[5] A. Sommerfeld, *Ann. d. Physik* **51,** 1 (1916).
[6] J. C. Slater and N. H. Frank, *Mechanics*, McGraw-Hill, New York (1947).
[7] R. D. Evans, *The Atomic Nucleus*, McGraw-Hill, New York (1955), Appendix B.
[8] S. W. McCuskey, *Introduction to Celestial Mechanics*, Addison-Wesley, Reading, Massachusetts (1963).
[9] G. Joos, *Theoretical Physics*, Hafner, New York (1950), Chap. VI.
[10] H. Shapley, *A Sourcebook in Astronomy*, McGraw-Hill, New York (1929) (cf. Kepler's laws, p. 30).

2.2 CENTRAL FORCE MOTION

We need not find the actual orbit equation (1.7) to study motion in a Coulomb or gravitational field. Several aspects of the motion may be deduced from the energy equation. This approach [1], [2] permits us to draw qualitative conclusions about motion governed by more general force laws.

Let us introduce the radial component of momentum

$$p_r = mv_r = m\dot{r}, \tag{2.1}$$

to go along with the angular momentum

$$p_\phi = mrv_\perp = mr\dot{\phi}. \tag{2.2}$$

For motion in a Coulomb field (1.1) then gives

$$E = \frac{(p_r)^2}{2m} + \frac{(p_\phi)^2}{2mr^2} - \frac{e^2}{r}. \tag{2.3}$$

The energy, written as a function of *position* and *momenta* [rather than position and velocity, as in (1.1)] is called the *Hamiltonian.*

Because p_ϕ, like E, is constant with time, we can picture (2.3) as describing the motion of a hypothetical particle moving in a one-dimensional *effective potential* V':

$$E - V' = \frac{(p_r)^2}{2m}. \tag{2.4}$$

The effective potential is the sum of two parts: an attracting Coulomb potential and a repelling angular-momentum "potential":

$$V' \equiv V'(r, p_\phi) = \frac{(p_\phi)^2}{2mr^2} - \frac{e^2}{r}. \tag{2.5}$$

$V'(r)$ provides a simple example of a *central field:* a potential independent of angular position.

To illustrate the influence of angular momenta, Fig. 2.2 shows the effective potential for a particle of unit mass in a Coulomb field of unit charge:

$$V' = \frac{(p_\phi)^2}{2r^2} - \frac{1}{r}. \tag{2.6}$$

Although we have already found the exact solution for motion in a Coulomb field, it is useful to see how some of our previous conclusions emerge from a consideration of (2.4) and (2.5), without requiring an explicit determination of the orbit.

First, we can see that for *negative* energies E, the motion is bounded.

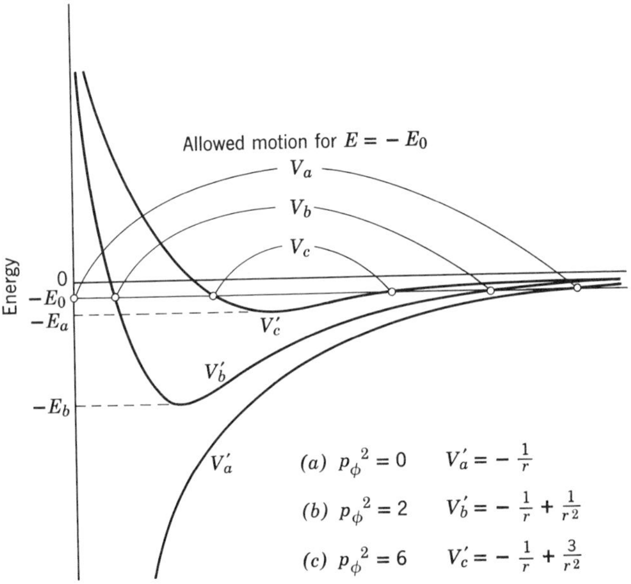

Fig. 2.2 Effective potentials of a Coulomb field for varying angular momentum.

That is, motion is restricted to a region of space for which r is greater than some minimum value $r_{\min}$ (possibly zero) and less than some maximum value $r_{\max}$. This restriction occurs because for very large values of r the effective potential becomes quite small and leaves the negative quantity E to dominate the left-hand side of (2.4):

$$E - V' \underset{r \to \infty}{\longrightarrow} E = -|E|. \tag{2.7}$$

Similarly, at sufficiently small r the quantity $(p_\phi)^2/2mr^2$ will dominate (unless $p_\phi = 0$):

$$E - V' \underset{r \to 0}{\longrightarrow} -\frac{(p_\phi)^2}{2mr^2}. \tag{2.8}$$

To avoid the contradiction of a negative quantity $(E - V')$ equaling the positive quantity $(p_r)^2/2m$ we conclude that radial motion is restricted to the region where

$$E - V'(r) \geq 0.$$

At the *turning points*, $r_{\max}$ and $r_{\min}$, defined as the points where

$$(p_r)^2 = 0,$$

the particle ceases its motion toward or away from the nucleus: $\dot{r} = 0$. The turning points occur at the intersections of the curve $V'(r)$ with the horizontal lines of constant energy:

$$V'(r) = E. \tag{2.9}$$

In the Coulomb field of (2.6) this condition, with

$$E = -\frac{1}{2(p_{\text{circ}})^2},$$

leads to the turning points

$$\begin{aligned} r_{\max}, r_{\min} &= (p_{\text{circ}})^2[1 \pm \sqrt{1 - (p_\phi/p_{\text{circ}})^2}\,] \\ &= (p_{\text{circ}})^2[1 \pm \epsilon]. \end{aligned} \tag{2.10}$$

The spacing between turning points is

$$r_{\max} - r_{\min} = 2(p_{\text{circ}})\sqrt{(p_{\text{circ}})^2 - (p_\phi)^2} = 2(p_{\text{circ}})^2\epsilon. \tag{2.11}$$

Next, viewing Fig. 2.2 we can see that as angular momentum increases (for a fixed negative energy), the two turning points draw closer together. For sufficiently large angular momentum, the turning points coalesce ($r_{\max} = r_{\min}$) and the motion is circular. If the angular momentum exceeds this critical value p_{circ}, motion is impossible: the curve $V'(r)$ lies everywhere above E, so that $E - V'$ is never positive.

Suppose we consider motion of a particle (a point charge) in a force field somewhat more general than the Coulomb field $-e/r^2$ of a point-charge nucleus. Let the potential energy be $-e^2f(r)/r$, where

$$\begin{aligned} f(r) &\to 1 \quad \text{for} \quad r \to \infty, \\ f(r) &\to Z \quad \text{for} \quad r \to 0. \end{aligned} \tag{2.12}$$

As we shall see, such a potential might govern the motion of one test electron in a neutral many-electron atom: close to the nucleus, the electron feels the full attraction of the nuclear charge $+Ze$; further away, the remaining electrons intervene to screen this nuclear charge; at very large distances, only the net charge $+e$ affects the test electron.

The effective potential of this *screened field* is

$$V'(r, p_\phi) = \frac{(p_\phi)^2}{2mr^2} - \frac{e^2f(r)}{r}. \tag{2.13}$$

As with the pure Coulomb field, no torques act upon the point charge, so the angular momentum remains constant with time. The electrical potential now deepens more rapidly than a Coulomb field as we approach the nucleus (e.g., the potential changes from $-e^2/r$ to $-2e^2/r$ and finally becomes $-Ze^2/r$). This deviation from the Coulomb field $-e^2/r$ lowers the inner portions of the curves $V'(r)$.

The precise specification of the orbit of a particle in a screened field is more difficult than the simple results of Section 2.1. We can draw some useful conclusions, however, simply by examining Fig. 2.3.

First, we can see that (2.7) and (2.8) apply to the field specified by (2.12) and (2.13), so that motion in the screened field is bounded for negative energies.

Next, suppose we compare the motion in a Coulomb field and a screened field, for fixed values of p_ϕ and p_{circ} or, on the basis of (2.11), for fixed values of $(p_\phi)^2$ and $(r_{\max} - r_{\min})$. We see that the screened field permits the inner turning point to draw nearer to the origin than does the pure Coulomb field. To maintain the same value of $r_{\max} - r_{\min}$, the energy must be

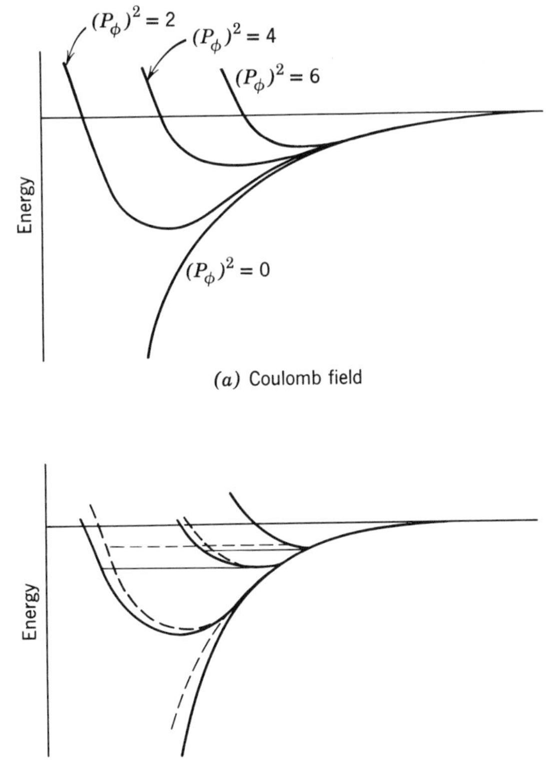

Fig. 2.3 Effective potential; Coulomb and screened fields.

lower. The energy difference between the Coulomb field and the screened field is most pronounced for orbits with low angular-momentum.

As another way of describing this dependence of energy on angular momentum, one can label orbits by the value of the *phase integrals* or *action angle variables*,

$$I_\phi = \int_0^{2\pi} p_\phi \, d\phi, \tag{2.14}$$

$$I_r = 2\int_{r_{\min}}^{r_{\max}} p_r \, dr, \tag{2.15}$$

associated with them. This approach formed the basis of the *old quantum theory*, exploited largely between 1913 and 1926. Nearly all references in Bibliography 4 discuss this approach. For a more modern discussion of these classical integrals see Goldstein [3].

Because p_ϕ remains constant around an orbit, I_ϕ is simply

$$I_\phi = 2\pi p_\phi. \tag{2.16}$$

I_ϕ takes this same value for motion in any central field. The radial integral was evaluated by Sommerfeld [4], for a Coulomb field (cf. Goldstein [3]):

$$\begin{aligned} I_r &= 2\pi p_\phi \left[\frac{1}{\sqrt{1-\epsilon^2}} - 1 \right] \\ &= 2\pi [p_{\text{circ}} - p_\phi]. \end{aligned} \tag{2.17}$$

This integral is proportional to the area under the curve $\sqrt{E - V'(r)}$ between $r_{\min}$ and $r_{\max}$. Therefore to maintain a given value of I_r when $V'(r)$ is altered from a Coulomb field to a screened field, the energy associated with the given orbit must be lowered. Again we find the largest energy shift is associated with smallest angular momenta.

A third line of reasoning further reinforces this conclusion. We can see from Fig. 2.3 that the energy of a circular orbit of given angular momentum will be lower for the screened field than for the Coulomb field. If, for given angular momentum, we label the orbits according to the excess energy over the energy in a circular orbit, we see that the screened field shifts this array of energies downward. Once again we see that the difference between Coulomb and screened field is largest for low angular momenta.

REFERENCES

[1] J. C. Slater and N. H. Frank, *Mechanics*, McGraw-Hill, New York (1947).

[2] H. Goldstein, *Classical Mechanics*, Addison-Wesley, Reading, Massachusetts (1950), Chap. 3.

[3] H. Goldstein, Ref. 2, Chap. 9.
[4] A. Sommerfeld, *Atomic Structure and Spectral Lines* (translated by H. L. Brose from 5th German ed. of 1931), Dutton, New York (1934); *Ann. Physik* **51,** 1 (1916).

2.3 CORRECTION FOR FINITE MASS

The motion of a small satellite about a massive attracting body actually deviates slightly from the perfect elliptical orbit of the last section, because the heavy body moves slightly under influence of the encircling satellite. To describe the motion more accurately, we should assume that each body moves freely under the influence of the other. The nucleus of mass M at position $\mathbf{r}_1$ moves according to the force $\mathbf{F}_1$ exerted by the satellite,

$$M\ddot{\mathbf{r}}_1 = \mathbf{F}_1, \tag{3.1}$$

while the satellite with mass m at $\mathbf{r}_2$ moves under the influence of the nuclear attraction $\mathbf{F}_2$,

$$m\ddot{\mathbf{r}}_2 = \mathbf{F}_2. \tag{3.2}$$

(Here, as elsewhere in this book, boldface symbols denote vector quantities.) The force exerted *by* the satellite is equal in magnitude and opposite in direction to the force exerted *on* it:

$$\mathbf{F}_1 = -\mathbf{F}_2. \tag{3.3}$$

Combining these equations, we find

$$M\ddot{\mathbf{r}}_1 + m\ddot{\mathbf{r}}_2 = \mathbf{F}_1 + \mathbf{F}_2 = \mathbf{F}_1 - \mathbf{F}_1 = 0, \tag{3.4}$$

$$\ddot{\mathbf{r}}_2 - \ddot{\mathbf{r}}_1 = \frac{\mathbf{F}_2}{m} - \frac{\mathbf{F}_1}{M} = \left(\frac{1}{m} + \frac{1}{M}\right)\mathbf{F}_1. \tag{3.5}$$

From (3.4) we see that the *center of mass*, with coordinates

$$\mathbf{R} \equiv \frac{M\mathbf{r}_1 + m\mathbf{r}_2}{M + m}, \tag{3.6}$$

is not accelerated, and so must move with constant velocity $\dot{\mathbf{R}}$. Furthermore, according to (3.5) the relative separation $\mathbf{r}$,

$$\mathbf{r} \equiv \mathbf{r}_1 - \mathbf{r}_2, \tag{3.7}$$

satisfies the equation

$$\mu\ddot{\mathbf{r}} = \mathbf{F}_1, \tag{3.8}$$

where the *reduced mass* μ is given by

$$\mu = \left(\frac{1}{m} + \frac{1}{M}\right)^{-1} = \frac{mM}{m + M}. \tag{3.9}$$

Equation 3.8 is the equation of motion for a particle of mass μ about a fixed center of attraction; the reduced mass μ appears in place of the satellite mass m. The energy in the new coordinates becomes

$$E = \frac{M}{2}(\dot{\mathbf{r}}_1)^2 + \frac{m}{2}(\dot{\mathbf{r}}_1)^2 + V(\mathbf{r}_1 - \mathbf{r}_2) \tag{3.10a}$$

$$= \frac{(m+M)}{2}(\dot{\mathbf{R}})^2 + \frac{\mu}{2}(\dot{\mathbf{r}})^2 + V(\mathbf{r}). \tag{3.10b}$$

Equation (3.10b) is identical with that describing the energy of a satellite of mass μ moving in the potential $V(\mathbf{r})$, except for the additive constant $\frac{1}{2}(m + M)(\dot{\mathbf{R}})^2$. This constant is the kinetic energy of the atom as a whole. Because only energy *differences* are ever observable, we shall always neglect such additive constants to the energy terms. We thereby exclude the study of motions of entire atoms, and concentrate upon the motion of electrons within the atoms.

From (3.9) we see that, for a system comprising two attracting particles of equal mass m, the reduced mass is half the free mass,

$$\mu = \tfrac{1}{2}m, \tag{3.11a}$$

and the center of mass lies midway between the particles:

$$\mathbf{R} = \tfrac{1}{2}(\mathbf{r}_1 + \mathbf{r}_2). \tag{3.12a}$$

Alternatively, when one particle is much more massive, $m \ll M$, the reduced mass tends toward the mass of the lighter particle,

$$\mu = \frac{m}{1 + (m/M)} = m\left[1 - \frac{m}{M} + \left(\frac{m}{M}\right)^2 + \cdots\right], \tag{3.11b}$$

and the center of mass nearly coincides with the position $\mathbf{r}_1$ of the heavier particle:

$$\mathbf{R} = \left(\mathbf{r}_1 + \frac{m}{M}\mathbf{r}_2\right)\frac{\mu}{m}. \tag{3.12b}$$

For the hydrogen atom, m/M is the ratio of electron to proton mass:

$$\frac{m}{M} = \frac{1}{1836.1}.$$

2.4 QUANTIZED ENERGY LEVELS

We observed in Section 2.1 that either the semimajor axis a or the circular angular momentum p_{circ} serves to set the scale of energies for a particle moving in an elliptical orbit. Let us see why angular momentum should be more fundamental than orbit size for the description of atomic structure.

In Section 1.5 we mentioned evidence (Planck's formula for blackbody radiation; Einstein's formula for the photoelectric effect) indicating that electromagnetic radiation is quantized into photons carrying the energy

$$E = h\nu \quad \text{or} \quad E = \hbar\omega. \tag{4.1}$$

An electromagnetic field carries not only energy, but momentum and angular momentum as well. Therefore, because the photon carries a quantum of energy, it should also carry a unit of angular momentum.

$$p_\phi = n\hbar \equiv n\frac{h}{2\pi}, \tag{4.2}$$

where n is an integer. If, following Bohr, we equate the angular momentum carried off by the photon to the angular momentum in a circular orbit, (1.19) gives

$$E = \frac{-me^4}{2(p_{\text{circ}})^2} = -\left(\frac{me^4}{2\hbar^2}\right)\frac{1}{n}. \tag{4.3}$$

These quantized energy levels, first derived by Bohr in 1913, produce the integers (the *principal quantum numbers* n) required for the empirical *term values* T_n:

$$T_n = -hcE_n = \frac{R}{n^2}\ \text{cm}^{-1}, \quad \text{with} \quad R = \left(\frac{me^4}{4\pi\hbar^3 c}\right). \tag{4.4}$$

Moreover, when Bohr derived (4.3), he found that the bracketed term equaled the observed Rydberg energy, within the uncertainty of e, c, $\hbar$, and m. As we shall see, quantum-mechanical calculations reproduce the result in (4.3).

Bohr proposed that spectral lines originate in transitions between stationary states whose energies are given by (4.3). Applying the relation $E = h\nu = hc\bar{\nu}$, Bohr predicted the several well-known series of hydrogen lines and forecast the existence of others still undiscovered:

$$\bar{\nu} = \frac{E_2}{hc} - \frac{E_1}{hc} = R\left[\frac{1}{(n_1)^2} - \frac{1}{(n_2)^2}\right]. \tag{4.5}$$

For an electron circling a nucleus of charge Ze, (4.3) gives the energy levels

$$E_n = -\frac{mZ^2e^4}{2\hbar^2}\frac{1}{n^2} = -hcR\frac{Z^2}{n^2}. \tag{4.6}$$

Such a one-electron system should exhibit a hydrogen-like spectrum, with series governed by the formula

$$\tilde{\nu} = Z^2 R \left[\frac{1}{(n_1)^2} - \frac{1}{(n_2)^2} \right]. \tag{4.7}$$

As we have seen [in (3.7) of Chapter 1], this formula does indeed describe the series observed in He II, Li III, Be IV, etc.

A. The Rydberg Constant

As Bohr noted in a second paper [1], the mass appearing in the energy expression (4.3) should properly be the reduced mass μ of an electron circling the nuclear mass M:

$$\mu = \frac{m}{1 + m/M} = m\left(1 - \frac{m}{M} + \cdots\right). \tag{4.8}$$

The difference between μ and m (the mass of a free electron) is negligible for very heavy atoms, but it is readily observable for light atoms. Consequently, the conventional symbol for the Rydberg constant includes a subscript indicating the atom in question. To obtain the Rydberg constant R_∞, the Rydberg frequency Ry, and the Rydberg energy hcR_∞ for an infinitely massive nucleus set $\mu = m$ in (4.4):

$$R_\infty = \frac{me^4}{4\pi\hbar^3 c} = 109737.31 \text{ cm}^{-1},$$

$$\text{Ry} \equiv cR_\infty = \frac{me^4}{4\pi\hbar^3} = 3.28984 \times 10^{15} \text{ Hz},$$

$$hcR_\infty = \frac{me^4}{2\hbar^2} = 2.17972 \times 10^{-11} \text{ erg}$$

$$= 13.6054 \text{ eV}.$$

For lighter atoms the Rydberg constant becomes

$$R_\text{A} = R_\infty\left(\frac{\mu_\text{A}}{m}\right) = \frac{R_\infty}{1 + (m/M_\text{A})}, \tag{4.9a}$$

where M_A is the mass of the *nucleus* of atom A. Expressed in terms of the mass of the *neutral atom*, $M_\text{A}^* = M_\text{A} + m$, (4.9*a*) reads:

$$R_\text{A} = R_\infty \frac{(M_\text{A}^* - m)}{M_\text{A}^*}. \tag{4.9b}$$

The values for hydrogen are

$$R_\text{H} = 109677.576 \text{ cm}^{-1},$$
$$cR_\text{H} = 3.288051 \times 10^{15} \text{ Hz},$$
$$hcR_\text{H} = 13.5794 \text{ eV}.$$

About 1.6% of the atoms of the natural element hydrogen possess a nucleus with roughly twice the mass of a proton. These *deuterium* atoms maintain a single electron orbiting around a singly charged nucleus consisting of a proton and a neutron. Chemically, deuterium is nearly indistinguishable from hydrogen. (We reserve the name *hydrogen* for the atom with a nucleus comprised of a single proton.) However, the spectrum of deuterium differs slightly from that of hydrogen, because of the larger reduced mass for the deuterium electron. The so-called $D\alpha$ line of deuterium occurs 1.8 Å toward the violet of the corresponding $H\alpha$ line at 6562.8 Å. The Rydberg constant for deuterium is [2]

$$R_D = 109.707.419 \text{ cm}^{-1}.$$

Most other elements also consist of mixtures of *isotopes* (atoms carrying the same nuclear charge yet differing in atomic weight). Two isotopes of a given element differ by the number of neutrons bound in the nucleus.

As found in nature, the element helium is a mixture of He^3 (two protons, one neutron in the nucleus) and He^4 (two protons, two neutrons) having the Rydberg constants [3]

$$R_{He^3} = 109{,}717.345 \text{ cm}^{-1},$$
$$R_{He4} = 109{,}722.267 \text{ cm}^{-1}.$$

The measurement of wavelength or wavenumber differences can be carried out with very high accuracy (about two parts in 10^9). Consequently the Rydberg constant R_∞ is one of the most accurately known physical constants. The combination $(me^4/\hbar^2)$ is known to a few parts in 10^9, whereas the individual values for e, $\hbar$, and m are good to five decimal places at best [3]. In dealing with atomic properties, it often proves convenient to take the electron charge e, the electron mass m, and the Dirac constant $\hbar = h/2\pi$ as the basic quantitative units. We can then set $e = m = \hbar = 1$ in all equations. The following paragraphs discuss these *atomic units*. Appendix A gives additional examples. (Physicists frequently use an alternative system with $c = \hbar = 1$.)

B. The Bohr Radius

The radius of the circular orbit obtained from (1.16) with $p_{circ} = 1\hbar$ corresponds, in the Bohr theory, to the smallest permissible orbit for hydrogen. This unit of length, commonly denoted a_0, is called the *Bohr radius* (more precisely, the first Bohr radius for a hydrogen atom with infinitely heavy nucleus):

$$a_0 = \frac{\hbar^2}{me^2} = 5.29167 \times 10^{-9} \text{ cm}.$$

According to the Bohr theory, as well as the subsequent quantum theory, this unit indicates the general order of magnitude of atomic radii. Various observations (such as spacing of atoms in a crystal and the effective sizes of colliding gas molecules) verify that atoms are indeed a few angstrom units (10^{-8} cm) in diameter. In discussions of atomic phenomena lengths are commonly expressed in units of a_0 (*atomic units*).

According to (1.18) and (4.2), the semimajor axes of successively larger hydrogen orbits follow the relationship

$$a = a_0 n^2. \tag{4.10}$$

The orbits around a nucleus of charge Ze possess the semimajor axes

$$a = \frac{\hbar^2 n^2}{mZe^2} = a_0 \frac{n^2}{Z}. \tag{4.11}$$

(These results again emerge from quantum theory.) The energy for an electron in such an orbit (4.6) can be written

$$E = -\frac{Ze^2}{2a} = -\frac{e^2}{2a_0}\frac{Z^2}{n^2}. \tag{4.12}$$

We should note a further quantization: the ratio of semiminor axis to semimajor axis is

$$\frac{b}{a} = \sqrt{1 - \varepsilon^2}. \tag{4.13}$$

But from (1.17)

$$\varepsilon^2 = 1 - \frac{(p_\phi)^2}{(p_{\text{circ}})^2}, \tag{4.14}$$

therefore the fraction b/a is equal to the ratio of actual angular momentum p_ϕ to the angular momentum p_{circ} in a circular orbit with the same energy:

$$\frac{b}{a} = \left(\frac{(p_\phi)^2}{(p_{\text{circ}})^2}\right)^{1/2} = \frac{p_\phi}{p_{\text{circ}}}. \tag{4.15}$$

Quantization of angular momentum has thus led to a quantization of orbit shape as well as orbit energy. This quantization may also be expressed in terms of the classical turning points introduced in Section 2.2,

$$\begin{aligned} r_{\max} - r_{\min} &= 2(p_{\text{circ}})^2\varepsilon \\ &= 2(p_{\text{circ}})\sqrt{(p_{\text{circ}})^2 - (p_\phi)^2}, \end{aligned}$$

or in terms of the action variables of Section 2.2,

$$\begin{aligned} I_\phi &= 2\pi p_\phi, \\ I_r &= 2\pi(p_{\text{circ}} - p_\phi), \end{aligned}$$

as first proposed by Wilson [4], Ishiwara [5], and Sommerfeld [6].

C. The Atomic Unit of Velocity

The velocity of an electron in a circular orbit may be obtained from the circular angular momentum p_{circ}:

$$v_{\text{circ}} = \frac{p_{\text{circ}}}{ma} = \frac{Ze^2}{n\hbar}. \tag{4.16}$$

This velocity is most conveniently expressed in terms of c, the speed of light, with the aid of Sommerfeld's dimensionless *fine-structure constant* [1] α:

$$\alpha \equiv \frac{e^2}{\hbar c} = \frac{1}{137.0388} = 7.29720 \times 10^{-3}.$$

The circular velocity is

$$v_{\text{circ}} = \frac{Z}{n}\alpha c = \frac{Z}{n} \times 2.1877 \times 10^8 \frac{\text{cm}}{\text{sec}}.$$

The circular velocity in the first Bohr orbit of hydrogen, $v_0 \equiv \alpha c$, provides the conventional *atomic unit of velocity.*

Classically, the speed is greatest at pericenter, where it takes the value

$$v = v_{\text{circ}} \frac{1+\varepsilon}{1-\varepsilon}. \tag{4.17}$$

Evidently orbits with large eccentricity (i.e., small angular momentum) may require very high velocities near pericenter. When we discuss speeds approaching the speed of light, we must incorporate the theory of relativity into our discussion. (The relativistic effects in the spectrum of hydrogen are briefly mentioned in chapter 8.) Relativistic effects become important for small orbits in highly charged nuclei or for highly eccentric orbits.

D. The Atomic Unit of Time

The period of motion in an elliptical orbit does not depend on the eccentricity. From (1.28) we find the period

$$\tau = \frac{\pi p_{\text{circ}}}{(-E)} = \frac{1}{(2cR)} \frac{n^3}{Z^2}. \tag{4.18}$$

We may anticipate that this period roughly indicates the time scale for atomic motions. The time required for an electron to move through one radian ($\frac{1}{2}\pi$ revolution) in the first Bohr orbit of hydrogen, apart from the reduced mass effect, is

$$\frac{\tau_0}{2\pi} = (4\pi c R_\infty)^{-1} = \frac{\hbar^3}{me^4} = \frac{a_0}{v_0} = 2.4189 \times 10^{-17} \text{ sec.}$$

This interval provides the conventional *atomic unit of time*. As we shall see later, the time intervals involved for radiation processes are typically of the order of 10^{-8} sec or longer and are therefore longer than atomic intervals by roughly 10^9.

E. Ionization

All of the orbits mentioned so far represent *bound* states of atoms. The total energy is *negative* and the orbits never extend to infinitely large distances. If we add energy to a bound electron by the influence of external forces, the electron orbit increases in size. Given sufficient energy, the electron can escape into a parabolic or hyperbolic orbit, leaving behind an ionized atom. The energy is then unquantized (i.e., the energy is not restricted to discrete quantized values).

In order to escape from an orbit whose energy is $-E_n$ the electron must receive energy *at least* equal to E_n. The minimum energy required to remove an electron from an energy level is called the *binding energy* of the electron. The *ionization energy* is the binding energy of an electron in the lowest energy level (the *ground level*); for example, the lowest energy of the hydrogen atom is

$$E_0 = -\frac{hcR_{\mathrm{H}}}{1^2}.$$

Thus the ionization energy for hydrogen is hcR_{H}. This is the minimum amount of energy that must be given up by a free electron in combining with a proton to form stable hydrogen. The energy difference between the ground level and a higher level (an excited level) is the *excitation energy*.

Conventionally, ionization energies are measured in terms of the kinetic energy acquired by an electron in dropping through an electric potential of one volt. This unit, the *electron volt*, abbreviated eV, is [1]

$$1 \text{ eV} = 1.60210 \times 10^{-12} \text{ erg}.$$

The ionization energy in electron volts and the electric potential in volts are both commonly referred to as the *ionization potential*, abbreviated IP. (More precisely, one should express the ionization potential in volts and the ionization energy in electron volts, but this distinction is commonly neglected.) For hydrogen the ionization potential is [2]

$$\text{IP} = \frac{hcR_{\mathrm{H}}}{e/c} = 13.59765 \text{ V}.$$

Atoms with two or more electrons exhibit several ionization limits. Conventionally, we define the second ionization potential as the energy required to just remove one electron, leaving the resultant ion in its second energy state. Higher ionization potentials, for which the ion is left in higher energy levels, are similarly defined.

REFERENCES

[1] N. Bohr, *Nature* **92**, 231 (1913).

[2] E. R. Cohen, K. M. Crowe, and J. W. M. DuMond, *Fundamental Constants of Physics*, Interscience, New York (1957).

[3] E. R. Cohen and J. W. M. DuMond, *Proceedings of the Second International Conference on Nuclidic Masses and Related Constants*, p. 152, Springer, Vienna (1964); Natl. Bur. Stds. Tech. News Bull. **47**, 175 (October 1963).

[4] W. Wilson, *Phil. Mag.* **29**, 795 (1915); **31**, 156 (1916).

[5] J. Ishiwara, *Tokyo Math. Phys. Proc.* **8**, 106 (1915).

[6] A. Sommerfeld, *Sitzber. München* (1915), pp. 425, 459; (1916), p. 131; (1917), p. 83; *Ann. d. Physik* **51**, 1 (1916).

2.5 MAGNETIC MOMENTS

Because every electric current or moving charge creates a magnetic field, we anticipate that a circling electron creates the field of a small current loop. As viewed *from the stationary nucleus*, the moving charge creates a field given by Ampère's law,

$$\mathbf{H}(\mathbf{r}) = -\frac{e}{c}\frac{\mathbf{r} \times \mathbf{v}}{r^3} \tag{5.1}$$

($-e$ is the electron charge in esu, $-e/c$ the charge in emu). At the nucleus, this field is perpendicular (i.e. *normal*) to the orbital plane; that is, antiparallel to the angular momentum of the electron:

$$\mathbf{H}_{\text{orb}}(0) = \frac{-e}{mcr^3}\,\mathbf{p}_\phi. \tag{5.2}$$

In an elliptic orbit, r does not remain constant, and we must introduce an average value of the quantity r^{-3}, weighted according to the probability of finding a given r.

As viewed from *very far outside* a small current loop, the magnetic field is the same as that of a small bar magnet. We idealize this field as that of an infinitesimal dipole, a *magnetic moment* $\boldsymbol{\mu}$. The magnetic moment of a current loop points normal to the plane of the current, with the magnitude

$$\mu = \text{current} \times \text{orbit area}. \tag{5.3}$$

For a current caused by an orbiting charge, we can write

$$\mu = \frac{\text{charge}}{\text{period}} \times \text{orbit area}; \tag{5.4}$$

but, according to Kepler's second law (1.25), the ratio of area to period has the constant value $(p_\phi/2m)$. Thus the magnetic moment of an orbiting point electron, with charge $-e/c$ (emu), is

$$\boldsymbol{\mu} = -\frac{e}{2mc}\,\mathbf{p}_\phi. \tag{5.5}$$

The ratio of magnetic moment to angular momentum (here $-e/2mc$) is known as the *gyromagnetic ratio.*

In dealing with phenomena on an atomic scale, we find it convenient to measure angular momentum in atomic units of

$$\hbar = 1.05450 \times 10^{-27} \text{ erg-sec},$$

instead of the macroscopic cgs units, erg-sec. We therefore introduce the dimensionless vector quantity **L** by writing

$$\mathbf{p}_\phi = \text{orbital angular momentum} = \hbar\mathbf{L}. \tag{5.6}$$

Equation 5.3 then reads

$$\boldsymbol{\mu} = -\beta\mathbf{L}, \tag{5.7}$$

where the *Bohr magneton* β (also denoted by μ_B) is the atomic unit of magnetic moment:

$$\mu_B \equiv \beta \equiv \frac{e\hbar}{2mc} = 9.2732 \times 10^{-21}\,\frac{\text{erg}}{\text{gauss}}.$$

When no external field is present, we have no way of distinguishing the various possible orientations of the orbital plane and magnetic moment. A magnetic field provides a reference direction; magnetic moments tend to align themselves along field lines of force. If a dipole is oriented at an angle θ with a uniform field **H**, the field produces a torque:

$$\text{torque} = -\,|\mu H|\,\sin\theta, \tag{5.8}$$

which tends to turn the dipole antiparallel to the field. The dipole is stably oriented only when it points directly along the field. In order to turn the dipole from this stable position to the orientation θ, we must do work against the field:

$$\text{work} = \int (\text{torque})\,d\theta = |\mu H|\,\cos\theta \equiv \boldsymbol{\mu}\cdot\mathbf{H}. \tag{5.9}$$

Thus we can ascribe to a magnetic moment in a uniform field a potential energy ΔE:

$$\Delta E = -\boldsymbol{\mu}\cdot\mathbf{H}. \tag{5.10}$$

We therefore expect that an energy level for a single-electron atom will be shifted by an amount proportional to **H** and to the component of angular momentum **L** along the field direction:

$$\Delta E_L = -\beta\mathbf{L}\cdot\mathbf{H}. \tag{5.11}$$

This analysis assumes, of course, that the orbit size remains unaffected by the external field. If the field is sufficiently strong, this assumption cannot be correct. We should anticipate that (5.11) will hold only as long as the force of the field remains a minor perturbation on the Coulomb force. In other words, this picture can be correct only if the orientation energy ΔE is small compared with the separation of the normal energy levels. We will consider more general cases in Chapter 11.

The foregoing simple arguments show that atomic energy levels will be influenced by magnetic fields; either fields of external origin or fields resulting from currents and moments in neighboring atoms. Before we discuss the actual observations, however, we should note a further influence of magnetic fields.

In a nonuniform field the force on one end of a dipole exceeds the opposing force on the opposite end, and a net force as well as a torque results. If the magnetic moment of a particle points parallel to the field, the particle will be repelled from the region of strong field. If the moment is antiparallel to the field the particle accelerates into the strong region. Quantitatively, the magnitude of the force on a dipole moment pointing antiparallel to a field in the z direction is

$$F_z = \mu \frac{\partial}{\partial z} H_z. \tag{5.12}$$

For an arbitrary orientation the force is a more complicated function, but we can use the vector operator ∇ (read "del"),

$$\nabla \equiv \mathbf{e}_x \frac{\partial}{\partial x} + \mathbf{e}_y \frac{\partial}{\partial y} + \mathbf{e}_z \frac{\partial}{\partial z} \tag{5.13}$$

(where $\mathbf{e}_x$, $\mathbf{e}_y$, and $\mathbf{e}_z$ are unit vectors along the coordinate axes), to write the force as

$$\mathbf{F} = (\boldsymbol{\mu}\cdot\nabla)\mathbf{H}; \tag{5.14a}$$

that is, the force in the z direction is

$$F_z = \mu_x \frac{\partial}{\partial x} H_z + \mu_y \frac{\partial}{\partial y} H_y + \mu_z \frac{\partial}{\partial z} H_z.$$

We can also write (5.14*a*) as

$$\mathbf{F} = \nabla(\boldsymbol{\mu}\cdot\mathbf{H}), \tag{5.14b}$$

by using an identity from vector analysis,

$$\nabla(\mathbf{A}\cdot\mathbf{B}) = (\mathbf{A}\cdot\nabla)\mathbf{B} + (\mathbf{B}\cdot\nabla)\mathbf{A} + \mathbf{A}\times(\nabla\times\mathbf{B}) + \mathbf{B}\times(\nabla\times\mathbf{A}), \tag{5.15}$$

and the facts that $\boldsymbol{\mu}$ is constant and $\mathbf{H}$ satisfies

$$\nabla\times\mathbf{H} = 0. \tag{5.16}$$

Using (5.7), we again find the magnetic field exerts an influence proportional to the component of angular momentum along a preferred direction. The influence here is a net force, and the preferred direction is that along which the field changes most rapidly:

$$\mathbf{F} = -\beta(\mathbf{L}\cdot\nabla)\mathbf{H}. \tag{5.17}$$

We thus conclude that atoms will possess magnetic moments that reveal themselves in two ways. First, in the presence of a uniform field the normal energy levels will be altered slightly according to the orientation of the atom in the field. Second, an inhomogeneous magnetic field will separate a collection of atoms according to the orientations of their magnetic moments.

Both these effects are actually observed. Atoms *do* possess magnetic moments roughly the size of a Bohr magneton. However, the full explanation of observed atomic moments requires a source of magnetic moment in addition to the orbital moment of (5.7). As we shall see in the following sections, the observations can be understood only if we assume that the electron possesses an "intrinsic" magnetic moment. This must be a permanent property of an electron, independent of its motion, just as charge and mass are intrinsic characteristics. In 1925 George Uhlenbeck and Samuel Goudsmit suggested [1] that the electron possesses an intrinsic angular momentum and a consequent magnetic moment. They pictured the electron as a tiny, spinning, charged sphere, possessing a magnetic moment as a result of its spinning motion. Although it is not necessary to rely on such a concrete picture of the electron, the designation *spin* has become firmly established as the name for the intrinsic angular momentum of any particle. As with orbital angular momentum, spin $\mathbf{S}$ is measured in atomic units:

$$\text{spin angular momentum} = \hbar\mathbf{S}. \tag{5.18}$$

For a negatively charged particle (in particular an electron), the intrinsic (or spin) magnetic moment will point antiparallel to the spin, by extension of (5.12). Introducing a proportionality factor g_S we can write the spin moment as

$$\boldsymbol{\mu}_S = -g_S\beta\mathbf{S}. \tag{5.19}$$

The preceding discussion suggests that an atom with a single valence electron should possess a total magnetic moment resulting from the vector sum of the spin moment $\boldsymbol{\mu}_S$ and the orbital moment (5.7):

$$\boldsymbol{\mu}_L = -\beta\mathbf{L}. \tag{5.20}$$

The resultant moment for the atom would be

$$\begin{aligned}\boldsymbol{\mu} &= \boldsymbol{\mu}_S + \boldsymbol{\mu}_L \\ &= -\beta(g_S\mathbf{S} + \mathbf{L}).\end{aligned} \tag{5.21}$$

This formula does indeed apply for many energy levels, as we shall see in Section 2.12 F.

In the years since 1925, it has been found that the proton and neutron, as well as many (but not all) atomic nuclei possess a magnetic moment and an intrinsic angular momentum or spin. Nuclear magnetic moments are found to be smaller than electron moments by roughly a factor of a thousand, as we expect from applying (5.8) to the heavy mass of a proton ($M_P \cong 1836m$). The conventional unit for nuclear moments is the *nuclear magneton* β_N:

$$\beta_N = \frac{e\hbar}{2M_Pc} = \frac{m}{M_P}\beta = 5.0505 \times 10^{-24} \text{ erg/gauss}.$$

REFERENCE

[1] G. E. Uhlenbeck and S. Goudsmit, *Naturwiss.* **13,** 953 (1925); *Physica* **5,** 266 (1925); *Zeits. f. Phys.* **35,** 618 (1926); *Nature* **117,** 264 (1926).

2.6 QUANTIZED ORIENTATION

A magnetic field produces a remarkable effect on atoms: the normal energy levels split into several uniformly spaced sublevels (often called

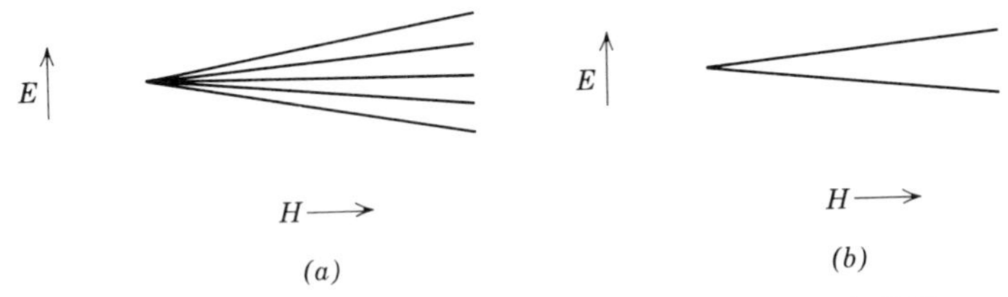

Fig. 2.4 Splitting of energy levels in a magnetic field.

states), symmetrically arranged about the normal level. Schematically, the field produces a splitting such as that shown in Fig. 2.4. The splitting is directly proportional to the field strength for sufficiently weak fields. Thus the splitting follows a pattern which may be written as

$$E_0 \rightarrow \begin{cases} E_0 + bH\,(J) \\ E_0 + bH\,(J-1) \\ E_0 + bH\,(J-2), \\ \cdot \\ \cdot \\ \cdot \\ E_0 - bH\,(J-1) \\ E_0 - bH\,(J) \end{cases} \tag{6.1}$$

where b is simply a proportionality factor and J is an integer or half-integer. Typically, a field of 20 kilogauss (kG) produces a splitting of about 1 kayser (1 reciprocal centimeter).

The evidence for such splitting takes many forms. Historically, the first indication of energy-level splitting came from Peter Zeeman's observations [1] of the splitting of spectral lines in a magnetic field. We shall discuss this *Zeeman effect* in the next section.

Further evidence comes from the fact that one can observe radiative transitions at the frequency bH/h, corresponding to the energy difference between two successive sublevels. Such transitions (various types of *magnetic resonance* phenomena [2]) are usually observed at radio frequencies, rather than optical frequencies. Comparison of the observed frequencies with magnetic field strength reveals that the parameter b, although varying from pattern to pattern, is roughly 1 β (one Bohr magneton).

It is reasonable to suppose that these discrete energy sublevels correspond to discrete orientations of atomic magnetic moments in the magnetic field. This is indeed the explanation, as Otto Stern and Walther Gerlach first demonstrated [3] in 1921. They passed a stream of neutral silver atoms through an inhomogeneous magnetic field and observed two resulting beams, corresponding to two possible orientations of the silver magnetic moment.

Let us write the energy splitting in terms of the Bohr magneton β and a dimensionless factor g, the *Landé g factor* [4] (or *Landé splitting factor*):

$$E_0 \rightarrow \begin{cases} E_0 + g\beta H\,(J) \\ E_0 + g\beta H\,(J-1) \\ \cdot \\ \cdot \\ \cdot \\ E_0 - g\beta H\,(J). \end{cases} \tag{6.2}$$

It is also convenient to introduce a *magnetic quantum number* M, such that M takes the values

$$M = J, \ldots, \tfrac{5}{2}, \tfrac{3}{2}, \tfrac{1}{2}, -\tfrac{1}{2}, -\tfrac{3}{2}, \ldots, -J \tag{6.3a}$$

for half-integral J, or the values

$$M = J, \ldots, 3, 2, 1, 0, -1, -2, \ldots, -J \tag{6.3b}$$

for integral J. We can then write a typical energy shift (6.2) as

$$E_0 \rightarrow E_0 + Mg\beta H. \tag{6.4}$$

In any given species of atom, the splitting produces either an *even* number of sublevels from every level (and therefore the J values are all integers) or it produces an *odd* number of sublevels (and therefore the J values are all half-integers).

The observed energy shifts are what we should expect for the orientation energy of a magnetic moment

$$\boldsymbol{\mu} = g\beta\mathbf{J}, \tag{6.5}$$

if the angular momentum $\mathbf{J}$ takes only orientations such that

$$\mathbf{J}\cdot\mathbf{H} = M|\mathbf{H}|, \tag{6.6}$$

where successive M values differ by unity. Positive values of M mean $\mathbf{J}$ points along the direction of $\mathbf{H}$, negative M means $\mathbf{J}$ points in the direction opposite to that of $\mathbf{H}$. The number J must represent the maximum component of the vector $\mathbf{J}$ along the field direction. It does not follow, however, that the vector $\mathbf{J}$ has the "length" J. We can say only that the length $|\mathbf{J}|$ is less than $J + \frac{1}{2}$:

$$J \leq |\mathbf{J}| < J + \tfrac{1}{2}. \tag{6.7}$$

As is shown in chapter 6, the length

$$\begin{aligned} |\mathbf{J}| &= \sqrt{\mathbf{J}\cdot\mathbf{J}} \\ &= \sqrt{J(J+1)} = J + \tfrac{1}{2} - \tfrac{1}{8}J + \cdots \end{aligned} \tag{6.8}$$

can be attributed to the vector $\mathbf{J}$. Some authors use the notation $\mathbf{J}^*$ in place of our $\mathbf{J}$ to emphasize that $|\mathbf{J}^*|$ is not equal to J. Our notation is more prevalent, however: we let $\mathbf{J}$ stand for an angular-momentum vector, and J stand for a quantum number.

A simple heuristic vector model enables one to picture the values of M that can occur for a given J value. For a vector $\mathbf{J}$ of length between 3 and $3\frac{1}{2}$ we can expect the components -3, -2, -1, 0, $+1$, $+2$, and $+3$. Figure 2.5 illustrates these orientations. (Only the polar angle is fixed; the plane of the diagram is undetermined.)

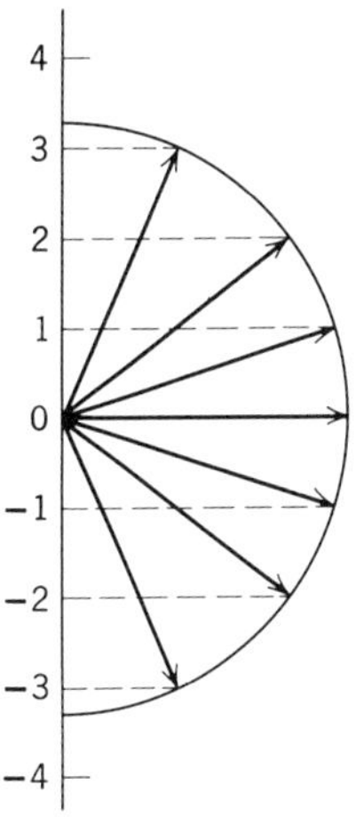

Fig. 2.5 Orientations of $\mathbf{J}$ for $J = 3$.

Conventionally, the vector **J** defined in this manner is called the *total angular momentum*. J is the *inner quantum number* of older literature. Equations 6.5 and 6.6, in providing essentially an observational definition of **J**, give no indication of how **J** (or $\boldsymbol{\mu}$) relates to the angular momenta of individual electrons; the equations simply express the observed energy splitting. The task of explaining the observed g values (i.e., the magnitude of the splitting) and the observed **J** (i.e., the number of sublevels) motivates our detailed discussion of angular momentum in Chapter 6.

In some instances, such as the experiment by Stern and Gerlach on silver, it is possible to attribute the atomic moment entirely to the spin of a single electron. Such observations indicate that the electron spin can take only *two* orientations. The two orientations should differ by one unit of angular momentum. Thus we should have

$$\mathbf{S}\cdot\mathbf{H} = \pm\tfrac{1}{2}|\mathbf{H}| \tag{6.9a}$$

or

$$\mathbf{S}\cdot\mathbf{H} = M_s|\mathbf{H}|, \qquad M_s = +\tfrac{1}{2}, -\tfrac{1}{2}. \tag{6.9b}$$

This proposal does indeed withstand the test of experiments. [We will discuss the experimental consequences of (6.9) in the following sections.] We therefore speak of the electron as a particle with *spin one-half*, meaning that the *component* of intrinsic angular momentum along a preferred direction takes the value $+\frac{1}{2}\hbar$ erg-sec or $-\frac{1}{2}\hbar$ erg-sec.

For an energy level whose magnetic splitting comes entirely from the spin moment of a single electron (i.e., $\mathbf{J} = \mathbf{S}$), the energy shift of (6.4) reads

$$E_0 \to E_0 + M_S g_S \beta|\mathbf{H}|. \tag{6.10}$$

Since $M_S = \pm\frac{1}{2}$, a measurement of such splitting provides the electron g factor. The present experimental value is

$$g_S = 2.002290716.$$

REFERENCES

[1] H. P. Zeeman, *Phil. Mag.* **43,** 226 (1897).
[2] C. P. Slichter, *Principles of Magnetic Resonance*, Harper and Row, New York (1963).
[3] O. Stern, *Z. Physik* **7** (1921); W. Gerlach and O. Stern, *Z. Physik* **8,** 10 (1921); **9,** 349 and 353 (1922); O. Stern and W. Gerlach, *Ann. d. Physik* **74,** 673 (1924).
[4] A. Landé, *Z. Physik* **5,** 231 (1921).

2.7 ZEEMAN EFFECT

Historically, the first indication of quantized atomic orientations came from the *Zeeman effect* [1]. A magnetic field shifts a normal spectral line

$$\hbar\omega_0 = E - E' \tag{7.1}$$

to the frequencies

$$\begin{aligned}\hbar\omega &= (E + \Delta E) - (E' + \Delta E') \\ &= \hbar\omega_0 + \beta H(gM - g'M').\end{aligned} \tag{7.2}$$

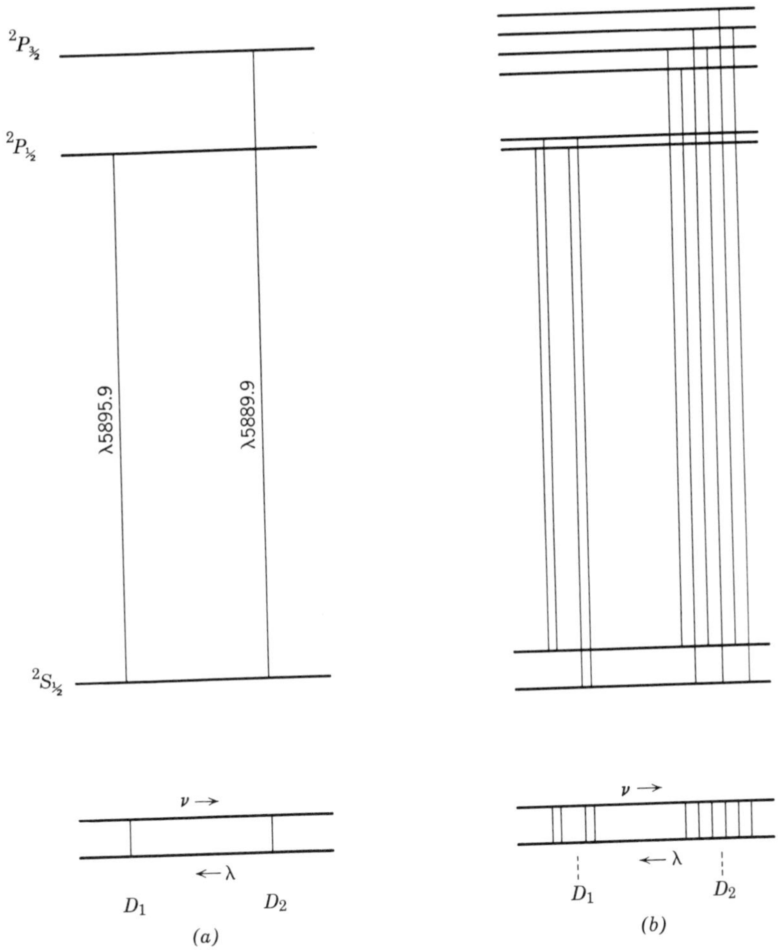

Fig. 2.6 Zeeman effect on sodium *D* lines: (*a*) without field; (*b*) with magnetic field.

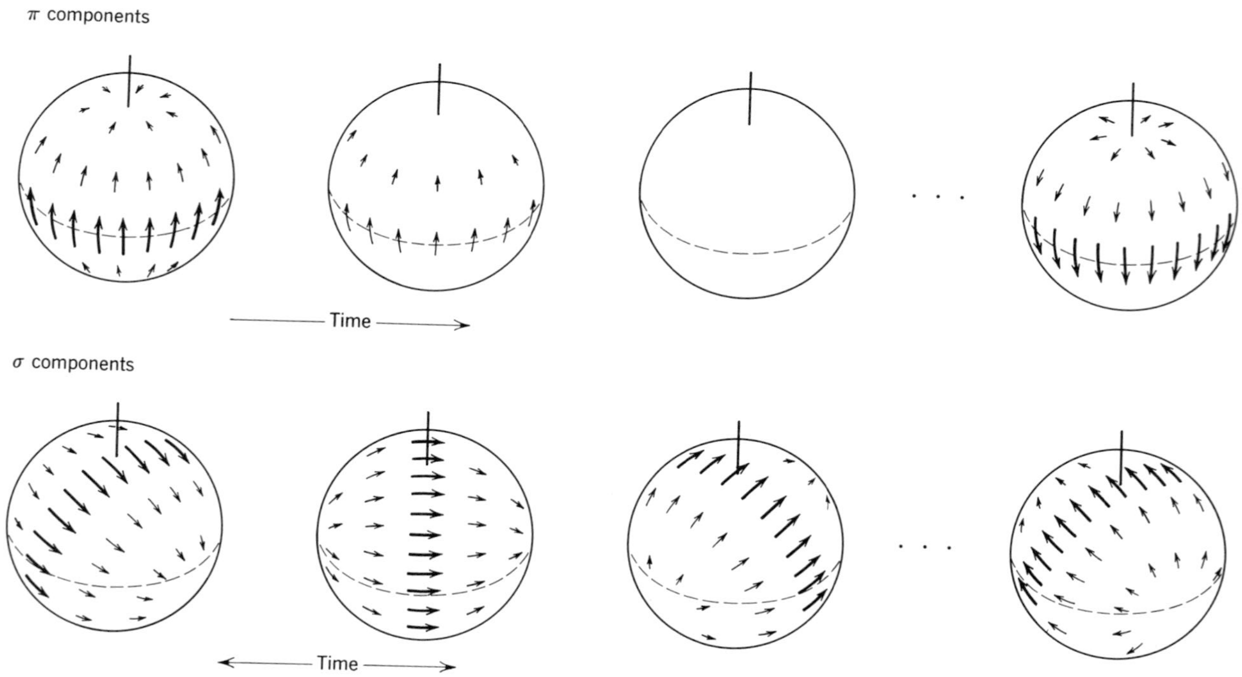

Fig. 2.7 Electric field of Zeeman components.

Numerically, the shift in wavenumbers is

$$\tilde{\nu} = \tilde{\nu}_0 + \frac{4.66858 \times 10^{-5}}{\text{cmG}} H(gM - g'M').$$

A simplified energy diagram illustrates the modern interpretation of Zeeman splitting. Figure 2.6*a* shows the normal energy levels responsible for the strong yellow *D* lines of sodium, D_1 at 5895.9 Å and D_2 at 5889.9 Å. Figure 2.6*b* portrays the effect of a magnetic field, with the splitting slightly exaggerated for clarity. A field of 20 to 30 kG splits the sodium lines by a few tenths of an angstrom.

All spectral lines exhibit some splitting in a magnetic field. The number of Zeeman components varies for different transitions, but, as Thomas Preston discovered [2] in 1898, all lines in a spectral series exhibit the same Zeeman pattern. More generally, the number of components and their polarization and relative intensities provide important clues for interpreting spectra.

As Zeeman discovered, the observed pattern depends markedly on the direction of the field axis with respect to the observer. He further found that the component spectral lines are polarized, although he did not resolve the components in his early studies. Viewing perpendicular to the field (the *transverse* effect commonly employed in the laboratory) one sees a pattern of linearly polarized components symmetrically arranged about the undisturbed wavelength. The outermost components are polarized perpendicular to the field, and are known as "σ components" (σ or s from the German *senkrecht* for perpendicular). The central components are polarized parallel to the field, and are known as "π components" (π or p for parallel). Looking along the field axis (the *longitudinal* effect) one no longer sees the central components, and the outermost components now appear circularly polarized.

The somewhat-complicated behavior of Zeeman patterns viewed from different directions can be understood when we realize that monochromatic light is an *electromagnetic field* whose amplitude varies sinusoidally at an angular frequency ω. In some sense, the light of a spectral line is a radiation field surrounding minute atomic antennas comprising the light source. An external magnetic field separates the antenna pattern from various atoms by shifting the radiation frequency according to the orientation of the antenna.

The intensity of light is proportional to the square of the amplitude of the electric vector of the radiation, and the polarization indicates the direction of the time-averaged electric vector. Thus by mapping out intensity and polarization distribution we map out the average electric field of the radiation. Figure 2.7 portrays the electric field at several instants in time.

The fields illustrated in Fig. 2.7 are particular examples of *multipole fields*, which are discussed in chapters 10 and 11. These particular fields are dipole fields—more specifically, electric-dipole (or $\mathcal{E}1$) fields. An ordinary unpolarized spectral line, originating in the absence of an external magnetic field, comprises a mixture of *three* basic dipole fields: a π-component field and two σ-component fields. (Strictly, the appellations "σ" and "π" refer to particular cases of linear polarization and are therefore inapplicable to longitudinal observations. Nevertheless, to simplify our present discussion, we shall for the moment label the three types of fields by the Greek letters that describe the transverse observations.)

The simplest Zeeman pattern (and the first to be explained) is the *normal Zeeman effect:* one π component between two σ components. As (7.2) shows, this pattern occurs when $g = g' = 1$. More often the pattern consists of a group of π components between groups of σ components—the so-called *anomalous Zeeman effect.*

In a uniform field the intensity of an individual σ component of a normal Zeeman triplet follows the distribution

$$I_\sigma(\theta) = \frac{I_0}{4}(1 + \cos^2\theta), \tag{7.3}$$

where θ is the polar angle between the field direction and the viewing direction. The intensity is independent of the azimuthal angle ϕ about the field axis. The σ components are, in general, elliptically polarized, with the ratio of minor and major axes equal to $\cos\theta$. Thus the polarization ranges from circular ($\theta = 0$ or 180°, viewing along the field axis) to linear ($\theta = 90°$, viewing transversely).

The intensity of the π component of a normal Zeeman triplet varies with θ according to the pattern

$$I_\pi(\theta) = \frac{I_0}{2}\sin^2\theta. \tag{7.4}$$

Like the σ components, the intensity is symmetrical around the field axis. In a uniform field the polarization of the π component is linear, parallel to the field.

The sum of the intensities of two σ components and one π component is

$$2I_\sigma(\theta) + I_\pi(\theta) = \frac{I_0}{2}[1 + \cos^2\theta + \sin^2\theta] = I_0, \tag{7.5}$$

independent of θ; an unresolved triplet is unpolarized and shows no angular variation of intensity.

The J values for the two energy levels involved in a transition can usually be inferred from the number of Zeeman components, whereas the g values can be determined from the magnitude of the splitting if the field is accurately known. Detailed measurements have been carried out for a few complex atoms. (Values may be found in reference [3].)

The linear relationship between magnetic field strength and the splitting of spectral lines finds an important application in the detection and measurement of magnetic fields in the sun and other stars. Individual Zeeman components blend together in stellar spectra. The pattern generally consists of a blend of σ components in the violet, a blend of π components in the center of the pattern, and a blend of σ components in the red. For a field directed *toward* the observer, the *violet* σ components are *left-circularly* polarized, the *red* σ components are *right-circularly* polarized. Measurement of the splitting between these two groups of σ components provides a measure of the field strength *along the line of sight* (H. W. Babcock discusses [4] this application of Zeeman splitting).

The linear dependence of Zeeman splitting on field strength persists only as long as the spread of Zeeman components from each line is much smaller than the spacing between lines. In very strong fields the linear dependence fails and the relative intensities of the components change as well. The "strong-field" effect is known as the *Paschen–Back* effect [5]. We will consider the Zeeman and Paschen–Back effects in more detail in chapter 11.

Further discussion of the Zeeman effect will be found in the monograph by Back and Landé [6], in the review by White [7], and in the article by van den Bosch [8].

REFERENCES

[1] H. P. Zeeman, *Phil. Mag.* **43,** 226 (1897).
[2] T. Preston, *Trans. Roy. Soc. Dublin* **7,** 7 (1899).
[3] C. E. Moore, *Atomic Energy Levels*, Nat. Bur. Stds. Circ. 467, vol. I (1949), vol. II (1952), vol. III (1958).
[4] H. W. Babcock, *Astronomical Techniques*, University of Chicago Press, Chicago, Illinois (1962), chap. 5.
[5] F. Paschen and E. Back, *Ann. Phys.* **39,** 897 (1912); **40,** 959 (1913); *Physica* **1,** 261 (1921).
[6] E. Back and A. Landé, *Zeemaneffekt und Multiplettstruktur*, Springer, Berlin (1925).
[7] H. E. White, *Rept. Prog. Phys.* **6,** 145 (1939).
[8] J. C. van den Bosch, The Zeeman Effect, *Handbuch der Physik* **28,** 296 (1957).

2.8 FINE STRUCTURE

As we noted in Section 2.3, the energy diagram of a monovalent atom actually consists of series of closely spaced double levels (only the S terms exhibit no doubling). Such doubling appears in the energy structure of all atoms (and ions) possessing a single valence electron.

It is natural to seek an explanation for this *fine-structure* doubling in the intrinsic structure of the electron, that is, the electron spin. The magnetic moment arising from electron spin should feel the influence not only of any external field, but also of the magnetic field produced by the orbiting electron itself. As seen from an electron, the atomic nucleus appears to be a circling positive charge of Ze. According to Ampère's law, the electron must react under the influence of this magnetic field,

$$\mathbf{H}' = \frac{Ze}{c}\frac{\mathbf{r} \times \mathbf{v}}{r^3}. \tag{8.1a}$$

(The prime signifies a field in the coordinate system at rest with the electron, rather than at rest in the laboratory.) If the Coulomb field is modified to a general radial electric field $\mathbf{E}$ derived from the potential $U(r)$,

$$\mathbf{E} = \mathbf{grad}\ U(r) = \nabla\ U(r) = \frac{\mathbf{r}}{r}\frac{\partial}{\partial r}\ U(r)$$

then the magnetic field acting on the electron is

$$\mathbf{H}' = \mathbf{E} \times \frac{\mathbf{v}}{c} = \frac{1}{cr}\frac{\partial U}{\partial r}\mathbf{r} \times \mathbf{v}. \tag{8.1b}$$

As Llewellyn H. Thomas pointed out [1] in 1926, if the coordinate system is fixed with the atom rather than the accelerating electron the effective magnetic field should be lower by half. (This purely kinematical correction is discussed by Kemble [2].) Including this *Thomas correction*, we can write the field in the reference system of the nucleus as

$$\mathbf{H}_{\text{orb}} = \frac{1}{2mc}\frac{\partial U}{\partial r}\frac{1}{r}\mathbf{p}_\phi = \frac{\hbar}{2mc}\frac{\partial V}{\partial r}\frac{\mathbf{L}}{r} \tag{8.2a}$$

or, for a hydrogen-like atom, where $U = -Ze/r$,

$$\mathbf{H}_{\text{orb}} = \frac{Ze}{2mc}\frac{\mathbf{p}\phi}{r^3} = Z\beta\frac{\mathbf{L}}{r^3}. \tag{8.2b}$$

In this field the orientation energy of the spin magnetic moment is

$$\Delta E_{SL} = \boldsymbol{\mu}_S \cdot \mathbf{H}_{\text{orb}} = \xi(r)\mathbf{S}\cdot\mathbf{L}, \tag{8.3}$$

where, for a hydrogenic atom,

$$\xi(r) = \frac{g_s Z\beta^2}{r^3} \tag{8.4a}$$

or, more generally,

$$\xi(r) = g_S \frac{\hbar^2}{2m^2c^2} \frac{1}{r} \frac{\partial U}{\partial r} . \tag{8.4b}$$

We thus observe a splitting of the energy levels increasing proportionally to the orbital angular momentum $\mathbf{L}$ and the nuclear charge Z, and decreasing as the effective orbit radius becomes larger.

The splitting of the energy levels of monovalent atoms into *two* sublevels demonstrates that only *two* spin orientations exist: spin parallel to $\mathbf{L}$, and spin antiparallel to $\mathbf{L}$. This helps confirm the hypothesis that an electron possesses a spin of one half.

We will see in Chapter 6 that the number $\mathbf{S}\cdot\mathbf{L}$ takes the values $+L/2$ and $-(L+1)/2$ when $S = \frac{1}{2}$. Thus the energy levels of a one-electron atom form closely spaced pairs

$$\begin{aligned} &E_0 + \zeta \frac{L}{2} , \\ &E_0 - \zeta \frac{(L+1)}{2} , \end{aligned} \tag{8.5}$$

where ζ denotes the average value of $\xi(r)$.

To estimate the size of this splitting, consider a hydrogen-like atom, for which

$$E_0 = -\frac{Ze^2}{2a} = -(hcR)\frac{Z^2}{n^2} ,$$

$$\xi = \frac{2Z\beta^2}{r^3} .$$

Here $a = a_0 n^2/Z$ is the semimajor axis of the given orbit. We might note that the Bohr magneton β is related to the Bohr radius a_0 by

$$\beta = \frac{e\hbar}{2mc} = \frac{e}{2}\left(\frac{e^2}{\hbar c}\right)\left(\frac{\hbar^2}{me^2}\right) = ea_0 \frac{\alpha}{2} , \tag{8.6}$$

where α is the fine-structure constant. Thus ξ can be written

$$\xi = \frac{Z(ea_0\alpha)^2}{2}\left(\frac{1}{r}\right)^3 = \left(\frac{e^2}{2a_0}\right)\frac{\alpha^2 Z^4}{n^6}\left(\frac{a}{r}\right)^3 . \tag{8.7}$$

This expression gives as the fine-structure splitting between the levels of (8.5):

$$\Delta E = \tfrac{1}{2}\zeta = 5.822 \frac{Z^4}{n^6}\left\langle\frac{a^3}{r^3}\right\rangle_{\text{av}} \text{cm}^{-1} . \tag{8.8}$$

Equation 8.8 closely predicts the observed separations of many alkali doublets [3].

REFERENCES

[1] L. H. Thomas, *Nature* **117,** 514 (1926); *Phil. Mag.* **3,** 1 (1927).
[2] E. C. Kemble, *The Fundamental Principles of Quantum Mechanics*, McGraw-Hill, New York (1937) [reprinted by Dover, New York (1958)], p. 502.
[3] E. U. Condon and G. H. Shortley, *The Theory of Atomic Structure*, Cambridge University Press, Cambridge, England (1935), p. 145.

2.9 HYPERFINE STRUCTURE

Atomic nuclei feel the effect of fields resulting from electronic motion and electronic spin, even in the absence of external fields. The nuclear alignment energy

$$\Delta E_{\text{nucl}} = \beta_{\text{N}} g_{\text{N}} \mathbf{I} \cdot \mathbf{H}_{\text{orb}} \tag{9.1}$$

gives a very small splitting (called *hyperfine splitting*) to atomic energy levels.

Equation 5.2 predicts a magnetic field at the nucleus of the order of

$$|\mathbf{H}_{\text{orb}}| \sim \frac{e\hbar}{mc{a_0}^3} = \frac{\alpha^2}{\beta}(hcR_\infty) = 1.245 \times 10^5 \text{ G},$$

caused by the orbital motion of an electron. This crude guess tends to overestimate the field, since in most atoms the effective radius of the valence electron orbit is somewhat larger than a_0. The fact remains that for free atoms the field at the nucleus can be appreciable: estimates given by Kopfermann [1] run from 10^5 G for neutral alkali atoms to 6×10^6 G for quadruply ionized bismuth. (Except for ferromagnetic atoms, these large fields disappear when the atoms coalesce into molecules or crystals. This process is commonly referred to as *quenching* of angular momentum.)

The orientation energy of the nucleus is quite small, but the splitting effect has been observed and studied in optical spectra. The energy difference between nuclear orientations generally corresponds to radio-frequency radiation, and it is more common to study nuclear moments by inducing transitions between the various quantized orientations. The subject of *nuclear magnetic resonance*, based on the observation of such transitions, has received considerable attention [2].

Hydrogen provides an example of this quantization important in astronomy. The energy difference between the only two possible orientations of the hydrogen nucleus, with respect to the magnetic field axis defined by the electron spin, gives the 21-cm radiation observed from hydrogen atoms in interstellar space. Hydrogen atoms emit this radiation when the electron and proton "flip" their relative orientations from parallel to antiparallel.

Discussions of hyperfine structure will be found in the texts by Kopfermann [1], Ramsey [3], Kuhn [4], Candler [5] and reference [6].

REFERENCES

[1] H. Kopfermann, *Nuclear Moments*, Academic, New York (1958), p. 132.
[2] C. P. Slichter, *Principles of Magnetic Resonance*, Harper and Row, New York (1963).
[3] N. F. Ramsey, *Nuclear Moments*, Wiley, New York (1953).
[4] H. G. Kuhn, *Atomic Spectra*, Academic, New York (1961), Chap. VI.
[5] C. Candler, *Atomic Structure and the Vector Model*, Van Nostrand, Princeton, New Jersey (1964).
[6] A. J. Freeman and R. B. Frankel, eds., *Hyperfine Interactions*, Academic, New York (1967).

2.10 ELECTRON ORBITALS

As we have noted, the spectra of the alkali metals exhibit series reminiscent of hydrogen. In turn, the term values follow a pattern similar to that of hydrogen except that Z^2/n^2 is no longer the ratio of two integers. This similarity suggests that a single, active, valence electron is responsible for the spectra. Further support for such a model comes from studies of chemical behavior: each alkali element ordinarily provides a single valence electron when it forms a chemical compound.

On the basis of such spectroscopic and chemical evidence, we envisage an alkali atom as having a single valence electron in orbit about a *core* of inactive electrons and a nucleus. The major effect of the core is to shield the valence electron from the strong nuclear attraction. Thus a valence electron moving in a large circular orbit feels simply the single net positive charge of an alkali ion, whereas an electron that moves in an elongated, penetrating ellipse will pass close to the nucleus and encounter a greater charge. Under these conditions, the valence electron will behave like a particle in a central field, following the motion discussed in Section 2.3.

As we saw there, an orbit in a screened field has lower energy than the corresponding orbit in a pure Coulomb field. The distinction between the two fields is slight for circular orbits (large angular momentum), but becomes quite pronounced for very elliptical orbits (small angular momentum). In terms of a Rydberg formula involving an *effective quantum number* $n^* = n - \Delta$,

$$E_n = -(hcR)\left(\frac{Z}{n^*}\right)^2,$$

high angular momentum will correspond to a small quantum defect Δ, whereas small angular momentum will be associated with a larger quantum defect (hence with lower energy).

These expectations are borne out in the observed structure of the energy levels of alkali atoms. As we noted in Chapter 1, the levels were early classified according to the principal quantum number n and a letter label S, P, D, . . . indicative of the spectral series (sharp, principal, diffuse, . . .). We can now see that this classification is simply an angular-momentum classification. Evidently only discrete values of angular momentum occur. The orbit responsible for the S term has the lowest angular momentum; successively higher values of angular momenta are associated with P, D, F, etc. terms.

Comment on notation: we shall generally employ capital letters to label spectroscopic terms or energy levels according to angular momentum. Lower-case letters will be used for orbit labels. Thus a P energy level may arise from the motion of an electron in a p orbit. For monovalent atoms, we can associate the spectroscopic terms with orbits of a single active electron, and the distinction between, say, a P term and a p orbit is unnecessary. However, this unique correspondence does not hold for more complex atoms, in which the energy structure often reflects cooperative motion of several valence electrons.

It should now be evident that the optical spectra of hydrogen and the alkali metals provide an important source of information about the motion of a single valence electron. Let us summarize a few general conclusions we can draw.

First, an integer n, the principal quantum number, characterizes the major aspects of the motion: it fixes the semimajor axis of the orbit, and largely determines the energy.

Second, superposed upon the effect of orbit size, we found a smaller energy dependence attributable to orbit eccentricity or angular momentum. For a given value of n we find n orbits of different eccentricity, each differing from the next by one unit of angular momentum. The larger the semimajor axis (or n), the more units of angular momentum in a circular orbit. For $n = 1$ apparently only one value of angular momentum occurs, the $1s$ orbit. For $n = 2$, two possible angular momenta can evidently occur, the $2s$ and the $2p$ orbits. From examining the alkali energy-level structure, we decide that an s orbit is always the most penetrating (lowest angular momentum). Thus we find the following types of orbits:

$1s$	$2s$	$3s$	$4s$	$5s$	$\cdots$	∞
	$2p$	$3p$	$4p$	$5p$		
		$3d$	$4d$	$5d$		
			$4f$	$5f$		
				$5g$.		

Principal quantum number increases from left to right, angular momentum increases down a column. Orbits with the same principal quantum number and same angular momentum are called *equivalent orbits*, and, in a given atom, the electrons occupying such orbits are called *equivalent electrons.*

Third, only particular discrete orientations of the orbits occur, as determined by integral values of the component of angular momentum along a preferred direction. If $2l + 1$ orientations can be observed, we can denote the orbital angular momentum by the quantum number l. Conversely, we know that $2l + 1$ different (i.e., distinguishable) orbits can be associated with the angular momentum l. The magnetic quantum number m_l characterizes the component of orbital angular momentum along a preferred direction: $m_l = -l, \ldots, 0, \ldots, +l$.

Fourth, the electron possesses an internal degree of freedom, apparent as a component of intrinsic angular momentum along a preferred direction, which takes two values. The quantum number m_s specifies this value: $m_s = -\frac{1}{2}$ or $+\frac{1}{2}$.

Thus the motion of an electron can be characterized by *four* quantum numbers. We shall use the term *orbital* as a generalization of "orbit" to denote the motion of an electron described by these four quantum numbers. We can think of the *orbital* of an electron as simply the orbit with the added specification of spin direction. Were it not for spin, the terms *orbit* and *orbital* would be synonymous.

By identifying the labels *s*, *p*, *d*, etc. with the following *orbital angular-momentum quantum numbers l*,

orbit label:	*s*	*p*	*d*	*f*	*g*	*h*	...,
l value:	0	1	2	3	4	5	...,

Table 2.1 Number of Equivalent Orbitals

n =	1	2	3	4	5	6
shell =	*K*	*L*	*M*	*N*	*O*	*P*
orbital = *s*	2	2	2	2	2	2
p		6	6	6	6	6
d			10	10	10	10
f				14	14	14
g					18	18
h						22
total =	2	8	18	32	50	72
running total =	2	10	28	60	110	182

we can write down the total number of distinguishable orbitals of various kinds. With a factor of 2 from the spin, this number is $2(2l + 1)$. The number of equivalent orbitals is displayed in Table 2.1.

Following x-ray notation, we sometimes refer to orbitals with $n = 1$ as K-shell orbitals, orbitals with $n = 2$ as L-shell orbitals, and so on. These shell labels appear in Table 2.1. These letter designations have no connection with the capital letters used as labels for orbital angular momentum.

It is reasonable to suppose that this collection of discrete orbitals somehow represents a basic set of orbits, and that the various electrons in any atom exist only in such orbitals. This view proves quite useful when we apply quantum theory to complex atoms. However, one vital fact has not yet been mentioned. Observations show that an unexcited valence electron occupies the following orbitals:

neutral element:	H	Li	Na	K	Rb	Cs	Fr
valence electron orbital:	1*s*	2*s*	3*s*	4*s*	5*s*	6*s*	7*s*
number of inner electrons:	0	2	10	18	36	54	86

Evidently the orbitals with low principal quantum number (hence low energy) are not available to higher members of the alkali family. We conclude that these low-energy orbitals are somehow filled by the preceding electrons.

This conclusion is indeed correct, as we can infer by tracing the position of the 1*s*, 2*s*, and succeeding levels through the list of chemical elements by means of their x-ray spectra. We are thus led to a simple form of the *exclusion principle* proposed by Wolfgang Pauli in 1925 [1]:

Only one electron can occupy any one orbital.

We may state this slightly differently, in terms of some set of four quantum numbers that correspond to semimajor axis (n), angular momentum (l), angular momentum orientation ($2l + 1$ values), and spin orientation (two values). The alternative statement is:

Occupied orbitals differ in at least one quantum number.

Basically, the Pauli exclusion principle is a weaker version of the statement that two particles cannot be in precisely the same place at the same time. In place of the usual four coordinates (three spatial coordinates and time) we instead have four discrete quantum numbers. For N electrons, we require $4N$ quantum numbers.

We can enumerate four quantum numbers in a variety of ways. For some simple purposes the handiest classification of orbits goes according to values of:

$$
\begin{aligned}
n &= 1, 2, \ldots &&= \text{principal quantum number (semimajor axis),}\\
l &= 0, 1, \ldots, n-1 &&= \text{orbital angular momentum (ellipticity),}\\
m_l &= -l, \ldots, +l &&= \text{magnetic quantum number (component of } l \text{ along preferred direction),}\\
m_s &= -\tfrac{1}{2}, +\tfrac{1}{2} &&= \text{spin magnetic quantum number (component of spin along preferred direction).}
\end{aligned}
$$

This classification is sometimes referred to as the *m scheme.*

REFERENCE

[1] W. Pauli, *Z. Physik* **31,** 765 (1925).

2.11 THE PERIODIC SYSTEM

When we adopt the Pauli principle as a basic law of nature, we can immediately begin to see why the chemical elements exhibit such striking chemical and spectroscopic periodicities.

A normal atom exists in the state of lowest internal energy. In this state, the electrons will occupy the orbitals with lowest energy. A simple "thought experiment" (German, *Gedankenexperimente*) first suggested by Bohr helps clarify this statement. Imagine a bare nucleus of charge Ze, to which we add Z electrons in succession. As we add each electron, it cascades down through various energy levels, emitting characteristic spectral lines as it occupies successively smaller orbitals with lower energy. At last the electron can proceed no further. It has reached the lowest unoccupied orbital.

Following this "building-up" principle (German, *Aufbauprinzip*), we imagine atoms constructed by the addition of electrons to an atomic nucleus. Each successive electron finally enters the unoccupied orbital of lowest energy.

In the normal hydrogen atom, the single unexcited electron travels in a $1s$ orbital. As we proceed to helium with its two electrons, we should expect to find both electrons in the low-energy $1s$ orbitals. Analysis of the helium spectrum bears this out.

With helium we have exhausted the two possible orbitals with $n = 1$. The two $1s$ electrons are tightly bound; it requires some 21 eV to excite one of these electrons to the next orbital. Such a tightly bound group of electrons is commonly called a *closed shell* or *filled shell*, implying an electron arrangement that is disturbed only with difficulty and participates reluctantly in chemical reactions. Such closed shells characterize the noble gases. In terms of energy levels, a closed shell of electrons means that a sizeable energy gap exists between the ground state of the atom and the first excited state. The greater the energy difference between the uppermost *occupied* orbital and the lowest *empty* orbital, the more inert is the shell. The uppermost occupied level is sometimes called the *Fermi level.*

Lithium, the third chemical element, has its first two electrons in $1s$ orbitals to form a helium-like core. The next available orbital in the hierarchy should clearly be the most penetrating of the $n = 2$ orbitals; that is, a $2s$ orbital. Indeed, analysis of the lithium spectrum shows that the valence electron normally occupies a $2s$ orbital. Thus in the ground state of lithium, electrons occupy orbitals labeled by $1s$, $1s$, and $2s$.

This list of occupied orbitals (more precisely the list of quantum numbers n and l of occupied orbitals) is called the electronic *configuration.* Using an exponent notation, with superscripts denoting the number of electrons in a given type of orbital, we may label the ground configuration of lithium by

$$\text{Li:} \quad 1s^2\, 2s.$$

In the fourth chemical element, beryllium, two electrons fill the $n = 1$ orbital (or K shell), and the remaining pair of valence electrons occupy two $2s$ orbitals, as verified through analysis of the spectrum. The configuration of beryllium in the ground state is

$$\text{Be:} \quad 1s^2\, 2s^2.$$

The first excited level in beryllium occurs only a few electron volts above the ground state, so the filled pair of $2s$ orbitals do not form a strongly bound shell. Orbitals with common angular momentum and common principal quantum number n are called a *subshell;* in beryllium the $2s$ subshell is filled.

We should expect to find the succeeding six chemical elements filling the $2p$ orbitals in their lowest energy state, and this prediction proves correct. In their lowest energy levels the elements have the configurations:

B	$1s^2\, 2s^2\, 2p$
C	$1s^2\, 2s^2\, 2p^2$
N	$1s^2\, 2s^2\, 2p^3$
O	$1s^2\, 2s^2\, 2p^4$
F	$1s^2\, 2s^2\, 2p^5$
Ne	$1s^2\, 2s^2\, 2p^6$.

With neon the $n = 2$ orbitals are completely filled. The first excited level of neon occurs some 17 eV above the ground level, so the $n = 2$ electrons form a distinctly stable configuration. These electrons thus form a distinct closed shell.

Beyond element 11, sodium, the valence electrons begin filling the $n = 3$ shell, with 10 electrons forming closed K and L shells. As with the previous elements, the $3s$ orbitals are the most penetrating. They therefore have the lowest energies, and hence fill first. Element 12, magnesium, possesses a ground configuration having a complete $3s$ subshell. In the succeeding six elements, aluminum, silicon, phosphorus, sulfur, chlorine, and argon, the $3p$ orbitals become filled. In these elements, the energies of the nearly circular $3d$ orbitals lie above those of the penetrating $4s$ and $4p$ orbitals. The energy gap above the last $3p$ orbital causes argon, with a full $3p$ subshell, to exhibit the characteristics of an element with a closed shell.

The $3d$ orbitals begin filling with element 21, scandium. For the succeeding 10 elements, the $4s$ and $3d$ orbitals have nearly comparable energies. The elements, scandium through nickel, comprise the so-called *iron group*. For these elements, one must pay careful attention to the influence of the electrons on one another and the influence of external fields. Element 36, krypton, has filled $3s$, $4p$, and $3d$ subshells and presents the appearance of an atom with a closed shell.

The next row of elements, from rubidium (37) to xenon (54) follows the pattern of the preceding row, filling generally the $5s$, the $4d$, and then the $5p$ subshells.

With the sixth row, we first encounter an occupied f orbital in the ground configuration of an element. The $5d$ and $4f$ orbitals have comparable energy in lanthanum and cerium. Lanthanum has a ground configuration of $6s^2\,5d$ outside an argon-like core, whereas cerium has $6s^2\,5d4f$ outside this core. The succeeding elements fill the $4f$ shell while generally retaining the $6s^2\,5d$ electrons. The elements with partially filled $4f$ subshells are the rare earths. Beyond ytterbium, the last of the rare earths, the $5d$ orbitals fill up, followed by the $4p$ orbitals. This sequence ends with the noble gas radon, which has the configuration $6s^2\,4f^{14}\,5d^{10}\,6p^6$, outside the argon core.

As we proceed along the list of chemical elements, we might note the behavior of the $n = 1$ and $n = 2$ electron shells observed in x-ray spectra. As outlying valence orbitals envelop them, the increasing nuclear charge draws these inner orbits closer to the nucleus. In these inner shells, the difference between an s orbital and a p orbital becomes less pronounced. On an energy-level diagram, these very deep energies appear as a distinct group, and the shell structure becomes pronounced. Figure 1.11 shows the gross trends with increasing atomic number.

For neutral atoms, electrons generally fill preferentially the orbitals with lowest value of $(n + l)$. For orbits with equal $(n + l)$, preference goes to large l. Figure 2.8 displays this rule of thumb for orbital filling. Although this rule correctly reflects the general trend of the filling process, the details

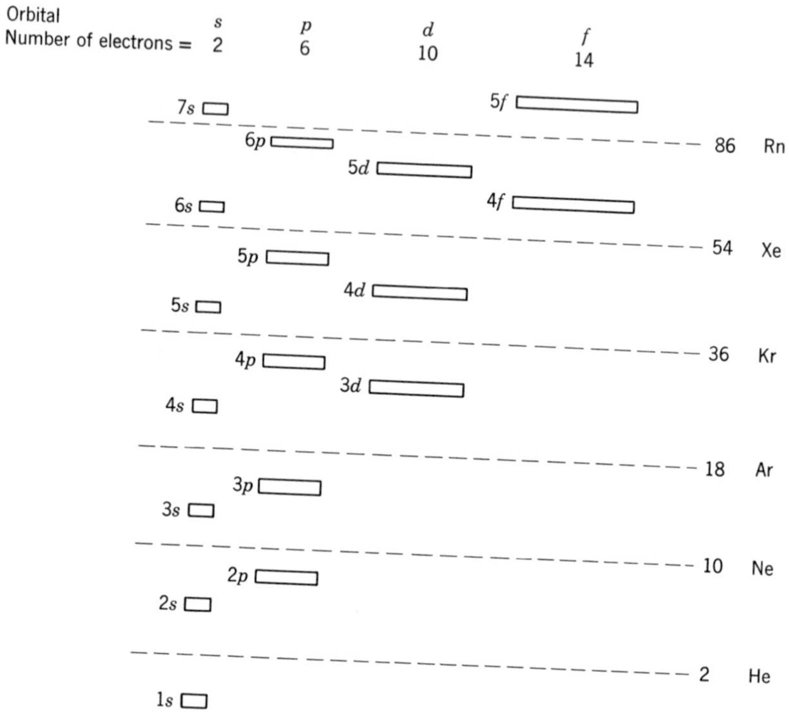

Fig. 2.8 Approximate filling order of orbitals in neutral atoms.

are often more involved. In particular, the filling of the *d* and *f* subshells reveals an interesting tendency for electrons having the same *n* and *l* to pair up. Further, the notion of "ground configuration" has less significance for elements with partially filled *d* or *f* subshells, where different configurations may have overlapping energy levels. For a more detailed description, we must consider the influence of the electrons upon one another.

When one considers ions, the hierarchy of orbitals tends toward a hydrogen-like ordering, and the influence of *n* predominates over *l*.

We should remark that several definitions of a "shell" exist in the literature. Historically, the chemical notion of a shell implied a group of inert electrons. The energy levels of inner electrons in heavy elements group themselves in distinct shells according to *n*. This shell structure is quite pronounced in x-ray spectra. On the other hand, outer- or valence-electron energy levels reveal a strong dependence on *l*. Thus authors like Slater, and Condon and Shortley refer to a complete set of $2(2l + 1)$ orbitals with given *n and l* as a closed *shell*. In this book, we shall refer to such an n, l group as a *subshell* and apply the term *closed shell* when all orbitals of given n are filled.

The foregoing discussion hints at the way we can relate chemical properties to energy-level structure. However, we have passed all too quickly over a crucial problem: how to label the observed energy levels with appropriate configurations. For simple atoms, with one and two valence electrons, it is usually fairly easy to interpret the observed levels in terms of single-particle orbitals. However, as we proceed to atoms with several valence electrons, such as iron, the single-particle nature of the spectrum is no longer obvious.

2.12 THE VECTOR MODEL

A. Coupling

We have seen that the valence electron in a monovalent atom possesses two types of angular momentum: *orbital* angular momentum (l), and an intrinsic angular momentum or *spin*. Quantization of the orbital angular momentum explains the series of energy levels labeled by S, P, D, F, . . . , and quantization of spin accounts for the doubling of the energy levels (the S levels are excepted from this doubling). What properties of divalent (or more complex) atoms correspond to these single-particle attributes? In this section we find a partial answer, based on empirical evidence. In chapters 6 and 9 we discuss the theory behind the present empirical rules.

In an atom like helium, with two valence electrons, we observe two *systems* of levels, distinguished by their multiplicity: a *singlet system* comprising singlet terms and a *triplet system* comprising triplet terms. Both systems exhibit a series structure similar to that of a monovalent atom, and we can classify the levels according to a principal quantum number n and an orbital angular momentum L. The triplet terms consist of three closely-spaced energy levels (only the S levels do not exhibit this fine structure). The terms of the singlet system, as the name indicates, reveal no such fine structure.

We have previously attributed the doublet structure of the alkali energy levels to the two possible orientations of a spin of $\frac{1}{2}$ along the angular-momentum direction—the two values of the spin–orbit interaction $\mathbf{L}\cdot\mathbf{S}$. It is natural to attribute the helium *triplet* structure to *three* quantized values of $\mathbf{L}\cdot\mathbf{S}$ and the *singlet* structure to a *single* value. We thus hypothesize that the triplet system has a spin quantum number $S = 1$, whereas the singlet system has $S = 0$. In Section 2.6 a simple vector diagram illusattred the connection between a vector $\mathbf{J}$ and its $2J + 1$ quantized orienta-

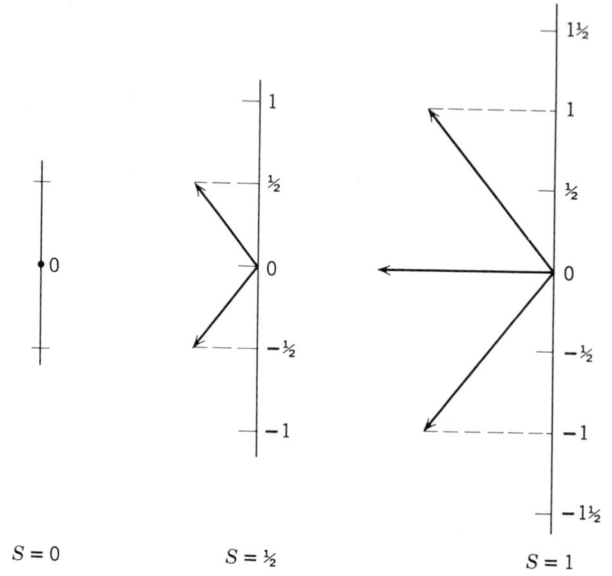

Fig. 2.9 Possible spin orientations, $S = 0, \frac{1}{2}, 1$.

tions. If we assume that multiplicity describes the number of orientations of a vector **S** with respect to the axis **L** (that is, the number of values for $\mathbf{S}\cdot\mathbf{L}$), we deduce that this number should be $2S + 1$. (Or, if $|\mathbf{L}| < |\mathbf{S}|$, the number of orientations is $2L + 1$.) Figure 2.9 illustrates some possible S values. We therefore associate multiplicities with the spin quantum number S as follows:

system =	singlet	doublet	triplet	quartet	quintet	···
multiplicity =	1	2	3	4	5	···
spin quantum number, S =	0	$\frac{1}{2}$	1	$\frac{3}{2}$	2	···.

Evidently the spin angular momenta of the two valence electrons compound into a single resultant quantized spin. The process of combining two angular momenta into a resultant angular momentum is generally called *coupling*. Denoting the total spin of the atom by **S** and the spin of the two electrons by **s**(1) and **s**(2), respectively, we can symbolize the observed coupling of angular momenta as

$$\begin{array}{llllll} \text{spins:} & \mathbf{s}(1) & + \ \mathbf{s}(2) & = \mathbf{S} & \\ \text{quantum numbers:} \left\{ \begin{array}{l} \\ \\ \end{array} \right. & \frac{1}{2} & \frac{1}{2} & \rightarrow 0 & \text{singlet system} \\ & \frac{1}{2} & \frac{1}{2} & \rightarrow 1 & \text{triplet system.} \end{array} \qquad (12.1)$$

In contrast to this coupling of spins, the orbital-angular-momentum structure of the neutral helium term-diagram retains the simplicity of a one-electron atom. This suggests that the observed energy levels result from the motion of a single active electron, with the inactive electron remaining in an unexcited 1*s* orbital. Only the altered multiplicity structure reveals the presence of the inactive electron. Nevertheless, we can express this observation in the form of an equation for the two individual orbital angular momenta $\mathbf{l}(1)$ and $\mathbf{l}(2)$ combining to the total orbital angular momentum $\mathbf{L}$:

$$\begin{array}{rcccl} \text{orbital angular momenta:} & \mathbf{l}(1) + \mathbf{l}(2) = \mathbf{L} & & & \\ \text{quantum numbers} \left\{ \begin{array}{l} \\ \\ \\ \end{array} \right. \!\!\!\!\!\!\!\! & \begin{array}{lll} 0 & 0 & \rightarrow 0 \\ 0 & 1 & \rightarrow 1 \\ 0 & 2 & \rightarrow 2 \end{array} & \begin{array}{l} S \text{ terms} \\ P \text{ terms} \\ D \text{ terms.} \end{array} & & (12.2) \end{array}$$

We have also seen that a third type of quantized angular momentum described by the quantum number J, is required for the labeling of the several energy levels that comprise a spectroscopic term, and for the explanation of energy-level splitting in a magnetic field. These J values can be determined by experiment even for complex atoms. (Indeed, it is nearly always possible to assign a value of J to a level even when assignment of other quantum numbers is ambiguous or impossible.) Since we attribute the magnetic effects to the orientation of the total atomic magnetic moment, it is natural to identify $\mathbf{J}$ as the total angular momentum of the atom. In the absence of external torques, the total angular momentum of any system remains constant. It is therefore natural that the total angular momentum of an atom (as distinct from possible partial angular momenta such as spin) manifest itself. Chapter 4 will present more substantial evidence for this identification.

What is the relationship between $\mathbf{J}$ and the more elementary angular momenta $\mathbf{S}$ and $\mathbf{L}$? Observations suggest that often $\mathbf{L}$ and $\mathbf{S}$ couple [in the sense of (12.1) and (12.2)] to give a resultant $\mathbf{J}$. Consider the two ^2P levels responsible for the pair of sodium D lines. The upper level is known to have $J = \frac{1}{2}$ and the lower level has $J = \frac{3}{2}$. We have previously identified the p orbital with a quantum number $l = 1$, and the spin with the value $\frac{1}{2}$. Thus we observe the coupling:

$$\begin{array}{rcl} \text{angular momenta:} & \mathbf{L} + \mathbf{S} = \mathbf{J}, & \\ \text{quantum numbers:} & \left\{ \begin{array}{lll} 1 & \frac{1}{2} & \rightarrow \frac{3}{2} \\ 1 & \frac{1}{2} & \rightarrow \frac{1}{2} \end{array} \right\} \; {}^2P \text{ levels.} & (12.3a) \end{array}$$

In the same way, we find that the ground level of sodium, ^2S, associated with the coupling:

$$\begin{array}{llll} \text{angular momenta:} & \mathbf{L} + \mathbf{S} = \mathbf{J}, & & \\ \text{quantum numbers:} & 0 \quad \tfrac{1}{2} \rightarrow \tfrac{1}{2} & {}^2S \text{ level.} & \end{array} \tag{12.3b}$$

Similarly, we can observe the following coupling of angular momenta in helium:

$$\begin{array}{ll} \text{angular momenta:} & \mathbf{L} + \mathbf{S} = \mathbf{J}, \\ \text{quantum numbers:} & \begin{cases} 0 \quad 0 \rightarrow 0 \quad {}^1S \text{ level} \\ 1 \quad 0 \rightarrow 1 \quad {}^1P \text{ level} \\ 0 \quad 1 \rightarrow 1 \quad {}^3S \text{ level} \\ \left.\begin{array}{l} 1 \quad 1 \rightarrow 0 \\ 1 \quad 1 \rightarrow 1 \\ 1 \quad 1 \rightarrow 2 \end{array}\right\} {}^3P \text{ levels.} \end{cases} \end{array} \tag{12.3c}$$

Similar tables may be drawn for ${}^1D$, ${}^3D$, etc.

Since the quantum numbers L, S, and J represent the maximum components of the angular momenta **L**, **S**, and **J**, we may picture the coupling between $L = 1$, and $S = \frac{1}{2}$ of ${}^2P$ by the vector diagram of Fig. 2.10. We have introduced this vector diagram simply as a device to describe the apparent coupling properties of angular momentum, as deduced from empirical evidence. The real justification for such diagrams emerges from the quantum mechanics of angular momentum, discussed in Chapter 6. We should keep in mind that the magnitude of the angular momentum **J** (or **L** or **S**) need not be equal to the quantum number J, which takes integral or half-integral values. In fact, we shall see in Chapter 6 that the magnitude of **J** is $|\mathbf{J}| = \sqrt{J(J+1)}$.

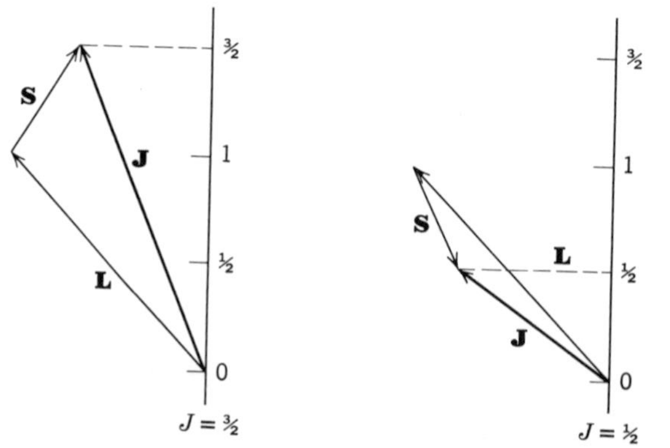

Fig. 2.10 Vector addition of $\mathbf{L} + \mathbf{S} = \mathbf{J}$ for $L = 1$, $S = \frac{1}{2}$.

The preceding observations lead us to the following *triangle rule* for coupling angular momenta:

For $\mathbf{J}_1 + \mathbf{J}_2 = \mathbf{J}$, the *quantum numbers* J_1, J_2, J form a triangle with integral or half-integral sides. (Rule 1)

For $\mathbf{J}_1 + \mathbf{J}_2 = \mathbf{J}$ we may substitute $\mathbf{s}(1) + \mathbf{s}(2) = \mathbf{S}$ (12.1), or $\mathbf{l}(1) + \mathbf{l}(2) = \mathbf{L}$ (12.2), or $\mathbf{S} + \mathbf{L} = \mathbf{J}$ (12.3), or a similar equation for any three angular momenta.

We may further note that, for a given L and S, the several observed J values differ by unity. If the multiplicity is even (i.e., if S is half-integral) then J must be half-integral. We may summarize this result in the second basic rule for compounding angular momenta, the *even-perimeter rule.*

For $\mathbf{J}_1 + \mathbf{J}_2 = \mathbf{J}$, the sum of the (positive) quantum numbers $J_1 + J_2 = J$ is an *even integer.* (Rule 2)

Applying these two rules, we readily calculate the permissible combinations of L, S, and J given in Table 2.2. The table shows the conventional spectroscopic notation for an energy level characterized by the quantum numbers L, S, and J: the multiplicity $(2S + 1)$ appears as a *preceding* superscript; the letter symbol S, P, D, etc., is used for $L = 0, 1, 2$, etc.; and J appears as a *following subscript.*

Table 2.2 Possible *LS*-Coupling Levels

	$S = 0$ Singlets	1/2 Doublets	1 Triplets	3/2 Quartets	2 Quintets
$L = 0$	$^1S_0$	$^2S_{1/2}$	$^3S_1$	$^4S_{3/2}$	$^5S_2$
$L = 1$	$^1P_1$	$^2P_{3/2,\,1/2}$	$^3P_{2,1,0}$	$^4P_{5/2,\,3/2,\,1/2}$	$^5P_{3,2,1}$
$L = 2$	$^1D_2$	$^2D_{5/2,\,3/2}$	$^3D_{3,2,1}$	$^4D_{7/2,\,5/2,\,3/2,\,1/2}$	$^5D_{4,3,2,1,0}$
$L = 3$	$^1F_3$	$^2F_{7/2,\,5/2}$	$^3F_{4,3,2}$	$^4F_{9/2,\,7/2,\,5/2,\,3/2,\,1/2}$	$^5F_{5,4,3,2,1}$

The triangle rules are easily illustrated with simple diagrams, such as those in Fig. 2.11.

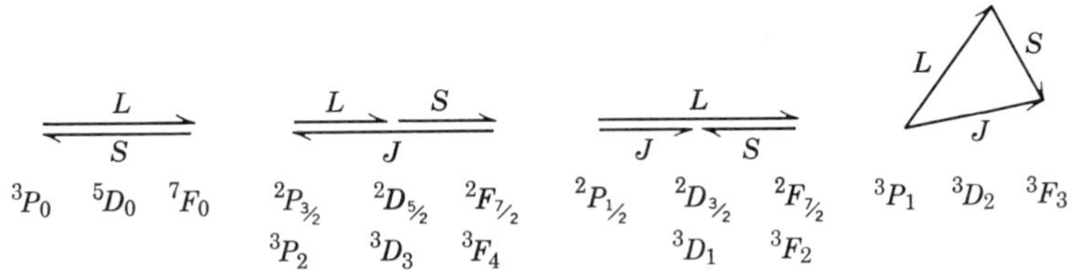

Fig. 2.11 Quantum number triangles.

In many atoms having two valence electrons, we observe examples of the coupling of individual angular momenta according to these rules. The individual spins couple according to (12.1), and the individual orbital angular momenta couple in a similar way:

$$\text{angular momenta: } \mathbf{l}(1) + \mathbf{l}(2) = \mathbf{L} \tag{12.4}$$

$$\text{quantum numbers} \begin{cases} 0 & 0 & \rightarrow 0 & ssS \text{ terms} \\ 0 & 1 & \rightarrow 1 & spP \text{ terms} \\ 1 & 0 & \rightarrow 1 & psP \text{ terms} \\ 1 & 1 & \rightarrow 0 & ppS \text{ terms} \\ 1 & 1 & \rightarrow 1 & ppP \text{ terms} \\ 1 & 1 & \rightarrow 2 & ppD \text{ terms.} \end{cases}$$

This proposal for coupling angular momenta is known as the *Russell–Saunders* coupling scheme [1], or *LS-coupling* scheme. Couple the spins to a resultant **S** and couple the orbital angular momenta to a resultant **L**, then couple **L** and **S** to give a total angular momentum **J**. (Other coupling schemes may also occur; we discuss them in Chapter 6.)

B. Excited Terms

The structure of calcium provides an example of *LS* coupling for two valence electrons. When the atom is unexcited, these electrons both occupy 4*s* orbitals, giving the spectroscopic term

$$4s^2 \ {}^1S.$$

The atom exhibits several series of terms in which one electron is excited, such as

$$\begin{matrix} 4s\ 5s\ {}^1S, & 4s\ 6s\ {}^1S, & \cdots \\ 4s\ 4p\ {}^1P, & 4s\ 5p\ {}^1P, & \cdots \end{matrix}$$

(with similar triplet series). Other terms have been observed in which both valence electrons are excited. (Such spectroscopic terms have been called "displaced terms," "primed terms," and "dashed terms". We refer to them as *doubly excited terms*); for example,

$$\begin{matrix} 4p^2\ {}^1S, & 4p\ 5p\ {}^1S, & \cdots \\ 4p^2\ {}^3P, & 4p\ 5p\ {}^3P, & \cdots. \end{matrix}$$

Often these doubly excited terms have energies exceeding the first ionization limit—more than enough energy to permit one electron to leave the atom. This occurs, for example, with the helium terms

$$2s\ 2p\ {}^1P, \qquad 2s\ 3p\ {}^1P, \qquad \cdots.$$

The atom can remain briefly in such a state because the energy is shared by two electrons—neither one alone has sufficient energy to leave the atom. In time, if selection rules permit, the energy will concentrate in one of the electrons while the other reverts to a less energetic orbital of ionized helium. If this occurs before the atom can radiate away its excess energy, the result is a spontaneous ionization, *autoionization* [2]–[4], according to the reaction

$$\mathrm{He}(2s\ 3p\ ^1P) \rightarrow \mathrm{He}^+(1s) + \text{electron}.$$

The free electron carries off the energy difference:

$$E\,(\text{electron}) = E(2s\ 3p\ ^1P) - E(1s\ \infty p\ ^1P).$$

This radiationless de-excitation process is also referred to as the Auger (pronounced "ozhay") effect [5]–[7], after P. Auger [5]. In heavier elements, the doubly excited terms need not lie above an ionization limit.

Table 2.3 Possible *LS*-Coupling Terms for Two Nonequivalent Orbitals

ss':	$^1S,\ ^3S$	
sp:	$^1P,\ ^3P$	
sd:	$^1D,\ ^3D$	
sf:	$^1F,\ ^3F$	
pp':	$^1(SPD)$	$^3(SPD)$
pd:	$^1(PDF)$	$^3(PDF)$
pf:	$^1(DFG)$	$^3(DFG)$
dd':	$^1(SPDFG)$	$^3(SPDFG)$
df:	$^1(PDFGH)$	$^3(PDFGH)$
ff':	$^1(SPDFGHI)$	$^3(SPDFGHI)$

C. Several Electrons

Using the vector model, we can easily predict all the spectroscopic terms that arise from *LS* coupling of two orbitals. For example, we find that an s orbital coupled to another orbital produces the terms

$$s's:\ ^1S,\ ^3S,$$
$$ps:\ ^1P,\ ^3P,$$
$$ds:\ ^1D,\ ^3D,$$

and two p orbitals give the terms

$$p'p:\ ^1S,\ ^1P,\ ^1D,\ ^3S,\ ^3P,\ ^3D.$$

Table 2.3 lists the possible terms arising from the coupling of two orbitals.

We can go a step further and couple a third orbital to these two. Regarding spin and orbital angular momenta as independent vectors, we couple the added spin onto the preceding resultant, for a new resultant **S**. Similarly we couple an additional **l** onto the two-electron **L** to obtain a new resultant **L**. From each parent term of the configuration *nl*, *n'l'*, we obtain several terms of the configuration *nl*, *n'l'*, *n''l''*. For example, from the terms of *pp'* we obtain:

$pp'\ (^1S)\ p''$: ^2P
$pp'\ (^3S)\ p''$: ^1P, ^3P
$pp'\ (^1P)\ p''$: ^2S, ^2P, ^2D
$pp'\ (^3P)\ p''$: ^2S, ^4S, ^2P, ^4P, ^2D, ^4D
etc.

We remark here that the term

$$pp'\ (^1S)p''\ ^2P$$

is not the same as the term

$$pp'\ (^1P)p''\ ^2P.$$

These two ^2P terms are distinguished by their *parentage* (or *genealogy* [4])—the quantum numbers of the term to which the last p'' electron was coupled.

Table 2.4 Possible Multiplicities

One electron:	doublet
Two electrons:	singlet, triplet
Three electrons:	doublet, quartet
Four electrons:	singlet, triplet, quintet
Five electrons:	doublet, quartet, sextet
Six electrons:	singlet, triplet, quintet, septet
Seven electrons:	doublet, quartet, sextet, octet

As a corollary to the rule of integer perimeters for angular-momentum triangles, we can state that *an even number of electrons has odd multiplicity; an odd number has even multiplicity*. Table 2.4 shows the possible multiplicities.

D. Equivalent Orbitals

Our discussion of *LS* coupling has assumed that spin and orbital angular momentum are independent coordinates. An important exception to this assumption occurs when we treat equivalent orbitals, for then the exclusion principle introduces a connection between spatial coordinates and spin. To cite an example, two electrons occupying the 1s orbitals must have the quantum numbers:

	n	l	m_s	m_l
orbital 1:	1	0	$+\frac{1}{2}$	0,
orbital 2:	1	0	$-\frac{1}{2}$	0.

The spins of the electrons are therefore antiparallel. If we wish a triplet state, $S = 1$, the spins must be parallel. But the exclusion principle forbids this possibility. A singlet is therefore the only allowed term.

Another important case occurs when a shell of equivalent electrons is filled [i.e., $2(2l + 1)$ electrons with orbital angular momentum l and the same principle quantum number]. For each electron characterized by quantum numbers n, l, m_s, m_l, another electron has quantum numbers n, l, $-m_s$, $-m_l$. Therefore the angular momenta must completely cancel; a closed shell has $L = S = J = 0$.

Because of this cancellation of angular momenta in a closed shell, a configuration with one electron fewer than a closed shell (i.e., one *hole*) has many of the attributes of the configuration with only a single electron: p^5 is similar to p; d^9 is similar to d. The similarity extends even further: two vacancies (or holes) in a shell act like two particles; three holes act like three particles; etc. Actually the analogy between particles and holes is not quite complete, because (as we shall see in Chapter 9) the *sign* of $\mathbf{S}\cdot\mathbf{L}$ differs.

The exclusion principle sharply reduces the number of terms available for equivalent orbitals. F. Hund examined [8] this problem in detail and drew up the list of terms shown in Table 2.5 [8]–[11]. Hund's method for eliminating the forbidden terms is described in several standard works [12]–[14]. We will take up this question from a different viewpoint in Chapter 9.

The following simplified procedure suggested by Tuttle [15] permits rapid enumeration of the spectroscopic terms allowed by the Pauli principle. Consider the terms of the configuration l^q, and let x be the lesser of q and $2l + 1$. Draw $2x + 3$ columns: x columns for "spin-up" ($m_S = +\frac{1}{2}$), x columns for "spin-down" ($m_S = -\frac{1}{2}$) and 3 columns for values of M_S and M_L and the term symbol ^{2S+1}L. Now proceed through the following steps.

1. Enter values of m_l in a row sequentially, from left to right, starting with $m_l = l$ in column 1, according to the following rule: *within the "spin-up" section (or the spin-down section) values of m_l must decrease from left to right, without repeating values.* If $q > 2l + 1$, the electrons fill the spin-up section and extend into the spin-down section, where the values of m_l start again at $m_l = l$ in column $x + 1$.

Table 2.5 Allowed *LS*-Coupling Terms of Equivalent Orbitals*

s electrons:								
s^2:	^1S							
s:		^2S						
p electrons:								
p^6:	^1S							
p or p^5:		^2P						
p^2 or p^5:	$^1(SD)$		^3P					
p^3:		$^2(PD)$		^4S				
d electrons:								
d^{10}:	^1S							
d or d^9:		^2D						
d^2 or d^8:	$^1(SDG)$		$^3(PF)$					
d^3 or d^7:		$^2(PDFGH)$		$^4(PF)$				
d^4 or d^6:	$^1(S_2D_2FG_2I)$		$^3(P_2DF_2GH)$		^5D			
d^5:		$^2(PD_2FGH)$		$^4(SPD_2F_2G_2I)$		^6S		
f electrons:								
f^{14}:	^1S							
f or f^{13}:		^2F						
f^2 or f^{12}:	$^1(SDGI)$		$^3(PFH)$					
f^3 or f^{11}:		$^2(PD_2F_2G_2H_2IKL)$		$^4(SDFGI)$				
f^4 or f^{10}:	$^1(S_2D_2FG_4H_2I_3KL_2N)$		$^3(P_3D_2F_4G_3H_3I_2K_2LM)$		$^5(SDFGI)$			
f^5 or f^9:		$^2(P_4D_5F_7G_6H_7I_5K_5L_3M_2NO)$		$^4(SP_2D_3F_4G_4H_3I_3K_2LM)$		$^6(PFH)$		
f^6 or f^8:	$^1(S_4PD_6F_4G_8H_4I_7K_3L_4M_2N_2Q)$		$^3(P_6D_5F_9G_7H_9I_6K_6L_3M_3NO)$		$^5(SPD_3F_2G_3H_2I_2KL)$		^7F	
f^7:		$^2(S_2P_5D_7FGH_9I_9K_7L_5M_4N_2OQ)$		$^4(S_2P_2D_6F_5G_7H_5I_5K_3L_3MN)$		$^6(PDFGHD)$		^8S

* Subscripts denote the number of terms that occur with a given L and S.

2. Determine M_S and M_L as the algebraic sums of the m_s and m_l values.

3. Determine a term symbol ^{2S+1}L by the following procedure. For the first row of the chart, the term is simply $S = M_S$ and $L = M_L$. As the chart grows longer, rows of given M_S and M_L must repeat all the preceding terms for which $S \geq M_S$ and $L \geq M_L$. You will have *at least* as many rows having the given M_S and M_L as you have terms previously found with $S \geq M_S$ and $L \geq M_L$. If you have *more* rows than terms, you have a *new* term (or terms), for which $S = M_S$ and $L = M_L$.

4. Now decrease M_L by unity (unless M_L is already 0) and repeat steps **1–3**. Tabulate a new row for each appropriate combination of m_l values that add to M_L. Continue until you complete the case $M_L = 0$.

5. After completion of the case $M_L = 0$, start over from step **1** with M_S lower by 1. This time start the row of m_l values in column 2 (or subsequent

+			−	M_S	M_L	Term
2	1	0		$\frac{3}{2}$	3	^4F *
2	1	−1		$\frac{3}{2}$	2	(^4F)
2	1	−2		$\frac{3}{2}$	1	(^4F)
2	0	−1		$\frac{3}{2}$	1	^4P *
2	0	−2		$\frac{3}{2}$	0	(^4F)
1	0	−1		$\frac{3}{2}$	0	(^4P)
	2	1	2	$\frac{1}{2}$	5	^2H *
	2	1	1	$\frac{1}{2}$	4	(^2H)
	2	0	2	$\frac{1}{2}$	4	^2G *
	2	1	0	$\frac{1}{2}$	3	(^4F)
	2	0	1	$\frac{1}{2}$	3	(^2H)
	2	−1	2	$\frac{1}{2}$	3	(^2G)
	1	0	2	$\frac{1}{2}$	3	^2F *
	2	1	−1	$\frac{1}{2}$	2	(^4F)
	2	0	0	$\frac{1}{2}$	2	(^2H)
	2	−1	1	$\frac{1}{2}$	2	(^2G)
	1	0	1	$\frac{1}{2}$	2	a^2D *
	1	−1	2	$\frac{1}{2}$	2	b^2D *

+		−	M_S	M_L	Term
2	1	−2	$\frac{1}{2}$	1	(^4F)
2	0	−1	$\frac{1}{2}$	1	(^4P)
2	−1	0	$\frac{1}{2}$	1	(^2H)
2	−2	1	$\frac{1}{2}$	1	(^2G)
1	0	0	$\frac{1}{2}$	1	(^2F)
1	−1	1	$\frac{1}{2}$	1	(a^2D)
1	−2	2	$\frac{1}{2}$	1	(b^2D)
1	−1	2	$\frac{1}{2}$	1	^2P *
2	0	−2	$\frac{1}{2}$	0	(^4F)
2	−1	−1	$\frac{1}{2}$	0	(^4P)
1	0	−1	$\frac{1}{2}$	0	(^2G)
1	−1	0	$\frac{1}{2}$	0	(^2F)
1	−2	1	$\frac{1}{2}$	0	(a^2D)
1	−1	1	$\frac{1}{2}$	0	(b^2D)
0	−2	2	$\frac{1}{2}$	0	(^2P)

Fig. 2.12 Enumeration of allowed terms of d^3.

Table 2.6 Ground Levels of Neutral Atoms

Z		Element	Configuration			IP
1	H	Hydrogen	$1s$		$^2S_{1/2}$	13.595
2	He	Helium	$1s^2$		$^1S_0$	24.581
3	Li	Lithium	$2s$		$^2S_{1/2}$	5.390
4	Be	Beryllium	$2s^2$		$^1S_0$	9.320
5	B	Boron	$2s^2$	$2p$	$^2P_{1/2}$	8.296
6	C	Carbon	$2s^2$	$2p^2$	$^3P_0$	11.256
7	N	Nitrogen	$2s^2$	$2p^3$	$^4S^\circ_{3/2}$	14.53
8	O	Oxygen	$2s^2$	$2p^4$	$^3P_2$	13.614
9	F	Fluorine	$2s^2$	$2p^5$	$^2P^\circ_{3/2}$	17.42
10	Ne	Neon	$2s^2$	$2p^6$	$^1S_0$	21.559
(helium core)						
11	Na	Sodium	$3s$		$^2S_{1/2}$	5.138
12	Mg	Magnesium	$3s^2$		$^1S_0$	7.644
13	Al	Aluminum	$3s^2$	$3p$	$^2P^\circ_{1/2}$	5.984
14	Si	Silicon	$3s^2$	$3p^2$	$^3P_0$	8.149
15	P	Phosphorus	$3s^2$	$3p^3$	$^4S^\circ_{3/2}$	10.484
16	S	Sulfur	$3s^2$	$3p^4$	$^3P_2$	10.357
17	Cl	Chlorine	$3s^2$	$3p^5$	$^2P^\circ_{3/2}$	13.01
18	A	Argon	$3s^2$	$3p^6$	$^1S_0$	15.755
(neon core)						
19	K	Potassium	$4s$		$^2S_{1/2}$	4.339
20	Ca	Calcium	$4s^2$		$^1S_0$	6.111
21	Sc	Scandium	$3d$	$4s^2$	$^2D_{3/2}$	6.54
22	Ti	Titanium	$3d^2$	$4s^2$	$^3F_2$	6.82
23	V	Vanadium	$3d^3$	$4s^2$	$^4F_{3/2}$	6.74
24	Cr	Chromium	$3d^5$	$4s$	$^7S_3$	6.763
25	Mn	Manganese	$3d^5$	$4s^2$	$^6S_{5/2}$	7.433
26	Fe	Iron	$3d^6$	$4s^2$	$^5D_4$	7.90
27	Co	Cobalt	$3d^7$	$4s^2$	$^4F_{9/2}$	7.86
28	Ni	Nickel	$3d^8$	$4s^2$	$^3F_4$	7.633

Table 2.6 (*continued*)

Z	Element		Configuration			IP
29	Cu	Copper	$3d^{10}$	$4s$	$^2S_{1/2}$	7.724
30	Zn	Zinc	$3d^{10}$	$4s^2$	$^1S_0$	9.391
31	Ga	Gallium	$*4s^2$	$4p$	$^2P^\circ_{1/2}$	6.00
32	Ge	Germanium	$*4s^2$	$4p^2$	$^3P_0$	7.88
33	As	Arsenic	$*4s^2$	$4p^3$	$^4S^\circ_{3/2}$	9.81
34	Se	Selenium	$*4s^2$	$4p^4$	$^3P_2$	9.75
35	Br	Bromine	$*4s^2$	$4p^5$	$^2P^\circ_{3/2}$	11.813
36	Kr	Krypton	$*4s^2$	$4p^6$	$^1S_0$	13.996

* means $3d^{10}$

(argon core)

37	Rb	Rubidium	$5s$		$^2S_{1/2}$	4.176
38	Sr	Strontium	$5s^2$		$^1S_0$	5.692
39	Y	Yttrium	$4d$	$5s^2$	$^2D_{3/2}$	6.5
40	Zr	Zirconium	$4d^2$	$5s^2$	$^3F_2$	6.84
41	Nb	Niobium(Columbium)	$4d^4$	$5s$	$^6D_{1/2}$	6.88
42	Mo	Molybdenum	$4d^5$	$5s$	$^7S_3$	7.10
43	Tc	Technecium	$4d^5$	$5s^2$	$^6S_{5/2}$	7.28
44	Ru	Ruthenium	$4d^7$	$5s$	$^5F_5$	7.364
45	Rh	Rhodium	$4d^8$	$5s$	$^4F_{9/2}$	7.46
46	Pd	Palladium	$4d^{10}$		$^1S_0$	8.33
47	Ag	Silver	$*5s$		$^2S_{1/2}$	7.574
48	Cd	Cadmium	$*5s^2$		$^1S_0$	8.991
49	In	Indium	$*5s^2$	$5p$	$^2P^\circ_{1/2}$	5.785
50	Sn	Tin	$*5s^2$	$5p^2$	$^3P_0$	7.342
51	Sb	Antimony	$*5s^2$	$5p^3$	$^4S^\circ_{3/2}$	8.639
52	Te	Tellurium	$*5s^2$	$5p^4$	$^3P_2$	9.01
53	I	Iodine	$*5s^2$	$5p^5$	$^2P^\circ_{3/2}$	10.454
54	Xe	Xenon	$*5s^2$	$5p^6$	$^1S_0$	12.127

* means $4d^{10}$

(krypton core)

Table 2.6 (*continued*)

Z		Element	Configuration				IP
55	Cs	Cesium	$6s$			$^2S_{1/2}$	3.893
56	Ba	Barium	$6s^2$			$^1S_0$	5.210
57	La	Lanthanum	$5d$	$6s^2$		$^2D_{3/2}$	5.577
58	Ce	Cerium	$4f$	$5d$	$6s^2$	$^1G_4^{\circ}$	5.65
59	Pr	Praseodymium	$4f^3$	$6s^2$		$^4I_{9/2}^{\circ}$	5.42
60	Nd	Neodymium	$4f^4$	$6s^2$		$^5I_4$	5.49
61	Pm	Prometheum	$4f^5$	$6s^2$		$^6H_{5/2}^{\circ}$	5.55
62	Sm	Samarium	$4f^6$	$6s^2$		$^7F_0$	5.63
63	Eu	Europium	$4f^7$	$6s^2$		$^8S_{7/2}^{\circ}$	5.68
64	Gd	Gadolinium	$4f^7$	$5d$	$6s^2$	$^9D_2^{\circ}$	6.16
65	Tb	Terbium	$(4f^9$	$6s^2$		$^6H_{15/2})$	(5.85)
66	Dy	Dysprosium	$4f^{10}$	$6s^2$		$^5I_8$	5.93
67	Ho	Holmium	$4f^{11}$	$6s^2$		$^4I_{15/2}^{\circ}$	6.02
68	Er	Erbium	$4f^{12}$	$6s^2$		$^3H_6$	6.10
69	Tm	Thulium	$4f^{13}$	$6s^2$		$^2F_{7/2}^{\circ}$	6.18
70	Yb	Ytterbium	$4f^{14}$	$6s^2$		$^1S_0$	6.25
71	Lu	Lutecium	$*5d$	$6s^2$		$^2D_{3/2}$	—
72	Hf	Hafnium	$*5d^2$	$6s^2$		$^3F_2$	—
73	Ta	Tantalum	$*5d^3$	$6s^2$		$^4F_{3/2}$	7.88
74	W	Tungsten(Wolfram)	$*5d^4$	$6s^2$		$^5D_0$	7.98
75	Re	Rhenium	$*5d^5$	$6s^2$		$^6S_{5/2}$	7.87
76	Os	Osmium	$*5d^6$	$6s^2$		$^5D_4$	8.7
77	Ir	Iridium	$*5d^7$	$6s^2$		$^4F_{9/2}$	9
78	Pt	Platinum	$*5d^9$	$6s$		$^3D_3$	9.0
79	Au	Gold	$*5d^{10}$	$6s$		$^2S_{1/2}$	9.22
80	Hg	Mercury	$*5d^{10}$	$6s^2$		$^1S_0$	10.43
81	Tl	Thallium	$\dagger 6s^2$	$6p$		$^2P_{1/2}^{\circ}$	6.106
82	Pb	Lead	$\dagger 6s^2$	$6p^2$		$^3P_0$	7.415
83	Bi	Bismuth	$\dagger 6s^2$	$6p^3$		$^4S_{3/2}^{\circ}$	7.287
84	Po	Polonium	$\dagger 6s^2$	$6p^4$		$^3P_2$	8.43
85	At	Astatine	$\dagger 6s^2$	$6p^5$		$^2P_{3/2}^{\circ}$	—
86	Rn	Radon	$\dagger 6s^2$	$6p^6$		$^1S_0$	10.746

* means $4f^{14}$

† means $4f^{14}\ 5d^{10}$

(xenon core)

Table 2.6 (*continued*)

Z		Element	Configuration		IP
87	Fr	Francium	$7s$	$^2S_{1/2}$	—
88	Ra	Radium	$7s^2$	$^1S_0$	5.277
89	Ac	Actinium	$6d\ \ 7s^2$	$^2D_{3/2}$	—
90	Th	Thorium	$6d^2\ \ 7s^2$	$^3F_2$	—
91	Pa	Protactinium	$5f^2\ \ 6d\ \ 7s^2$	$^4K_{11/2}$	—
92	U	Uranium	$5f^3\ \ 6d\ \ 7s^2$	$^5L^\circ_6$	—
93	Np	Neptunium	$5f^4\ \ 6d\ \ 7s^2$	$^6L_{11/2}$	—
94	Pu	Plutonium	$5f^6\ \ 7s^2$	$^7F_0$	—
95	Am	Americium	$5f^7\ \ 7s^2$	$^8S^\circ_{7/2}$	—
96	Cm	Curium	$5f^7\ \ 6d\ \ 7s^2$	$^9D^\circ_2$	—
97	Bk	Berkelium	$(5f^8\ \ 6d\ \ 7s^2$	$^8G_{15/2})$	—
98	Cf	Californium	$(5f^{10}\ \ 7s^2$	$^5I_8)$	—
99	E	Einsteinium	$5f^{11}\ \ 7s^2$	$^4I^\circ_{15/2}$	—
100	Fm	Fermium	$5f^{12}\ \ 7s^2$	$^3H_6$	—
101	Mv	Mendelevium	$5f^{13}\ \ 7s^2$	$^2F^\circ_{7/2}$	—
102	No	Nobelium	$5f^{14}\ \ 7s^2$	$^1S_0$	—
103	Lw	Lawrencium	$5f^{14}\ \ 6d\ \ 7s^2$	$^2D_{3/2}$	—

B. G. Wybourne, *Spectroscopic Properties of Rare Earths*, Interscience, New York (1965).

C. E. Moore, *Atomic Energy Levels*, Natl. Bur. Stds. Circ. 467, vol. 1 (1949), vol. 2 (1952), vol. 3 (1958).

J. Sugar and J. Reader, *J. Opt. Soc. Am.* **55,** 1286 (1965); J. Reader and J. Sugar, *J. Opt. Soc. Am.* **56,** 1189 (1966).

columns as calculations proceed) instead of column 1. Continue with steps **1–4** until you have completed the case $M_L = 0$ and $M_S = 0$ or $\frac{1}{2}$.

As an example, Fig. 2.12 illustrates the procedure for determining the allowed terms of d^3. We have placed an asterisk beside term symbols the first time they appear, and enclosed repeated symbols in parentheses.

The preceding tabulation enumerates the allowed terms but it does *not* tell us the connection between a set of individual quantum numbers $\{m_l, m_s\}$ and the collective quantum numbers S and L when more than one term occurs with a given M_S and M_L. We discuss this connection in Chapter 6.

Hund went further than simply providing a list of allowed terms. Drawing on empirical evidence, he proposed two rules for determining the relative positions of these terms.

1. *Of the terms arising from equivalent orbitals, those with largest multiplicity lie lowest.*

2. *Of the terms with given multiplicity, and arising from equivalent orbitals, that with largest L value lies lowest.*

Hund's rules predict, for example, that the lowest-lying terms of the d^n configurations should be

$$d^2\ {}^3F, \quad d^3\ {}^4F, \quad d^4\ {}^5D, \quad \text{etc.}$$

Hund also noted the following:

3a. *For terms arising from less than half-filled shells, the level with lowest J lies lowest ("normal order").*

3b. *For terms arising from more than half-filled shells, the level with highest J lies lowest ("inverted order").*

To these we may add:

3c. *Terms arising from half-filled shells show only very slight fine-structure splitting.*

Hund was quite successful in predicting the lowest terms and levels of many atoms. However, exceptions do occur.

For reference, Table 2.6 gives the ground configuration and energy level for the elements, as given in the National Bureau of Standards monographs *Atomic Energy Levels* [16] and in more recent publications.

E. Landé Interval Rule

It is interesting to note a consequence of our simple model for coupling angular momentum. Suppose we regard

$$\mathbf{J} = \mathbf{L} + \mathbf{S} \tag{12.5}$$

as an ordinary vector equation. Then we obtain:

$$\mathbf{J}\cdot\mathbf{J} = \mathbf{L}\cdot\mathbf{L} + 2\mathbf{L}\cdot\mathbf{S} + \mathbf{S}\cdot\mathbf{S}. \tag{12.6}$$

This relation permits us to write the spin–orbit splitting energy (6.3) as

$$\Delta E = \zeta\mathbf{S}\cdot\mathbf{L} = \tfrac{1}{2}\zeta[\mathbf{J}\cdot\mathbf{J} - \mathbf{L}\cdot\mathbf{L} - \mathbf{S}\cdot\mathbf{S}]. \tag{12.7}$$

We might suppose that replacement of the product $\mathbf{J}\cdot\mathbf{J}$ by J^2, etc., should yield the formula for fine-structure splitting. This prescription proves incorrect. The correct formula,

$$\Delta E_{SLJ} = \tfrac{1}{2}\zeta[J(J+1) - L(L+1) - S(S+1)], \tag{12.8}$$

was discovered by A. Landé [17] from empirical studies. We derive his formula from quantum theory in Chapter 9. *Landé's formula* (12.8) predicts that the separation between adjacent levels of a spectroscopic term should be

$$\Delta E_{SLJ} - \Delta E_{SLJ-1} = \tfrac{1}{2}\zeta[J(J+1) - (J-1)J] = \zeta J. \qquad (12.9)$$

Thus if $J_{\max}$ is the largest value of J (so that $J_{\max} = S + L$), the energy difference between the level $J_{\max}$ and successive levels follow the ratios

$$J_{\max} : J_{\max} - 1 : J_{\max} - 2 : \cdots$$

These expressions, known as the *Landé interval rule*, describe the fine structure of atoms that follow LS coupling. For example, it predicts the levels of a ^3D term as:

$$\begin{aligned} E(^3D_3) &= E_0(^3D) + 2\zeta \\ &\qquad]\ \text{difference} = 3\zeta \\ E(^3D_2) &= E_0(^3D) - 1\zeta \\ &\qquad]\ \text{difference} = 2\zeta \\ E(^3D_1) &= E_0(^3D) - 3\zeta \end{aligned}$$

To obtain the average energy of the ^3D term (its *center of gravity*) we weight each level by its statistical weight or degeneracy, $2J + 1$ (i.e., the number of Zeeman states comprising the level):

$$\bar{E}(^3D) = \tfrac{7}{15}E(^3D_3) + \tfrac{5}{15}E(^3D_2) + \tfrac{3}{15}E(^3D_1) = E_0(^3D).$$

This equation illustrates the general result,

$$\sum_J (2J+1)[J(J+1) - L(L+1) - S(S+1)] = 0, \qquad (12.10)$$

with summation from $J = |L - S|$ to $J = L + S$. In other words, the spin–orbit interaction does not shift the center of gravity of a term.

When $S = \frac{1}{2}$, Landé's formula gives the doublet splitting used in (8.5):

$$\Delta E_{J=L+1/2} = \zeta\,\frac{L}{2},$$

$$\Delta E_{J=L-1/2} = -\zeta\,\frac{(L+1)}{2}. \qquad (12.11)$$

Although many of the levels of complex atoms follow Landé's rule, large deviations occur as well; such deviations indicate that the assumption of LS coupling does not apply to that particular term.

F. Landé *g* Factor

We have suggested [with (5.22)] that the magnetic moment of a monovalent element is the resultant of a spin moment and an orbital moment.

Suppose we generalize that suggestion to the Russell–Saunders coupling model:

$$\boldsymbol{\mu} = \beta(g_s\mathbf{S} + \mathbf{L}). \tag{12.12}$$

With $g_s = 2$ this reads

$$\boldsymbol{\mu} = \beta(2\mathbf{S} + \mathbf{L}) = \beta(\mathbf{S} + \mathbf{J}). \tag{12.13}$$

It follows that the component of $\boldsymbol{\mu}$ along $\mathbf{J}$ is

$$\boldsymbol{\mu}\cdot\mathbf{J} = \beta(\mathbf{S}\cdot\mathbf{J} + \mathbf{J}\cdot\mathbf{J}). \tag{12.14}$$

If we now solve the equation

$$\mathbf{L}\cdot\mathbf{L} = (\mathbf{J} - \mathbf{S})\cdot(\mathbf{J} - \mathbf{S}) = \mathbf{J}\cdot\mathbf{J} - 2\mathbf{J}\cdot\mathbf{S} + \mathbf{S}\cdot\mathbf{S},$$

for $\mathbf{J}\cdot\mathbf{S}$, then we can write (12.14) as

$$\boldsymbol{\mu}\cdot\mathbf{J} = \tfrac{1}{2}\beta[3\mathbf{J}\cdot\mathbf{J} + \mathbf{S}\cdot\mathbf{S} - \mathbf{L}\cdot\mathbf{L}]. \tag{12.15}$$

Now the Zeeman splitting can be written

$$\Delta E = -\boldsymbol{\mu}\cdot\mathbf{H} = \beta g\mathbf{J}\cdot\mathbf{H}. \tag{12.16}$$

This equation states that only the compound of $\boldsymbol{\mu}$ along $\mathbf{J}$ contributes to the Zeeman splitting. We therefore write

$$\boldsymbol{\mu}\cdot\mathbf{H} = \frac{(\boldsymbol{\mu}\cdot\mathbf{J})(\mathbf{J}\cdot\mathbf{H})}{(\mathbf{J}\cdot\mathbf{J})} = \beta\left[\frac{3\mathbf{J}\cdot\mathbf{J} + \mathbf{S}\cdot\mathbf{S} - \mathbf{L}\cdot\mathbf{L}}{2\mathbf{J}\cdot\mathbf{J}}\right]M|\mathbf{H}|. \tag{12.17}$$

Comparison of (12.16) and (12.17) then gives the Landé g factor as

$$g = \frac{3\mathbf{J}\cdot\mathbf{J} + \mathbf{S}\cdot\mathbf{S} - \mathbf{L}\cdot\mathbf{L}}{2\mathbf{J}\cdot\mathbf{J}} = \frac{3}{2} + \frac{(\mathbf{S}\cdot\mathbf{S}) - (\mathbf{L}\cdot\mathbf{L})}{2(\mathbf{J}\cdot\mathbf{J})}. \tag{12.18}$$

Landé found [17] that this formula could indeed apply to many energy levels if $J(J + 1)$ were substituted for $\mathbf{J}\cdot\mathbf{J}$, etc.:

$$g = \frac{3}{2} + \frac{S(S + 1) - L(L + 1)}{2J(J + 1)}. \tag{12.19}$$

Quantum-mechanical calculations (Chapter 11) confirm the applicability of Landé's formula to many (but by no means all) energy levels. Table 2.7 provides values of g according to (12.19); note that g need not lie between the limits $g = 1$ and $g = 2$, nor need g be positive.

Given a table of g factors, it is a straightforward exercise to predict the pattern of Zeeman components from the formula

$$\tilde{\nu} = \tilde{\nu}_0 + \beta(Mg - M'g')|\mathbf{H}| = \tilde{\nu}_0 + \beta(M\,\Delta g - g'\,\Delta M)|\mathbf{H}|. \tag{12.20}$$

For example, the transition ${}^2P_{3/2} \rightarrow {}^2S_{1/2}$ (e.g., the sodium D_2 line) has:

$$g({}^2P_{3/2}) = \tfrac{4}{3},\quad g'({}^2S_{1/2}) = 2,\quad \Delta g = -\tfrac{2}{3},\quad M = \tfrac{3}{2}, \tfrac{1}{2}, -\tfrac{1}{2}, -\tfrac{3}{2},\quad M' = \tfrac{1}{2}, -\tfrac{1}{2}.$$

Table 2.7 Landé g Factors for Russell-Saunders Terms [a]

		$L = S$	P	D	F	G	H
Singlets ($S = 0$)	$J = L$	0	1	1	1	1	1
Doublets ($S = \frac{1}{2}$)	$J = L - \frac{1}{2}$		0.667	0.800	0.857	0.889	0.909
	$L + \frac{1}{2}$	2	1.333	1.200	1.143	1.111	1.091
Triplets ($S = 1$)	$J = L - 1$		0	0.500	0.667	0.750	0.800
	L		1.500	1.167	1.083	1.050	1.033
	$L + 1$	2	1.500	1.333	1.250	1.200	1.167
Quartets ($S = \frac{3}{2}$)	$J = L - \frac{3}{2}$			0	0.400	0.571	0.667
	$L - \frac{1}{2}$		2.667	1.200	1.029	0.984	0.970
	$L + \frac{1}{2}$		1.733	1.371	1.238	1.172	1.133
	$L + \frac{3}{2}$	2	1.600	1.429	1.333	1.273	1.231
Quintets ($S = 2$)	$J = L - 2$			0	0	0.333	0.500
	$L - 1$			1.500	1	0.917	0.900
	L		2.500	1.500	1.250	1.150	1.100
	$L + 1$		1.833	1.500	1.350	1.267	1.214
	$L + 2$	2	1.667	1.500	1.400	1.333	1.286

[a] After E. U. Condon and G. H. Shortley, *Theory of Atomic Spectra*, Cambridge University Press, London (1935) p. 382.,
For more detailed tables, see C. E. Moore, *Atomic Energy Levels* National Bureau of Standards Circular 467 (1949), vol. I. pp. XX–XXVII.

Therefore σ^+ components ($\Delta M = +1$) occur at

$$\tilde{\nu}_0 + \beta|\mathbf{H}|\tfrac{5}{3},$$
$$\tilde{\nu}_0 + \beta|\mathbf{H}|\tfrac{3}{3};$$

π components ($\Delta M = 0$) occur at

$$\tilde{\nu}_0 + \beta|\mathbf{H}|\tfrac{1}{3},$$
$$\tilde{\nu}_0 - \beta|\mathbf{H}|\tfrac{1}{3};$$

and σ^- components ($\Delta M = -1$) occur at

$$\tilde{\nu}_0 - \beta|\mathbf{H}|\tfrac{3}{3},$$
$$\tilde{\nu}_0 - \beta|\mathbf{H}|\tfrac{5}{3}.$$

This pattern can be succinctly stated with a notation introduced by Back and Landé [18]:

$$^2P_{3/2} - {}^2S_{1/2}: \quad \frac{(1),\ 3,\ 5}{3}.$$

This Back–Landé symbol denotes components spaced symmetrically about ν_0, at $\pm\frac{1}{3}$, $\pm\frac{3}{3}$, and $\pm\frac{5}{3}$ in units of βH; parentheses indicate π components. The Back–Landé symbol is independent of which level, $^2P_{3/2}$ or $^2S_{1/2}$, is the upper (initial) level.

REFERENCES

[1] H. N. Russell and F. A. Saunders, *Astrophys. J.* **61,** 38 (1925).
[2] A. G. Shenstone, *Phys. Rev.* **38,** 873 (1931); *Rept. Progr. Phys.* **5,** 210 (1939).
[3] E. Majorana, *Nuovo Cimento* **8,** 107 (1931).
[4] W. R. S. Garton, *Proc. Phys. Soc.* (*London*) **A65,** 268 (1952).
[5] P. Auger, *Compt. Rend.* **180,** 65 (1925); *J. Phys. Radium* **6,** 205 (1925); *Compt. Rend.* **182,** 773 (1926); *Ann. Phys.* (Paris) **6,** 183 (1926).
[6] E. H. S. Burhop, *The Auger Effect and Other Radiationless Transitions*, Cambridge University Press, New York (1952).
[7] E. U. Condon and G. H. Shortley, *The Theory of Atomic Spectra*, Cambridge University Press, Cambridge, England (1935), pp. 216, 276, 303.
[8] F. Hund, *Z. Physik* **33,** 345 (1925); *Linienspektren und Periodisches System der Elemente*, Springer-Verlag, Berlin (1927).
[9] G. Breit, *Phys. Rev.* **29,** 782 (1927).
[10] R. C. Gibbs, D. T. Wilber, and H. E. White, *Phys. Rev.* **29,** 790 (1927).
[11] H. N. Russell, *Phys. Rev.* **29,** 782 (1927).
[12] L. Pauling and S. Goudsmit, *The Structure of Line Spectra*, McGraw-Hill, New York (1930).
[13] J. C. Slater, *Quantum Theory of Atomic Structure*, McGraw-Hill, New York (1960), Vol. I.
[14] G. Herzberg, *Atomic Spectra and Atomic Structure*, Dover, New York (1944).
[15] E. R. Tuttle, *Am. J. Phys.* **35,** 26 (1967).
[16] C. E. Moore, *Atomic Energy Levels*, Nat. Bur. Std. Circ. 467, Vol. 1 (1949); Vol. 2 (1952); Vol. 3 (1958).
[17] A. Landé, *Z. Physik* **15,** 189 (1923); **19,** 112 (1923); **5,** 231 (1921).
[18] E. Back and A. Landé, *Zeemaneffekt und Multiplettstruktur*, Springer, Berlin (1925).

2.13 THE ANALYSIS OF COMPLEX SPECTRA

Now that we have outlined the theory of the vector model let us see how that theory will aid us in analyzing spectra. The spectrum of a complex atom may consist of many thousands of lines, each of which is to be identified with some transition between two atomic levels of different energies, say E_u and E_l, where the indices denote upper and lower, respectively. The wavenumber $\tilde{\nu}$ and the wavelength in vacuum λ are determined by

$$\tilde{\nu} = \frac{1}{\lambda} = \frac{(E_u - E_l)}{(hc)}. \tag{13.1}$$

In practice we use observed wavelengths to deduce the energy levels. Accordingly, we first reduce the measured wavelengths in air to wavenumbers, using tables of wavenumbers or a computer program for the refractive index n_{air}.

$$\tilde{\nu} = \frac{n_{\text{air}}}{\lambda_{\text{air}}}. \tag{13.2}$$

The result of our analysis is a map of atomic energy levels on a wavenumber scale.

The energy levels of the atom fall generally into two groups: even and odd parity. With certain restrictions imposed by other selection rules, transitions occur from levels of one group to those of another, thereby giving rise to spectral lines. The general principle of analysis is shown in Fig. 2.13. The diagram indicates two pairs of levels of opposite parity. Illustrative values of inner quantum numbers J, which are presumed to be identical for the respective pairs, are given. Four lines result for wavenumbers A, B, C, D.

Let a, b, c, and d represent the energies (expressed in wavenumber units) of the four respective levels, as measured from the ground or any other convenient level of the atom. Then we see from the diagram that

$$B = d - b, \qquad D = d - a, \qquad A = c - b, \qquad C = c - a.$$

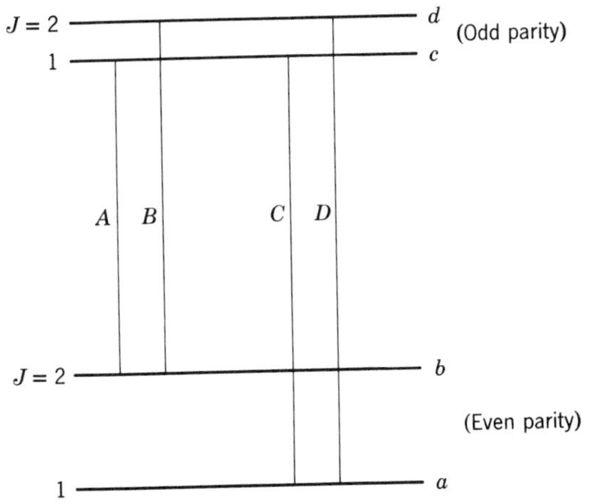

Fig. 2.13 Schematic diagram of a multiplet.

A, *B*, *C* and *D*, the observed quantities, measure the wavenumber differences. Now note that

$$B - A = D - C = d - c \quad \text{and} \quad B - D = A - C = b - a.$$

We have found two constant differences, indicating two pairs of lines arising from the same sets of levels. If, above *c* and *d*, there exist another pair of (odd) levels, *e* and *h*, the constant differences $b - a$ will appear again. The four lines may be arranged to form a square array, with the differences of energy given in parentheses:

	$(b - a)$	
	B	D
$(d - c)$		
	A	C

The analysis of complex spectra is greatly facilitated by the existence of multiple terms, whose related levels characterized by individual *J* values lie close together. The group of related lines formed by the transitions from one term to another is called a *multiplet*. The significance of a multiplet is seen most easily from a hypothetical example.

Let us suppose that in the spectrum of a certain atom we find nine lines relatively close together of similar behavior with reference to excitation in flame, electric furnace, arc, and spark. Knowledge of the laboratory behavior is usually very helpful. The wave numbers are

20920, 20963, 20995, 21000, 21013, 21025, 21075, 21088, 21095.

Between these nine lines 36 differences exist, only a few of which are significant.

From these differences we may assemble the lines into a characteristic multiplet pattern:

		(100)		(75)		(50)		(25)	
	21095		20995		20920				
(93)									
			21088		21013		20963		
(62)									
					21075		21025		21000

The differences are shown in parentheses. The two extra lines, 21000 and 21095, have been fitted in to give a symmetrical pattern consistent with regular increase of intervals. Note that pairs at opposite corners of a square, such as 21088 and 20920, cannot be interchanged without upsetting either the intervals or the general increase of wavenumber toward the left or toward the bottom of the multiplet. The student will verify that the

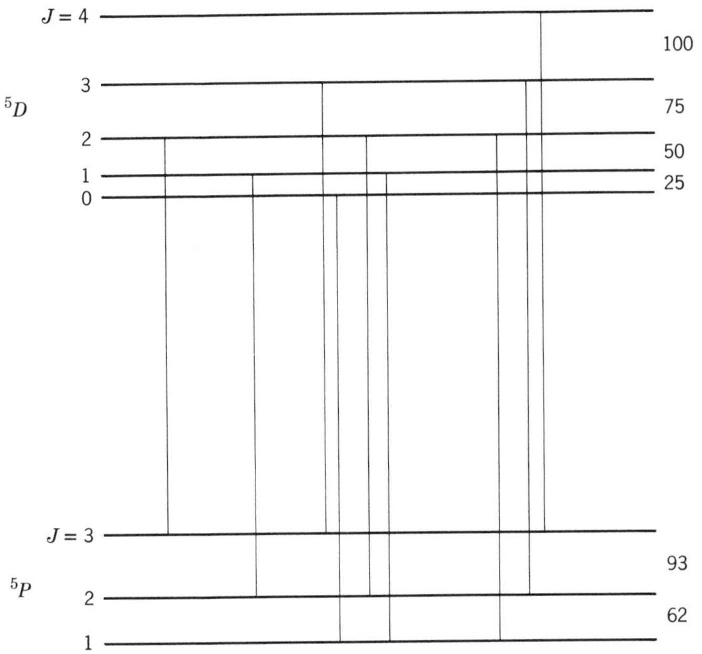

Fig. 2.14 A ^5D–^5P multiplet.

wave numbers are consistent with transitions between one term consisting of five levels and another of three levels, as shown in Fig. 2.14.

The ratios for the term intervals for the upper and lower levels are

$$4:3:2:1 \quad \text{and} \quad 3:2,$$

respectively. By the Landé interval rule the inner quantum numbers for the two upper levels must be 4 and 3. This conclusion is confirmed by the nature of the pattern. By reference to Table 2.2 we see that the upper term is a ^5D. The lower term may be either a ^5P or a ^3D. In the absence of other information to the contrary we conclude that the former assignment is more likely because transitions between levels of different multiplicity are usually fairly weak. We have drawn the ^5D level at the top, but we cannot tell whether this is correct until further levels have been located. Figure 2.15 displays schematically the origin of various representative multiplets. An X indicates that the line is forbidden by the $J = 0 \rightarrow J = 0$ selection rule.

A complete analysis will often show dozens of multiplets arising from the same term going to higher and lower terms of opposite parity. As the

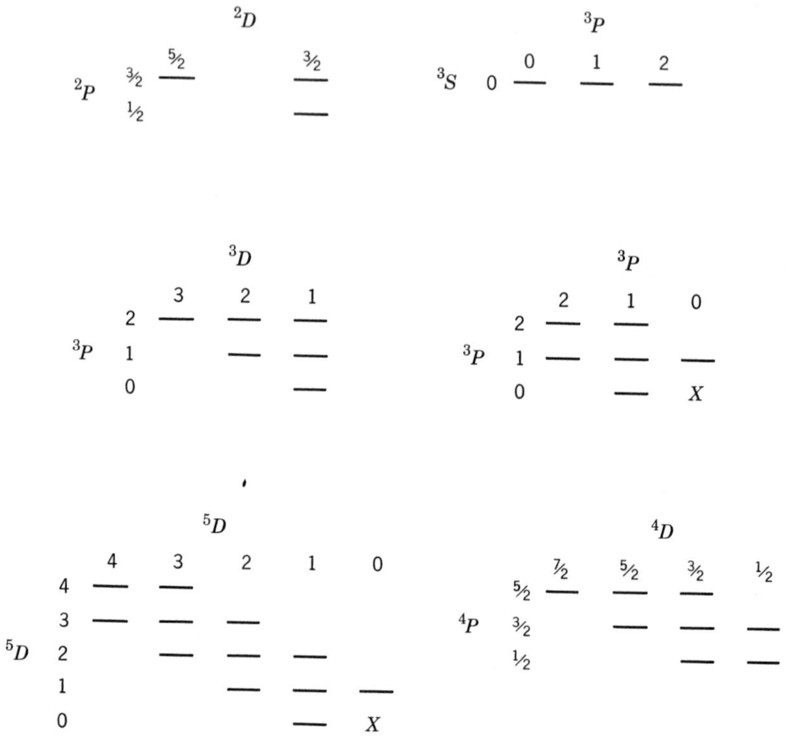

Fig. 2.15 The origin of representative multiplets.

analysis progresses, assignment of J values becomes easier. Irregular terms that deviate markedly from the Landé interval rule may be identified by means of the levels they combine with. In the actual work the relative intensities of the multiplet lines, as discussed in Chapter 10, aid in the identification. Measures of the Zeeman effect also give valuable information.

2.14 TERMINOLOGY

At this point we pause to define and review some conventional terminology associated with atomic energy levels.

State. The *state* of an atom is the condition of motion of all the electrons. To specify a *state*, one must list *four* quantum numbers for each electron (or $4N$ quantum numbers for N electrons). (Actually, five quantum numbers are implied, but the fifth number, the electron spin, is always $\frac{1}{2}$, so we need not include it in our list.) The quantum numbers need not be specifically associated with particular electrons, as we shall see. If several states have the same energy, they are *degenerate*. The state with lowest energy is the *ground state*.

Level. A collection of states having the same energy in the absence of an external electric or magnetic field all correspond to an *energy level*. A *level* is distinguished by a particular value of the *total angular momentum*, the quantum number J. The level with lowest energy is the *ground level*.

Sublevel. An external field splits an energy *level* into several *sublevels*, distinguished by a magnetic quantum number (or several magnetic quantum numbers). Sublevels are often called *Zeeman states* or simply *states*.

Term. In many atoms, the *levels* cluster in related groups which can be labeled by *multiplicity* (i.e., spin) and *orbital angular momentum*. Such a collection of levels comprises a *spectroscopic term*. For example, one speaks of a ^3D *term*, meaning the weighted average energy of the $^3D_3$, $^3D_2$, and $^3D_1$ levels.

Configuration. Specification of the quantum numbers n and l for the orbital of each electron defines a *configuration;* we use an exponent to indicate the number of electrons sharing a given n and l. For example, $1s^2$, $2p$ and $1s^2$, $2s^2$, $2p^6$, $5f$. The orbitals are conventionally listed according to increasing n, then by increasing l, that is, $1s$, $2s$, $2p$, $3s$, $3p$, $3d$, $4s$, $4p$, $4d$, $4f$, $5s$, $5p$, $5d$, $5f$, $5g$, $\cdots$.

Equivalent Orbitals. Orbitals with the same n and l are *equivalent*. (The electrons in equivalent orbitals are sometimes called *equivalent electrons*.)

Statistical Weight. The number of distinct states in a specified collection is the statistical weight. The statistical weight of a level is $2J + 1$; for a term, it is $(2S + 1)(2L + 1)$; for a single electron with a specified n it is $2n^2$.

Spectral lines are commonly categorized according to the following nomenclature:

A transition between two *sublevels* is called a *component*. (For nondegenerate sublevels, this is a transition between two particular states.)

A transition between two *levels* is a *line*. (A *line* is a blend of *components*.)

The collection of transitions between two *terms* is called a *multiplet*. (A *multiplet* consists of from one to a dozen or more *lines*.)

The collection of transitions between two configurations is referred to as a *transition array*. (A *transition array* may comprise hundreds of *lines* in a dozen or more *multiplets*.)

Allowed transitions between the ground level and higher levels are known as *resonance lines* (these include the Lyman series of hydrogen and the principal series of alkalis). The particular resonance line of lowest frequency is often called *the resonance line.*

APPENDIX A. ATOMIC UNITS

Quantity	Expression	Value[1]	SI[2]	CGS[3]
Length				
Bohr radius	$a_0 = \frac{\hbar^2}{me^2} = a_0 = \frac{\alpha}{4\pi R_\infty}$	5.29167 (7)	10^{-11} m	**10^{-9} cm**
Compton wavelength of electron	$\lambda_c = \frac{h}{mc} = 2\pi\alpha(a_0) = \frac{\alpha^2}{2R_\infty}$	2.42621 (6)	10^{-12} m	10^{-10} cm
Reduced Compton wavelength of electron	$\lambdabar_c = \frac{\hbar}{mc} = \alpha(a_0)$	3.86144 (9)	10^{-13} m	10^{-11} cm
Classical radius of electron	$r_e = \frac{e^2}{mc^2} = \alpha^2(a_0)$	2.81777 (11)	10^{-15} m	10^{-13} cm
Wavelength of a 1 eV photon	$\frac{hc}{e} = \frac{2\pi}{\alpha}$ (e)	1.23981 (4)	10^{-6} eV m	10^{-4} eV cm
. . .	$\frac{4\pi\hbar^3 c}{3me^4} = \frac{4\pi}{3\alpha}(a_0) = \frac{1}{3R_\infty}$	3.03756	10^{-12} eV m	10^{-10} eV cm

APPENDIX A. ATOMIC UNITS *(continued)*

Quantity	Expression	Value[1]	SI[2]	CGS[3]
Area				
Square of Bohr radius	$\frac{\hbar^4}{m^2e^4} = (a_0)^2$	2.80018	10^{-23} m^2	10^{-19} cm^2
Square of classical radius of electron	$(r_e)^2 = \frac{e^4}{m^2c^4} = \alpha^4(a_0)^2$	7.9398 (6)	10^{-30} m^2	10^{-26} cm^2
Thompson cross section	$\sigma = \frac{8\pi}{3}\frac{e^4}{m^2c^4} = \frac{8\pi}{3}\alpha^4(a_0)^2$	6.6516 (5)	10^{-29} m^2	10^{-25} cm^2
Wavenumber				
Atomic unit	$\frac{me^2}{\hbar^2} = \left(\frac{1}{a_0}\right) = \frac{4\pi R_\infty}{\alpha}$	1.88976	10^{11} m^{-1}	10^9 cm^{-1}
Wavenumber $\bar{\nu}$ of 1 atomic unit energy	$\frac{1}{hc}\frac{e^2}{a_0} = \frac{\alpha}{2\pi}\left(\frac{1}{a_0}\right) = 2R_\infty$	2.194746	10^7 m^{-1}	10^5 cm^{-1}
Rydberg constant	$R_\infty = \frac{me^4}{4\pi\hbar^3c} = \frac{\alpha}{4\pi}\left(\frac{1}{a_0}\right)$	1.0973731 (3)	10^7 m^{-1}	10^5 cm^{-1}
Wavenumber of 1 eV photon	$\frac{e}{hc} = \frac{\alpha}{2\pi}\left(\frac{1}{e}\right)$	8.06573 (23)	10^5(eV)$^{-1}$ m^{-1}	10^3(eV)$^{-1}$ cm^{-1}

Time				
Atomic unit	$\frac{\hbar^3}{me^4} = \left(\frac{\hbar a_0}{e^2}\right) = \frac{1}{4\pi c R_\infty}$	2.41888	10^{-17} sec	10^{-17} sec
Frequency				
Atomic unit	$\frac{me^4}{\hbar^3} = \left(\frac{e^2}{\hbar a_0}\right) = 4\pi c R_\infty$	4.134138	10^{16} Hz	10^{16} s^{-1}
Rydberg frequency	$R_y = \frac{me^4}{4\pi\hbar^3} = \frac{1}{4\pi}\left(\frac{e^2}{\hbar a_0}\right) = cR_\infty$	3.289842	10^{15} Hz	10^{15} s^{-1}
Cyclotron frequency of electron	$\nu_H = \frac{e}{2\pi mc} = \frac{\alpha}{2\pi}\left(\frac{ea_0}{\hbar}\right)$	2.799211	10^6 Hz G^{-1}	10^0 Mc sec^{-1} G^{-1}
Frequency of a 1-eV photon	$\frac{e}{h} = \frac{1}{2\pi}\left(\frac{e}{\hbar}\right)$	2.41804 (7)	10^{14} Hz$(eV)^{-1}$	10^8 Mc sec^{-1} $(eV)^{-1}$
Mass				
Electron rest mass	$m = \frac{M}{1836.1}$	9.1091 (4) 5.48597 (9)	10^{-31} kg 10^{-4} u	10^{-28} g 10^{-4} u
Proton rest mass	$M = 1836.1m$	1.67252 (8) 1.00727663 (24)	10^{-27} kg u	10^{-24} g u
Unified atomic mass unit ($\frac{1}{12}$ mass of C^{12} nucleus)	u	1.66043	10^{-27} kg	10^{-24} g

APPENDIX A. ATOMIC UNITS *(continued)*

Quantity	Expression	Value[1]	SI[2]	CGS[3]
Velocity				
Atomic unit	$v_0 = \left(\frac{e^2}{\hbar}\right) = \alpha c$	2.18765	10^6 m sec^{-1}	10^8 cm sec^{-1}
Speed of light	$c = \frac{1}{\alpha}\left(\frac{e^2}{\hbar}\right)$	2.997925 (3)	10^8 m sec^{-1}	10^{10} cm sec^{-1}
Momentum				
Atomic unit	$\left(\frac{me^2}{\hbar}\right) = \alpha mc$	1.9927	10^{-24} kg m sec^{-1}	10^{-19} g cm sec^{-1}
Angular Momentum				
Atomic unit	$\hbar = \frac{h}{2\pi}$	1.05450 (7)	10^{-34} J sec	10^{-27} erg sec
Energy				
Atomic unit	$\frac{me^4}{\hbar^2} = \left(\frac{e^2}{a_0}\right) = 2hcR_\infty$	2.72106	10^1 eV	10^1 eV
Rydberg energy	$\frac{me^4}{2\hbar^2} = \frac{1}{2}\left(\frac{e^2}{a_0}\right) = hcR_\infty$	{2.17972 1.36054	10^{-18} J 10^1 eV	10^{-11} erg 10^1 eV

Electron rest energy	mc^2	$= \frac{1}{\alpha^2}\left(\frac{e^2}{a_0}\right)$	5.11006 (5)	10^5 eV	10^5 eV
Proton rest energy	Mc_2		9.38256 (15)	10^8 eV	10^8 eV
Energy of a 1-eV electron	eV		1.60210 (7)	10^{-19} J	10^{-12} erg
Electrical					
Electron charge		e	1.60210 (7) 4.80298 (20)	10^{-19} C —	10^{-20} emu 10^{-10} esu
Charge-to-mass ratio of electron		$\frac{e}{m}$	1.758796 (19) 5.27274 (6)	10^{11} C kg^{-1} —	10^7 emu g^{-1} 10^{17} esu g^{-1}
Atomic unit of electric potential		$\frac{me^3}{\hbar^2} = \frac{e}{a_0} = \frac{2hcR_\infty}{e}$	2.72106 9.07649	10^1 V —	10^1 V 10^{-2} esu
Atomic unit of electric field intensity		$\frac{m^2e^5}{\hbar^4} = \frac{e}{(a_0^2)}$	5.14216 1.71524	10^{11} V m^{-1} —	10^9 V cm^{-1} 10^7 esu
Atomic unit of electric dipole moment		$\frac{\hbar^2}{me^3} = ea_0$	8.4778 2.54158	10^{-30} C m —	— 10^{-18} esu cm

APPENDIX A. ATOMIC UNITS (*continued*)

Quantity	Expression	Value[1]	SI[2]	CGS[3]
Magnetic				
e' emu = e/c esu; e' SI = e SI)				
Bohr magneton	$\mu_B \equiv \beta = \frac{\hbar e'}{2m} = \frac{\alpha}{2}(ea_0)$	9.2732 (6)	10^{-24} J T^{-1}	10^{-21} erg G^{-1}
Cyclotron frequency of electron	$\nu_H = \frac{e'}{2\pi m} = \frac{\alpha}{2\pi}\left(\frac{ea_0}{\hbar}\right) = \frac{\beta}{\pi\hbar}$	2.79921	10^{10} Hz T^{-1}	10^0 Mc sec^{-1} G^{-1}
Lorentz unit of Zeeman displacement	$\frac{e'}{4\pi mc} = \frac{\alpha^2}{4\pi}\left(\frac{a_0}{e}\right) = \frac{\beta}{2\pi\hbar c}$	4.66858 (4)	10^1 m^{-1} T^{-1}	10^{-5} cm^{-1} G^{-1}
Quantum of magnetic flux	$\frac{h}{e'} = \frac{2\pi}{\alpha}(e)$	4.13556 (12)	10^{-15} J sec C^{-1}	10^{-7} cm^2 G^{-1}
Atomic unit of magnetic field intensity	$\frac{m^2e^2}{\hbar^4} = \frac{e}{(a_0)^2} = \frac{\alpha}{\beta}(hcR_\infty)$	1.71524	10^3 T	10^7 G
Temperature				
Boltzmann's constant	k	1.38054 (18)	10^{-23} J °K^{-1}	10^{-16} erg °K^{-1}

Temperature of 1 eV	$\frac{e}{k}$	1.16049 (16)	10^4 °K(eV)$^{-1}$	10^4 °K(eV)$^{-1}$
Temperature of 1 atomic unit energy	$\frac{me^4}{k\hbar^2} = \frac{2hcR_\infty}{k}$	3.15779	10^5 °K	10^5 °K
Atomic specific-heat constant	$\frac{h}{k}$	4.7993 (6)	10^{-11} sec °K	10^{-11} sec °K
Second radiation constant	$\frac{hc}{k}$	1.43879 (19)	10^{-2} m °K	10^0 cm °K
Miscellaneous				
Sommerfeld fine-structure constant	$\alpha = \frac{e^2}{\hbar c} = \alpha$	7.29720 (10)	10^{-3}	10^{-3}
	$\frac{e^2}{hc} = \frac{\alpha}{2\pi}$	1.161385 (16)	10^{-3}	10^{-3}
	$\frac{\hbar c}{e^2} = \frac{1}{\alpha}$	137.0388 (19)	10^0	10^0
	α^2	5.32492 (14)	10^{-5}	10^{-5}
	α^3	3.88570	10^{-9}	10^{-9}
	$\frac{1}{\alpha^3}$	2.57354	10^8	10^8

APPENDIX A. ATOMIC UNITS (*continued*)

Quantity	Expression	Value[1]	SI[2]	CGS[3]
Miscellaneous				
Planck's constant	$h = 2\pi\hbar$	6.6256 (5)	10^{-34} J sec	10^{-27} erg sec
Dirac's constant	$\hbar$	1.05450 (7)	10^{-34} J sec	10^{-27} erg sec
	hc	1.9863	10^{-9} J m	10^{-16} erg cm
	$\frac{hc}{e}$	1.23981 (4)	10^{-6} eV m	10^{-4} eV cm
First radiation constant	$2\pi hc^2$	3.7405 (3)	10^{-8} W m^2	10^{-5} erg cm^2 s^{-1}
Gas constant	R	8.3143 (12)	10^0 J °K^{-1} mol^{-1}	10^7 erg °K^{-1} mol^{-1}
Avogadro's number	N	6.02252 (28)	10^{23} mol^{-1}	10^{23} mol^{-1}
Stephan–Boltzmann constant	$\sigma = \left(\frac{\pi^2}{60}\right)\left(\frac{k^4}{\hbar^3 c^2}\right)$	5.6697 (29)	10^{-8}W m^{-2} (°K)$^{-4}$	10^{-5} erg cm^{-2} sec^{-1} (°K)$^{-4}$
pi	π	3.141592654	10^0	10^0
	$\frac{1}{\pi}$	3.183098862	10^{-1}	10^{-1}

[1] Values shown with error estimates (three standard deviations) are from E. R. Cohen and J. W. M. DuMond least-squares values tabulated in a. *Natl. Bur. Stds. Tech. News.* Bull., October 1963. b. *Handbook of Mathematical Functions*, Natl. Bur. Stds. Applied Math. Series 55 (June 1964). c. *J. Opt. Soc. Am.* **54**, 282 (1964).

[2] SI = Système International (MKSA): C = coulomb, T = tesla = 1 weber/m^2 = 10^4 gauss, Hz = hertz = 1 cycle/sec, J = joule = 10^7 erg, N = newton = 10^5 dyne.

[3] CGS system: G = gauss.

3. Wave Mechanics

3.1 WAVELIKE PROPERTIES OF MATTER

The Bohr–Sommerfeld quantization, used in the last chapter, selects from the continuum of particle orbits those for which the angular momentum takes particular discrete values. This method leads to discrete term values in accord with spectroscopic observations. But the grafting of quantum conditions on classical mechanics is not wholly satisfactory. We need a variety of empirical rules, such as the introduction of $L(L + 1)$ for $\mathbf{L} \cdot \mathbf{L}$. This approach offers little hope for a consistent, quantitative treatment of the structure of atoms having several valence electrons.

In 1925 two complementary approaches pointed the way to a consistent atomic mechanics. The first theory, *matrix mechanics*, was proposed by Werner Heisenberg [1]. The second theory was developed a few months later by Erwin Schrödinger [2] as *wave mechanics*. Schrödinger's approach provides the more direct means of picturing an atom, and we therefore discuss his theory first. As we shall see, the two approaches are mathematically equivalent. They describe complementary aspects of what is now called *quantum mechanics*.

Schrödinger's mechanics emerged from a suggestion by Louis de Broglie [3] that particles should exhibit wavelike properties. De Broglie reasoned that, since electromagnetic waves display attributes of particles (e.g., the photoelectric effect) as well as waves (e.g., diffraction), then for the sake of symmetry in nature, particles such as electrons should be capable of wavelike behavior. As we shall see in Section 3.2, de Broglie's theory was quantitative and made explicit predictions concerning the relationship between momentum of the particle and its associated wavelength: $p = h/\lambda$, where h is Planck's constant. De Broglie's hypothesis was soon confirmed by C. J. Davisson and L. H. Germer [4], who, bombarding a nickel crystal

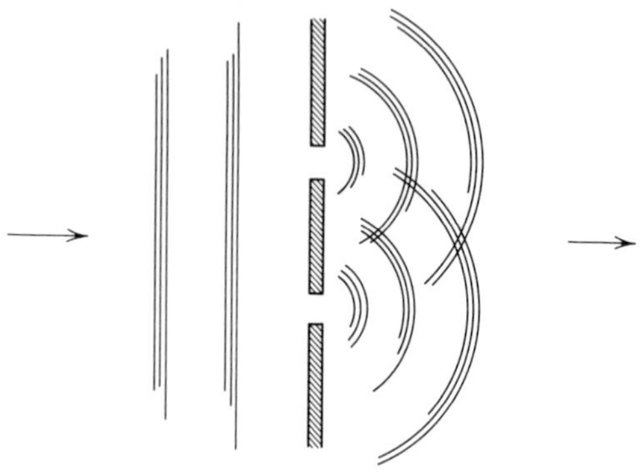

Fig. 3.1 Diffraction by two apertures.

with a beam of electrons, observed a diffraction pattern in the distribution of scattered electrons. Since then, neutron diffraction and other experiments have amply demonstrated the wavelike nature of matter.

A diffraction experiment offers a clear example of wave phenomena. Imagine a wave passing from left to right through the slits in Fig. 3.1. Beyond the slit barrier to the right, the amplitude of disturbance is the sum of two disturbances, each moving outward from one of the slits. This *principle of superposition* was first noted by Christian Huygens. The resulting disturbance will have wave crests (or valleys) wherever waves from two apertures combine crests (or valleys), and will have a null value wherever crests and valleys cancel. The resulting interference pattern from light waves shows a sequence of alternating bright and dark regions on a screen intersecting the waves. The screen is bright wherever the *intensity* (the *square* of the amplitude) is large, and is dark wherever the intensity is small (a null point of the wave front). When we record the interference pattern on a photographic plate, we measure the intensity of the wave disturbance rather than the amplitude.

Suppose we replace the photographic plate by an array of photoelectric detectors, and decrease the illumination on the aperture. We now observe discrete electrical impulses from each detector. We shall further discover, after a suitable time, that the number of impulses recorded at any position is proportional to the intensity of the wave disturbance observed previously with the photographic plate. This experiment demonstrates that radiation energy comes in quanta or *photons*. Each impulse of a photoelectric detector indicates the absorption of a photon. Such a detector is therefore called a *photon counter*. (A photographic plate, examined under magnification, also reveals the discrete nature of radiation: the image consists of dark grains in each of which a photon was absorbed, surrounded by areas where no photon was absorbed.)

A similar experiment, wherein a beam of electrons replaces the beam of light, would reveal a similar result. The diffraction pattern can be recorded on a fluorescent screen or photographic plate or, alternatively, observed as individual electrons with an array of electron counters. We should find the intensity of the electron wave (revealed by the screen) proportional to the number of particles (recorded by the counters).

Such experiments reveal the *dual* nature of both matter and radiation. We can observe single photons and electrons or we can observe large numbers of them. At low intensities, light exhibits properties of particles (the photons), whereas at higher intensities the wave properties emerge. The references in Bibliography 5 provide further discussion of the fundamental observations.

REFERENCES

[1] W. Heisenberg, *Z. Physik* **34,** 858 (1925).

[2] E. Schrödinger, *Ann. Physik* **79,** 361 (1925); **79,** 489 and 734 (1925); **80,** 487 (1926); **81,** 109 (1926).
These are reprinted in E. Schrödinger, "Die Wellenmechanik," in *Dokumente der Naturwissenschaft*, A. Hermann (ed.), Ernst Battenberg Verlag, Stuttgart (1963), vol. 3.

[3] L. de Broglie, *Phil. Mag.* **47,** 446 (1924); *Ann. Phys.* (Paris) **3,** 22 (1925).

[4] C. Davisson and L. Germer, *Nature* **119,** 558 (1927); *Phys. Rev.* **30,** 705 (1927); *Proc. Natl. Acad. of Sci.* **14,** 317 and 619 (1928); J. Franklin Inst. **205,** 597 (1928).

3.2 EQUATIONS FOR WAVES

Let us accept the fact that the electron can exhibit wavelike properties. How can we incorporate this behavior into our picture of an atom?

Suppose that we wish to describe a wavelike disturbance progressing steadily through free space. For mathematical convenience, let the direction of motion be the positive x axis, and ignore any possible variation of the wave in the y and z directions. We can describe this *plane wave* by the following equation for the *wave amplitude* $\psi(x, t)$:

$$\psi = A \cos\left[\frac{2\pi}{\lambda}(x - ct + \delta)\right], \qquad (2.1)$$

where λ is the wavelength, c the phase velocity, and A and δ determine the amplitude and the position of a wave crest (phase), respectively, in terms of the arbitrary origin and scale of our coordinate system. Observe that a given value of ψ occurs for a given value of $(x - ct)$. As time increases, this value occurs at progressively greater values of x. In time t, this value of x will be length ct larger. We might describe the wave equally well by a sine function if we set the phase δ equal to $\frac{1}{2}\pi$. We lose nothing by writing (2.1) with unit amplitude and zero phase:

$$\psi = \cos(kx - \omega t), \tag{2.2}$$

where, for simplicity, we follow common practice and introduce the *wave vector*,

$$k \equiv \frac{2\pi}{\lambda} = 2\pi\tilde{\nu} = \frac{2\pi\nu}{c}, \tag{2.3}$$

and the *angular frequency*,

$$\omega \equiv 2\pi\nu = 2\pi\tilde{\nu}c = \frac{2\pi}{\lambda}c. \tag{2.4}$$

(Some authors refer to k as a *wave number;* it differs from the *wavenumber* $\tilde{\nu}$ by a factor of 2π.) The two new parameters k and ω are linked, in this simple plane wave, by the relation

$$\omega = kc. \tag{2.5}$$

An equation relating k and ω is called a *dispersion relation*. As a last simplification of (2.1), note that Euler's formula

$$e^{i\phi} = \cos\phi + i\sin\phi, \tag{2.6}$$

where $i \equiv \sqrt{-1}$, permits us to write a plane wave as

$$\psi = \exp i(kx - \omega t), \tag{2.7}$$

with the understanding that the real part of any expression involving ψ represents the physically meaningful quantity.

Next, we inquire for the differential equation satisfied by the wave of (2.7). The partial derivatives are

$$\begin{aligned} \frac{\partial\psi}{\partial t} &= -i\omega\psi, & \frac{\partial\psi}{\partial x} &= ik\psi, \\ \frac{\partial^2\psi}{\partial t^2} &= -\omega^2\psi, & \frac{\partial^2\psi}{\partial x^2} &= -k^2\psi. \end{aligned} \tag{2.8}$$

Then, replacing ω^2 by k^2c^2 according to (2.5), we find

$$\frac{\partial^2\psi}{\partial t^2} = -k^2c^2\psi = c^2\frac{\partial^2\psi}{\partial x^2}. \tag{2.9}$$

The time-dependent equation,

$$\frac{\partial^2 \psi}{\partial x^2} - \frac{1}{c^2}\frac{\partial^2 \psi}{\partial t^2} = 0, \tag{2.10}$$

is often called the *wave equation* in texts on electromagnetic theory or hydrodynamics, since it describes the plane waves encountered in those disciplines. The time-independent equation for a wave of a particular angular frequency ω is

$$\frac{\partial^2 \psi}{\partial x^2} + k^2\psi = 0. \tag{2.11}$$

A wave in a material medium characterized by a refractive index n also follows the form of (2.7) but now the phase velocity is c/n. The angular frequency becomes

$$\omega = \frac{2\pi}{n\lambda}c = k\frac{c}{n}, \tag{2.12}$$

with n a function of k. The wave equation becomes

$$\frac{\partial^2 \psi}{\partial x^2} - \frac{n^2}{c^2}\frac{\partial^2 \psi}{\partial t^2} = 0, \tag{2.13}$$

or, with (2.9),

$$\frac{\partial^2 \psi}{\partial x^2} + \frac{n^2\omega^2}{c^2}\psi = 0. \tag{2.14}$$

Thus far we have discussed waves of definite angular frequency. A single-frequency (pure) sine wave, however, has infinite extension along the x axis. Suppose instead we consider a *packet* of waves. A hypothetical stationary observer would see this wave disturbance pass by, within a short period of time, followed by no disturbance at all, as illustrated in Fig. 3.2. Our interest in wave packets comes from a presumption, justified below, that such a localized disturbance may describe a particle more adequately than a wave extending indefinitely in time. Mathematically, we can construct such a wave packet by superposing monochromatic waves of slightly different frequency such that the amplitudes all add coherently at a point

Fig. 3.2 A wave packet.

x, but get progressively out of phase and cancel as we move away from this point. Adding together waves of the form of (1.7), each with an amplitude $f(k)$, over a succession of small intervals dk, gives the disturbance

$$\psi(x, t) = \frac{1}{\sqrt{2\pi}} \int_{-\Delta k}^{+\Delta k} f(k) \exp i[kx - \omega(k)t]\, dk, \tag{2.15}$$

where we introduce a factor $\sqrt{2\pi}$ for later convenience. The position of constructive interference occurs where the argument η of the exponential,

$$\eta \equiv (kx - \omega t), \tag{2.16}$$

varies least as we vary k; for values of k for which η changes rapidly over an interval dk, the fluctuation of $e^{i\eta}$ will cancel out. In other words, the wave packet centers on the point x_0 where $\eta(x)$ is an extremum; that is, where

$$\frac{d\eta}{dk} = 0 = \frac{d}{dk}\,[kx - \omega(k)t]. \tag{2.17}$$

This equation shows that the center is located at

$$x_0 = \frac{d\omega}{dk}\, t. \tag{2.18}$$

The packet thus moves with the *group velocity*

$$v_g = \frac{x_0}{t} = \frac{d\omega}{dk}\,. \tag{2.19}$$

Now let us identify the location of this wave packet with the position of a particle. We equate the group velocity of the wave to the *particle velocity* v,

$$v_g = v = \frac{p}{m}\,. \tag{2.20}$$

Next, we note that the energy of a free particle is entirely kinetic energy:

$$E = \tfrac{1}{2}mv^2.$$

We can use (2.20) to write this energy as a function of momentum rather than velocity (the *Hamiltonian function* $\mathcal{H}$):

$$E = \frac{p^2}{2m} = \mathcal{H}(p). \tag{2.21}$$

For a wave, Einstein's equation $E = h\nu$ or $E = \hbar\omega$ expresses energy in terms of the frequency as the fundamental observable quantity. We might reasonably assume that, for a particle, this same equation should conversely prescribe the frequency in terms of the energy as the fundamental observable quantity. We therefore write

$$\omega = \frac{E}{\hbar} = \frac{1}{\hbar}\frac{p^2}{2m}. \tag{2.22}$$

Then (2.19) becomes

$$\frac{p}{m} = \frac{d}{dk}\left(\frac{1}{\hbar}\frac{p^2}{2m}\right) \tag{2.23}$$

or

$$\frac{dp}{dk} = \hbar. \tag{2.24}$$

Integration gives $p = \hbar k$, since the integration constant merely sets the zero point of measurement. We thus obtain the relation proposed by de Broglie [1]:

$$p = \frac{h}{\lambda} \equiv \hbar k. \tag{2.25}$$

The momentum of the particle is proportional to the wave vector of the wave. Alternatively, the *de Broglie relation* (2.25) states that the wavelength associated with a particle of momentum p is the *de Broglie wavelength*

$$\lambda = \frac{h}{p}, \tag{2.26}$$

as Davisson and Germer first confirmed [2].

We might note that the relationship of (2.25) between momentum and wavelength also follows from the condition, discussed in texts on electromagnetic theory, that the momentum density p of an electromagnetic wave of energy density E is

$$p = \frac{E}{c}. \tag{2.27}$$

This equation, combined with the Einstein condition $E = \hbar\omega$, leads again to the result

$$p = \frac{\hbar\omega}{c} = \hbar k.$$

Our discussion of motion in a single direction readily generalizes to motion in three dimensions. We replace (2.7) by a three-dimensional wave, with wave vectors k_x, k_y, and k_z:

$$\psi = \exp i(k_x x + k_y y + k_z z - \omega t). \tag{2.28}$$

The notation simplifies if we consider a wave vector $\mathbf{k}$ with components k_x, k_y, and k_z:

$$\psi = \exp i(\mathbf{k}\cdot\mathbf{r} - \omega t). \tag{2.29}$$

The wave equation (2.13) becomes

$$\frac{\partial^2\psi}{\partial x^2} + \frac{\partial^2\psi}{\partial y^2} + \frac{\partial^2\psi}{\partial z^2} - \frac{n^2}{c^2}\frac{\partial^2\psi}{\partial t^2} = 0, \tag{2.30}$$

with (1.5) now reading

$$\omega^2 = (k_x{}^2 + k_y{}^2 + k_z{}^2)c^2 \equiv k^2c^2. \tag{2.31}$$

The *Laplacian operator* ∇^2 (read "del squared"; sometimes written as Δ), defined in rectangular coordinates as

$$\nabla^2 \equiv \frac{\partial^2}{\partial x^2} + \frac{\partial^2}{\partial y^2} + \frac{\partial^2}{\partial z^2}, \tag{2.32}$$

simplifies the form of (2.30) to

$$\nabla^2\psi - \frac{n^2}{c^2}\frac{\partial^2\psi}{\partial t^2} = 0. \tag{2.33}$$

With the substitution of $\partial^2\psi/\partial t^2$ from (2.8), we obtain the three-dimensional Helmholtz equation:

$$\nabla^2\psi - \left(\frac{n\omega}{c}\right)^2\psi = 0. \tag{2.34}$$

All of the wave equations discussed above, both for one-dimensional and three-dimensional waves, share one similarity: the wave disturbance ψ is a *scalar* quantity. That is, the wave phenomenon is completely described at a given point x (or $\mathbf{r}$) and a given time t by a *single number*, $\psi(x, t)$ [or $\psi(\mathbf{r}, t)$]. Examples might be a wave of temperature or pressure. For some wave phenomena, a single number gives insufficient information. An electromagnetic wave, for example, has not only amplitude but also *polarization* (the direction of the electric field). It requires that we specify more than one *component*, or value, at a given point. The wave disturbance ψ might be a vector such as

$$\psi = \mathbf{e}_x\psi_x + \mathbf{e}_y\psi_y + \mathbf{e}_z\psi_z, \tag{2.35}$$

where $\mathbf{e}_x$, $\mathbf{e}_y$, and $\mathbf{e}_z$ are unit vectors along the coordinate axes. For other types of wave ψ might be some other mathematical quantity with several components. We discuss some of these quantities in later chapters. Each component, such as ψ_x of (2.35), will satisfy (2.33).

For the waves of hydrodynamics, ψ may represent the amplitude of a pressure disturbance. For radio waves it might represent the magnitude of one component of the electric-field intensity. What is the physical significance of the wave disturbance ψ that we associated with a particle in the last section? The discussion at the beginning of this section suggests that we should associate the wave intensity at a point x_0 [$\psi^2(x_0)$ for a real function ψ and $\psi^*(x_0)\psi(x_0)$ for a complex function], with the probability of observing a particle at that point. Let dP be the probability of observing a given particle in the volume dv. Then we have the probability in the volume Δv of

$$\int^{\Delta v} dP = \int^{\Delta v} |\psi|^2 \, dv. \tag{2.36}$$

To ensure that we will definitely observe the particle *somewhere* we require that the probability be unity when the volume Δv encloses all space:

$$\int^{\infty} dP = 1 = \int^{\infty} |\psi|^2 \, dv. \tag{2.37}$$

This condition requires us to *normalize* our wavefunctions, to make the integral equal to unity. In principle we easily satisfy this condition. Let φ be an arbitrary solution of (2.30) (or of any other linear differential equation). The integral of $|\varphi|^2$ will then have some value, say N:

$$\int^{\infty} |\varphi|^2 \, dv = N. \tag{2.38}$$

We then construct a *normalized* solution ψ by dividing by $\sqrt{N}$:

$$\psi = \frac{1}{\sqrt{N}} \varphi, \qquad \int^{\infty} |\psi|^2 \, dv = 1. \tag{2.39}$$

This procedure requires the integral of $|\varphi|^2$ to have a finite upper bound as the integration volume tends toward infinity—otherwise the value N would be infinite. Physically, this restriction corresponds to a function concentrated within a finite region of space. Functions that satisfy this condition [for example, a Gaussian $\varphi(x) = \exp(-x^2)$] are called *normalizable*. Functions that do not meet these requirements [for example $\varphi(x) = \sin kx$] are called *unnormalizable;* they describe a particle that cannot be localized with certainty inside any finite volume.

REFERENCES

[1] L. de Broglie, *Phil. Mag.* **47,** 446 (1924); *Ann. Phys. (Paris)* **3,** 22 (1925).
[2] C. Davisson and L. H. Germer, *Nature* **119,** 558 (1927); *Phys. Rev.* **30,** 705 (1927); *Proc. Natl. Acad. Sci.* **14,** 317 and 619 (1928); *J. Franklin Inst.* **205,** 597 (1928).

3.3 THE SCHRÖDINGER EQUATION FOR A SINGLE PARTICLE

Starting from the de Broglie relation $\mathbf{p} = \hbar\mathbf{k}$, we can readily obtain a scalar wave equation (a wave with only one component) describing the motion of a particle. For simplicity, we first consider the one-dimensional case of a free particle. We start with the equation for the energy expressed in terms of momentum (the Hamiltonian function). The de Broglie relation then gives

$$E\psi = \mathcal{H}\psi = \frac{p^2}{2m}\psi = \frac{\hbar^2 k^2}{2m}\psi. \tag{3.1}$$

We now substitute for k^2 from (2.8),

$$k^2\psi = -\frac{\partial^2\psi}{\partial x^2}, \tag{3.2}$$

to find

$$E\psi = -\frac{\hbar^2}{2m}\frac{\partial^2\psi}{\partial x^2}. \tag{3.3}$$

This differential equation is known as the time-independent *Schrödinger equation* for a free particle (in one dimension).

In the presence of a potential $V(x)$ the energy or Hamiltonian function in (2.1) must include V to give

$$E\psi = \mathcal{H}\psi = \left(\frac{p^2}{2m} + V\right)\psi. \tag{3.4}$$

Retracing the steps of (2.1) and (2.2), we obtain the Schrödinger equation for a particle in a potential field:

$$\frac{\partial^2}{\partial x^2}\psi - \frac{2m}{\hbar^2}V(x)\psi = -\frac{2m}{\hbar^2}E\psi. \tag{3.5}$$

Let us state explicitly the steps that led us to the Schrödinger equation:

First, we wrote the electron energy as the sum of a potential energy (which depends on position) and a kinetic energy (a function of momentum).

Next, we set this expression, the Hamiltonian, equal to a constant, the energy E.

Finally, we introduced the substitution

$$p^2\psi \to -\hbar^2\frac{\partial^2}{\partial x^2}\psi.$$

This procedure amounts to the replacement of p by the differential operator

$$p \longrightarrow \frac{\hbar}{i}\frac{\partial}{\partial x}.$$

We can readily follow this same route in three dimensions. The Hamiltonian function becomes the sum of three kinetic-energy terms and a potential-energy term:

$$\mathcal{H}(x, y, z, p_x, p_y, p_z) = \frac{p_x^2}{2m} + \frac{p_y^2}{2m} + \frac{p_z^2}{2m} + V(x, y, z). \tag{3.6}$$

[In special cases, $V(x, y, z)$ may, but not necessarily, separate into the sum of $V(x)$, $V(y)$, and $V(z)$.] Replacement of the momenta by (partial) differential operators,

$$p_x \longrightarrow \frac{\hbar}{i}\frac{\partial}{\partial x}, \qquad p_y \longrightarrow \frac{\hbar}{i}\frac{\partial}{\partial y}, \qquad p_z \longrightarrow \frac{\hbar}{i}\frac{\partial}{\partial z}. \tag{3.7}$$

then gives the three-dimensional Schrödinger equation

$$\frac{\partial^2}{\partial x^2}\psi + \frac{\partial^2}{\partial y^2}\psi + \frac{\partial^2}{\partial z^2}\psi + \frac{2m}{\hbar^2}V\psi = \frac{2m}{\hbar^2}E\psi \tag{3.8}$$

for the wavefunction $\psi(x, y, z)$. With the notation ∇^2 for the Laplacian operator, (2.32), the Schrödinger equation becomes

$$\nabla^2\psi + \frac{2m}{\hbar^2}(E - V)\psi = 0. \tag{3.9}$$

To obtain a time-dependent equation employ the equation $E = \hbar\omega$ and require that the wavefunction have the time dependence $\exp(-i\omega t)$, as in (2.7). Then from (2.8),

$$E\psi = \hbar\omega\psi = i\hbar\frac{\partial}{\partial t}\psi, \tag{3.10}$$

we obtain the *time-dependent Schrödinger equation*,

$$-\frac{\hbar^2}{2m}\nabla^2\psi + V\psi = i\hbar\frac{\partial}{\partial t}\psi. \tag{3.11}$$

This "derivation" of the Schrödinger equation provides no rigorous foundation for quantum mechanics, though the heuristic procedure we followed makes it *plausible* that we can employ a wave equation to describe a particle. The true test can come only through comparison of observations with predictions of the Schrödinger equation. Such comparisons over the last several decades have indeed shown that the Schrödinger equation provides an acceptable description of atoms and molecules.

The identification of $|\psi(x)|^2$ with probability holds for both time-dependent wavefunctions $\psi(x, t)$ and steady-state functions $\psi(x)$. The time-dependent function is a solution to (3.11) and with the probability interpretation we may consider following the course of a single particle or wave packet. We shall be more concerned, in the study of electron motion within atoms, with the steady-state or time-independent Schrödinger equation (3.9). In this case the probability distribution in a region of space will not change with time. We may then think of the probability distribution either as a smeared-out distribution of a single electron or as a statistical result of many observations.

The appearance of $i \equiv \sqrt{-1}$ in (3.10) implies that the function ψ is a complex quantity. Suppose we write ψ as

$$\psi = f + ig \tag{3.12}$$

where f and g are real. We then see, on substituting (3.12) into (3.11) and separating the result into real and imaginary parts, that f and g are linked by the equations

$$-\frac{\hbar}{m}\nabla^2 f + Vf = -\hbar\frac{\partial}{\partial t}g, \tag{3.13a}$$

$$-\frac{\hbar}{m}\nabla^2 g + Vg = +\hbar\frac{\partial}{\partial t}f, \tag{3.13b}$$

so that neither f nor g alone is a solution to the time-dependent Schrödinger equation, (3.11). Thus for such an equation we must use a complex function. To form the *complex conjugate* function, ψ^*, we by definition replace every i in the original function by $-i$:

$$\psi^* = f - ig. \tag{3.14}$$

Note that the quantity $\psi^*\psi$ is always real and positive:

$$\psi^*\psi \equiv |\psi|^2 = (f - ig)(f + ig) = f^2 + g^2. \tag{3.15}$$

Because i does not appear in the time-independent Schrödinger equation (3.9), f and g of (3.13) both satisfy the same equation as ψ, and we need not deal with complex wavefunctions. In this book we are usually concerned with the time-independent equation, and consequently we may use real rather than complex functions whenever this procedure simplifies the mathematics.

3.4 BOUNDARY CONDITIONS AND QUANTIZATION

In the remaining sections of this chapter we examine in some detail the solutions to the time-independent Schrödinger equation for some simple potentials. In a sense we shall merely be studying applied differential equations, but the mathematical properties of these solutions have important physical consequences. In developing purely mathematical tools we obtain some insight into the physical nature of the system our equations describe. For further discussion consult the references in Bibliography 6.

A differential equation serves only as a partial statement of a given physical problem. In general, an infinite number of functions will satisfy the equation. For example, the equation

$$\frac{\partial^2 \psi}{\partial x^2} - \frac{1}{c^2}\frac{\partial^2 \psi}{\partial t^2} = 0 \tag{4.1}$$

has as a solution

$$\psi = f(x \pm ct), \tag{4.2}$$

where $f(\zeta)$ is an arbitrary function of the argument ζ. To pick out any particular solution, and thus to connect the differential equation with a particular physical problem, we must specify suitable *boundary conditions* for ψ. For example, we might require that ψ take certain values along the edge of a membrane, or we might require a function to have a particular value of $\partial\psi/\partial t$ when $t = 0$.

The appropriate one-dimensional boundary conditions on the Schrödinger wavefunction ψ follow from our identification of $|\psi|^2$ with probability. If the probability of observing a particle in some finite interval dx is to remain finite, then $|\psi|^2$ must remain finite. Hence we exclude functions that become infinite at some point or that increase without bound for large values of x. Furthermore, $\partial\psi/\partial x$ must not be infinite anywhere if $\partial^2\psi/\partial x^2$ is to have meaning. Thus ψ must be continuous in the variable x. If we deal with a one-dimensional potential, $V(x)$, which remains finite, (3.5) shows that $\partial^2\psi/\partial x^2$ will remain finite. This restriction means $\partial\psi/\partial x$ must be continuous.

In addition to providing boundary conditions on ψ, our probability interpretation leads to the requirement that $|\psi|^2$ be a single-valued function of x, and apart from a phase $e^{i\phi}$, ψ must also be single-valued. To summarize these conditions and the exceptions:

$\psi(x, t)$ single valued (apart from a phase), finite, and continuous;

$$\frac{\partial\psi}{\partial t}, \frac{\partial\psi}{\partial x} \quad \text{finite and continuous (unless } V \to \pm\infty);$$

$$\frac{\partial^2\psi}{\partial x^2} \quad \text{finite (unless } V \to \pm\infty).$$

Similar conditions hold in three dimensions. However, the arguments are not so simple, except in Cartesian coordinates. For example, if the volume element is

$$dv = f(x_1x_2x_3)\, dx_1\, dx_2\, dx_3,$$

then $f\,|\psi|^2$ rather than simply $|\psi|^2$ must remain finite.

These simple boundary conditions will lead inevitably to quantization in many cases in the sense that *integers* appear naturally in expressions for energy, angular momentum, and other classically defined quantities.

3.5 THE SCHRÖDINGER EQUATION IN ONE DIMENSION

The problem of a "particle in a box" has received attention in every text on quantum mechanics, for it is one of the simplest models that illustrates how boundary conditions lead to quantization of energy levels. We create a mathematical "box" in one dimension by proposing an idealized potential $V(x)$, infinite for $x < 0$ (region A) and $x > L$ (region C) and zero for $0 < x < L$ (region B). (See Fig. 3.3.) We next write the one-dimensional Schrödinger equation for a particle of energy E (unspecified for the moment):

$$\frac{\hbar^2}{2m}\frac{\partial^2\psi}{\partial x^2} = (V - E)\psi. \tag{5.1}$$

In regions A and C, where $V \to \infty$, we have

$$\psi = \frac{1}{(V - E)}\frac{\hbar^2}{2m}\frac{\partial^2\psi}{\partial x^2} \to 0 \tag{5.2}$$

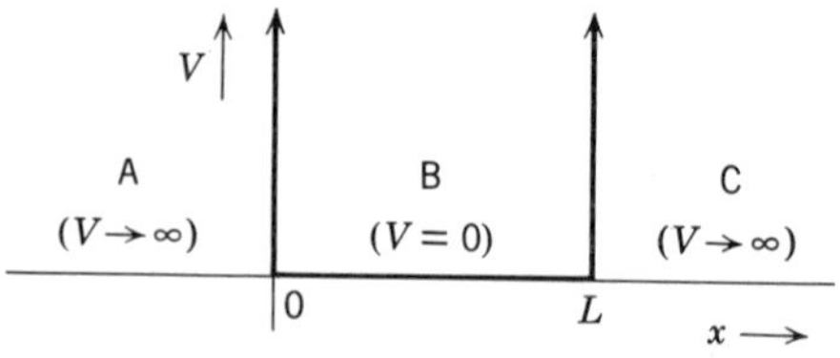

Fig. 3.3 Potential for one-dimensional box.

and the wavefunction vanishes outside the box. This is our way of saying that the particle is certainly (probability unity) inside the box. In region B the equation becomes

$$\frac{\partial^2 \psi}{\partial x^2} = -\frac{2mE}{\hbar^2}\psi, \tag{5.3}$$

with the boundary condition that ψ be zero at the edges of the box so as to join continuously the solutions in regions A and C:

$$\begin{aligned} \psi(0) &= 0, \\ \psi(L) &= 0. \end{aligned} \tag{5.4}$$

(We cannot require continuity of $\partial\psi/\partial x$ at $x = 0$ and $x = L$ in the limit of $V \to \infty$.) Next we look for a solution to (5.3) and (5.4) of the form

$$\psi = a \sin kx + b \cos kx,$$

because

$$\frac{d^2}{dx^2} \sin kx = k^2 \sin kx$$

and

$$\frac{d^2}{dx^2} \cos kx = k^2 \cos kx. \tag{5.5}$$

This trial solution satisfies (5.3) if

$$k^2 = \frac{2mE}{\hbar^2}, \tag{5.6}$$

and it satisfies (5.4) if

$$\begin{aligned} \psi(0) &= 0 = 0 + b, \\ \psi(L) &= 0 = a \sin kL + b \cos kL. \end{aligned} \tag{5.7}$$

The first of these boundary conditions requires $b = 0$. Then, because $\sin(n\pi) = 0$ for integer n, the second boundary condition requires

$$kL = \left(\frac{2mE}{\hbar^2}\right)^{1/2} L = n\pi, \tag{5.8}$$

where n is an integer. Only certain values of E, the *eigenvalues*

$$E = \frac{\pi^2\hbar^2}{2mL^2} n^2, \tag{5.9}$$

give acceptable solutions to the Schrödinger equation; that is, solutions consistent with our boundary conditions of Section 3.4. The *eigenfunctions* or acceptable wavefunctions are

$$\psi(x) = a \sin\left(\frac{\pi n}{L}x\right) = a \sin\left[\left(\frac{2mE}{\hbar^2}\right)^{1/2} x\right]. \tag{5.10}$$

The constant a is fixed by our normalization requirement

$$\int_0^L \psi^2(x)\,dx = 1, \tag{5.11}$$

which gives

$$\begin{aligned} a^2 \int_0^L \sin^2\left(\frac{\pi n}{L}x\right) dx &= a^2\left(\frac{L}{\pi n}\right)\left[\frac{1}{2}\left(\frac{\pi n x}{L}\right) - \frac{1}{4}\sin^2\left(\frac{2\pi n x}{L}\right)\right]_0^L \\ &= a^2\left(\frac{L}{\pi n}\right)\frac{\pi n}{2} = 1 \end{aligned} \tag{5.12}$$

or $a = \sqrt{2/L}$. The normalized eigenfunction associated with the nth eigenvalue is

$$\psi_n(x) = \left(\frac{2}{L}\right)^{1/2} \sin\left(\frac{\pi n}{L}x\right). \tag{5.13}$$

These eigenfunctions have the spatial appearance of standing waves in a cavity or vibrations of a violin string. The nth eigenfunction has $n - 1$ *nodes* (places where $\psi = 0$) between the walls, and the energy increases quadratically with this number of nodes plus one (i.e., with n).

Although our mathematical "box" differs from the potential wells encountered in nature because of the abrupt change of potential at the "walls" and the infinite potential "outside" the box, several observations about this problem remain qualitatively true for any similar "confined" particle.

First, we see that the energy is restricted to a discrete set of values, the eigenvalues. Such a situation occurs whenever boundary conditions require that an integral number of nodes occur in a fixed region.

Second, as the box becomes smaller ($L \to 0$), the energy of the lowest allowed energy state increases. For example, (5.9) shows that the least energy a particle can have when confined to a "box" of atomic dimensions (say 5×10^{-9} cm or one Bohr radius, a_0) is

$$E = \frac{\pi^2\hbar^2}{2ma_0^2}\,1^2 = \pi^2 \times \frac{me^4}{2\hbar^2} \approx 136 \text{ eV}.$$

This energy exceeds the ionization energy of hydrogen, $(me^4/2\hbar^2) = 13.6$ eV, because the hydrogenic electron is not confined by fixed walls and actually ranges over a distance much larger than a_0. As we squeeze in the walls of our container, the kinetic energy of the electron increases. Confinement of the electron to nuclear dimensions, 10^{-13} cm, requires hundreds of GeV. (The GeV or giga-electron volt is 10^9 eV. This value is also denoted BeV for billion electron volts.) For comparison, the rest energy of an electron, mc^2, is 0.5×10^6 eV.

Third, the existence of nodes signifies regions in which the particle will not be found—positions in which $|\psi(x)|^2 = 0$. As we proceed to higher energy of excitation ($n \to \infty$), the wavefunction has more oscillations across the box, until within any interval there are as many nodes as we might choose. The probability of finding the electron in any interval—the square of the wavefunction—thus tends to average out toward a uniform value over the box, as we look at higher electron energies. At very high energies, the particle has equal likelihood of being anywhere within the box. This is just what we should expect for a "classical" particle in a box: it is just as likely to be near a wall as near the center. Thus we see the classical description emerging from the quantum-mechanical description as we go to high-excitation energy.

Next consider the more realistic problem of a particle moving in the one-dimensional potential of Fig. 3.4. We encountered such a potential with the Bohr-atom electron and we will discuss it in detail in the next sections. Let ψ'' denote $\partial^2\psi/\partial x^2$, the curvature of the function ψ. Then the Schrödinger equation, which we can write as

$$\frac{\psi''}{\psi} = \frac{2m}{\hbar^2}(V - E). \tag{5.14}$$

implies that the curvature of the wavefunction depends on $(V - E)$. When V is *less than E*, the curvature is always *toward* the x axis: positive curvature

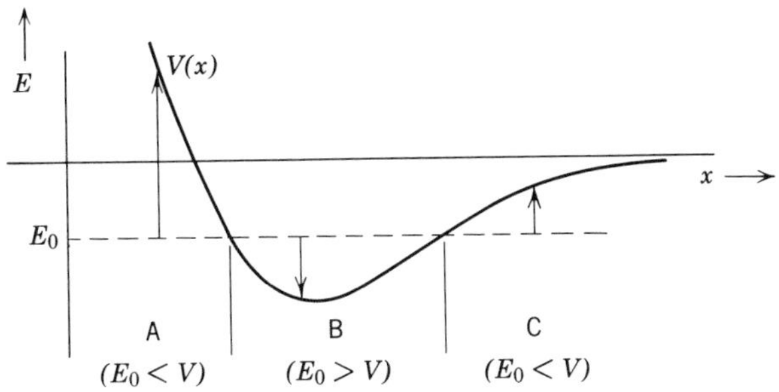

Fig. 3.4 A one-dimensional potential well. Arrows show the difference $V - E_0$ at different positions.

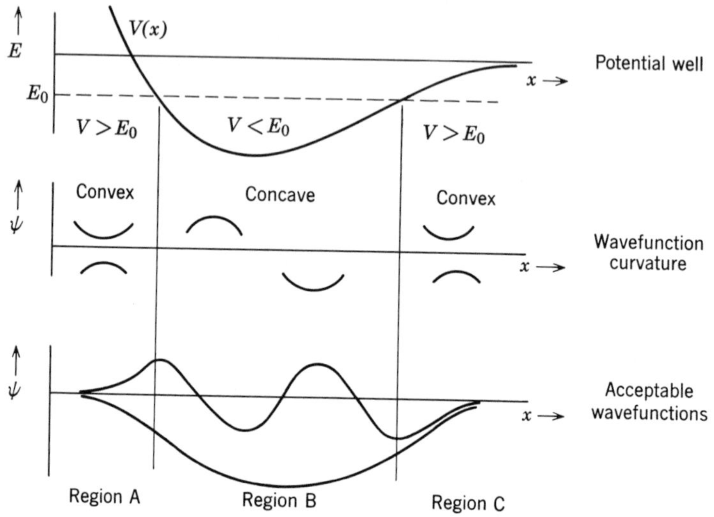

Fig. 3.5

for negative ψ and negative curvature for positive ψ. When V is *greater than E*, the wave function curves *away from* the x axis. If V were constant over a small region, these conditions would correspond to an *oscillatory solution* for $V < E$ and an *exponential solution* for $V > E$. Figure 3.5 presents these arguments graphically.

The wavefunction must pass smoothly from one region to the next, according to our boundary condition. This condition requires the magnitude of the function to increase from zero in region A, bend back or oscillate in region B, and decrease again to zero in region C. Such variation

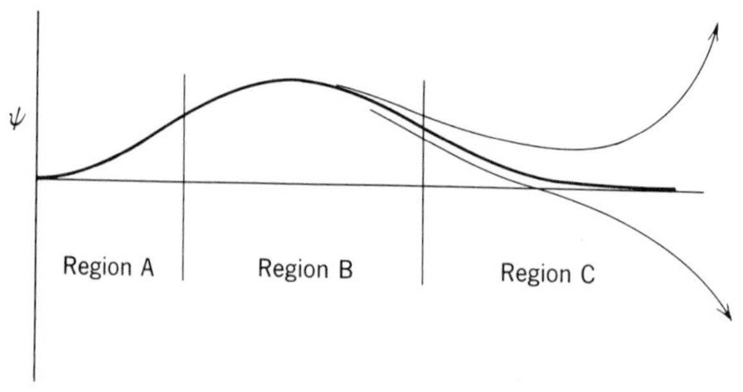

Fig. 3.6 Result of integrating wave equation.

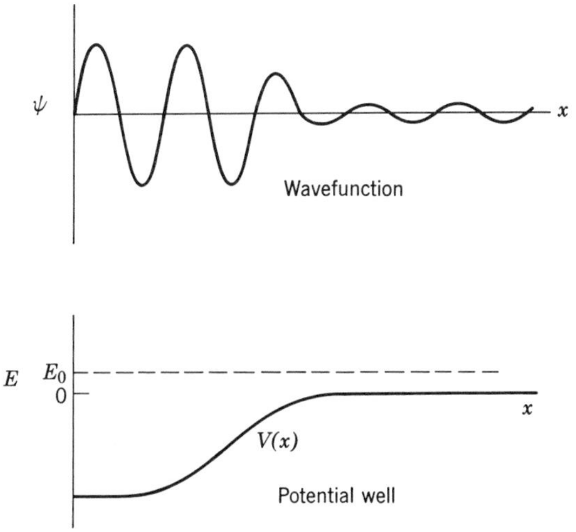

Fig. 3.7 Resonance.

will occur only if the curvature of the wavefunction is properly adjusted by suitable choice of the constant E.

If we were to perform a numerical integration of (5.14), starting from a zero value in region A, we should generally find that, for an arbitrary but negative E, the function would become unboundedly large as we progressed into region C. Figure 3.6 depicts this behavior. Only for the proper choice of E, an eigenvalue of (5.14), will the function behave acceptably, and we then obtain an eigenfunction solution. As with the particle in a box, the energy increases with the number of nodes. The greater the curvature in region B, the more times will the wavefunction cross the x axis.

For positive energy this quantization is no longer necessary; the wavefunction will oscillate sinusoidally at large distances without growing. Thus negative energies [with respect to the zero point, $V(\infty)$] are quantized while positive energies are not. This lack of quantization does not imply, however, that the continuum of positive energies is without structure. It may happen that, for a particular positive energy, the wavefunction can oscillate strongly within the potential well and join smoothly to a small-amplitude sine wave outside the well. Such an energy produces a *potential-well resonance*, illustrated in Fig. 3.7.

3.6 THE SCHRÖDINGER EQUATION IN THREE DIMENSIONS

We have seen that the one-dimensional Schrödinger equation,

$$\frac{d^2\psi}{dx^2} + \frac{2m}{\hbar^2}[E - V(x)] = 0, \tag{6.1}$$

describes the steady-state or time-independent distribution of a particle or wave packet. We now extend our study to the three-dimensional equation,

$$\left(\nabla^2 + \frac{2m}{\hbar^2}V\right)\psi = \frac{2m}{\hbar^2}E\psi. \tag{6.2}$$

The solution of this equation for the wavefunction, ψ, determines the spatial distribution of probability amplitude for a particle. That is, the probability of finding the particle in some volume ΔV is

$$\int^{\Delta V} |\psi|^2\, dV. \tag{6.3}$$

Although we have used Cartesian coordinates x, y, z to extend the one-dimensional Schrödinger equation to three dimensions, the resulting equa-

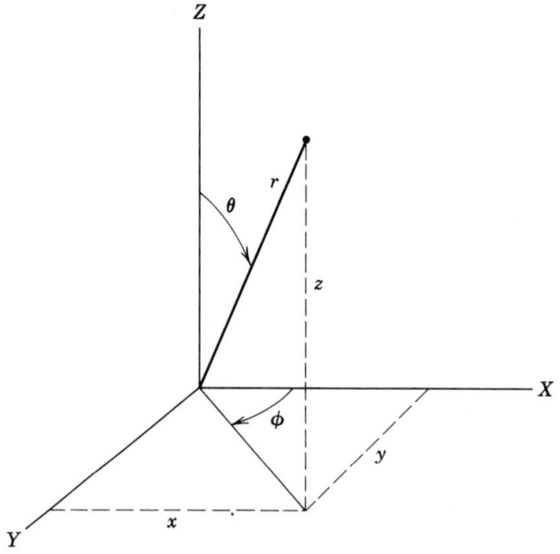

Fig. 3.8 Spherical coordinates.

tion (6.2) serves in any coordinate system. In atomic physics spherical polar coordinates provide the most commonly used coordinate system, because in these coordinates the symmetry of free atoms and the predominantly radial nature of most atomic potentials leads, as we shall see, to simple solutions. Spherical polar coordinates consist of the radial distance r, the polar angle (or colatitude) θ, and azimuthal angle ϕ (see Fig. 3.8). These relate to the Cartesian coordinates by

$$\begin{aligned} r &= (x^2 + y^2 + z^2)^{1/2}, & x &= r \sin\theta \cos\phi, \\ \theta &= \arctan \frac{(x^2 + y^2)}{z}, & y &= r \sin\theta \sin\phi, \\ \phi &= \arctan \frac{y}{x}, & z &= r \cos\theta. \end{aligned} \tag{6.4}$$

Substituting these coordinates and the appropriate derivatives [1] into (6.3) produces the Laplacian operator in spherical coordinates:

$$\nabla^2\psi = \frac{1}{r}\frac{\partial^2}{\partial r^2} r\psi + \frac{1}{r^2}\frac{1}{\sin\theta}\frac{\partial}{\partial\vartheta}\sin\theta\frac{\partial\psi}{\partial\vartheta}\frac{1}{\sin^2\theta}\frac{\partial^2\psi}{\partial\phi^2}. \tag{6.5}$$

For the moment we introduce the differential operators

$$\mathfrak{N}(r)\psi = -\frac{1}{r}\frac{\partial^2}{\partial r^2} r\psi \tag{6.6}$$

and

$$\mathfrak{M}(\theta, \phi)\psi = -\left[\frac{1}{\sin\theta}\frac{\partial}{\partial\theta}\sin\theta\frac{\partial\psi}{\partial\theta} + \frac{1}{\sin^2\theta}\frac{\partial^2\psi}{\partial\phi^2}\right]. \tag{6.7}$$

(We will frequently use script letters to denote differential operators.) The $\mathfrak{M}$ operator has the alternative useful form,

$$\mathfrak{M}\psi = -\left[\frac{\partial^2\psi}{\partial\theta^2} + \cot\theta\frac{\partial\psi}{\partial\theta} + (1 + \cot^2\theta)\frac{\partial^2\psi}{\partial\phi^2}\right]. \tag{6.8}$$

The Hamiltonian, as an operator, now reads

$$\mathcal{H} = -\frac{\hbar^2}{2m}\nabla^2 + V = \frac{\hbar^2}{2m}\mathfrak{N}(r) + \frac{\hbar^2}{2mr^2}\mathfrak{M}(\theta, \phi) + V(r, \theta, \phi), \tag{6.9}$$

and the Schrödinger equation becomes

$$\mathfrak{N}\psi + \frac{\mathfrak{M}}{r^2}\psi + \frac{2m}{\hbar^2}(E - V)\psi = 0. \tag{6.10}$$

The operators $\mathfrak{M}$ and $\mathfrak{N}$ have direct physical significance as we can see by examining the energy equation for a particle moving in a plane ($\theta = \pi$):

$$E = \tfrac{1}{2}mv^2 + V(r) = \tfrac{1}{2}m[\dot{r}^2 + (r\dot{\phi})^2] + V(r). \tag{6.11}$$

If we substitute the radial momentum $p_r = m\dot{r}$ and the angular momentum $p_\phi = mr^2\dot{\phi}$, this becomes

$$E = \frac{p_r^{\,2}}{2m} + \frac{p_\phi^{\,2}}{2mr^2} + V. \tag{6.12}$$

Comparison of (6.12) with (6.8) suggests we identify $\mathfrak{N}$ as the operator for the square of the radial momentum $p_r^{\,2}$, and $\mathfrak{M}$ as the operator for the square of the angular momentum (when $\theta = \pi$, this is $p_\phi^{\,2}$). Such identification is indeed possible, as we can see by examining the operators that should correspond to the components of angular momentum. For a classical point-particle the angular momentum about the (arbitrary) coordinate origin is, by definition, the moment of momentum, or the linear momentum times the length of the lever arm. More conveniently, we may express the angular momentum as the vector product of the linear momentum **p** and the distance from the origin **r**:

$$\hbar \mathbf{L} = \mathbf{r} \times \mathbf{p}. \tag{6.13}$$

We have introduced the factor $\hbar = h/2\pi$ in this definition in order to simplify subsequent formulas: we always express angular momentum in units of $\hbar$. The components of **L** along Cartesian axes are therefore

$$\hbar L_x = yp_z - zp_y, \qquad \hbar L_y = zp_x - xp_z, \qquad \hbar L_z = xp_y - yp_x. \tag{6.14}$$

In the transition to wave mechanics we replace linear momenta by differential operators, according to (3.7.) The angular-momentum components thereby become operators, $\mathbf{L} \rightarrow \mathfrak{L}$:

$$\begin{aligned}
\mathfrak{L}_x &= -i\left(y\frac{\partial}{\partial z} - z\frac{\partial}{\partial y}\right),\\
\mathfrak{L}_y &= -i\left(z\frac{\partial}{\partial x} - x\frac{\partial}{\partial z}\right),\\
\mathfrak{L}_z &= -i\left(x\frac{\partial}{\partial y} - y\frac{\partial}{\partial x}\right).
\end{aligned} \tag{6.15}$$

To transform these operators into polar coordinates, we substitute the coordinates and derivatives. For example,

$$\mathcal{L}_z = -ir\sin\theta\cos\phi\left(\frac{\partial r}{\partial y}\frac{\partial}{\partial r} + \frac{\partial\theta}{\partial y}\frac{\partial}{\partial\theta} + \frac{\partial\phi}{\partial y}\frac{\partial}{\partial\phi}\right)$$

$$+ ir\sin\theta\sin\phi\left(\frac{\partial r}{\partial x}\frac{\partial}{\partial r} + \frac{\partial\theta}{\partial x}\frac{\partial}{\partial\theta} + \frac{\partial\phi}{\partial x}\frac{\partial}{\partial\phi}\right)$$

$$= -ir\sin\theta\cos\phi\left(\frac{\cos\phi}{r\sin\theta}\frac{\partial}{\partial\phi}\right) - ir\sin\theta\sin\phi\left(\frac{\sin\phi}{r\sin\theta}\frac{\partial}{\partial\phi}\right)$$

$$= -i\frac{\partial}{\partial\phi}. \tag{6.16a}$$

Similarly,

$$\mathcal{L}_x = i\left(\sin\theta\frac{\partial}{\partial\theta} + \cot\theta\cos\phi\frac{\partial}{\partial\phi}\right), \tag{6.16b}$$

$$\mathcal{L}_y = i\left(-\cos\theta\frac{\partial}{\partial\theta} + \cot\theta\sin\phi\frac{\partial}{\partial\phi}\right). \tag{6.16c}$$

Multiplying these out, we obtain

$$\mathcal{L}^2 \equiv \mathcal{L}_x{}^2 + \mathcal{L}_y{}^2 + \mathcal{L}_z{}^2$$

$$= -\left[\frac{\partial^2}{\partial\theta^2} + \cot\theta\frac{\partial}{\partial\theta} + (1+\cot^2\theta)\frac{\partial^2}{\partial\phi^2}\right] = \mathfrak{M}. \tag{6.17}$$

Here we see more evidence supporting our interpretation of $\mathfrak{M}$ as the square of the angular momentum. Still further proof will appear with the solutions to the Schrödinger equation and the implications of experiments. We therefore replace $\mathfrak{M}$ by $\mathcal{L}^2$.

The electron in hydrogen, the simplest atom, moves under the infiuence of the central potential e^2/r, as we saw in Chapter 2. In alkali atoms (sodium, potassium, etc.) the outermost or valence electron also seems to move in a central field, though not one with a simple r^{-1} potential. We shall therefore investigate the Schrödinger equation for a general central field, $V = V(r)$. Then (6.19) may be written

$$r^2\mathfrak{N}(r)\psi + \frac{2mr^2}{\hbar^2}[V(r) - E]\psi = -\mathcal{L}^2(\theta, \phi)\psi. \tag{6.18}$$

With a partial differential equation of this form, in which the separate terms are either radial operators or angular operators, but never a combination of the two, we proceed most easily by the method of *separation of variables*. Let $\psi(r, \theta, \phi)$ be expressed as the product of $R(r)$, a function of r, and $Y(\theta, \phi)$, a function of angles. We substitute

$$\psi(r, \theta, \phi) = R(r)Y(\theta, \phi) \tag{6.19}$$

into (6.18) and then divide both sides by RY to obtain

$$r^2 \frac{\mathfrak{N} R(r)}{R(r)} + \frac{2mr^2}{\hbar^2}[V(r) - E] = -\frac{\mathfrak{L}^2 Y(\theta, \phi)}{Y(\theta, \phi)}. \tag{6.20}$$

The $Y(\theta, \phi)$ has canceled from the left-hand side, since $\mathfrak{N}$ is a differential operator acting only on the radial coordinate r, and $R(r)$ has similarly canceled from the right-hand side. Equation 6.20 states that some function of r is equal to some function of θ and ϕ:

$$f(r) = g(\theta, \phi).$$

This equation can hold only if both sides are in fact just a constant, say $-\lambda$:

$$r^2 \frac{\mathfrak{N} R(r)}{R(r)} + \frac{2mr^2}{\hbar^2}[V(r) - E] = -\lambda, \tag{6.21}$$

$$\frac{\mathfrak{L}^2 Y(\theta, \phi)}{Y(\theta, \phi)} = \lambda. \tag{6.22}$$

We thereby obtain an ordinary differential equation for the radial factor $R(r)$ and a partial differential equation for $Y(\theta, \phi)$:

$$-\frac{1}{r}\frac{d^2}{dr^2}(rR) + \frac{2m}{\hbar^2}V(r)R + \frac{\lambda}{r^2}R = \frac{2m}{\hbar^2}ER, \tag{6.23}$$

$$\frac{\partial^2 Y}{\partial \theta^2} + \cot\theta \frac{\partial Y}{\partial \theta} + (1 + \cot^2\theta)\frac{\partial^2}{\partial \phi^2} Y = -\lambda Y. \tag{6.24}$$

Multiply the Y equation by $\sin^2\theta$ and it breaks into operators in θ and an operator in ϕ:

$$\sin^2\theta \frac{\partial^2 Y}{\partial \theta^2} + \sin\theta\cos\theta \frac{\partial Y}{\partial \theta} + \lambda \sin^2\theta\, Y = -\frac{\partial^2 Y}{\partial \phi^2}. \tag{6.25}$$

Thus we can separate this partial differential equation into two ordinary differential equations by substituting

$$Y(\theta, \phi) = \Theta(\theta)\Phi(\phi)$$

and dividing by $\Theta\Phi$:

$$\frac{\sin^2\theta}{\Theta}\frac{d^2\Theta}{d\theta^2} + \frac{\sin\theta\cos\theta}{\Theta}\frac{d\Theta}{d\theta} + \lambda \sin^2\theta = -\frac{1}{\Phi}\frac{d^2\Phi}{d\phi^2}. \tag{6.26}$$

As with (6.20), each side must equal some constant, say $-\mu$.

We have thus obtained the two angular equations:

$$\frac{d^2\Phi}{d\phi^2} = \mu\Phi, \tag{6.27}$$

$$\frac{d^2\Theta}{d\theta^2} + \cot\theta \frac{d\Theta}{d\theta} + \mu(1 + \cot^2\theta)\Theta = -\lambda\Theta. \tag{6.28}$$

The radial equation, (6.23), takes a simpler form if we substitute the variable $P(r)$,

$$P(r) = rR(r), \tag{6.29}$$

to give

$$-\frac{d^2P}{dr^2} + \frac{2m}{\hbar^2}V(r)P + \frac{\lambda}{r^2}P = \frac{2m}{\hbar^2}EP. \tag{6.30}$$

Any solution to (6.27) through (6.30),

$$\psi(r, \theta, \phi) = \frac{P(r)}{r}\Theta(\theta)\Phi(\phi), \tag{6.31}$$

describes the spatial probability-amplitude distribution of a particle moving in a central field of force. This is a steady-state distribution, since the Schrödinger equation (6.2) contains no time dependence. We shall shortly connect some of the properties of these solutions with the properties of the valence electron in hydrogen and alkali atoms. However, not all the observed electronic properties will emerge from these equations. For one thing, these equations do not provide for any structure of either the electron or the atomic nucleus, whereas in fact both particles possess an internal degree of freedom called *spin*. Second, the energy equation from which we began (6.2) neglects the variation of mass with velocity. Relativity theory tells us this effect must become important for velocities approaching c, the velocity of light. In spite of these two limitations, many important conclusions remain unaffected by these corrections.

The most important result of the next sections will be that the separation constants μ and λ, as well as the energy E—all of which appear as eigenvalues in (6.27) through (6.30)—take on only certain restricted values. This comes about, just as in the one-dimensional equation, because we impose certain simple boundary conditions on the solutions P, Θ, and Φ. Physical arguments dictate that $|\psi|^2r^2\sin\theta$ should not become infinite anywhere, and should have one unique value at each point. These conditions suffice to select from the infinity of possible solutions just those "quantized" solutions that represent observed atomic states.

REFERENCES

[1] H. Eyring, J. Walter, and G. E. Kimball, *Quantum Chemistry*, Wiley, New York (1944), p. 40:
D. H. Menzel, *Mathematical Physics*, Dover, New York (1961), Sec. 32;
P. M. Morse and H. Feshbach, *Methods of Theoretical Physics*, McGraw-Hill, New York (1953), Chap. 1.

3.7 THE SEPARATED ϕ-EQUATION

As we can readily see by direct substitution, the equation for $\Phi(\phi)$,

$$\frac{d^2}{d\phi^2}\Phi = \mu\Phi, \tag{7.1}$$

has periodic solutions for negative values of μ (say $\mu = -m^2$, where m is real):

$$e^{im\phi} \quad \text{and} \quad e^{-im\phi} \qquad \text{or} \qquad \sin m\phi \quad \text{and} \quad \cos m\phi.$$

It also has nonperiodic solutions for positive μ (say $\mu = m^2$):

$$e^{m\phi} \quad \text{and} \quad e^{-m\phi} \qquad \text{or} \qquad \sinh m\phi \quad \text{and} \quad \cosh m\phi.$$

If $|\Phi|^2$ represents a probability distribution, it should have one unique value everywhere. Because $\phi = 0$ and $\phi = 2\pi$ both denote the same angle, we require that

$$\Phi(0) = \Phi(2\pi). \tag{7.2}$$

This condition immediately rules out the nonperiodic solutions. Further, (7.2) requires that m must be an integer, for then

$$e^{im0} = 1 = e^{im2\pi}.$$

Thus the acceptable solutions have the form

$$\Phi = Ae^{im\phi}, \qquad m = 0, \pm 1, \pm 2, \ldots, \tag{7.3}$$

where A is a constant, and the eigenvalues of (7.1) are

$$\mu = -1, -4, -9, \ldots, -m^2, \ldots. \tag{7.4}$$

Because the probability of finding the particle in a volume ΔV is

$$\int^{\Delta V} |\psi|^2 \, dv = \int^{\Delta V} \psi^*\psi \, dv,$$

we see that the probability of observing the particle within the angular wedge $\Delta\phi$ is

$$\int^{\Delta\phi} \Phi^*\Phi \, d\phi = |A|^2 \int^{\Delta\phi} e^{-im\phi} e^{+im\phi} \, d\phi = |A|^2 \int^{\Delta\phi} d\phi = |A|^2 \, \Delta\phi.$$

This probability depends, not on the angle ϕ but only on the width of the wedge $\Delta\phi$. The probability of observing the particle *somewhere*, that is, in the interval $0 \leq \phi \leq 2\pi$, must be unity. Therefore we require

$$1 = |A|^2 \int_0^{2\pi} d\phi = |A|^2 2\pi.$$

Thus we are able to fix the absolute value of the *normalizing constant A:*

$$|A| = \frac{1}{\sqrt{2\pi}}.$$

We have yet no constraint on the phase of A, say η, if we view A as a complex number:

$$A = |A| e^{i\eta}.$$

We shall adopt the *convention* that A is real ($\eta = 0$).

Actually, the argument that Φ must be single-valued, (7.2), is not quite correct. Because we can only observe $|\Phi|^2$, we can require only that

$$\Phi(0) = \pm\Phi(2\pi).$$

This procedure would then allow m to take on half-integral values, $m = 0, \pm\frac{1}{2}, \pm 1, \pm\frac{3}{2}, \ldots$. However, Blatt and Weisskopf pointed out [1] that the half odd-integer values $\pm\frac{1}{2}, \pm\frac{3}{2}, \ldots$ lead to unacceptable probability currents. (This point is further discussed in articles by Merzbacher [2], Buchdahl [3], and Pauli [4].) Therefore the only physically acceptable solutions are the eigenfunctions

$$\ldots, \frac{e^{-i\phi}}{\sqrt{2\pi}}, \frac{1}{\sqrt{2\pi}}, \frac{e^{+i\phi}}{\sqrt{2\pi}}, \frac{e^{+2i\phi}}{\sqrt{2\pi}}, \frac{e^{+3i\phi}}{\sqrt{2\pi}}, \ldots.$$

These eigenfunctions, obtained as the solutions to (7.1), also satisfy the equation:

$$\frac{d}{d\phi} \frac{e^{im\phi}}{\sqrt{2\pi}} = im \frac{e^{im\phi}}{\sqrt{2\pi}}, \tag{7.5}$$

or, with the subscript m on Φ_m denoting the eigenvalue,

$$\mathfrak{L}_z \Phi_m \equiv -i \frac{\partial}{\partial\phi} \Phi_m = m\Phi_m. \tag{7.6}$$

Thus the Φ_m functions are eigenfunctions of the operator $\mathfrak{L}_z$, which we have identified with the z component of angular momentum. What is the physical significance of this? The answer comes from observations of the

Zeeman effect, the Stern–Gerlach effect, and other experiments that distinguish one component of angular momentum. In such experiments we observe only certain integral values of the angular-momentum component—integral multiples of our unit of angular momentum, $\hbar$. Thus we interpret $m\hbar$ as the permissible values of the z component of angular momentum. (The z axis is arbitrary; we can choose it to be whatever direction appears appropriate to the problem at hand.) When we allow for an additional intrinsic angular momentum (spin) for particles, this interpretation does indeed completely explain the observations of "space quantization," as we shall later see.

We should not be too surprised that these eigenfunctions appear in the description of the ϕ distribution of probability, because any well-behaved function of ϕ for $0 \leq \phi \leq 2\pi$ can be expressed in a complex Fourier series,

$$f(\phi) = \sum_{m=-\infty}^{\infty} a_m \frac{e^{im\phi}}{\sqrt{2\pi}}, \tag{7.7}$$

where the a_m are called the *Fourier coefficients*. The significant point is that each *Fourier component* $e^{im\phi}/\sqrt{2\pi}$ is an acceptable steady-state solution or wavefunction. A linear combination, such as (7.7) with more than one non-zero a_m, also represents a steady-state wavefunction, but it is not an eigenfunction of $\mathfrak{L}_z = (\hbar/i)(\partial/\partial\phi)$.

REFERENCES

[1] J. Blatt and V. Weisskopf, *Theoretical Nuclear Physics*, Wiley, New York (1952).
[2] E. Merzbacher, *Am. J. Phys.* **30**, 237 (1962).
[3] H. Buchdahl, *Am. J. Phys.* **30**, 289 (1962); **31**, 829 (1963).
[4] W. Pauli, *Handbuch der Physik*. **5**/1, Springer, Berlin (1958).

3.8 THE SEPARATED θ-EQUATION: SERIES SOLUTION

No single "best" method exists for solving differential equations such as (6.30), the θ equation, and (6.31), the r equation. Both were studied a century ago and a greal deal of literature exists on the solutions [1]–[6]. For many practical purposes, a power series provides the most useful solution to a differential equation. We assume the unknown function $P(x)$ can be written as

$$P(x) = \sum_{k=\epsilon}^{K} A_k x^k, \tag{8.1}$$

where the coefficients A_k and the limits of summation ϵ and K are all to be determined. We can illustrate this approach with the θ equation (6.28) (recall $\mu = -m^2$):

$$\frac{d^2}{d\theta^2}\Theta + \cot\theta\frac{d\Theta}{d\theta} + \left(\lambda - \frac{m^2}{\sin^2\theta}\right)\Theta = 0. \tag{8.2}$$

For convenience we replace the variable θ by $x = \cos\theta$, noting that

$$\frac{d}{d\theta} = \frac{dx}{d\theta}\frac{d}{dx} = -\sin\theta\frac{d}{dx} = -(1 - x^2)^{1/2}\frac{d}{dx}.$$

Thus,

$$(1 - x^2)\frac{d^2}{dx^2}\Theta - 2x\frac{d\Theta}{dx} + \left(\lambda - \frac{m^2}{1 - x^2}\right)\Theta = 0. \tag{8.3}$$

An additional change of variable,

$$\Theta = (\sin\theta)^m T(\cos\theta) = (1 - x^2)^{m/2}T(x),$$

gives the equation

$$(1 - x^2)\frac{d^2}{dx^2}T - 2x(m + 1)\frac{d}{dx}T + [\lambda - m(m + 1)]T = 0. \tag{8.4}$$

Substitution of the series (8.1) for $T(x)$ now gives

$$\sum_k \{k(k - 1)A_k x^{k-2} + [\lambda - m(m + 1) - k(k - 1) - 2k(m + 1)]A_k x^k\} = 0. \tag{8.5}$$

For this equation to hold for all values of x, the coefficient of each power of x in (8.5) must separately vanish. We assumed $A_\epsilon x^\epsilon$ was the first term of the series expansion in (8.1). Hence from (8.5) we see that the coefficient of $x^{\epsilon-2}$ is

$$\epsilon(\epsilon - 1)A_\epsilon = 0. \tag{8.6}$$

This is called an *indicial equation;* it shows (since A_ϵ is assumed to be the lowest nonzero coefficient) that the series can begin either with $x^0 = 1$ (when $\epsilon = 0$) or with $x^1 \equiv x$ (when $\epsilon = 1$). For higher powers of x. we can rewrite (8.5) as

$$\sum_k x^k\{(k + 2)(k + 1)A_{k+2} + [\lambda - (k + m)(k + m + 1)]A_k\} = 0. \tag{8.7}$$

Setting the coefficient of x^k equal to zero gives a *recursion relation* relating different coefficients:

$$A_{k+2} = \frac{(k + m)(k + m + 1) - \lambda}{(k + 2)(k + 1)}A_k. \tag{8.8}$$

Using this relation, we can obtain all the A_k's from A_0 and A_1.

If the series (8.1) is an infinite series ($K \to \infty$), the function $\Theta(x)$ becomes infinite when $x \to -1$ (i.e., $\theta \to 2\pi$) (cf. Courant and Hilbert [4], p. 326). The function $|\Theta|^2 \sin\theta$ also becomes infinite when $\theta \to 2\pi$. Since such an infinite value is not permissible in a wavefunction, the series must terminate with some finite power K. Setting $A_{K+2} = 0$ in (8.8) then gives

$$[(K + m)(K + m + 1) - \lambda]A_K = 0.$$

For this equation to hold, the eigenvalue λ must have the form

$$\lambda = l(l + 1) \quad \text{where} \quad K = l - m, \quad l \text{ a real integer,} \tag{8.9}$$

in which case the series for $T(x)$ terminates with $x^K \equiv x^{l-m}$. Note that if this termination condition holds for $l - m$ *even* (odd) it will *not* hold for $l - m$ *odd* (even). We must then set A_1 (A_0) identically zero, giving $T(x)$ as an even (odd) polynomial in x.

For the *even* series we have

$$T = \sum_{2k=0}^{2k=l-m} A_k x^{2k}, \tag{8.10}$$

with the recursion relation

$$\begin{aligned} \frac{A_{k+1}}{A_k} &= \frac{(2k + m)(2k + m + 1) - l(l + 1)}{(2k + 1)(2k + 2)} \\ &= -\frac{(l - m - 2k)(l + m + 2k + 1)}{(2k + 1)(2k + 2)}. \end{aligned} \tag{8.11}$$

It is useful to compare this with the recursion relation for the *hypergeometric function* ${}_2F_1(a, b;\ c;\ x)$ defined as

$${}_2F_1(a, b; c; x) = 1 + \frac{ab}{c}\frac{x}{1!} + \frac{a(a + 1)b(b + 1)}{c(c + 1)}\frac{x^2}{2!} + \cdots. \tag{8.12}$$

With the conventional notation

$$\begin{aligned} (a)_0 &\equiv 1, \\ (a)_1 &\equiv a, \\ (a)_n &\equiv a(a + 1)(a + 2)\cdots(a + n - 1), \end{aligned}$$

the function takes the form

$$\begin{aligned} {}_2F_1(a, b; c; x) &= \sum_{n=0} \frac{(a)_n(b)_n}{(c)_n}\frac{x^n}{n!} \\ &\equiv 1 + \frac{ab}{c}x + \frac{a(a + 1)b(b + 1)}{c(c + 1)}\frac{x^2}{2} + \cdots \\ &\equiv \sum_n A_n x^n. \end{aligned} \tag{8.13}$$

Depending on the values of a, b, and c, the series (8.13) may extend indefinitely, or it may terminate after a finite number of terms. From (8.13) we immediately see that the A_n coefficients for the hypergeometric function satisfy the equation

$$\frac{A_{n+1}}{A_n} = \frac{(a)_{n+1}}{(a)_n}\frac{(b)_{n+1}}{(b)_n}\frac{(c)_n}{(c)_{n+1}}\frac{n!}{(n+1)!} = \frac{(a+n)(b+n)}{(c+n)(n+1)}. \tag{8.14}$$

We can place the recursion relation (8.11) into the form of (8.14) by dividing all terms by 2:

$$\frac{A_{k+1}}{A_k} = \frac{[\frac{1}{2}(m-l)+k][\frac{1}{2}(l+m+1)+k]}{(\frac{1}{2}+k)(k+1)}. \tag{8.15}$$

Thus the T polynomial is proportional to a hypergeometric function. With a particular choice of proportionality,

$$T^m_{l-m}(x) = \frac{1\cdot 3\cdot 5\cdots(l+m-1)}{2\cdot 4\cdot 6\cdots(l-m)}\ {}_2F_1\left(\frac{m-l}{2},\ \frac{m+l+1}{2};\ \frac{1}{2};\ x^2\right), \qquad (\textit{even series}) \tag{8.16}$$

we obtain *Gegenbauer polynomials* (cf. Morse and Feshbach [2], p. 782). Note that the subscript on T gives the rank of T as a polynomial in x^2.

For the *odd* series, we have

$$T = \sum_{2k=0}^{2k=l-m-1} A_k x^{2k-1}, \tag{8.17}$$

with the relation

$$\frac{A_{k+1}}{A_k} = -\frac{(l-m-2k-1)(l+m+2k+2)}{(2k+3)(2k+2)}$$
$$= \frac{[\frac{1}{2}(m-l+1)+k][\frac{1}{2}(m+l+2)+k]}{(\frac{3}{2}+k)(k+1)}. \tag{8.18}$$

Again we obtain a hypergeometric series. With the conventional choice of the proportionality constant for the Gegenbauer polynomials we have

$$T^m_{l-m}(x) = (-1)^{l-m}\frac{1\cdot 3\cdot 5\cdots(l+m)}{2\cdot 4\cdot 6\cdots(l-m-1)}(x)$$
$$\times\ {}_2F_1\left(\frac{m-l+1}{2},\ \frac{m+l+2}{2};\ \frac{3}{2};\ x^2\right). \qquad (\textit{odd series}) \tag{8.19}$$

These two equations, (8.16) and (8.19), are usually combined into a single equation for the Gegenbauer polynomials:

$$T_{l-m}^{m}(x) = \frac{(2l-1)!!}{(l-m)!} x^{l-m} {}_2F_1\left(\frac{m-l}{2}, \frac{m-l+1}{2}; \frac{1}{2}-l; \frac{1}{x^2}\right). \tag{8.20}$$

The double factorial notation means

$$(2n-1)!! = \frac{(2n)!}{2^n(n)!} = 1\cdot 3\cdot 5\cdot 7\cdots(2n-1).$$

Mathematics texts refer to the polynomials [7]

$$C_n^{m+½} = \left[\frac{2^m(m)!}{(2m)!}\right] T_n^m = \frac{T_n^m}{(2m-1)!!} \tag{8.21}$$

as the *Gegenbauer polynomials* (or *ultraspherical polynomials*). That is,

$$C_n^{½} = T_n^0, \qquad C_n^{3/2} = T_n^1, \qquad C_n^{7/2} = \frac{T_n^3}{15}, \quad \text{etc.}$$

Table 3.1 Gegenbauer Polynomials $T_{l-m}^{m}(z)$

$T_0^0 = 1$	$T_1^0 = z$	$T_2^0 = \frac{1}{2}(3z^2 - 1)$	$T_3^0 = \frac{1}{2}(5z^3 - 3z)$
$T_0^1 = 1$	$T_1^1 = 3z$	$T_2^1 = \frac{3}{2}(5z^2 - 1)$	$T_3^1 = \frac{5}{2}(7z^3 - 3z)$
$T_0^2 = 3$	$T_1^2 = 15z$	$T_2^2 = \frac{15}{2}(7z^2 - 1)$	$T_3^2 = \frac{105}{2}(3z^3 - z)$
$T_0^3 = 15$	$T_1^3 = 105z$	$T_2^3 = \frac{105}{2}(9z^2 - 1)$	$T_3^3 = \frac{315}{2}(11z^3 - z)$

Table 3.1 gives some of these polynomials. The *associated Legendre polynomials* $P_l^m(x)$ are defined [7] as

$$P_l^m(x) = (1-x^2)^{m/2} T_{l-m}^m(x) = \frac{(1-x^2)^{m/2}}{(2m-1)!!} C_{l-m}^{m+½}(x)$$

or

$$P_l^m(\cos\theta) = (\sin\theta)^m T_{l-m}^m(\cos\theta). \tag{8.22}$$

Apart from a numerical factor these are the desired Θ functions. Our normalization requirement fixes that factor; the associated Legendre polynomials give the integral

$$\int_{-1}^{+1} |P_l^m(x)|^2\,dx = \frac{2}{2l+1}\,\frac{(l+m)!}{(l-m)!}. \tag{8.23}$$

We therefore have:

$$\Theta_l^m(\cos\theta) = \left[\frac{(2l+1)}{2}\frac{(l+m)!}{(l-m)!}\right]^{1/2} P_l^m(\cos\theta)$$

$$= \left[\frac{(2l+1)}{2}\frac{(l+m)!}{(l-m)!}\right]^{1/2} (\sin\theta)^m T_{l-m}^m(\cos\theta).$$

$$= \frac{(2l-1)!!}{(l-m)!}\left[\frac{(2l+1)}{2}\frac{(l+m)!}{(l-m)!}\right]^{1/2} (\cos\theta)^{l-m}$$

$$\times\, {}_2F_1\left(\frac{m-l}{2}, \frac{m-l+1}{2}; \frac{1-2l}{2}; (\cos\theta)^{-2}\right). \tag{8.24}$$

The complete angular eigenfunctions are the products of these functions with the Φ_m of the last chapter:

$$Y_{lm}(\theta, \phi) = \left[\frac{(2l+1)}{4\pi}\frac{(l+m)!}{(l-m)!}\right]^{1/2} (\sin\theta)^m T_{l-m}^m(\cos\theta)\, e^{im\phi}, \tag{8.25}$$

We have passed somewhat cavalierly over several important points, but the discussion does illustrate the solution of differential equations by means of series-expansion. Rather than pursue the omissions in more detail, we shall introduce an alternative approach, somewhat more abstract, which provides practice in the use of differential operators. The abstract approach leads to the same results, although we employ a different argument to obtain quantization.

REFERENCES

[1] E. T. Whittaker and G. N. Watson, *A Course in Modern Analysis*, Cambridge University Press, Cambridge, England (1927).

[2] P. M. Morse and H. Feshbach, *Methods of Theoretical Physics*, McGraw-Hill, New York (1953).

[3] D. H. Menzel, *Mathematical Physics*, Dover, New York (1961).

[4] R. Courant and D. Hilbert, *Methods of Mathematical Physics*, Interscience, New York (1953), vol. I.

[5] F. B. Hildebrand, *Advanced Calculus for Engineers*, Prentice-Hall, Englewood Cliffs, New Jersey (1949).
J. Mathews and R. L. Walker, *Mathematical Methods of Physics*, Benjamin, New York (1965).

[6] H. Margenau and G. M. Murphy, *The Mathematics of Physics and Chemistry*, Van Nostrand, Princeton, New Jersey (1956), 2nd ed.

[7] M. A. Abramowitz and I. A. Stegun (eds.), *Handbook of Mathematical Functions*, Natl. Bur. Stds. Appl. Math. Series 55; Washington, D. C. (1964).

3.9 THE ANGULAR EQUATION: OPERATOR APPROACH

So far in this chapter we have concentrated on differential equations and their solutions. After all, if the wave-like qualities of electrons enable them to form atoms, it seems only natural to investigate atoms through "wave" equations—differential equations. Yet many of our questions about atoms concern not the probability distribution of the electrons, but rather certain average properties such as dipole moments and polarizability. Furthermore, a central problem of atomic structure is the determination of the energy levels of atoms. We can solve such problems without ever explicitly solving a differential equation. In this section we see how a few general *operator* properties of certain differential operators lead to the results derived from differential equations, as well as a few new results. The operator method looks more formal and abstract at first, though in many ways it is simpler than the approach via differential equations. Operator techniques have found wide application throughout applied mathematics, since they provide important general results without detailed calculation of series solutions. We will further pursue the study of operators in the next chapter.

With this introduction, we return to Section 3.6 and ask: What are the properties of the angular factor Y,

$$\psi(r, \theta, \phi) = R(r)Y(\theta, \phi)$$

in the solutions to (6.20),

$$\mathfrak{N}\psi + \frac{\mathfrak{L}^2}{r^2}\psi + \frac{2mV}{\hbar^2}\psi = \frac{2m}{\hbar^2}E\psi? \tag{9.1}$$

The separation constant λ, introduced in (6.22), appears in that equation as an eigenvalue of the operator $\mathfrak{L}^2$. In other words, the operator serves merely to multiply the function Y by a constant:

$$\mathfrak{L}^2 Y = \lambda Y. \tag{9.2}$$

We have identified $\mathfrak{L}^2$ with the square of the total angular momentum, through (6.17). Equation 9.2 therefore says that the Y function is an eigenfunction of angular momentum squared which possesses the eigenvalue λ. We anticipate that more than one eigenfunction and eigenvalue satisfy this equation, so we shall distinguish the various eigenvalues by means of an index l, as λ_l. In Section 3.7 we saw that Φ_m, the ϕ-dependent factor of $Y(\theta, \phi)$, was an eigenfunction of $\mathfrak{L}_z$, possessing eigenvalue m. Hence Y is both an eigenfunction of $\mathfrak{L}^2$ with eigenvalue λ_l, and an eigenfunction of $\mathcal{L}_z$ with eigenvalue m. We therefore distinguish the functions by two subscripts:

$$\mathcal{L}^2 Y_{lm} = \lambda_l Y_{lm}, \tag{9.3a}$$

$$\mathcal{L}_z Y_{lm} = m Y_{lm}. \tag{9.3b}$$

(Recall that physical angular momentum corresponds to $\hbar\mathcal{L}_z$ and the square corresponds to $\hbar^2\mathcal{L}^2$.) In this section we determine properties of Y and l, using only the operator properties of $\mathcal{L}^2$ and $\mathcal{L}_z$ and rather general restrictions. We shall frequently omit the index l in what follows, with the understanding that such an equation holds for any l.

We begin by introducing three differential operators in polar coordinates, derived from the angular-momentum operators of Section 6 (the reader should verify these equations):

$$\begin{aligned}
\mathcal{L}_0 &\equiv \mathcal{L}_z = -i\frac{\partial}{\partial\phi},\\
\mathcal{L}_+ &\equiv -\frac{\mathcal{L}_x + i\mathcal{L}_y}{\sqrt{2}} = -e^{i\phi}\frac{(\partial/\partial\theta + i\cot\theta[\partial/\partial\phi])}{\sqrt{2}},\\
\mathcal{L}_- &\equiv \frac{\mathcal{L}_x - i\mathcal{L}_y}{\sqrt{2}} = -e^{-i\phi}\frac{(\partial/\partial\theta - i\cot\theta[\partial/\partial\phi])}{\sqrt{2}}.
\end{aligned} \tag{9.4}$$

Our choice of signs and the factor $2^{-1/2}$ anticipates results of later chapters. Then, for an arbitrary function $F(\theta, \phi)$,

$$\begin{aligned}
\mathcal{L}_0\mathcal{L}_0 F &= -\frac{\partial^2}{\partial\phi^2}F,\\
\mathcal{L}_+\mathcal{L}_- F &= \frac{1}{2}e^{i\phi}\left(\frac{\partial}{\partial\theta} + i\cot\theta\frac{\partial}{\partial\phi}\right)e^{-i\phi}\left(\frac{\partial}{\partial\theta} - \cot\theta\frac{\partial}{\partial\phi}\right)F\\
&= \frac{1}{2}\left(\frac{\partial^2}{\partial\theta^2} + \cot\theta\frac{\partial}{\partial\theta} + \cot^2\theta\frac{\partial^2}{\partial\phi^2} - i\frac{\partial}{\partial\phi}\right)F,\\
\mathcal{L}_-\mathcal{L}_+ F &= \frac{1}{2}\left(\frac{\partial^2}{\partial\theta^2} + \cot\theta\frac{\partial}{\partial\theta} + \cot^2\theta\frac{\partial^2}{\partial\phi^2} + i\frac{\partial}{\partial\phi}\right)F\\
&= \mathcal{L}_+\mathcal{L}_- F - \mathcal{L}_0 F.
\end{aligned} \tag{9.5}$$

(Again, the reader should verify these relations.)

In passing, note that the operator $\mathcal{L}^2$ of (6.17),

$$\mathcal{L}^2 = -\left(\frac{\partial^2}{\partial\theta^2} + \cot\theta\frac{\partial}{\partial\theta} + \cot^2\theta\frac{\partial^2}{\partial\phi^2} + \frac{\partial^2}{\partial\phi^2}\right),$$

can be rewritten as

$$\mathcal{L}^2 = -\mathcal{L}_+\mathcal{L}_- + \mathcal{L}_0\mathcal{L}_0 - \mathcal{L}_-\mathcal{L}_+. \tag{9.6}$$

The similarity between (9.6) and (6.17),

$$\mathcal{L}^2 = \mathcal{L}_x\mathcal{L}_x + \mathcal{L}_y\mathcal{L}_y + \mathcal{L}_z\mathcal{L}_z,$$

will prove useful in section 3.10.

Now consider a solution $Y(\theta, \phi)$ to (6.24), rewritten here:

$$-\left(\frac{\partial^2}{\partial\theta^2} + \cot\theta + \cot^2\theta\,\frac{\partial^2}{\partial\phi^2}\right)Y - \frac{\partial^2}{\partial\phi^2}Y = \lambda Y. \tag{9.7}$$

Rewrite this equation using the $\mathcal{L}$ operators of (9.4) and (9.5) as

$$(2\mathcal{L}_-\mathcal{L}_+ + \mathcal{L}_0 + \mathcal{L}_0\mathcal{L}_0)Y = \lambda Y. \tag{9.8}$$

We saw in Section 3.7 that $Y = \Theta\Phi$ is an eigenfunction of $\mathcal{L}_z$ (or $\mathcal{L}_0$), having the eigenvalue m, say:

$$\mathcal{L}_0 Y_m \equiv \mathcal{L}_0\Theta(\theta)\Phi_m(\phi) = mY_m.$$

Thus (9.8) becomes

$$\mathcal{L}_-\mathcal{L}_+Y_m = -\tfrac{1}{2}[\lambda - m(m+1)]Y_m. \tag{9.9}$$

In a similar way we find that

$$\mathcal{L}_+\mathcal{L}_-Y_m = -\tfrac{1}{2}[\lambda - m(m-1)]Y_m. \tag{9.10}$$

From these two operator equations we can immediately deduce an important property of the $\mathcal{L}_+$ and $\mathcal{L}_-$ operators. First multiply (9.9) by $\mathcal{L}_+$:

$$\mathcal{L}_+\mathcal{L}_-\mathcal{L}_+Y_m = -\tfrac{1}{2}[\lambda - m(m+1)]\mathcal{L}_+Y_m.$$

Then compare this expression with (9.7), but replace m by $m + 1$:

$$\mathcal{L}_+\mathcal{L}_-Y_{m+1} = -\tfrac{1}{2}[\lambda - m(m+1)]Y_{m+1}.$$

We see that $\mathcal{L}_+Y_m$ satisfies the same equation as Y_{m+1}. Hence the two functions can differ only by some numerical factor C_m (independent of θ and ϕ):

$$\mathcal{L}_+Y_m = -C_mY_{m+1}. \tag{9.11}$$

$\mathcal{L}_+$ is a *step-up* or *raising operator* acting on the parameter m. Operating on Y_m, an eigenfunction of $\mathcal{L}_0$ with eigenvalue m, it produces the eigenfunction Y_{m+1} with the next higher value of m. A similar argument, using the equation

$$\mathcal{L}_-\mathcal{L}_+\mathcal{L}_-Y_m = -\tfrac{1}{2}[\lambda - m(m-1)]\mathcal{L}_-Y_m$$

proves that $\mathcal{L}_-$ is a *step-down* or *lowering operator* and we write

$$\mathcal{L}_-Y_m = C_{m-1}Y_{m-1}. \tag{9.12}$$

[Our method of introducing the constants C_m and C_{m-1} in (9.11) and (9.12) anticipates what follows. Using, say, C_m^+ and C_m^-, leads to the same normalization.] Either (9.9) or (9.10) fixes the constant C_m apart from an arbitrary sign. Substituting (9.11) and (9.12) into (9.9) gives

$$\mathcal{L}_-\mathcal{L}_+Y_m = -C_m\mathcal{L}_-Y_{m+1} = -C_m{}^2Y_m = -\tfrac{1}{2}[\lambda - m(m+1)]Y_m,$$

so that

$$C_m{}^2 = \tfrac{1}{2}[\lambda - m(m+1)].$$

If C_m were a complex number, $|C_m|e^{ip}$, this equation would fix only the magnitude $|C_m|$. We may choose the phase, e^{ip}, as we please. The usual phase convention assumes C_m to be real and positive:

$$C_m = \left[\frac{\lambda - m(m+1)}{2}\right]^{1/2} \tag{9.13}$$

However, C_m will be real only if the quantity $\lambda - m(m+1)$ never becomes negative. The argument given at the end of this section, in (9.32)–(9.37), assures us that this condition must hold in the cases of physical interest. We therefore obtain the condition:

$$\lambda - m(m+1) \geq 0. \tag{9.14}$$

Armed with this condition, we can immediately infer λ from the relation

$$\mathcal{L}_+Y_{lm} = -\left[\frac{\lambda_l - m(m+1)}{2}\right]^{1/2} Y_{lm+1}, \tag{9.15}$$

in the following way. Consider some fixed value of λ_l. Then successive applications of $\mathcal{L}_+$ to Y_{lm} will raise m, producing Y_{lm+1}, Y_{lm+2}, . . . , Y_{lm+i}, ... Eventually the value $(m+i)(m+i+1)$ will exceed the assigned λ_l, and condition (9.14) will not hold. To avoid this, we must require that m not exceed some maximum value l, depending on λ_l. To meet this requirement we must have

$$\lambda_l = l(l+1), \tag{9.16}$$

for then (9.15) gives

$$\mathcal{L}_+Y_{ll} = -\left[\frac{l(l+1) - l(l+1)}{2}\right]^{1/2} Y_{ll+1} = 0. \tag{9.17}$$

Thus the $\mathcal{L}_+$ can never produce a function Y_{lm} with $m > l$.

In a similar way, successive applications of $\mathcal{L}_-$ lower m from the maximum value l down to zero and on to negative values, according to the relation [from (9.8) and (9.9)]

$$\mathcal{L}_-Y_{lm} = \left[\frac{l(l+1) - m(m-1)}{2}\right]^{1/2} Y_{lm-1}. \tag{9.18}$$

But we can prove that $l(l+1) - m(m-1)$ must always be positive. Merely use $\mathfrak{L}_-\mathfrak{L}_+$ instead of $\mathfrak{L}_+\mathfrak{L}_-$. Thus m takes the minimum value $m = -l$; (9.18) reads for this case:

$$\mathfrak{L}_- Y_{l,-l} = \left[\frac{l(l+1) - (-l)(-l-1)}{2}\right]^{1/2} Y_{l,-l-1} = 0. \tag{9.19}$$

These simple arguments prove that, *for a given value of the eigenvalue* $l(l+1)$ *of* $\mathfrak{L}^2$, *the eigenvalue* m *of* $\mathfrak{L}_z$ *can have any of* $2l+1$ *different values:* $-l, -l+1, \ldots, 0, \ldots, l-1, l$.

From (9.17) we readily find the analytic expression for Y_{ll}. Using the definition of $\mathfrak{L}_+$, we have

$$e^{i\phi}\left(\frac{\partial}{\partial\theta} + i\cot\theta\,\frac{\partial}{\partial\phi}\right) Y_{ll} = 0. \tag{9.20}$$

Substituting $Y = \Theta\Phi$ and using the properties of Φ, we get

$$\frac{\partial}{\partial\theta}\Theta_l^l\Phi_l - l\cot\theta\,\Theta_l^l\Phi_l = 0$$

or

$$\frac{(d/d\theta)\Theta_l^l}{\Theta_l^l} = \frac{l\cos\theta}{\sin\theta} = \frac{l(d/d\theta)\sin\theta}{\sin\theta}$$

This equation integrates directly, giving

$$\log\Theta_l^l = l\log\sin\theta - \log N \tag{9.21}$$

(N a normalizing constant of integration) so that

$$\Theta_l^l = N(\sin\theta)^l. \tag{9.22}$$

We can fix N by normalizing Θ:

$$\int \Theta_l^l\Theta_l^l \sin\theta\, d\theta = 1 = N^2\int_0^\pi (\sin\theta)^{2l+1}\, d\theta.$$

Evaluating the integral through successive integration by parts, we obtain

$$2\int^{\pi/2}(\sin\theta)^{2l+1}\, d\theta = 2\,\frac{2\cdot 4\cdots(2l)}{1\cdot 3\cdot 5\cdots(2l+1)} = \frac{2(2^l l!)^2}{(2l+1)!} = \frac{1}{N^2}\,.$$

Since only the magnitude of N is fixed, we follow Condon and Shortley [1] and include a factor of $(-1)^l$. (Other choices occasionally occur in the literature.) With

$$N = (-1)^l\frac{1}{2^l l!}\left[\frac{(2l+1)!}{2}\right]^{1/2}, \tag{9.23}$$

and the results of Section 3.7 for Φ, we then have the formula for Y_{ll},

$$Y_{ll} = \frac{(-1)^l}{2^l l!}\left[\frac{(2l+1)!}{4\pi}\right]^{1/2} e^{il\phi}(\sin\theta)^l. \tag{9.24}$$

From Y_{ll} we can construct the function Y_{lm} through repeated application of the lowering operator $\mathcal{L}_-$. From (9.18) and (9.19) we have

$$Y_{ll-1} = \frac{\mathcal{L}_-}{\sqrt{l}}Y_{ll} = \frac{(-1)}{\sqrt{l}}e^{-i\phi}\left(\frac{\partial}{\partial\theta} - i\cot\theta\frac{\partial}{\partial\phi}\right)Y_{ll}.$$

Then, using (9.22), we have

$$Y_{ll-1} = N_l\frac{(-1)}{\sqrt{2l}}\frac{e^{i(l-1)\phi}}{\sqrt{2\pi}}\left(\frac{d}{d\theta} + l\cot\theta\right)(\sin\theta)^l.$$

Now we use the identity (for any function F of θ and ϕ)

$$\frac{1}{(\sin\theta)^m}\frac{d}{d\theta}(\sin\theta)^m F = \frac{dF}{d\theta} + m\cot\theta F$$

to write

$$Y_{ll-1} = N_l\frac{(-1)}{\sqrt{2l}}\frac{e^{i(l-1)\phi}}{\sqrt{2\pi}}\frac{1}{(\sin\theta)}\frac{d}{d\theta}(\sin\theta)^{2l}.$$

A second application of $\mathcal{L}_-$ gives

$$\begin{aligned} Y_{ll-2} &= \frac{\mathcal{L}_-}{\sqrt{2l-1}}Y_{ll-1} \\ &= \frac{N_l(-1)^2}{\sqrt{(2l)(2l-1)1\cdot 2}}\frac{e^{i(l-2)\phi}}{\sqrt{2\pi}}\frac{1}{(\sin\theta)^{l-1}}\frac{d}{d\theta}\frac{1}{\sin\theta}\frac{d}{d\theta}(\sin\theta)^{2l}. \end{aligned}$$

Repeating this application $l - m$ times gives

$$Y_{lm} = N_l(-1)^{l-m}\frac{(l+m)!}{(l-m)!(2l)!}\frac{e^{im\phi}}{\sqrt{2\pi}}\frac{1}{(\sin\theta)^m}\left(\frac{1}{\sin\theta}\frac{d}{d\theta}\right)^{l-m}(\sin\theta)^{2l}.$$

Or, from the identity

$$\frac{d}{d\cos\theta} = -\frac{1}{\sin\theta}\frac{d}{d\theta},$$

the result can be written

$$Y_{lm} = \frac{(-1)^l}{2^l l!}\left(\frac{2l+1}{4\pi}\right)^{1/2}\left[\frac{(l+m)!}{(l-m)!}\right]^{1/2}\frac{e^{im\phi}}{(\sin\theta)^m}\left(\frac{d}{d\cos\theta}\right)^{l-m}(\sin\theta)^{2l}. \tag{9.25a}$$

We can obtain an alternative expression by acting on the function

$$Y_{l-l} = \frac{1}{2^l l!}\left[\frac{(2l+1)!}{4\pi}\right]^{1/2} e^{-il\phi}(\sin\theta)^l \tag{9.26}$$

with the operator $(\mathcal{L}_+)^{l+m}$. The result is

$$Y_{lm} = \frac{(-1)^{l+m}}{2^l l!}\left(\frac{2l+1}{4\pi}\right)^{1/2}\left[\frac{(l-m)!}{(l+m)!}\right]^{1/2} e^{im\phi}\,(\sin\theta)^m\left(\frac{d}{d\cos\theta}\right)^{l+m}(\sin\theta)^{2l}. \tag{9.25b}$$

Table 3.2 Spherical Harmonics Y_{lm}

$l = 0$	$Y_{00} =$	$\frac{1}{\sqrt{4\pi}}$	
$l = 1$	$Y_{10} =$	$\sqrt{\frac{3}{4\pi}}\,\frac{z}{r}$	$= \sqrt{\frac{3}{4\pi}}\cos\theta$
	$Y_{1\pm1} = \mp$	$\sqrt{\frac{3}{8\pi}}\,\frac{(x \pm iy)}{r}$	$= \mp\sqrt{\frac{3}{8\pi}}\sin\theta\, e^{\pm i\phi}$
$l = 2$	$Y_{20} =$	$\sqrt{\frac{5}{16\pi}}\,\frac{(3z^2 - r^2)}{r^2}$	$= \sqrt{\frac{5}{16\pi}}(2\cos^2\theta - \sin^2\theta)$
			$= \sqrt{\frac{5}{16\pi}}(3\cos^2\theta = 1)$
	$Y_{2\pm1} = \mp$	$\sqrt{\frac{15}{8\pi}}\,\frac{z(x \pm iy)}{r^2}$	$= \mp\sqrt{\frac{15}{8\pi}}\cos\theta\sin\theta\, e^{\pm i\phi}$
	$Y_{2\pm2} =$	$\sqrt{\frac{15}{32\pi}}\,\frac{(x \pm iy)^2}{r^2}$	$= \sqrt{\frac{15}{32\pi}}\sin^2\theta\, e^{\pm 2i\phi}$
$l = 3$	$Y_{30} =$	$\sqrt{\frac{7}{16\pi}}\,\frac{z(5z^2 - 3r^2)}{r^3}$	$= \sqrt{\frac{7}{16\pi}}(2\cos^3\theta - 3\cos\theta\sin^2\theta)$
	$Y_{3\pm1} = \mp$	$\sqrt{\frac{21}{56\pi}}\,\frac{(x \pm iy)(5z^2 - r^2)}{r^3}$	$= \pm\sqrt{\frac{21}{56\pi}}(4\cos^2\theta\sin\theta - \sin^3\theta)\, e^{\pm i\phi}$
	$Y_{3\pm2} =$	$\sqrt{\frac{15}{32\pi}}\,\frac{z(x \pm iy)^2}{r^3}$	$= \sqrt{\frac{15}{32\pi}}\cos\theta\sin^2\theta\, e^{\pm 2i\phi}$
	$Y_{3\pm3} = \mp$	$\sqrt{\frac{35}{48\pi}}\,\frac{(x \pm iy)^3}{r^3}$	$= \mp\sqrt{\frac{35}{48\pi}}\sin^3\theta\, e^{\pm 3i\phi}$

The function $Y_{lm}(\theta, \phi)$ is usually called a *spherical harmonic* (also *surface harmonic* and *tesseral harmonic*). The polynomial $r^l Y_{lm}$ is occasionally called a *solid harmonic*. Table 3.2 gives the spherical harmonics through $l = 3$. As defined here (the so-called *Condon and Shortley* [1] *phase convention*), the spherical harmonic Y_{lm} differs from $Y_{l,-m}$ by the phase (-1^m):

$$Y_{lm} = (-1)^m Y_{l,-m}. \tag{9.27}$$

Harmonics with positive odd m have a negative sign. The Y_{lm} may also be written in terms of the *associated Legendre polynomial* P_l^m:

$$Y_{lm}(\theta, \phi) = (-1)^m \left(\frac{2l+1}{4\pi}\right)^{1/2} \left[\frac{(l-|m|)!}{(l+|m|)!}\right]^{1/2} e^{im\phi}\, P_l^{|m|}(\cos\theta) \quad (m > 0) \tag{9.25c}$$

$$= + \left(\frac{2l+1}{4\pi}\right)^{1/2} \left[\frac{(l-|m|)!}{(l+|m|)!}\right]^{1/2} e^{im\phi}\, P_l^{|m|}(\cos\theta) \quad (m < 0) \tag{9.25d}$$

where, following Edmonds [2],

$$P_l^m(x) = \frac{(1-x^2)^{m/2}}{2^l l!} \left(\frac{d}{dx}\right)^{l+m} (x^2-1)^l \tag{9.28a}$$

or

$$P_l^m(\cos\theta) = \frac{(-1)^l}{2^l l!} (\sin\theta)^m \left(\frac{d}{d\cos\theta}\right)^{l+m} (\sin\theta)^{2l}. \tag{9.28b}$$

Note that with this definition,

$$P_l^{-m}(x) = (-1)^m \frac{(l-m)!}{(l+m)!} P_l^m(x).$$

Although most texts on quantum mechanics now follow the phase convention here used, other definitions do occur. Schiff [3] and Bethe and Salpeter [4] omit the phase $(-1)^m$ in (9.27*a*).

It is useful to note that, according to (9.28), the associated Legendre polynomial is an even function of x if $l + m$ is an even integer:

$$P_l^m(-x) = (-1)^{l+m} P_l^m(x). \tag{9.29}$$

This relation, taken with

$$e^{im(\phi-\pi)} = (-1)^m e^{im\phi}, \tag{9.30}$$

permits us to obtain the *inversion symmetry* of the spherical harmonics:

$$Y_{lm}(\theta-\pi, \phi-\pi) = (-1)^l Y_{lm}(\theta, \phi). \tag{9.31}$$

(The direction θ, ϕ is opposite the direction $\theta - \pi, \phi - \pi$.) This symmetry property is known as *parity: Y_{lm}* has *even parity* if l is an even integer, and has *odd parity* if l is odd.

PROOF OF AN OPERATOR INEQUALITY

We assumed in (9.13) that C_m was real. To see that this assumption must be correct, consider the following integral involving two different functions of θ and ϕ, say $f(\theta, \phi)$ and $g(\theta, \phi)$, over all angles:

$$I \equiv \int f^*(\mathcal{L}_+ g)\, d\Omega.$$

(Here $d\Omega \equiv \sin\theta\, d\theta\, d\phi$, and f^* indicates the complex conjugate of f.) Using the definition of $\mathcal{L}_+$, we have

$$I = -\frac{1}{\sqrt{2}}\int_0^{2\pi} e^{i\phi}\, d\phi \int_0^{\pi} f^*\left(\frac{\partial g}{\partial\theta}\right)\sin\theta\, d\theta$$
$$-\frac{i}{\sqrt{2}}\int_0^{\pi}\cot\theta\sin\theta\, d\theta\int_0^{2\pi} e^{i\phi} f^*\left(\frac{\partial g}{\partial\phi}\right) d\phi. \quad (9.32)$$

Next, we integrate this by parts. The first term becomes

$$-\frac{1}{\sqrt{2}}\int_0^{2\pi} e^{i\phi}\, d\phi\left[(f^*g\sin\theta)_0^{\pi} - \int_0^{\pi} f^*g\cos\theta\, d\theta - \int_0^{\pi} g\,\frac{\partial f^*}{\partial\theta}\sin\theta\, d\theta\right],$$

and the second becomes

$$-\frac{i}{\sqrt{2}}\int_0^{\pi}\cot\theta\sin\theta\, d\theta\left[(e^{i\phi} f^*g)_0^{2\pi} - i\int_0^{2\pi} e^{i\phi} f^*g\, d\phi - \int_0^{2\pi} e^{i\phi}\, g\,\frac{\partial f^*}{\partial\phi}\, dg\right].$$

The bracketed terms $[\cdots]$ vanish from both terms, either because $\sin\pi = \sin 0 = 0$ or because f and g are periodic over $0 \le \phi \le 2\pi$. The integrals $\int d\phi \int d\theta\, e^{i\phi}\cos\theta\, f^*g$ cancel, leaving

$$I = \frac{1}{\sqrt{2}}\int_0^{2\pi} e^{i\phi}\, d\phi\int_0^{\pi}\left(\frac{\partial f^*}{\partial\theta}\right) g\sin\theta\, d\theta$$
$$+\frac{i}{\sqrt{2}}\int_0^{\pi}\cot\theta\sin\theta\, d\theta\int_0^{\pi} e^{i\phi}\left(\frac{\partial f^*}{\partial\phi}\right) g\, d\phi, \quad (9.33)$$

or

$$I = -\frac{1}{\sqrt{2}}\int g\left(-e^{i\phi}\,\frac{\partial f^*}{\partial\theta} - i\cot\theta\, e^{i\phi}\,\frac{\partial f^*}{\partial\phi}\right) d\Omega.$$

Referring to the definition of $\mathcal{L}_-$ we see that

$$I = -\int g(\mathcal{L}_- f)^*\, d\Omega.$$

Operators $\mathcal{Q}^+$ and $\mathcal{Q}^-$, satisfying the relation

$$\int f^*(\mathcal{Q}^+ g)\, dv = \int (\mathcal{Q}^- f)^* g\, dv, \tag{9.34}$$

are called *Hermitian adjoint* operators. In the present example, $(-\mathcal{L}_-)$ is the adjoint of $\mathcal{L}_+$. As we can see, operators are adjoint only with respect to functions that fulfill specified boundary conditions.

The second step of our argument begins with the integral

$$\int Y^*_{lm} \mathcal{L}_+ \mathcal{L}_- Y_{lm}\, d\Omega. \tag{9.35}$$

From (9.10) this integral gives

$$-\tfrac{1}{2}[\lambda_l - m(m+1)] \int Y^*_{lm} Y_{lm}\, d\Omega = -\tfrac{1}{2}[\lambda_l - m(m+1)] \int |Y_{lm}|^2\, d\Omega.$$

When we use the adjoint property of $\mathcal{L}_+$, the integral reduces to

$$-\int (\mathcal{L}_- Y_{lm})^* (\mathcal{L}_- Y_{lm})\, d\Omega = -\int |\mathcal{L}_- Y_{lm}|^2\, d\Omega. \tag{9.36}$$

Thus we find

$$\int |\mathcal{L}_- Y_{lm}|^2\, d\Omega = \tfrac{1}{2}[\lambda_l - m(m+1)] \int |Y_{lm}|^2\, d\Omega.$$

Since neither of the integrals can be negative, we conclude that $\lambda_l - m(m+1)$ must be real and nonnegative:

$$\lambda_l - m(m+1) \geq 0. \tag{9.37}$$

REFERENCES

[1] E. U. Condon and G. H. Shortley, *The Theory of Atomic Spectra*, Cambridge University Press, New York (1935).
[2] A. R. Edmonds, *Angular Momentum in Quantum Mechanics*, Princeton University Press, Princeton, New Jersey (1955).
[3] L. I. Schiff, *Quantum Mechanics*, McGraw-Hill, New York (1955), 2nd ed.
[4] H. A. Bethe and E. E. Salpeter, *Quantum Mechanics of One- and Two-Electron Atoms*, Academic, New York (1957).

3.10 ANGULAR FUNCTIONS AND SPHERICAL TENSORS

We have now found that the spherical harmonic $Y_{lm}(\theta, \phi)$ gives the angular dependence of the probability amplitude $\psi(r, \theta, \phi)$ for an electron in a central field. Because this function is the solution of the steady-state or time-independent Schrödinger equation, it has a large amplitude where the electron spends much time and low amplitude in directions where the electron is less likely to be found. The motion of the electron evidently differs considerably from planetary motion, for the probability amplitude is not confined to a plane. The various solutions Y_{lm} are distinguished by the eigenvalue $l(l + 1)$ of the operator $\mathfrak{L}^2$ and the eigenvalue m for the operator $\mathfrak{L}_z$. We refer to $\mathfrak{L}$ as the operator of *orbital angular momentum* (to distinguish from *spin* angular momentum). $\mathfrak{L}_z$ then represents the *projection* (or *component*) of orbital angular momentum along a chosen direction. The z direction might be, for example, a molecular axis, an axis of crystal symmetry, or the direction of a magnetic field.

Linear differential equations, such as the Schrödinger equation

$$-\nabla^2\psi + \frac{2m}{\hbar^2}(V - E)\psi = 0, \qquad (10.1)$$

possess the important property that if ψ_1 and ψ_2 are two solutions, then any linear combination

$$a\psi_1 + b\psi_2$$

is also a solution. In Section 3.11 we see that E does not depend on m, so that a combination of functions $\psi = RY_l^m$ with different m for fixed l will also satisfy (10.1). The significance of the individual spherical harmonics appears when we can distinguish wavefunctions with different projections of angular momentum.

Traditionally, wavefunctions are labeled by letters to designate the value of l:

$l =$	0	1	2	3	4	5	6	7	8	9	...
label $=$	s	p	d	f	g	h	i	k	l	m	...

That is, a p electron has a wavefunction whose angular part is Y_{1-1}, Y_{10}, or Y_{11}, or some linear combination of these. For a given value of l, the eigenvalue m can take the values $-l, -(l - 1), -(l - 2), \ldots, 0, \ldots, (l - 1), l$ or a total of $2l + 1$ different values. Thus there will be one s wavefunction, three p wavefunctions, five d wavefunctions, and so on.

The spherical harmonics have complex values, because of the $e^{im\phi}$ factor. For convenience in picturing them, we combine functions that differ only by the sign of m. Introducing the *spherical tensor* $C_m^{(l)}$ of Racah [1] (see Table 3.3),

$$C_m^{(l)}(\Omega) \equiv \left(\frac{4\pi}{2l + 1}\right)^{1/2} Y_{lm}(\theta, \phi), \qquad (10.2)$$

Table 3.3 Racah Spherical Tensors $C^{(k)}$

$k=0$	$C_0^{(0)} = 1$		
$k=1$	$rC_0^{(1)} = r_0 = z$	$=$	$r\cos\theta$
	$rC_{\pm1}^{(1)} = r_{\pm1} = \mp \dfrac{(x \pm iy)}{\sqrt{2}}$	$= \mp$	$\dfrac{r\sin\theta\, e^{\pm i\phi}}{\sqrt{2}}$
$k=2$	$r^2C_0^{(2)} = r_0r_0 + r_{+1}r_{-1}$	$=$	$\dfrac{r^2}{2}(3\cos^2\theta - 1)$
	$r^2C_{\pm1}^{(2)} = \mp\sqrt{3}\, r_0r_{\pm1}$	$= \mp$	$\dfrac{r^2}{\sqrt{2}}\cos\theta\sin\theta\, e^{\pm i\phi}$
	$r^2C_{\pm2}^{(2)} = \sqrt{\dfrac{3}{2}}\, r_{\pm1}r_{\pm1}$	$=$	$\dfrac{r^2}{\sqrt{8}}\sin^2\theta\, e^{\pm 2i\phi}$
$k=3$	$r^3C_0^{(3)} = \dfrac{1}{2}(r_0r_0r_0 - 3r_{+1}r_{-1})$		
	$r^3C_{\pm1}^{(3)} = \mp\sqrt{\dfrac{3}{7}}\, r_{\pm1}(r_0r_0 - r_{+1}r_{-1})$		
	$r^3C_{\pm2}^{(3)} = \sqrt{\dfrac{15}{14}}\, r_0r_{\pm1}r_{\pm1}$		
	$r^3C_{\pm3}^{(3)} = \mp\sqrt{\dfrac{10}{3}}\, r_{\pm1}r_{\pm1}r_{\pm1}$		

($\Omega \equiv \theta, \phi$) we can write the unnormalized angular dependence of an electron wavefunction as follows.

<u>s electron ($l = 0$)</u>

$$s = 1 = C_0^{(0)}.$$

<u>p electrons ($l = 1$)</u>

$$p_z = \frac{z}{r} = C_0^{(1)}.$$

<u>d electrons ($l = 2$)</u>

$$d_{x^2-y^2} = \sqrt{\frac{3}{8}}\,\frac{x^2 - y^2}{r^2} = \frac{1}{2}\,[C_{+2}^{(2)} + C_{-2}^{(2)}].$$

$$d_{xy} = \sqrt{\frac{3}{2}}\,\frac{xy}{r^2} = -\frac{i}{2}\,[C_{+2}^{(2)} - C_{-2}^{(2)}].$$

$$d_{yz} = \sqrt{\frac{3}{2}}\,\frac{yz}{r^2} = \frac{i}{2}\,[C_{+1}^{(2)} - C_{-1}^{(2)}].$$

$$p_x = \frac{x}{r} = -\frac{1}{\sqrt{2}}[C_{+1}^{(1)} - C_{-1}^{(1)}]. \qquad d_{xz} = \sqrt{\frac{3}{2}}\frac{xz}{r^2} = -\frac{1}{2}[C_{+1}^{(2)} - C_{-1}^{(2)}].$$

$$p_y = \frac{y}{r} = \frac{1}{\sqrt{2}}[C_{+1}^{(1)} + C_{-1}^{(1)}]. \qquad d_{z^2} = \frac{3z^2 - r^2}{2r^2} = C_0^{(2)}.$$

Because of the property

$$\sum_m |Y_{lm}|^2 = \frac{2l+1}{4\pi} \qquad \text{or} \qquad \sum_m |C_m^{(l)}|^2 = 1,$$

we can see that the sum of the squares of all the wavefunctions for a given l is spherically symmetric.

$$|s|^2 = 1,$$
$$|p_x|^2 + |p_y|^2 + |p_z|^2 = 1,$$
$$|d_{x^2-y^2}|^2 + |d_{xy}|^2 + |d_{yz}|^2 + |d_{xz}|^2 + |d_{z^2}|^2 = 1.$$

The spherical harmonics satisfy the important relation

$$\int Y_{lm}^* Y_{l'm'}\, d\Omega = 0 \qquad \text{unless } m = m',\ l = l', \tag{10.3}$$

where $d\Omega = \sin\theta\, d\theta\, d\phi$. That is, functions of different l and m are *orthogonal*. The orthogonality with respect to m follows from direct integration (recall $Y_{lm} = \Theta_l^m \Phi_m$) of

$$\int \Phi_m^* \Phi_{m'}\, d\phi = \frac{1}{2\pi}\int e^{-im\phi} e^{im'\phi}\, d\phi.$$

If $m = m'$ we get

$$\frac{1}{2\pi}\int_0^{2\pi} d\phi = 1,$$

but if $m \neq m'$ we have

$$\frac{1}{2\pi}\int_0^{2\pi} e^{i(m'-m)\phi}\, d\phi = \frac{1}{2\pi}(1 - 1) = 0.$$

The l orthogonality follows [2] from the differential equation for Θ_l^m, (8.2) slightly rewritten:

$$\frac{1}{\sin\theta}\frac{d}{d\theta}\sin\theta\frac{d}{d\theta}\Theta + \left[l(l+1) - \frac{m^2}{\sin^2\theta}\right]\Theta = 0. \tag{10.4}$$

We multiply the left-hand side by $\Theta_{l'}^m$ (the same m, different l) and subtract the result from an equation identical with (10.4) except for an interchange of l and l':

$$\frac{\Theta_{l'}^m}{\sin\theta}\frac{d}{d\theta}\sin\theta\frac{d}{d\theta}\Theta_l^m - \frac{\Theta_l^m}{\sin\theta}\frac{d}{d\theta}\sin\theta\frac{d}{d\theta}\Theta_{l'}^m = [l'(l'+1) - l(l+1)]\Theta_{l'}^m\Theta_l^m.$$

We then multiply by the element of solid angle, $\sin\theta\, d\theta\, d\phi$, and integrate over all angles:

$$\int \Theta_{l'}^m \frac{d}{d\theta}\sin\theta\frac{d}{d\theta}\Theta_l^m\, d\theta - \int \Theta_l^m \frac{d}{d\theta}\sin\theta\frac{d}{d\theta}\Theta_{l'}^m\, d\theta$$
$$= [l'(l'+1) - l(l+1)]\int \Theta_{l'}^m\Theta_l^m \sin\theta\, d\theta. \qquad (10.5)$$

When we integrate the left-hand side by parts we obtain

$$\sin\theta\left(\Theta_{l'}^m\frac{d}{d\theta}\Theta_l^m - \Theta_l^m\frac{d}{d\theta}\Theta_{l'}^m\right)\Bigg|_{\theta=0}^{\theta=\pi}$$
$$-\int \sin\theta\left(\frac{d\Theta_l^m}{d\theta}\frac{d\Theta_{l'}^m}{d\theta} - \frac{d\Theta_{l'}^m}{d\theta}\frac{d\Theta_l^m}{d\theta}\right)d\theta.$$

The integrated term equals zero because of the factor $\sin\theta$, whereas the integral is identically zero. Since we have assumed $l \neq l'$, (10.5) gives

$$\int \Theta_{l'}^m\Theta_l^m \sin\theta\, d\theta = 0 \qquad \text{if} \quad l \neq l'. \qquad (10.6)$$

The Φ_m part of Y_{lm} thus provides orthogonality for different m values. The Θ_l^m factor provides orthogonality for different l values.

We see that the spherical harmonics $Y_{lm}(\theta, \phi)$ form an orthogonal and normalized set of functions (an *orthonormal* set). We can express this condition succinctly with the *Kronecker delta*, δ_{ab}, which is 1 if $a = b$ and 0 if $a \neq b$:

$$\int Y_{lm}^* Y_{l'm'}\, d\Omega = \delta_{ll'}\delta_{mm'}. \qquad (10.7)$$

The spherical harmonics also form a *complete set* of functions, in that one may express any well-behaved function of θ and ϕ as a linear combination of spherical harmonics:

$$f(\theta, \phi) = \sum_{l=0}^{\infty}\sum_{m=-l}^{+l} a_{lm}Y_{lm}(\theta, \phi). \qquad (10.8)$$

(For the proof of this assertion, see Whittaker and Watson [3], or Morse and Feshbach [4].) This procedure is analogous to a Taylor expansion of $f(x)$ in a power series in x^n or a Fourier expansion of $f(t)$ in a series in $\sin[(n/2\pi)t]$ and $\cos[(n/2\pi)t]$. The coefficients a_{lm} in (10.8) are *expansion coefficients* for the particular function $f(\theta, \phi)$. [They are sometimes called *Fourier coefficients* because of the resemblance of (10.8) to a Fourier series.] We can readily determine them (in principle) if we know $f(\theta, \phi)$: multiply (10.2) by $Y^*_{l'm'}$ and integrate over all angles. All the terms on the right side vanish because of orthogonality, except the term with $l = l'$ and $m = m'$.

$$\int f(\theta, \phi) Y_{l'm'}(\theta, \phi)\, d\Omega = \sum_l \sum_m a_{lm} \int Y^*_{lm} Y_{l'm'}\, d\Omega = a_{l'm'}.$$

Thus the expansion coefficients are

$$a_{lm} = \int Y^*_{lm} f(\theta, \phi)\, d\Omega. \tag{10.9}$$

As an illustration, let $f(\theta, \phi)$ be the function $g(\theta, \phi) Y_{l'm'}(\theta, \phi)$. According to (10.3) this expression has the expansion

$$g(\theta, \phi) Y_{l'm'}(\theta, \phi) = \sum_{l,m} a_{lm} Y_{lm}(\theta, \phi),$$

$$a_{lm} = \int Y^*_{lm} g Y_{l'm'}\, d\Omega.$$

Similarly, the function $(\partial/\partial \cos\theta) Y_{l'm'}$ has the expansion

$$\frac{\partial}{\partial \cos\theta} Y_{l'm'} = \sum_{l,m} a_{lm} Y_{lm},$$

with

$$a_{lm} = \int Y^*_{lm} \frac{\partial}{\partial \cos\theta} Y_{l'm'}\, d\Omega.$$

Both these examples are just special cases of expanding $\mathcal{A} Y_{l'm'}$ where $\mathcal{A}$ is some (possibly differential) operator:

$$\mathcal{A} Y_{l'm'} = \sum_{l,m} a_{lm} Y_{lm}, \tag{10.10}$$

$$a_{lm} = \int Y^*_{lm} \mathcal{A} Y_{l'm'}\, d\Omega. \tag{10.11}$$

Now the expansion coefficients a_{lm} of (10.10) depend on what operator we select for $\mathcal{A}$ and on which $Y_{l'm'}$ the operator acts. We really should show this explicitly by a better notation for the expansion coefficients. We therefore introduce the notation

$$\langle lm | \mathcal{A} | l'm' \rangle \equiv \int Y^*_{lm} \mathcal{A} Y_{l'm'}\, d\Omega \tag{10.12}$$

for the expansion coefficients

$$\mathfrak{A} Y_{l'm'} = \sum_{l,m} \langle lm|\mathfrak{A}|l'm'\rangle Y_{lm}. \tag{10.13}$$

We can view (10.12) and (10.13) in a particularly useful way if we arrange the values $\langle lm|\mathfrak{A}|l'm'\rangle$ into a square array or *matrix*. We label the columns by the indices $l'm'$ and the rows by the indices lm. The values in a particular column $l'm'$ of this matrix are the expansion coefficients for the function $\mathfrak{A} Y_{l'm'}$.

l	m	$l' =$	0	1			2	
		$m' =$	0	−1	0	+1	−2	···
0	0		D	x	x	x	x	
1	−1		x	D	x	x	x	
	0		x	x	D	x	x	
	+1		x	x	x	D	x	
2	−2		x	x	x	x	D	
	⋮							

Fig. 3.9 Matrix Elements.

We shall be particularly interested in operators represented by a *diagonal matrix*, whose only elements are located down the principal diagonal, $lm = l'm'$. These elements are labeled D in Fig. 3.9. For such operators there is no summation in (10.13):

$$\mathfrak{A} Y_{lm} = \langle lm|\mathfrak{A}|lm\rangle Y_{lm}. \tag{10.14}$$

This is just an eigenvalue equation; the diagonal elements of the matrix are the eigenvalues. We have already seen that the Y_{lm} are eigenfunctions of $\mathfrak{L}^2$ and $\mathfrak{L}_z$; these operators are represented by diagonal matrices,

$$\langle lm|\mathfrak{L}^2|l'm'\rangle = l(l+1)\delta_{ll'}\delta_{mm'}, \tag{10.15}$$

$$\langle lm|\mathfrak{L}_z|l'm'\rangle = m\delta_{ll'}\delta_{mm'}. \tag{10.16}$$

Of course, any quantity c that *does not depend on θ or ϕ* (it might depend on time or on r) will also have a diagonal matrix:

$$\langle lm|c|l'm'\rangle = c\delta_{ll'}\delta_{mm'}. \tag{10.17}$$

The $\mathfrak{L}_\pm$ operators, on the other hand, have matrix elements only *off* the diagonal. They have elements between m and $m \pm 1$ for the *same* values of l:

$$\langle lm|\mathfrak{L}_\pm|l'm'\rangle = \mp\left[\frac{l(l+1) - m(m\pm 1)}{2}\right]^{1/2}\delta_{ll'}\delta_{m,m\pm 1}. \tag{10.18}$$

In the previous sections [in (6.17) and (9.6)], we have seen that the operator $\mathcal{L}^2$ could be written as

$$\mathcal{L}^2 = \mathcal{L}_x\mathcal{L}_x + \mathcal{L}_y\mathcal{L}_y + \mathcal{L}_z\mathcal{L}_z = -\mathcal{L}_+\mathcal{L}_- + \mathcal{L}_0\mathcal{L}_0 - \mathcal{L}_-\mathcal{L}_+. \quad (10.19)$$

If we introduce the notation

$$\mathcal{L}_{+1} \equiv \mathcal{L}_+ \equiv \frac{-(\mathcal{L}_x + i\mathcal{L}_y)}{\sqrt{2}} = -\mathcal{L}^*_{-1},$$

$$\mathcal{L}_{-1} \equiv \mathcal{L}_- \equiv \frac{+(\mathcal{L}_x - i\mathcal{L}_y)}{\sqrt{2}} = -\mathcal{L}^*_{+1},$$

$$\mathcal{L}_0 \equiv \mathcal{L}_z = \mathcal{L}^*_0,$$

then we can write

$$\mathcal{L}^2 = \sum_q \mathcal{L}^*_q\mathcal{L}_q = \sum_q (-1)^q\mathcal{L}_q\mathcal{L}_{-q}. \quad (10.20)$$

We shall call the operators $\mathcal{L}_q$ the complex *spherical components* of the angular-momentum operator (they are also called *irreducible* components).

We can generalize these results to other vectors. For example, the position vector in rectangular coordinates,

$$\mathbf{r} = x\mathbf{e}_x + y\mathbf{e}_y + z\mathbf{e}_z, \quad (10.21)$$

with components (x, y, z), can be written with a set of *complex spherical unit vectors*, (see Table 3.4)

Table 3.4 Complex Spherical Unit Vectors

In Cartesian coordinates

$$\mathbf{e}_{+1} = -\frac{1}{\sqrt{2}}(\mathbf{e}_x - i\mathbf{e}_y) \qquad \mathbf{e}_x = \frac{1}{\sqrt{2}}(\mathbf{e}_{+1} - \mathbf{e}_{-1})$$

$$\mathbf{e}_{-1} = \frac{1}{\sqrt{2}}(\mathbf{e}_x - i\mathbf{e}_y) \qquad \mathbf{e}_y = \frac{i}{2}(\mathbf{e}_{+1} + \mathbf{e}_{-1})$$

$$\mathbf{e}_0 = \mathbf{e}_z$$

In polar coordinates

$$\mathbf{e}_{+1} = -\frac{e^{i\phi}}{\sqrt{2}}[\sin\theta\,\mathbf{e}_r + \cos\theta\,\mathbf{e}_\theta + i\sqrt{2}\,\mathbf{e}_\phi]$$

$$\mathbf{e}_{-1} = \frac{e^{-i\phi}}{\sqrt{2}}[\sin\theta\,\mathbf{e}_r + \cos\theta\,\mathbf{e}_\theta + i\sqrt{2}\,\mathbf{e}_\phi]$$

$$\mathbf{e}_0 = \cos\theta\,\mathbf{e}_r - \sin\theta\,\mathbf{e}_\theta$$

$$\left.\begin{aligned} \mathbf{e}_{+1} &= \frac{-(\mathbf{e}_x + i\mathbf{e}_y)}{\sqrt{2}}, \\ \mathbf{e}_0 &= \mathbf{e}_z, \\ \mathbf{e}_{-1} &= \frac{+(\mathbf{e}_x - i\mathbf{e}_y)}{\sqrt{2}}, \end{aligned}\right\} \tag{10.22}$$

as

$$\mathbf{r} = -r_{+1}\mathbf{e}_{-1} + r_0\mathbf{e}_0 - r_{-1}\mathbf{e}_{+1}. \tag{10.23}$$

We can readily find the components of $\mathbf{r}$ in this expansion by substituting the definitions (10.22) into (10.23) and comparing the result with (10.21). A bit of algebra reveals that

$$\left.\begin{aligned} r_{+1} &= \frac{-(x + iy)}{\sqrt{2}} = \frac{r \sin\theta\, e^{i\phi}}{\sqrt{2}}, \\ r_{-1} &= \frac{+(x - iy)}{\sqrt{2}} = \frac{r \sin\theta\, e^{-i\phi}}{\sqrt{2}}, \\ r_0 &= z = r\cos\theta, \end{aligned}\right\} \tag{10.24}$$

where we have written the magnitude of $\mathbf{r}$ as

$$r = (x^2 + y^2 + z^2)^{1/2}.$$

These components are just the spherical Racah tensors of order 1, multiplied by r:

$$r_q = r\left(\frac{3}{4\pi}\right)^{1/2} Y_{1q} = rC_q^{(1)}. \tag{10.25}$$

Note that, according to our definitions,

$$r_q^* = (-1)^q r_{-q} \quad \text{and} \quad \mathbf{e}_q^* = (-1)^q \mathbf{e}_{-q}, \tag{10.26}$$

so that we may write (10.23) as

$$\mathbf{r} = \sum_q (-1)^q r_q \mathbf{e}_{-q} = \sum_q r_q \mathbf{e}_q^* = \sum_q r_q^* \mathbf{e}_q. \tag{10.27}$$

We can also write the square of the magnitude

$$|\mathbf{r}|^2 \equiv x^2 + y^2 + z^2 \tag{10.28}$$

as

$$|\mathbf{r}|^2 = \sum_q (-1)^q r_q r_{-q} = \sum_q r_q r_q^*. \tag{10.29}$$

Similar relationships hold for any vector:

$$\mathbf{A} = A_x\mathbf{e}_x + A_y\mathbf{e}_y + A_z\mathbf{e}_z = \sum_q (-1)^q A_q \mathbf{e}_{-q} \tag{10.30}$$

where

$$A_{\pm 1} = \frac{\mp(A_x \pm iA_y)}{\sqrt{2}} \quad \text{and} \quad A_0 = A_z. \qquad (10.31)$$

We can take the scalar product of two vectors in either coordinate system:

$$\mathbf{A}\cdot\mathbf{B} = A_xB_x + A_yB_y + A_zB_z = \sum_q (-1)^q A_q B_{-q} = \sum_q A_q^* B_q. \qquad (10.32)$$

Using the orthogonality of the rectangular unit vectors,

$$\mathbf{e}_x\cdot\mathbf{e}_x = 1, \qquad \mathbf{e}_x\cdot\mathbf{e}_y = 0, \qquad \mathbf{e}_x\cdot\mathbf{e}_z = 0, \qquad \text{etc.},$$

and the definitions (10.22), we see that the complex spherical unit vectors satisfy the conditions

$$\mathbf{e}_{+1}\cdot\mathbf{e}_{-1} = -1, \qquad \mathbf{e}_{+1}\cdot\mathbf{e}_0 = 0, \qquad \mathbf{e}_{+1}\cdot\mathbf{e}_{+1} = 0, \qquad \text{etc.},$$

which can be stated as

$$\mathbf{e}_p^*\cdot\mathbf{e}_q = (-1)^p\mathbf{e}_{-p}\cdot\mathbf{e}_q = \delta_{pq}. \qquad (10.33)$$

We can create a more complicated object, a *dyadic*, by juxtaposing two vectors. (This procedure does *not* mean the scalar product. It is sometimes called the *outer product*.) The unit dyadic is defined as

$$\mathsf{I} = \mathbf{e}_x\mathbf{e}_x + \mathbf{e}_y\mathbf{e}_y + \mathbf{e}_z\mathbf{e}_z = -\mathbf{e}_{+1}\mathbf{e}_{-1} + \mathbf{e}_0\mathbf{e}_0 - \mathbf{e}_{+1}\mathbf{e}_{-1}.$$

It is then easy to see that the quadrupole dyadic, defined as

$$\mathsf{Q} \equiv \mathbf{r}\cdot\mathbf{r} - \frac{r^2}{3}\mathsf{I}, \qquad (10.34)$$

takes the explicit form

$$\begin{aligned}\mathsf{Q} = \left(x^2 - \frac{r^2}{3}\right)\mathbf{e}_x\mathbf{e}_x + xy\mathbf{e}_x\mathbf{e}_y + xz\mathbf{e}_x\mathbf{e}_z \\ + xy\mathbf{e}_y\mathbf{e}_x + \left(y^2 + \frac{r^2}{3}\right)\mathbf{e}_y\mathbf{e}_y + yz\mathbf{e}_y\mathbf{e}_z \\ + xz\mathbf{e}_z\mathbf{e}_x + yz\mathbf{e}_z\mathbf{e}_y + \left(z^2 - \frac{r^2}{3}\right)\mathbf{e}_z\mathbf{e}_z. \qquad (10.35)\end{aligned}$$

(Some authors call 3Q the quadrupole dyadic.) If we write this dyadic in the form

$$\mathsf{Q} = Q_{xx}\mathbf{e}_x\mathbf{e}_x + Q_{xy}\mathbf{e}_x\mathbf{e}_y + \cdots + Q_{zz}\mathbf{e}_z\mathbf{e}_z,$$

the array of numbers Q_{xx}, Q_{xy}, etc. is known as a *Cartesian tensor*. With a bit of algebra we can rewrite this equation in terms of spherical unit vectors and the spherical Racah tensors of order 2 given in Table 3.2:

$$\begin{aligned}\mathbf{Q} = {} & \sqrt{\tfrac{2}{3}}\, C_{-2}^{(2)}\mathbf{e}_{+1}\mathbf{e}_{+1} + \sqrt{\tfrac{1}{3}}\, C_{-1}^{(2)}\mathbf{e}_{+1}\mathbf{e}_{0} + \tfrac{1}{3}C_{0}^{(2)}\mathbf{e}_{+1}\mathbf{e}_{-1} \\ & + \sqrt{\tfrac{1}{3}}\, C_{-1}^{(2)}\mathbf{e}_{0}\mathbf{e}_{+1} - \tfrac{2}{3}C_{0}^{(2)}\mathbf{e}_{0}\mathbf{e}_{0} \qquad - \sqrt{\tfrac{1}{3}}\, C_{+1}^{(2)}\mathbf{e}_{0}\mathbf{e}_{-1} \\ & + \tfrac{1}{3}C_{0}^{(2)}\mathbf{e}_{-1}\mathbf{e}_{+1} - \sqrt{\tfrac{1}{3}}\, C_{+1}^{(2)}\mathbf{e}_{-1}\mathbf{e}_{0} + \sqrt{\tfrac{2}{3}}\, C_{+2}^{(2)}\,\mathbf{e}_{-1}\mathbf{e}_{-1}. \end{aligned} \tag{10.36}$$

The scalar product of two dyadics is defined as the number

$$\mathbf{A}:\mathbf{B} = A_{xx}B_{xx} + A_{xy}B_{xy} + A_{xz}B_{xz} + \cdots + A_{zz}B_{zz} = \sum_{ij} A_{ij}B_{ij}. \tag{10.37}$$

Thus the scalar (or *double dot*) product of any dyadic with itself is simply the sum of the squares of the components. For the dyadic $\mathbf{Q}$ this is

$$\mathbf{Q}:\mathbf{Q} = \tfrac{2}{3}(|C_{+2}^{(2)}|^2 + |C_{+1}^{(2)}|^2 + |C_{0}^{(2)}|^2 + |C_{-1}^{(2)}|^2 + |C_{-2}^{(2)}|^2). \tag{10.38}$$

We discuss dyadics further in chapter 6.

The Racah tensors with $m = 0$ do not depend on the angle ϕ. These tensors are polynomials in $\cos\theta$, the Legendre polynomials:

$$C_0^{(l)}(\theta, \phi) = P_l(\cos\theta).$$

From the power-series definition

$$P_l(x) = \sum_{r=0}^{l} (-1)^r \frac{(2l-2r)x^{l-2r}}{(2l)(r!)(l-r)!(l-2r)!} \tag{10.39}$$

and the multinomial expansion

$$(a + b + c + \cdots)^n = \sum_{\alpha\beta\gamma\cdots} \frac{n!}{\alpha!\beta!\gamma!\cdots} a^\alpha b^\beta c^\gamma \cdots \tag{10.40}$$

with

$$\alpha + \beta + \gamma + \cdots = n$$

we can prove *Rodrigues's formula* (cf. Whittaker and Watson [3], p. 303):

$$P_l(x) = \frac{1}{2^l l!}\frac{d^l}{dx^l}(x^2 - 1)^l. \tag{10.41}$$

The polynomials also satisfy (cf. Morse and Feshbach [4], p. 597)

$$P_l(x) = \frac{1}{l!}\left[\frac{d^l}{du^l}\left(\frac{1}{u^2 - 2ux + 1}\right)^{1/2}\right]_{u=0}. \tag{10.42}$$

From these results, one can find an extremely useful expansion for the inverse of the distance between point $\mathbf{R}$ (coordinates $R, \theta_R, \phi_R \equiv R, \Omega_R$) and point $\mathbf{r}$ (coordinates $r, \theta_r, \phi_r \equiv r, \Omega_r$). If $\mathbf{R}$ and $\mathbf{r}$ make an angle of ω, and $R > r$, then

$$\frac{1}{|\mathbf{R} - \mathbf{r}|} = \left(\frac{1}{R^2 - r^2 - 2rR\cos\omega}\right)^{1/2} = \sum_{l=0}^{\infty} \frac{\mathbf{r}^l}{\mathbf{R}^{l+1}} P_l(\cos\omega). \quad (10.43)$$

We can place this in an even more useful form by using the *addition theorem* (proved in Chapter 6, Section 6.5):

$$P_l(\cos\omega) = C_0^{(l)}(\omega) = \sum_{m=-l}^{+l} (-1)^m C_{-m}^{(l)}(\theta_R, \phi_R) C_m^{(l)}(\theta_r, \phi_r). \quad (10.44)$$

We shall often use the Racah summation convention to simplify writing:

$$\mathbf{C}^{(l)} \cdot \mathbf{C}^{(l)} \equiv \sum_{m=-l}^{+l} (-1)^m C_{-m}^{(l)} C_m^{(l)}. \quad (10.45)$$

Then (10.43) can be written

$$\frac{1}{|\mathbf{R} - \mathbf{r}|} = \sum_{l=0}^{\infty} \frac{r^l}{R^{l+1}} \mathbf{C}^{(l)}(\Omega_R) \cdot \mathbf{C}^{(l)}(\Omega_r). \quad (10.46)$$

When we have a *collection* of points $\mathbf{R}_i$ and points $\mathbf{r}_j$ $(R_i > r_j)$ we often need the interaction

$$\sum_{ij} \frac{1}{|R_i - r_j|} = \sum_{l=0}^{\infty} \sum_m (-1)^m \sum_i \frac{C_{-m}^{(l)}(\Omega_i)}{(R_i)^{l+1}} \sum_j (r_j)^l C_m^{(l)}(\Omega_j), \quad (10.47)$$

where Ω_i refers to the direction $\theta_i \phi_i$ to particle i. Here we have split the interaction into a factor $\mathbf{V}^{(l)}$ giving the influence of distant points, $\mathbf{R}_i$,

$$V_m^{(l)} \equiv \sum_i \frac{C_m^{(l)}(\Omega_i)}{(R_i)^{l+1}}, \quad (10.48)$$

and a factor, the *multipole tensor*, expressing the distribution of the points close to the origin:

$$Q_m^{(l)} \equiv \sum_i (r_i)^l C_m^{(l)}(\Omega_i). \quad (10.49)$$

We thus write

$$\sum_{ij} \frac{1}{|\mathbf{R}_i - \mathbf{r}_j|} = \sum_{l=0}^{\infty} \mathbf{V}^{(l)} \cdot \mathbf{Q}^{(l)}. \quad (10.50)$$

The $V_m^{(l)}$ tensors are related to the lth derivatives of the potential R^{-1}.

When the points cannot be divided clearly into distant points $\mathbf{R}_i$ and near points $\mathbf{r}_j$, we use instead the form

$$\sum_{ij} \frac{1}{|\mathbf{r}_i - \mathbf{r}_j|} = \sum_{l=0}^{l=\infty} \sum_{ij} \frac{(r_<)^l}{(r_>)^{l+1}} \mathbf{C}^{(l)}(\Omega_i) \cdot \mathbf{C}^{(l)}(\Omega_j), \quad (10.51)$$

where $r_>$ $(r_<)$ refers to the greater (lesser) of r_i and r_j.

It is also possible to expand the equation for a plane wave, with wave vector $\mathbf{k} = k_x\mathbf{e}_x + k_y\mathbf{e}_y + k_z\mathbf{e}_z$ in terms of spherical Bessel functions $j_l(kr)$ to obtain the *Rayleigh expansion* (see Blatt and Weisskopf [5]):

$$e^{i\mathbf{k}\cdot\mathbf{r}} = \sum_{l=0}^{l=\infty} (2l+1)i^l j_l(kr)\mathbf{C}^{(l)}(\Omega_k)\cdot\mathbf{C}^{(l)}(\Omega_r). \tag{10.52}$$

(The spherical Bessel functions are discussed in appendix B and by Morse and Feshbach [4], p. 1574.)

A spherical wave can be similarly expressed in terms of the spherical Hankel function, $h_l(kr)$ [Morse and Feshbach [4], p. 1574]:

$$\mathbf{R} \equiv \mathbf{r}_1 - \mathbf{r}_2,$$

$$\frac{e^{i\mathbf{k}\cdot\mathbf{R}}}{|\mathbf{R}|} = k\sum_{l=0}^{\infty}(2l+1)j_l(kr_<)h_l(kr_>)\mathbf{C}^{(l)}(\Omega_1)\cdot\mathbf{C}^{(l)}(\Omega_2). \tag{10.53}$$

Close to the origin (that is, $kr_< \to 0$) this relationship becomes

$$\xrightarrow[kr_>\to 0]{} k\sum_l (2l+1)\frac{(kr_<)^l}{1\cdot 3\cdot 5\cdots(2l+1)}h_l(kr_>)\mathbf{C}^{(l)}(\Omega_1)\cdot\mathbf{C}^{(l)}(\Omega_2),$$

whereas at large distances ($kr_> \to \infty$)

$$\xrightarrow[kr_>\to\infty]{} \frac{e^{ikr_>}}{r_>}\sum_l (i)^{-l-1}(2l+1)j_l(kr_<)\mathbf{C}^{(l)}(\Omega_1)\cdot\mathbf{C}^{(l)}(\Omega_2).$$

When both $kr_< \to 0$ and $kr_> \to \infty$, then the expansion approaches the expression:

$$\to \frac{ie^{ikr_>}}{r_>}\sum_l \frac{(-ikr_<)^l}{1\cdot 3\cdots(2l-1)}\mathbf{C}^{(l)}(\Omega_1)\cdot\mathbf{C}^{(l)}(\Omega_2).$$

It is sometimes useful to write the momentum operator, defined by

$$p = \frac{\hbar}{i}\nabla,$$

in spherical components by means of the angular-momentum operator

$$\hbar\mathfrak{L} = (\mathbf{r}\times p) = \frac{\hbar}{i}(\mathbf{r}\times\nabla).$$

To do this, we use an identity from vector analysis to write

$$\hbar\mathbf{r}\times\mathfrak{L} = \mathbf{r}\times(\mathbf{r}\times p) = r^2 p - \mathbf{r}(\mathbf{r}\cdot p). \tag{10.54}$$

The second term of this expression provides the radial component of ∇, which is $\partial/\partial r$:

Table 3.5 Expansion Formulas

a. $(r_{12})^{-1} = \sum_l \frac{r_<^l}{r_>^{l+1}} \mathbf{C}^{(l)}(1)\cdot\mathbf{C}^{(l)}(2)$

b. $(r_{12})^{-3} = \frac{1}{r_>^2 r_<^2} \sum_l \frac{r_<^l}{r_>^{l+1}} (2l+1)\mathbf{C}^{(l)}(1)\cdot\mathbf{C}^{(l)}(2)$

c. $(r_{12})^{-5} = \frac{1}{3(r_>^2 - r_<^2)^3} \sum_l \frac{r_<^l}{r_>^{l+1}} (2l+1)[(2l+3)r_>^2 - (2l-1)r_<^2]\mathbf{C}^{(l)}(1)\cdot\mathbf{C}^{(l)}(2)$

d. $\exp(i\mathbf{k}\cdot\mathbf{r}) = \sum_l (i)^l(2l+1)j_l(kr)\mathbf{C}^{(l)}(\Omega_{\mathbf{k}})\cdot\mathbf{C}^{(l)}(\Omega_{\mathbf{r}})$

e. $\frac{\exp(i\mathbf{k}\cdot\mathbf{r}_{12})}{r_{12}} = ik\sum_l (2l+1)j_l(kr_<)h_l(kr_>)\mathbf{C}^{(l)}(1)\cdot\mathbf{C}^{(l)}(2)$

where

$$\mathbf{r}_{12} \equiv \mathbf{r}_1 - \mathbf{r}_2, \qquad \mathbf{C}^{(l)}(i) \equiv \mathbf{C}^{(l)}(\Omega_i)$$

[b,c] B. R. Judd, *Operator Techniques in Atomic Spectroscopy*, McGraw-Hill, New York (1963), p. 88.

[d] A. R. Edmonds, *Angular Momentum in Quantum Mechanics*, Princeton University Press, Princeton, New Jersey (1955), p. 81.

[e] P. M. Morse and H. Feshbach, *Methods of Theoretical Physics*, McGraw-Hill New York (1953), p. 1574.

$$\frac{\mathbf{r}\cdot\boldsymbol{p}}{r} = \frac{\hbar}{i}\frac{\partial}{\partial r}.$$

When we recall that $\mathbf{r} = r\mathbf{C}^{(1)}$, we see that (10.53) gives the formula

$$\boldsymbol{p} = \hbar\frac{\mathbf{r}\times\mathfrak{L}}{r^2} - i\mathbf{C}^{(1)}\frac{\partial}{\partial r}. \tag{10.55}$$

[Note that $\mathbf{C}^{(l)}$ does not depend on the radial coordinate.]

Table 3.5 collects some of these formulas for later reference.

REFERENCES

[1] G. Racah, *Phys. Rev.* **62,** 438 (1942).

[2] D. H. Menzel, *Mathematical Physics*, Dover, New York (1961), section 1.18.

[3] E. T. Whittaker and G. N. Watson, *A Course of Modern Analysis*, Cambridge University Press, Cambridge, England (1940).

[4] P. M. Morse and H. Feshbach, *Methods of Theoretical Physics*, McGraw-Hill, New York (1953).
[5] J. M. Blatt and V. F. Weisskopf, *Theoretical Nuclear Physics*, Wiley, New York (1952), p. 784.

3.11 THE RADIAL EQUATION

Equation (6.31) for the radial function $P(r)$ [where $\psi = (P/r)Y$] has the form of a one-dimensional Schrödinger equation:

$$-\frac{d^2P}{dr^2} + \left[KV(r) + \frac{l(l+1)}{r^2}\right]P = KEP, \tag{11.1}$$

where we use K to denote the *Schrödinger constant* $2m/\hbar^2$. The bracketed expression is just the "effective potential" introduced in the study of Keplerian motion in Chapter 2—an attracting potential, $KV(r)$ (for hydrogen-like atoms this potential is $-KZe^2/r$), balanced by the repelling centrifugal potential $l(l+1)/r^2$. We have seen, in Section 3.4, *all positive* energies KE are possible, but only discrete "*quantized*" *negative* values permit acceptable P functions. We can readily see how K fixes the scale of r and E, that is, atomic sizes and energies. To do this, consider a hydrogenic atom, nuclear charge Ze, with zero angular momentum, $l = 0$:

$$\frac{d^2P_0}{dr^2} + K\left(\frac{Ze^2}{r} + E\right)P_0 = 0. \tag{11.2}$$

At large distances, we expect the function either to fall off exponentially with distance if $E < 0$, or to vary sinusoidally if $E > 0$, according to the arguments in Section 3.4. We first look at the case where $E < 0$. Near $r = 0$ the r^{-1} term dominates, and we anticipate P will then be proportional to r, in order to counter this. Suppose then, that the solution has the form

$$P_0 = C\frac{r}{a}e^{-r/a}, \tag{11.3}$$

where a and C are constants. Now

$$\frac{d^2P_0}{dr^2} = \frac{C}{a}\left(\frac{r}{a^2} - \frac{2}{a}\right)e^{-r/a}.$$

Thus the equation becomes

$$\frac{r}{a^2} - \frac{2}{a} + KZe^2 + KEr = 0. \tag{11.4}$$

As r approaches zero, the first and last terms become negligible, and we find

$$a = \frac{2}{KZe^2} = \frac{\hbar^2}{me^2Z} \equiv \frac{a_0}{Z} \simeq \frac{0.5}{Z} \times 10^{-8} \text{ cm.} \tag{11.5}$$

We recognize a_0 as the Bohr radius. As r becomes large, the first and last terms of (11.4) dominate, giving

$$E_0 = -\frac{Z^2}{Ka_0^2} = -\frac{mZ^2e^4}{2\hbar^2} = -13.6Z^2 \text{ eV}, \tag{11.6}$$

the ionization energy for an infinitely massive hydrogenic atom. The normalization of P_0 (or of $R_0 \equiv P_0/r$) gives $C = 1/\sqrt{2a}$:

$$\int (R_0)^2 r^2\, dr \equiv \int (P_0)^2\, dr = 1 = \frac{C^2}{a^2}\int_0^\infty r^2 e^{-r/a}\, dr = \frac{C^2}{a^2}\, 2a^3.$$

Since P_0 has no nodes, other than $r = 0$ and $r \to \infty$, this function must have the lowest eigenvalue.

The series solution to (11.1) is straightforward. The substitution $P(r) = e^{-r/a}G(r)$ gives the equation

$$\frac{d^2}{dr^2}G - \frac{2}{a}\frac{d}{dr}G + \frac{1}{a^2}G + \left[KE + \frac{KZe^2}{r} - \frac{l(l+1)}{r^2}\right]G = 0. \tag{11.7}$$

We insert the series

$$G = \sum_{k=\nu}^{\epsilon} A_k r^k \tag{11.8}$$

into (11.7) to obtain

$$\sum_k A_k r^{k-2}\left\{[k(k-1) - l(l+1)] + \left[-\frac{2k}{a} + KZe^2\right]r + \left[\frac{1}{a^2} + KE\right]r^2\right\} = 0. \tag{11.9}$$

For this equation to hold, the coefficient of each power of r must be zero. To obtain the indicial equation, set the coefficient of the lowest power of r, say r^ν, equal to zero:

$$\nu(\nu - 1) - l(l+1) = 0.$$

The solution to this equation, $\nu = l + 1$, shows that the series begins with r^{l+1}. Thus we can write

$$P(r) = e^{-r/a}\, r^{l+1} \sum_{i=0}^{\epsilon} A_i r^i, \tag{11.10}$$

where the A_i satisfy [according to (11.9) with the replacement $k = l + i + 1$] the equations

$$0 = \sum_i A_i \left[i(i + 1 + 2l)r^{l+i-1} + \frac{2}{a}\left(-l - i - 1 + \frac{KZe^2a}{2} \right) r^{l+i} + \left(\frac{1}{a^2} + KE \right) r^{l+i+1} \right]. \quad (11.11)$$

The coefficient of r^{l+i} in this sum must be zero. We increase (decrease) i by unity in the first (last) bracketed term, and obtain the recursion relation,

$$0 = (i + 1)(i + 2 + 2l)A_{i+1} - \frac{2}{a}\left(l + 1 + i - \frac{KZe^2a}{2} \right) A_i + \left(\frac{1}{a^2} + KE \right) A_{i-1}. \quad (11.12)$$

If there is to be a lowest term in (11.10) (and we saw that there must be one, viz. A_0), then the last bracket of (11.12) must be identically zero:

$$KE = -\frac{1}{a^2}. \quad (11.13)$$

Thus the A_i satisfy

$$\frac{A_{i+1}}{A_i} = \frac{(l + 1 - KZe^2a/2 + i)}{(2l + 2 + i)(i + 1)} \frac{2}{a}. \quad (11.14)$$

A comparison of this result with the definition of the *confluent hypergeometric function*,

$$_1F_1(b; c; x) = \sum_{i=0} \frac{(b)_i}{(c)_i} \frac{x^i}{i!} = \Sigma C_i x^i, \quad (11.15)$$

$$\frac{C_{i+1}}{C_i} = \frac{(b + i)}{(c + i)(i + 1)},$$

shows that our solution can be written in terms of the function $_1F_1(l + 1 - n; 2l + 2; 2r/a)$, where we have defined the number n (not yet assumed to be an integer) by

$$n \equiv \tfrac{1}{2}KZe^2a. \quad (11.16)$$

This definition is equivalent, according to (11.13), to writing

$$a = \frac{2n}{KZe^2} = \frac{n}{Z} a_0, \quad (11.17)$$

$$E = -\frac{KZ^2e^4}{4n^2} = \frac{Z^2}{n^2} E_0, \quad (11.18)$$

where E_0 is the lowest hydrogenic energy level in the Bohr theory. Only the (dimensionless) variable $2r/a = 2Zr/a_0n$ actually enters the solution.

The length scale for atomic structure is thus roughly set by Z/a_0. By including a normalizing factor N_{nl} in our solution, we can write (11.10) as

$$P_{nl}(r) = N_{nl}e^{-r/a}\left(\frac{2r}{a}\right)^{l+1} {}_1F_1\left(l + 1 - n; 2l + 2; \frac{2r}{a}\right). \qquad (11.19)$$

We have yet to determine the number n. When E is negative, corresponding to a bound state, our discussion of Chapter 2 shows that $P_{nl}(r)$ must decrease exponentially at large distances. This behavior means that the summation of (11.10) must terminate at some largest power of r (so that the exponential damping, which is a series comprising *all* powers, will dominate). The series terminates at i if $A_{i+1} = 0$. Then, from (11.14),

$$(E < 0): \quad \tfrac{1}{2}KZe^2a \equiv n = l + 1 + i = \text{an integer}, \qquad (11.20)$$

and we see that, because l is an integer, n must also be an integer, called the *principal quantum number*. From (11.17) we now retrieve the energy levels of the Bohr theory. The largest power of r in $P_{nl}(r)$ is

$$r^{l+1}r^{n-l-1} = r^n.$$

$P_{nl}(r)$, being a polynomial in r^n, has n radial nodes. For small distances it rises as

$$P_{nl}(r) \sim \left(\frac{2r}{a}\right)^{l+1}, \qquad r \to 0,$$

and at large distances it drops exponentially,

$$P_{nl}(r) \sim e^{-r/a}, \qquad r \to \infty.$$

Since i in (11.20) cannot be negative, *n must be greater than $l + 1$:*

$$n \geq l + 1.$$

The bound-state radial functions ($E < 0$) are often written in terms of the *associated Laguerre polynomials* $L_q^p(x)$. Unfortunately, two labeling conventions exist for these polynomials! Mathematicians (cf. Abramowitz and Stegun [1]; Bateman [2]; Magnus and Oberhettinger [3]; Morse and Feshbach [4]) usually define these polynomials by

$$L_q^p(x) = \frac{(p + q)!}{(p)!(q)!}\, {}_1F_1(-q; p + 1; x)$$

or, what is the same,

$$L_q^p(x) = (-1)^p \frac{d^p}{dx^p}[L_{p+q}^0],$$

$$L_n^0(x) = e^x \frac{d^n}{dx^n}(x^n e^{-x}). \qquad \text{(Notation 1)}$$

On the other hand, in the literature of wave mechanics and chemistry (cf. Condon and Morse [5]; Condon and Shortley [6]) these are defined by (here an unconventional bar will distinguish them)

$$\bar{L}_q^p(x) = \frac{d^p}{dx^p}[L_q^0] \qquad \text{(Notation 2)}$$

or

$$\bar{L}_q^p(x) = (-1)^p L_{q-p}^p = (-1)^p \frac{(q)!}{(p)!(q-p)!}\,{}_1F_1(p-q; p+1; x).$$

Clearly the expression for R_{nl} in terms of L_q^p depends on convention: mathematicians would write R_{nl} as L_{n-l-1}^{2l+1}, whereas physicists and chemists would write L_{n+l}^{2l+1} for the same polynomial. The use of the confluent hypergeometric function removes this difficulty and gives, in addition, an immediate prescription for constructing the polynomial and for extending it to positive energies.

As n increases the energy levels become more closely spaced, approaching a limit at $E = 0$. For positive energies, corresponding to an unbound or free electron, we see from (11.18) that n becomes imaginary:

$$(E > 0): \quad n = i\frac{Ze^2}{2}\left(\frac{K}{E}\right)^{1/2} = iZ\left(-\frac{E_0}{E}\right)^{1/2} \equiv i\kappa. \tag{11.21}$$

The function $P_{\kappa l}(r)$ now need not drop exponentially to zero, the series in (11.10) need not terminate, and the energy E is unrestricted (i.e. unquantized).

One often requires the value of integrals such as

$$I^k(nl, n'l') = \int P_{nl}(r)P_{n'l'}(r)r^k\,dr. \tag{11.22}$$

According to (11.19) these integrals can be written

$$I^k(nl, n'l') = NN'\left(\frac{2}{a}\right)^{l+1}\left(\frac{2}{a'}\right)^{l'+1}\int dr \exp\left[-\left(\frac{2}{a}+\frac{2}{a'}\right)r\right]$$
$$\times\, r^{l+l'+k+1}\,{}_1F_1\left(-n+l+1, 2l+2; \frac{2r}{a}\right)$$
$$\times\, {}_1F_1\left(-n'+l'+1, 2l'+2; \frac{2r}{a'}\right).$$

It is now a straightforward (albeit tedious) process to expand the ${}_1F_1$ functions into power series, multiply the series together, collect the terms involving a given power of r, and integrate term by term with the aid of the formula

Table 3.6 Hydrogenic Radial Functions [a] $R_{nl}(r) = P_{nl}(r)/r$ **divided by** $(Z/a_0)^{3/2}$

	$l = 0\ (s)$	$l = 1\ (p)$	$l = 2\ (d)$	$l = 3\ (f)$
$n = 1\quad (x \equiv Zr/a_0)$	$2e^{-x}$	—	—	—
$n = 2\quad (x \equiv Zr/2a_0)$	$\frac{1}{\sqrt{2}}(1 - x)\, e^{-x}$	$\frac{1}{\sqrt{6}}\, e^{-x}$	—	—
$n = 3\quad (x \equiv Zr/3a_0)$	$\frac{2}{\sqrt{27}}\left(1 - 2x + \frac{2}{3}x^2\right) e^{-x}$	$\frac{8}{9\sqrt{6}}\, x\left(1 - \frac{x}{2}\right) e^{-x}$	$\frac{4}{9\sqrt{30}}\, x^2\, e^{-x}$	—
$n = 4\quad (x \equiv Zr/4a_0)$	$\frac{1}{4}\left(1 - 3x + 2x^2 - \frac{1}{3}x^3\right) e^{-x}$	$\frac{\sqrt{15}}{12}\, x\left(1 - x + \frac{1}{5}x^2\right) e^{-x}$	$\frac{1}{4\sqrt{5}}\, x^2\left(1 - \frac{x}{3}\right) e^{-x}$	$\frac{1}{12\sqrt{35}}\, x^3\, e^{-x}$

[a] The hydrogenic wavefunctions are $\psi_{nlm}(\mathbf{r}) = R_{nl}(r)\, Y_{lm}(\Omega) = r^{-1} P_{nl}(r)\, Y_{lm}(\Omega)$. Multiply the functions shown above by $(Z/a_0)^{3/2}$ to get R_{nl}, and by $(a_0/r)(Z/a_0)^{3/2}$ to get P_{nl}.

$$\int_0^\infty e^{-br}\, r^m\, dr = \frac{m!}{b^{m+1}}. \tag{11.23}$$

The resulting expression for $I^k(nl, n'l')$ will, in general, be a series.

Integrals involving the bound-state hydrogenic functions (discrete n) have been evaluated by various authors [7], [8]. In particular, the normalization constant in (11.19) determined by,

$$1 = \int_0^\infty (P_{nl})^2\, dr = \int_0^\infty (R_{nl})^2 r^2\, dr,$$

is

$$N_{nl} = \frac{\sqrt{Z}}{n(2l+1)!}\left[\frac{(n+l)!}{(n-l-1)!}\right]^{1/2}. \tag{11.24}$$

The resulting normalized radial functions for bound states are, for r in units of a_0 (i.e., $e = \hbar = m = 1$),

$$\begin{aligned} P_{nl}(r) &= rR_{nl}(r) \\ &= \frac{\sqrt{Z}}{n(2l+1)!}\left[\frac{(n+l)!}{(n-l-1)!}\right]^{1/2}\left(\frac{2Zr}{n}\right)^{l+1}\exp\left(-\frac{Zr}{n}\right) \\ &\qquad \times {}_1F_1\left(-n+l+1; 2l+2; \frac{2Zr}{n}\right). \end{aligned} \tag{11.25}$$

The first few radial functions are given in Table 3.6, in terms of the convenient variable $x = Zr/n$.

Table 3.7 Average Value of $\langle r^n \rangle$ for Hydrogenic Atoms

$$\langle r \rangle = \frac{1}{2Z}\,[3n^2 - l(l+1)]a_0$$

$$\langle r^2 \rangle = \frac{n^2}{2Z^2}\,[5n^2 + 1 - 3l(l+1)](a_0)^2$$

$$\left\langle \frac{1}{r} \right\rangle = \frac{Z}{n^2}\,\frac{1}{a_0}$$

$$\left\langle \frac{1}{r^2} \right\rangle = \frac{Z^2}{n^3(l+\frac{1}{2})}\,\frac{1}{(a_0)^2}$$

$$\left\langle \frac{1}{r^3} \right\rangle = \frac{Z^3}{n^3(l+1)(l+\frac{1}{2})l}\,\frac{1}{(a_0)^3}$$

$$\left\langle \frac{1}{r^4} \right\rangle = \frac{Z^4[3n^2 - l(l+1)]}{2n^5(l+\frac{3}{2})(l+1)(l+\frac{1}{2})l(l-\frac{1}{2})}\,\frac{1}{(a_0)^4}$$

From (11.25) and the properties of the hypergeometric function, one can calculate various mean values of r^k,

$$\langle r^k \rangle \equiv \int_0^\infty (P_{nl})^2 r^k \, dr = I^k(nl, nl).$$

A few results are given in Table 3.7 (from Bethe and Salpeter [9]). The result for r^{-1} is just the negative of the mean value of the potential energy. It is particularly interesting to examine the quantity

$$\Delta r^2 \equiv \langle r - \langle r \rangle \rangle^2 = \langle r^2 \rangle - \langle r \rangle^2,$$

the mean-square deviation of the electron–nucleus distance. This is a quantum-mechanical measure of the eccentricity of the orbit. From the preceding table we find the fractional deviation is

$$\frac{\Delta r^2}{\langle r \rangle^2} = \frac{n^2(n^2 + 2) - l^2(l + 1)^2}{[3n^2 - l(l + 1)]^2}.$$

Classically, the most elliptical orbits have the lowest angular momentum for a given energy, whereas circular orbits have the highest possible angular momentum. Quantum mechanically, the $l = 0$ or s electrons are the most penetrating. The quantum mechanical counterparts of circular orbits are those with largest allowed angular momentum, $l = n - 1$:

$$\text{penetrating } (l = 0): \qquad \frac{\Delta r^2}{\langle r \rangle^2} = \frac{1}{9}\left(1 + \frac{2}{n^2}\right),$$

$$\text{circular } (l = n - 1): \qquad \frac{\Delta r^2}{\langle r \rangle^2} = \frac{1}{(2n + 1)}.$$

Because of the r^l dependence of $R_{nl}(r)$ near the origin, only the s electrons have an appreciable probability of being found within an atomic unit of distance, $Za_0 \simeq Z/2$ Å, of the nucleus.

REFERENCES

[1] M. A. Abramowitz and I. A. Stegun, *Handbook of Mathematical Functions*, Natl. Bur. Stds., Applied Mathematics Series 55 (1964).

[2] A. Erdelyi, W. Magnus, F. Oberhettinger, and F. G. Tricomi, Bateman Manuscript Project, *Higher Transcendental Functions*, McGraw-Hill, New York (1953).

[3] W. Magnus and F. Oberhettinger, *Special Functions of Mathematical Physics*, Chelsea, New York (1949).

[4] P. M. Morse and H. Feshbach, *Methods of Theoretical Physics*, McGraw-Hill, New York (1953).

[5] E. U. Condon and P. M. Morse, *Quantum Mechanics*, McGraw-Hill, New York (1929).

[6] E. U. Condon and G. H. Shortley, *Theory of Atomic Spectra*, Cambridge University Press, Cambridge, England (1935).
[7] D. H. Menzel, *Rev. Mod. Phys.* **36**, 613 (1964).
[8] W. Gordon, *Ann. d. Physik* **2**, 1031 (1929).
[9] H. Bethe and E. Salpeter, *Quantum Mechanics of One- and Two-Electron Atoms*, Springer, Berlin (1959).

APPENDIX A: THE METHOD OF LADDER OPERATORS

Eigenvalue equations involving a parameter l, of the form

$$\left[-\frac{d^2}{dx^2} + V(x, l)\right] F_n(x, l) = \lambda_n F_n(x, l), \tag{A.1}$$

occur frequently in physics and applied mathematics. That is, we have a sequence of eigenfunctions $F_1(x, l)$, $F_2(x, l)$, . . . which are functions of x and the parameter l. The functions have eigenvalues λ_1, λ_2, . . . which are independent of l. Usually there will be several values of l and therefore several different eigenfunctions $F_n(x, l)$ that satisfy (A.1) with the same eigenvalue λ_n.

An interesting method for solving such equations, the *factorization* method, is discussed in detail by Infeld and Hull [1] and by Morse and Feshbach [2]. We try to find a function $u(x, l)$ and two differential operators,

$$\begin{aligned} \mathfrak{D}_l^+ &= -\left[\frac{d}{dx} + u^+(x, l)\right], \\ \mathfrak{D}_l^- &= \left[\frac{d}{dx} - u^-(x, l)\right], \end{aligned} \tag{A.2}$$

such that the eigenvalue equation, (A.1), becomes

$$[\mathfrak{D}_l^+\mathfrak{D}_l^- + a(l)]F_n(x, l) = \lambda_n F_n(x, l), \tag{A.3a}$$

and

$$[\mathfrak{D}_{l+1}^-\mathfrak{D}_{l+1}^+ + a(l+1)]F_n(x, l) = \lambda_n F_n(x, l), \tag{A.3b}$$

where $a(l)$ is independent of x.

It follows from (A.3) that $\mathfrak{D}_l^+$ and $\mathfrak{D}_l^-$ will be step-up and step-down *ladder operators* acting on the parameter l, as we see by the following argument. Write

$$\mathfrak{D}_l^+\mathfrak{D}_l^- F_n(x, l) = [\lambda_n - a(l)]F_n(x, l) \tag{A.4}$$

from (A.3a) and write

$$\mathfrak{D}_l^-\mathfrak{D}_l^+ F_n(x, l-1) = [\lambda_n - a(l)]F_n(x, l-1) \tag{A.5}$$

from (A.3*b*). Multiply the latter by $\mathfrak{D}_l^+$:

$$\mathfrak{D}_l^+[\mathfrak{D}_l^-\mathfrak{D}_l^+F_n(x, l-1)] = \mathfrak{D}_l^+\mathfrak{D}_l^-[\mathfrak{D}_l^+F_n(x, l-1)]$$
$$= [\lambda_n - a(l)][\mathfrak{D}_l^+F_n(x, l-1)]. \qquad (A.6)$$

Comparison with (A.4) reveals that $\mathfrak{D}_l^+F_n(x, l-1)$ satisfies the same equation as $F_n(x, l)$. Thus $\mathfrak{D}_l^+$ has the effect of *increasing* the parameter l by unity. In a similar way, multiply (A.4) by $\mathfrak{D}_l^-$ and compare with (A.5) to see that $\mathfrak{D}_l^-$ *decreases* l by unity.

Because the $\mathfrak{D}$ operators are ladder operators, when they act on a function $F(x, l)$ they produce some constant multiple of the function with raised or lowered l values:

$$\begin{aligned}\mathfrak{D}_{l+1}^+F_n(x, l) &= C_{l+1}F_n(x, l+1),\\ \mathfrak{D}_l^-F_n(x, l) &= C_lF_n(x, l-1).\end{aligned} \qquad (A.7)$$

(We have chosen the subscripts on the constants C_l with an eye to simplifying the following results. Another choice would give the same normalization.) Then sequential application of (A.7) produces

$$\mathfrak{D}_l^+\mathfrak{D}_l^-F_n(x, l) = \mathfrak{D}_l^+C_lF_n(x, l-1) = C_lC_lF_n(x, l). \qquad (A.8)$$

But (A.4) shows that

$$\mathfrak{D}_l^+\mathfrak{D}_l^-F_n(x, l) = [\lambda_n - a(l)]F_n(x, l),$$

so that we must have

$$C_l^2 = \lambda_n - a(l). \qquad (A.9)$$

This fixes C_l and C_{l-1} within a phase factor, which we can choose as $+1$ by convention. Thus

$$\mathfrak{D}_{l+1}^+F_n(x, l) = \sqrt{\lambda_n - a(l+1)}\,F_n(x, l+1), \qquad (A.10a)$$
$$\mathfrak{D}_l^-F_n(x, l) = \sqrt{\lambda_n - a(l)}\,F_n(x, l-1). \qquad (A.10b)$$

In this way we can construct all the eigenfunctions of a given eigenvalue λ_n from a single eigenfunction, once we know $u(x, l)$, $a(l)$, and λ_n.

We can readily determine $u(x, l)$ and $a(l)$ from the $V(x, l)$ of (A.1). First suppose $u^+(x, l) = u^-(x, l)$. Neglecting l dependence for the moment, we have

$$\mathfrak{D}^+\mathfrak{D}^-F = -\left(\frac{d}{dx} + u\right)\left(\frac{d}{dx} - u\right)F = -\left(\frac{d^2}{dx^2}F - \frac{d}{dx}uF + u\frac{dF}{dx} - u^2F\right)$$
$$= -\left(\frac{d^2}{dx^2} - \frac{du}{dx} - u^2\right)F,$$

while

$$\mathfrak{D}^-\mathfrak{D}^+F = -\left(\frac{d}{dx} - u\right)\left(\frac{d}{dx} + u\right)F = -\left(\frac{d^2}{dx^2} + \frac{du}{dx} - u^2\right)F.$$

We eliminate d^2/dx^2 from these equations, using (A.1), to obtain

$$\mathfrak{D}_l^+\mathfrak{D}_l^- F_n(x, l) = \left[-V(x, l) + \lambda_n - \frac{du}{dx}(x, l) + u^2(x, l)\right] F_n(x, l),$$

$$\mathfrak{D}_l^-\mathfrak{D}_l^+ F_n(x, l-1)$$
$$= \left[-V(x, l-1) + \lambda_n + \frac{du}{dx}(x, l) + u^2(x, l)\right] F_n(x, l-1).$$

Thus (A.4) and (A.5) give

$$\left[-V(x, l) + \frac{d}{dx}u(x, l) + u^2(x, l) + a(l)\right] F_n(x, l) = 0, \quad \text{(A.11)}$$

$$\left[-V(x, l-1) - \frac{d}{dx}u(x, l) + u^2(x, l) + a(l)\right] F_n(x, l-1) = 0. \quad \text{(A.12)}$$

Multiply (A.11) by $F_n(x, l-1)$ and (A.12) by $F_n(x, l)$. Then, adding the two equations gives

$$2u^2(x, l) + 2a(l) = V(x, l) - V(x, l-1), \quad \text{(A.13)}$$

and subtracting gives

$$2\frac{d}{dx}u(x, l) = V(x, l) - V(x, l-1). \quad \text{(A.14)}$$

Differentiation of (A.13),

$$4u\frac{du}{dx} = \frac{d}{dx}V(x, l) + \frac{d}{dx}V(x, l-1),$$

then gives [after substitution from (A.14)] the solution for u:

$$u(x, l) = \frac{1}{2}\frac{(d/dx)V(x, l) + (d/dx)V(x, l-1)}{V(x, l) - V(x, l-1)} \quad \text{(A.15)}$$

(recall $u^+ = u^-$). The term $a(l)$ follows from (A.13):

$$a(l) = \tfrac{1}{2}\left[V(x, l) + V(x, l-1)\right] - u^2(x, l). \quad \text{(A.16)}$$

If the factorization method is to work, the potential $V(x, l)$ in (A.1) must be such that the expression on the right-hand side of (A.16) is independent of x (a may be identically zero). Equations A.15 and A.16 are not the most general solutions to (A.2) and (A.3), for we have assumed here that $u^+ = u^-$. Other assumptions could be made, leading to slightly different factorization.

Next, we note that the $\mathfrak{D}$ operators satisfy the following condition, for any functions $f(x, l)$ and $g(x, l)$ that vanish or are periodic on the boundary B to some region V:

$$\begin{aligned}\int_V g\mathfrak{D}^+ f\,dx &= -\int_V g\frac{df}{dx} - \int_V ugf\,dx \\ &= -gf\Big|_B + \int_V f\frac{d}{dx}g\,dx - \int_V ugf\,dx \\ &= 0 + \int_V f\mathfrak{D}^- g\,dx,\end{aligned}$$

where the second line follows by integrating by parts. $\mathfrak{D}^+$ is the Hermitian adjoint of $\mathfrak{D}^-$ and vice versa. Using this property we see that

$$\int F^*\mathfrak{D}^+\mathfrak{D}^- F\,dx = \int (\mathfrak{D}^- F^*)(\mathfrak{D}^- F)\,dx = \int \mathfrak{D}^- F^2\,dx,$$

a quantity that cannot be negative or imaginary. But from (A.4) we have

$$\begin{aligned}\int F_n^*(x, l)\mathfrak{D}_l^+\mathfrak{D}_l^- F_n(x, l)\,dx &= [\lambda_n - a(l)]\int F^*F\,dx \\ &= [\lambda_n - a(l)]\int |F_n(x, l)|^2\,dx,\end{aligned}$$

and this expression too cannot be negative. Hence:

$$\lambda_n - a(l) \geq 0. \tag{A.17}$$

In a similar way, we can use (A.5),

$$\int F_n(x, l)\mathfrak{D}_{l+1}^-\mathfrak{D}_{l+1}^+ F_n(x, l)\,dx = [\lambda_n - a(l+1)]\int |F_n(x, l)|^2\,dx,$$

to show that

$$\lambda_n - a(l+1) \geq 0. \tag{A.18}$$

These results assure us that the radicals in (A.10) will always be real.

Conditions (A.17) and (A.18) now provide the eigenvalues λ_n in terms of a. For suppose, first, that $a(l)$ is an *increasing* function of l, such as lc or $-c/l^2$. Then successive applications of $\mathfrak{D}_{l+1}^+$, as in (A.10*a*), produce larger values of l and $a(l+1)$. We can ensure that $a(l+1)$ never exceeds λ_n by requiring that for some maximum value of l, say $l = n$, the two are equal.

$$a(n+1) = \lambda_n, \qquad a(l) < a(l+1). \tag{A.19a}$$

Then the raising operator cannot increase l beyond the value $l = n$:

$$\mathfrak{D}_{n+1}^+ F_n(x, n) = 0. \tag{A.20a}$$

By similar reasoning, if $a(l)$ is a *decreasing* function of l, successive applications of $\mathfrak{D}_l^-$ produce smaller values of l but larger values of $a(l)$. We can satisfy (A.17) by requiring for some minimum value of l, say $l = n$, that

$$a(n) = \lambda_n, \qquad a(l) > a(l+1). \tag{A.19b}$$

This procedure leads to the equation

$$\mathfrak{D}_n^- F_n(x, n) = 0. \tag{A.20b}$$

Equations A.19 and A.20 provide not only the eigenvalues λ_n, but the eigenfunctions $F_n(x, n)$ as well. The equation for $F_n(x, n)$ from (A.20*a*) and the definition in (A.2) is

$$-\left[\frac{d}{dx} + u(x, n+1)\right] F_n(x, n) = 0$$

or

$$\frac{d}{dx} nF_n(x, n) = -u(x, n+1),$$

which integrates immediately to

$$F_n(x, n) = N_n \exp\left[-\int u(x, n+1)\, dx\right], \qquad a(l) < a(l+1), \tag{A.21a}$$

where N_n is an arbitrary constant. Similarly, the equation for $F_n(x, n)$ from (A.20*b*) is

$$F_n(x, n) = N_n \exp\left[\int u(x, n)\, dx\right], \qquad a(l) > a(l+1). \tag{A.21b}$$

These techniques serve to solve the $\Theta_l^m(\theta)$ equation and the $R_{nl}(r)$ equation of Sections 3.8 and 3.12 as well as numerous other equations. For further details, consult Infeld and Hull [1].

REFERENCES

[1] L. Infeld and T. E. Hull, *Rev. Mod. Phys.* **23,** 21 (1951).
[2] P. M. Morse and H. Feshbach, *Methods of Theoretical Physics*, McGraw-Hill, New York (1953), p. 729 ff.

APPENDIX B: THE SPHERICAL BESSEL FUNCTIONS

A useful application of the ladder-operator approach is to the *scalar Helmholtz equation,*

$$\nabla^2\psi - k^2\psi = 0. \tag{B.1}$$

If we set $\psi(r, \theta, \phi) = [f(r)/r]Y_l^m(\theta, \phi)$, the radial equation becomes [cf. (11.1)]:

$$\left[-\frac{d^2}{dr^2} + \frac{l(l+1)}{r^2}\right] f = k^2 f. \tag{B.2}$$

Note that the change of variable $x = kr$ will remove the explicit dependence of this equation on k. Hence f must be a function of kr, say $f_l(kr)$.

The preceding discussion of ladder operators provides the following factorization:

$$\mathfrak{D}_l^+ \mathfrak{D}_l^- f_l(kr) = k^2 f_l(kr), \tag{B.3}$$

where

$$\mathfrak{D}_l^\pm = \mp\left(\frac{d}{dr} \pm \frac{l}{r}\right). \tag{B.4}$$

The raising and lowering process is

$$-\mathfrak{D}_{l+1}^+ f_l(kr) \equiv \left(\frac{d}{dr} + \frac{l+1}{r}\right) f_l(kr) = -kf_{l+1}(kr), \tag{B.5a}$$

$$\mathfrak{D}_l^- f_l(kr) \equiv \left(\frac{d}{dr} - \frac{l}{r}\right) f_l(kr) = kf_{l-1}(kr). \tag{B.5b}$$

Because $a(l)$ is identically zero, the parameter l is not restricted by the values of k. [However, the initial assumption of $\psi = (f_l/r)Y_{lm}$ does restrict l to the positive integral values found with the spherical harmonics.] Therefore we *cannot* find an equation of the type

$$\mathfrak{D}^\pm f = 0$$

to start the ladder. Solutions exist for positive and negative l, and non-integral l. However, the original equation, with $l = 0$, is easy enough to solve:

$$\frac{d^2}{dr^2} f_0(kr) + k^2 f_0(kr). \tag{B.6}$$

This has solutions of the form sin (kr), cos (kr), and e^{ikr}. From any such solution we form others, using $\mathfrak{D}^+$ or $\mathfrak{D}^-$.

For many purposes it is more convenient to work directly with the complete radial function, $f(r)/r$. The $l = 0$ functions, $f_0(kr)/kr$, are known as

spherical Bessel functions: $\quad j_0(kr) = \sin\frac{(kr)}{kr},$

spherical Neumann functions: $\quad n_0(kr) = -\cos\frac{(kr)}{kr},$

spherical Hankel functions: $$h_0(kr) = -\frac{ie^{ikr}}{kr}.$$

The $j_l(kr)$ [and $n_l(kr)$ and $h_l(kr)$ as well] satisfy the differential equation

$$\left[\frac{d^2}{dr^2} + \frac{2}{r}\frac{d}{dr} - \frac{l(l+1)}{r^2}\right] j_l(kr) = k^2 j_l(kr). \tag{B.7}$$

If we introduce the notation

$$\mathcal{R}_l^- \equiv -\mathcal{D}_{l+1}^+ \equiv \left(\frac{d}{dr} + \frac{1}{r} + \frac{l}{r}\right), \tag{B.8a}$$

$$\mathcal{R}_l^+ \equiv \mathcal{D}_{l-1}^- \equiv \left(\frac{d}{dr} + \frac{1}{r} - \frac{l}{r}\right), \tag{B.8b}$$

this equation factors as

$$\mathcal{R}_{l+1}^- \mathcal{R}_{l+1}^+ j_l(kr) = \mathcal{R}_l^+ \mathcal{R}_l^- j_l(kr) = k^2 j_l(kr). \tag{B.9}$$

Since this equation has the same form as (A.3), the $\mathcal{R}$ operators are ladder operators acting on j_l. From the discussion following (A.3) we immediately see that

$$\mathcal{R}_{l+1}^+ j_l(kr) = \left(\frac{d}{dr} - \frac{l}{r}\right) j_l(kr) = kj_{l+1}(kr), \tag{B.10a}$$

$$\mathcal{R}_l^- j_l(kr) = \left(\frac{d}{dr} + \frac{l+1}{r}\right) j_l(kr) = kj_{l-1}(kr). \tag{B.10b}$$

These functions are discussed by Morse and Feshbach [1], pp. 622, 1465, and 1573. (See also [2].) They have the asymptotic forms:

	$x \to 0$	$x \to \infty$
$j_l(x) \to$	$\dfrac{x^l}{1\cdot 3\cdot 5\cdots(2l+1)}$	$\to \dfrac{1}{x}\cos\left[x - (l+1)\dfrac{\pi}{2}\right],$
$n_l(x) \to$	$-\dfrac{1\cdot 3\cdot 5\cdots(2l-1)}{x^{l+1}}$	$\to \dfrac{1}{x}\sin\left[x - (l+1)\dfrac{\pi}{2}\right],$
$h_l(x) =$	$j_l(x) + in_l(x)$	$\to (i)^{-l-1}\dfrac{e^{ix}}{x}.$

REFERENCES

[1] P. M. Morse and H. Feshbach, *Methods of Theoretical Physics*, McGraw-Hill, New York (1953).

[2] M. Abramowitz, and I. Stegun, *Handbook of Mathematical Functions*, Natl. Bur. Stds. Applied Math Series 55, Washington, D. C. (1964), Section 10.

4. Quantum Mechanics

4.1 THE UNCERTAINTY PRINCIPLE

A systematic treatment of atomic physics demands several basic alterations of our intuitive approach to physics. The change from the viewpoint of classical physics to that of quantum physics must leave intact many relationships, such as Newton's laws and Maxwell's equations, which we know hold true on the "macroscopic" scale. But when we consider phenomena on a "microscopic" scale, and deal with very small distances or with light waves of low intensity, new effects emerge that cannot be predicted solely from the macroscopic laws. In this chapter, we examine the basic changes needed in our formulation of physics as we turn from simple macroscopic bodies to complicated microscopic phenomena. Bibliography 7 provides sources of further discussion.

The first change occurs in our concept of a "particle." On the macroscopic scale, we sometimes idealize a planet or satellite as a point mass, traveling under the influence of a gravitational field. We apply Newton's laws (or Kepler's laws) and predict the motion of the particle. We can then measure, perhaps with radar, the position and velocity of the object at any time or at a sequence of times. Our measurement does not noticeably disturb the motion of the object. Even a powerful radar will not measurably affect the motion of a heavy satellite. But when we attempt to observe a very small particle, the radiation we employ to observe the particle may perceptibly change its trajectory. Radiation pressure becomes a significant force. Thus when we try to verify our predictions of how the particle behaves—predictions based on the laws of macroscopic motion—the very smallness of the particle frustrates our attempts. Our methods of interrogation induce erratic and unpredictable behavior.

Heisenberg's uncertainty principle [1] expresses these remarks mathematically: the product of uncertainty in position, Δx, and uncertainty in momentum, Δp_x, is always *finite*, *never* zero. The Dirac constant $\hbar$ ($\hbar = h/2\pi$) fixes the limit of uncertainty:

$$\Delta p_x \, \Delta x \geq \hbar = 1.0544 \times 10^{-27} \text{ erg sec.} \tag{1.1}$$

The uncertainty principle has its foundations in the classical theory of wave motion. Suppose we have a perfectly monochromatic sinusoidal wave, with angular frequency ω and wavelength $\lambda = 2\pi/k$, moving with velocity c:

$$\psi(x, t) = \sin(k_0 x - \omega t). \tag{1.2}$$

In order to be perfectly monochromatic, as we have assumed, the wave train must extend indefinitely in space and time. Any *actual* wave has only a finite extent. Mathematically, we describe this truncated train as a superposition of waves having wavelengths slightly different from $2\pi/k_0$. Denoting the amplitudes of these various superposed waves by $a(k)$, we have

$$\psi(x, t) = \sum_k a(k) \sin(kx - \omega t). \tag{1.3}$$

If the train persists over a large distance, only a few interfering sine waves are needed, each with nearly the same wave number. To build a shorter wave packet, we require more coefficients and a wider range in wave numbers. The spread in wave number, Δk, relates to the spread in position, Δx, roughly by

$$\Delta x = \frac{1}{\Delta k}. \tag{1.4}$$

That is, we need a spread of at least Δk to reduce the position to Δx. With de Broglie's identification of p_x with $\hbar k$ [Chapter 3, (1.26)] we have

$$\Delta x \, \Delta p_x \geq \hbar. \tag{1.5}$$

Similarly, a purely sinusoidal electrical signal,

$$\psi(t) = \sin(\omega_0 t), \tag{1.6}$$

must persist indefinitely. Termination of the signal introduces a superposition of sine terms with slightly different frequencies (recall Section 1.6*C*):

$$\psi(t) = \sum_\omega a(\omega) \sin(\omega t). \tag{1.7}$$

The more sharply we cut off the signal, the greater the frequency spread

$\Delta\omega$ introduced in the series. The spread in angular frequency is at least as great as the reciprocal of the time interval Δt over which the signal ceases

$$\Delta\omega \geq \frac{1}{\Delta t}. \tag{1.8}$$

With the identification $E = \hbar\omega$, we get

$$\Delta E\, \Delta t \geq \hbar. \tag{1.9}$$

Since $\hbar$ is so small (10^{-27} erg-sec), the uncertainty becomes important only for phenomena on an atomic scale.

For example, if we measure to within 1 μ (10^{-4} cm) the position of a dust particle weighing 0.1 μg, the Heisenberg uncertainty in velocity from (1.1) is only 10^{-14} cm/sec, far less than we can measure in practice. On the other hand, when we determine that an electron ($\sim 10^{-27}$ g) moves within an atomic diameter ($\sim 10^{-8}$ cm), the velocity must be uncertain by $\sim 10^8$ cm/sec. Thus we cannot verify any prediction of electron velocity to better than 10^8 cm/sec (an uncertainty of roughly 0.3% the velocity of light) and still know that the electron remains within the atom.

As another example, knowledge of the energy of an atomic transition frequency to only 0.1% gives an uncertainty of $\sim 10^{-13}$ erg in energy, so that we might hope to specify the time of the transition within 10^{-14} sec. During this interval the electron will make some 100 revolutions around the nucleus. It should be clear that we cannot expect to verify experimentally any conjectures or predictions of *precisely when*, on an atomic scale, an electron radiates energy during a transition.

The uncertainty principle, in either (1.1) or (1.9), is essentially a statement that "particles," such as electrons, protons, and even atoms, possess certain attributes of waves. These wave-like properties are experimentally well established. In the previous chapter this wave nature provided a foundation for a wave-mechanical description of particles. Since the uncertainty principle offers a succinct statement of the wave-like properties of matter, it enables us to construct a general formulation of dynamics on an atomic scale. In the next section we review several formulations of dynamics on the macroscopic scale, to appreciate how we might modify those approaches.

REFERENCE

[1] W. Heisenberg, *Z. Physik* **43,** 172 (1927).

4.2 MACROSCOPIC DYNAMICS

What are the essential questions posed by a problem in macroscopic dynamics? Typically, we wish to know the position of a particle at any moment, under the influence of a specified force. Knowing the trajectory, we then can calculate the velocity and the potential and kinetic energies, for all times. For a rigid body we must also know how the body twists and turns with time. To meet these requirements, our *formulation of dynamics* relates the coordinates of the body to the forces acting on it through a set of equations (physical laws). The problem reduces to finding the solution of these equations.

For example, in the *Newtonian formulation* the equation of motion for a particle of constant mass, m, relates acceleration $\mathbf{a}$ to force $\mathbf{F}$:

$$m\mathbf{a} = m\frac{d^2}{dt^2}\mathbf{r} = \mathbf{F}(\mathbf{r}, \mathbf{v}, t). \tag{2.1}$$

Simple cases of this equation can be solved for $\mathbf{r}(t)$ by direct integration. But (2.1) is a vector equation, which represents three separate equations, one in each component, say x, y, and z or r, θ, and ϕ. Therefore we may find direct integration too involved when the force depends on several coordinates. The Newtonian formulation becomes even less tractable when several particles interact.

The *Lagrangian* and *Hamiltonian formulations* provide a framework for handling such systems of particles by introducing *generalized coordinates*, q_i, tailored to the particular system. We express the position of the ith particle, $\mathbf{r}_i$, in terms of some set of coordinates q_i:

$$\mathbf{r}_i = \mathbf{r}_i(q_1, q_2, \ldots, q_r, t). \tag{2.2}$$

These may be distances, angles, areas, or any other convenient coordinate. For n particles, we require $3n$ generalized coordinates. Next we express the kinetic energy T and potential energy V in these generalized coordinates:

$$T = \sum_i \tfrac{1}{2}m_i\dot{\mathbf{r}}_i^2 = T(q_1, q_2, \ldots, t) \tag{2.3}$$

$$V = V(q_1, \ldots).$$

The potential energy is defined by the force on the ith particle,

$$\mathbf{F}_i = -\,\mathbf{grad}_i\, V = -\nabla_i V. \tag{2.4}$$

Since, in (2.3), we assume the masses m_i to be fixed, they do not appear explicitly as variable arguments of T or V. The Lagrangian formulation is limited to systems in which the forces are derivable from a potential, as in (2.4), and to certain other systems, for which the potential depends on velocity. All of the systems we shall consider fall into these classes. Defining a function $\mathcal{L}(q, \dot{q}, t)$, the *Lagrangian*, by

$$\mathcal{L} \equiv T - V, \tag{2.5}$$

we can express Newton's equation of motion (2.1) as a set of equations for the generalized coordinates

$$\frac{d}{dt}\frac{\partial \mathcal{L}}{\partial \dot{q}_i} = \frac{\partial \mathcal{L}}{\partial q_i}, \qquad i = 1, \ldots, n. \tag{2.6}$$

Thus in the *Lagrangian formulation* we first select a set of coordinates suitable to the particular system under study, then solve *Lagrange's equations* (2.6), and finally determine the positions of the particles. We often find out all we wish to know about a system from the solution of (2.6), without going on to calculate the positions of the particles, since we may be more interested in finding the general nature of motion than in following the particles in detail.

As we progress to more complicated systems, with numerous interacting particles, Lagrange's equations may become impossibly involved, even for solution on a computer. The complicated form of the equations of motion (2.6) and the intricate relation of the generalized coordinates to particle position in (2.2) force us to abandon hope of following an individual particle in its course. We must content ourselves with knowledge of average properties of the motion. Certain meaningful constants may characterize this complicated motion, just as period, line of nodes, and orbital inclination characterize planetary motion. Now Lagrange's equations (2.6) are of the second order. With, say, n generalized coordinates, we have $2n$ integration constants at our disposal. In simple cases the known initial values of $2n$ variables q_i and $\dot{q}_i$ might fix the $2n$ constants. In the sense of an initial-value problem we may say we have $2n$ variables q_i and $\dot{q}_i$ to specify. But we are not usually interested in specifying the integration constants as initial values. Can we find a formulation of dynamics in which the constants have special significance?

The *Hamiltonian formulation* satisfies this request; it introduces generalized momenta p_i, defined as

$$p_i \equiv \frac{\partial \mathcal{L}(q_i, \dot{q}_i, t)}{\partial \dot{q}_i}, \tag{2.7}$$

and the *Hamiltonian* $\mathcal{H}(p, q, t)$, defined as

$$\mathcal{H}(p, q, t) \equiv \sum_i \dot{q}_i p_i - \mathcal{L}(q, \dot{q}, t). \tag{2.8}$$

In this formulation we regard the q_i and p_i as the basic variables, and we express $\mathcal{H}$, T, and V as functions of q and p rather than of q and $\dot{q}$. When V is independent of time, then

$$\mathcal{H}(p, q, t) = T(p, q, t) + V(p, q), \tag{2.9}$$

and $\mathcal{H}$ is a constant, the total energy of the system. We denote the value of this constant by E. Then the relation

$$\mathcal{H}(p, q, t) = E \tag{2.10}$$

expresses conservation of energy. Hamilton's *canonical equations*, derived from (2.7) and (2.8), express the motion of the system:

$$\dot{q}_i = \frac{\partial \mathcal{H}}{\partial p_i}, \tag{2.11a}$$

$$-\dot{p}_i = \frac{\partial \mathcal{H}}{\partial q_i}. \tag{2.11b}$$

The great importance of these equations becomes evident from this observation: if the energy of a system does not depend on one of the coordinates q_i, the *canonically conjugate momentum* p_i remains constant with time:

$$-\dot{p}_i = \frac{\partial \mathcal{H}}{\partial q_i} = 0 \tag{2.12}$$

$$p_i = \text{const.}$$

For example, when the potential energy does not depend on the x coordinate, there is no force in the x direction,

$$F_x = -\frac{\partial V}{\partial x} = 0, \tag{2.13}$$

and the x component of momentum,

$$p_x = m\dot{x}, \tag{2.14}$$

remains constant.

As another example, take the polar angle ϕ as a generalized coordinate for a free particle ($V = 0$). The conjugate momentum is then the angular momentum p_ϕ:

$$p_\phi = \frac{\partial \mathcal{L}}{\partial \phi} = \frac{\partial}{\partial \phi}\left(\frac{m\dot{r}}{2} + \frac{mr\dot{\phi}}{2}\right) = mr^2\dot{\phi}; \tag{2.15}$$

since $\partial \mathcal{H}/\partial \phi = 0$, p_ϕ is constant with time. This is just a restatement of the principle that angular momentum is constant when no torque (the generalized force in this instance) acts.

Using the Hamiltonian formulation, we can exploit the symmetries in any particular system to find constants of the motion, such as energy, momentum, angular momentum, period of rotation, etc. These quantities tell us a great deal about the behavior of a system of particles over a period of time, just as Kepler's laws tell us a great deal about planetary motion. As we saw in the last section, the uncertainty principle limits the knowledge we can obtain experimentally about motion on a microscopic scale. There is little point in attempting to include in a system of microscopic dynamics, details of motion that we can never verify or observe. The Hamiltonian formulation provides an excellent framework for microscopic dynamics, for it enables us to deal with constants of motion rather than with the detailed paths of the individual particles. These constants—energy, momenta, and angular momenta—replace positions as the key dynamical quantities. We must abandon our intuitive concrete picture of the paths of particles and consider an alternative abstract notion of *constants of motion.* In the next section we shall see how to construct such a description and how the uncertainty principle affects our formulation.

4.3 STATES AND OBSERVABLES

How do we conveniently describe a physical *system*, such as an electron, a satellite, a bottle of gas, or an electrical circuit? In every case we look for a set of parameters that we can measure, perhaps as a function of time. For a satellite we might measure position (the coordinates are the parameters), whereas for an electrical circuit a set of voltages or currents describes the system.

In cases for which we cannot measure trajectories of individual particles because of statistical impracticality or quantum-mechanical impossibilities, we might measure temperature, pressure, mean velocities, or currents. P. A. M. Dirac introduced [1] the name *observables* for quantities susceptible of experimental determination. Measurement of an observable yields a *number* that characterizes the investigated system under certain conditions. Extending Dirac's usage slightly, we might say that any physical system can be characterized by a set of *observables.* For the sake of efficiency, we often want measurements of different observables to provide different information about the system. The observables thus should be *independent.* (Temperature and mean molecular speed of a gas are not independent; temperature and pressure are.) Furthermore, our picture of the system, as obtained from these measurements, should be as complete as possible. In other words, the observables should form a *complete* set, in the sense that no further measurement can yield new information. For a perfect gas, the variables pressure, volume, and number of atoms, or pressure, entropy, and number of atoms provide a complete description. The list of values for some complete set of observables specifies the *state* of the system. The notion of state, in the sense of specifying the condition of a physical system, extends beyond the disciplines of quantum mechanics and statistical mechanics.

Properly chosen observables provide all the information possible about a system. Additional measurements either verify known properties or they alter and disrupt the state of the system. We can organize this list of values of observables in a very useful way. Imagine each observable to be a coordinate axis in a space of many dimensions. The measured value of a particular observable we represent by a distance along the appropriate coordinate axis; a point in this space represents a *configuration* of the system, a set of values for the observables. In this way one can relate the study of a physical system to the study of points in an abstract many-dimensional space. This relationship forms the foundation of modern quantum mechanics, and motivates the discussion of abstract vector spaces in the following sections. Each point in the abstract space may be considered as the head of a vector, directed away from the origin. We can thus express relationships between points in abstract space (representing relationships between different physical states) in the language of vector calculus, and apply the mathematics of vectors to the study of physical systems.

REFERENCE

[1] P. A. M. Dirac, *The Principles of Quantum Mechanics*, Oxford University Press, New York (1958), 4th ed.

4.4 ABSTRACT VECTOR SPACES

One usually defines the vectors encountered in elementary physics—force, momentum, velocity, etc.—as "objects" with two "parts"; *length* or *magnitude*, and *direction*. Based on this definition, vector calculus is a set of rules governing the following five consequent properties of vectors: [1, 2, 3, 4, 5].

Property I. Vectors may be added together.

Property II. Vectors may be multiplied by numbers.

Property III. Two vectors have a scalar (or dot or inner) product.

Property IV. Vectors can be specified by components along coordinate axes.

(Property V). Two vectors have a vector [or cross or outer] product.

(Property V, which we include for completeness, is not required for the mathematical structure of a vector space.) Alternatively, the four properties I–IV by themselves, when stated more precisely, provide a definition for "abstract" vectors and the "space" in which they exist. *An "abstract vector space" is a collection of objects, called vectors, along with a number system, called scalars, that satisfy properties I through IV.* We shall follow the convention of indicating vectors by **bold face** Roman letters, such as **A** or **e**, and scalars by *italic* letters, usually lower case, such as a, b, or c. Let us examine these properties.

Property I. *Vectors may be added together.* This addition produces another vector which does not depend on the order in which we added the vectors together. We include the possibility of a vector of zero length, **0**, called the *null vector*. Using **0** we can define subtraction as the inverse to addition. Stated mathematically, *the operation of vector addition is*

commutative $$\mathbf{A} + \mathbf{B} = \mathbf{B} + \mathbf{A} = \mathbf{C} \tag{Ia}$$

and associative $$(\mathbf{A} + \mathbf{B}) + \mathbf{C} = \mathbf{A} + (\mathbf{B} + \mathbf{C}) \tag{Ib}$$

and a null vector exists $$\mathbf{A} + \mathbf{0} = \mathbf{A} \tag{Ic}$$

$$\mathbf{A} + (-\mathbf{A}) = \mathbf{0}. \tag{Id}$$

In the case of ordinary vectors in two dimensions we can picture the commutative and associative requirements of vector addition:

$$\mathbf{A} + \mathbf{B} = \mathbf{B} + \mathbf{A} \qquad (\mathbf{A} + \mathbf{B}) + \mathbf{C} = \mathbf{A} + (\mathbf{B} + \mathbf{C})$$

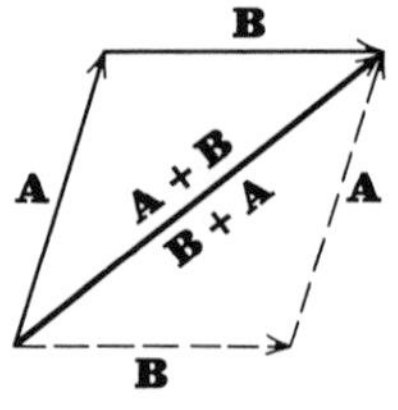

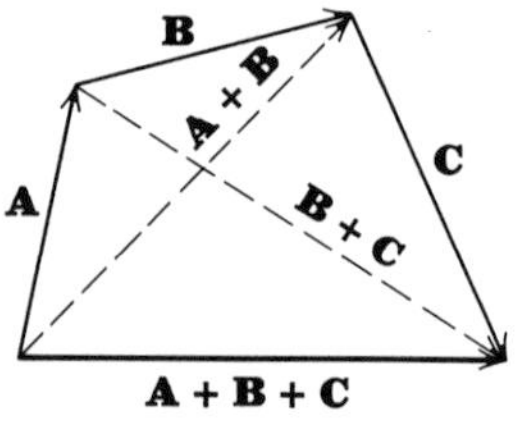

Property II. *Vectors may be multiplied by numbers.* The numbers (scalars) may be real or complex, and the result of this multiplication is another vector, either real or complex. (To be mathematically precise, the "numbers" need only be a *field*. Examples of fields are real numbers, rational numbers, complex numbers, and numbers of the form $a + b\sqrt{2}$ with a and b rational.) *This multiplication is*

distributive

$$(a + b)\mathbf{A} = a\mathbf{A} + b\mathbf{A} \tag{IIa}$$

$$a(\mathbf{A} + \mathbf{B}) = a\mathbf{A} + a\mathbf{B} \tag{IIb}$$

and associative

$$(ab)\mathbf{A} = a(b\mathbf{A}) \tag{IIc}$$

with the particular cases of multiplication by

$$\text{zero} \qquad 0\mathbf{A} = \mathbf{0}$$

$$\text{and unity} \qquad 1\mathbf{A} = \mathbf{A},$$

and division is possible. (Division by zero is excluded.) When dealing with complex scalars and complex vectors, we shall indicate complex conjugation (replacement of $i = \sqrt{-1}$ by $-i$) with an asterisk:

$$\text{if} \qquad c = a + ib \qquad \mathbf{C} = \mathbf{A} + i\mathbf{B}$$

$$\text{then} \qquad c^* = a - ib \qquad \mathbf{C}^* = \mathbf{A} - i\mathbf{B}.$$

when a, b, $\mathbf{A}$, and $\mathbf{B}$ are real.

Property III. *Two vectors have a scalar product*, sometimes called "dot product" or "inner product," which is a number (possibly complex). The scalar product is denoted by various authors as $\mathbf{A}\cdot\mathbf{B}$, $(\mathbf{A}, \mathbf{B})$, $(\mathbf{A}\ \mathbf{B})$, or $\langle\mathbf{A}|\mathbf{B}\rangle$. We shall follow Dirac and adopt the last notation.

For vectors consisting of directed line segments, the scalar product $\langle\mathbf{A}|\mathbf{B}\rangle$ is the magnitude of $\mathbf{A}$ times the magnitude of $\mathbf{B}$ times the cosine of the angle θ_{AB} between $\mathbf{A}$ and $\mathbf{B}$:

$$\langle\mathbf{A}|\mathbf{B}\rangle = AB\cos\theta_{AB} = AB\cos\theta_{BA} = \langle\mathbf{B}|\mathbf{A}\rangle. \tag{4.1}$$

We readily verify that this number, often referred to as the *projection* of $\mathbf{A}$ on $\mathbf{B}$ (or $\mathbf{B}$ on $\mathbf{A}$) has the following properties:

$$\text{symmetric:} \qquad \langle\mathbf{A}|\mathbf{B}\rangle = \langle\mathbf{B}|\mathbf{A}\rangle \tag{4.2}$$

$$\text{distributive:} \qquad \langle a\mathbf{A} + b\mathbf{B}|\mathbf{C}\rangle = a\langle\mathbf{A}|\mathbf{C}\rangle + b\langle\mathbf{B}|\mathbf{C}\rangle. \tag{4.3}$$

These two equations are all we need to define the scalar product, as long as we deal with only real numbers; the scalar product must then be a real number. However, when we include complex numbers in our number system, we need to modify our definitions slightly. We shall require that *the scalar product of two abstract vectors must satisfy the conditions*

$$\langle\mathbf{A}|\mathbf{B}\rangle^* = \langle\mathbf{B}|\mathbf{A}\rangle \tag{IIIa}$$

$$\langle a\mathbf{A} + b\mathbf{B}|\mathbf{C}\rangle = a^*\langle\mathbf{A}|\mathbf{C}\rangle + b^*\langle\mathbf{B}|\mathbf{C}\rangle \tag{IIIb}$$

$$\langle\mathbf{A}|\mathbf{A}\rangle = 0 \qquad \text{only if} \qquad \mathbf{A} = 0. \tag{IIIc}$$

The scalar product embodies the notion of length and angle, or, more generally speaking, the *metric* of the space. Conventionally the scalar product of any vector with itself is called the *norm* of the vector:

$$\text{norm } \mathbf{A} = \langle\mathbf{A}|\mathbf{A}\rangle = |A|^2. \tag{4.4}$$

From the definition of scalar product, the norm must be a real number. We then define the length or magnitude of **A** as the positive square root of the norm:

$$\text{length } \mathbf{A} \equiv A = +\sqrt{A^2} = +\sqrt{\langle\mathbf{A}|\mathbf{A}\rangle}. \tag{4.5}$$

We can similarly generalize (4.1) and define the cosine of the angle between two vectors by

$$\cos(\mathbf{A}, \mathbf{B}) \equiv \frac{\langle\mathbf{A}|\mathbf{B}\rangle}{AB} = \frac{\langle\mathbf{A}|\mathbf{B}\rangle}{\sqrt{\langle\mathbf{A}|\mathbf{A}\rangle\langle\mathbf{B}|\mathbf{B}\rangle}}; \tag{4.6}$$

when $\langle\mathbf{A}|\mathbf{B}\rangle = 0$ the vectors are *orthogonal;* when $\langle\mathbf{A}|\mathbf{B}\rangle = |A| \times |B|$ the vectors are parallel. The *distance* between the points at the terminations of vectors **A** and **B** is just the length of the vector $\mathbf{A} - \mathbf{B}$, or $|\mathbf{A} - \mathbf{B}|$. Several properties of "length" in abstract space follow directly from the defining properties of the scalar product: the *Cauchy–Schwarz inequality,*

$$|A|^2 \times |B|^2 \leq |\langle\mathbf{A}|\mathbf{B}\rangle|^2$$

and the *triangle inequality*

$$|\mathbf{A}| + |\mathbf{B}| \geq |\mathbf{A} + \mathbf{B}|.$$

From an arbitrary vector, **A**, we can form a vector $\mathbf{e}_A$ of unit length pointing along **A** by dividing **A** by its length (called *normalizing* **A**):

$$\mathbf{e}_A = \frac{\mathbf{A}}{\sqrt{\langle\mathbf{A}|\mathbf{A}\rangle}} = \frac{\mathbf{A}}{\sqrt{|A|^2}}. \tag{4.7}$$

This vector has unit length since

$$\langle\mathbf{e}_A|\mathbf{e}_A\rangle = \frac{\langle\mathbf{A}|\mathbf{A}\rangle}{|A|^2} = 1 \tag{4.8}$$

and it has the direction of **A** since it makes the same angle with any arbitrary vector **B** as does **A**:

$$\cos(\mathbf{B}, \mathbf{e}_A) = \frac{\langle\mathbf{B}|\mathbf{e}_A\rangle}{B} = \frac{\langle\mathbf{B}|\mathbf{A}\rangle}{BA} = \cos(\mathbf{B}, \mathbf{A}). \tag{4.9}$$

Throughout this book we reserve the letter **e** for vectors of unit length, and we designate the direction of **e** by a subscript. The scalar product of any vector **B** with $\mathbf{e}_A$ is the *projection* of **B** on **A** or the component of **B** along **A**.

As an example, consider the space composed of continuous functions of x over the interval $0 \le x \le 1$, so that $\mathbf{A} \equiv A(x)$ and $\mathbf{B} \equiv B(x)$. Then for real functions, the integral

$$\int_0^1 A(x)B(x)\,dx$$

or, for complex functions, the integral

$$\int_0^1 A^*(x)B(x)\,dx$$

has all the properties we require for the scalar product $\langle \mathbf{A} | \mathbf{B} \rangle$, and we can define such an integral to be the scalar product. The norm in this function space is

$$\text{norm } \mathbf{A} = \int_0^1 |A(x)|^2\,dx. \tag{4.10}$$

Strictly speaking, the allowable functions in the space must be not only continuous, but also *square integrable* as well, i.e., the integral of (4.10) must exist. *Function spaces*, L^p, are sometimes defined in mathematical analysis as linear spaces, with functions of x as the vectors, for which the norm given by

$$\int |f(x)|^p\,dx$$

exists. Such spaces have properties (I) and (II) (and IV) but there need be no scalar product defined between each two vectors constituting the space.

Property IV. *Vectors can be specified by components along coordinate axes.* For line segments in two dimensions we can write an arbitrary vector **A** as the sum of a vector in the x direction, $\mathbf{a}_x$, and a vector in the y direction, $\mathbf{a}_y$:

$$\mathbf{A} = \mathbf{a}_x + \mathbf{a}_y = A_x\mathbf{e}_x + A_y\mathbf{e}_y, \tag{4.11}$$

where $A_x = \langle \mathbf{A} | \mathbf{e}_x \rangle$ and $A_y = \langle \mathbf{A} | \mathbf{e}_y \rangle$ are the components along the coordinate axes. We say that **A** has been *resolved into components* along x and y. We could just as well resolve **A** into a component along the x axis and a component along an axis b at an angle of, say, 75° to the x axis:

$$\mathbf{A} = \mathbf{a}_x + \mathbf{a}_b = A_x\mathbf{e}_x + A_b\mathbf{e}_b. \tag{4.12}$$

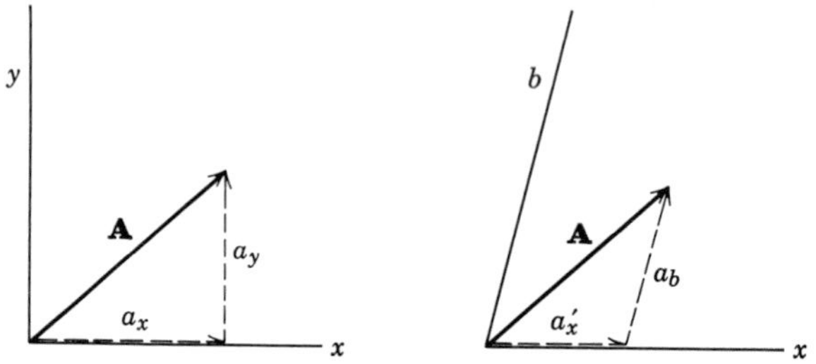

The x, y coordinates are orthogonal coordinates,

$$\langle \mathbf{e}_x | \mathbf{e}_y \rangle = 0,$$

whereas the x, b coordinates are *skew* coordinates,

$$\langle \mathbf{e}_x | \mathbf{e}_b \rangle = \cos 75°.$$

Note that the component of **A** along x depends on whether the second axis is y or b. We are at liberty to choose any two *independent* vectors as our coordinate vectors; *two* vectors because this is a two-dimensional space, and "independent" meaning that the vectors are not both in the same direction (they are not multiples of each other), although they need not be perpendicular.

Now we extend these notions to abstract vector spaces. Suppose we have a collection of vectors $\mathbf{a}_1, \mathbf{a}_2, \mathbf{a}_3, \ldots, \mathbf{a}_n$. These will be called *independent* if no one of them can be formed from some linear combination of the others, and *dependent* if any of them can be formed from the others. That is, they are dependent if a set of numbers $\{c_i\}$ exists such that

$$c_1\mathbf{a}_1 + c_2\mathbf{a}_2 + c_3\mathbf{a}_3 + \cdots + c_n\mathbf{a}_n = \mathbf{0}, \tag{4.13}$$

and they are independent if no such set of numbers exists (other than $c_1 = c_2 = c_3 = \cdots = c_n = 0$). If we can select n independent vectors from our collection and no more, we have an *n-dimensional space*, and these n vectors form what is called a *basis* for the space. The n basis vectors may be selected any way we choose, just so long as they are linearly independent. In fact, if we have a basis $\mathbf{a}_1, \ldots, \mathbf{a}_n$, any independent linear combinations of these will also provide a basis for the same space.

Since, by definition, we can have only n independent vectors, say $\mathbf{a}_1, \ldots, \mathbf{a}_n$, in an n-dimensional space, we know that any vector in the space must either be one of the vectors $\mathbf{a}_i$ or it must be some linear combination of them:

$$\mathbf{A} = \sum_{i=1}^{n} c_i\mathbf{a}_i. \tag{4.14}$$

This is true because we know that the set $\mathbf{a}_1, \ldots, \mathbf{a}_n$, $\mathbf{A}$ must be *dependent;* in other words, there exists a set of numbers $c_1, \ldots, c_n$ such that

$$c_1\mathbf{a}_1 + c_2\mathbf{a}_2 + c_3\mathbf{a}_3 + \cdots + c_n\mathbf{a}_n + \mathbf{A} = 0. \tag{4.15}$$

We can extend the notion of vector spaces from spaces with a finite number of dimensions, n, and n basis vectors, to spaces with an infinite number of dimensions and an infinite number of basis vectors. We must then require as a condition on the space that there exist a *complete* basis. That is, there must exist an infinite set of basis vectors $\{\mathbf{a}_i\}$, with which we can expand any vector:

$$\mathbf{A} = \sum_{i=1}^{\infty} c_i\mathbf{a}_i. \tag{4.16}$$

The distinction between (4.14) and (4.16) is important. For a finite-dimensional space, the dimension of the space, n, is defined in terms of the number of possible independent vectors, so that $n + 1$ vectors *must* be dependent; (4.13) just expresses this fact. On the other hand, we must *require* that a complete basis exist as part of our definition of an infinite-dimensional space. Such spaces are sometimes called *Hilbert spaces.* [Some authors reserve the term Hilbert space for a *denumerably* infinite dimensional space of functions, with the scalar product of (4.23).]

When we work with the components, operations with vectors become simple arithmetical operations. For example, the x component of the sum of several two-dimensional vectors is just the sum of the individual components:

$$\begin{aligned} \mathbf{A} &= A_x\mathbf{e}_x + A_y\mathbf{e}_y \\ \mathbf{B} &= B_x\mathbf{e}_x + B_y\mathbf{e}_y \\ (\mathbf{A} + \mathbf{B}) &= (A_x + B_x)\mathbf{e}_x + (A_y + B_y)\mathbf{e}_y. \end{aligned} \tag{4.17}$$

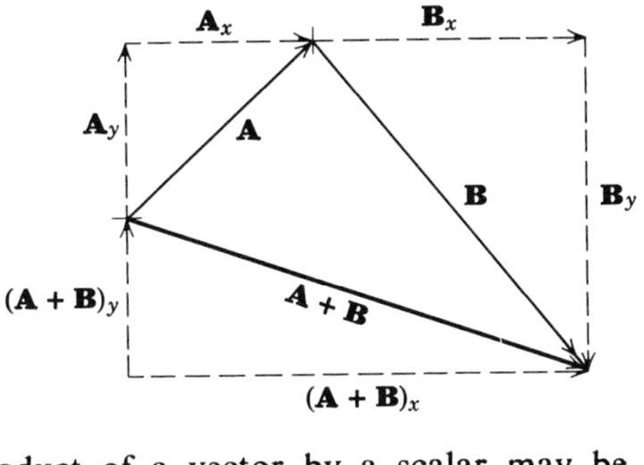

Similarly, the product of a vector by a scalar may be found from the components:

$$cA = (cA_x)e_x + (cA_y)e_y. \tag{4.18}$$

Using the properties of the vectors in (4.17), we obtain the scalar product

$$\langle \mathbf{A} | \mathbf{B} \rangle = A_x B_x + A_y B_y. \tag{4.19}$$

As a special case we obtain the Pythagorean theorem,

$$\langle \mathbf{A} | \mathbf{A} \rangle = A^2 = A_x^2 + A_y^2. \tag{4.20}$$

The components of a vector in a particular basis completely characterize the vector. From them we can determine lengths, angles, and any other desired property of a vector. Indeed, vectors are often *defined* as an ordered set of numbers, the vector components, satisfying equations of the form

$$(A_1, A_2, \ldots, A_n) + (B_1, B_2, \ldots, B_n) = (A_1 + B_1, A_2 + B_2, \ldots, A_n + B_n), \tag{4.21}$$

$$c(A_1, A_2, \ldots, A_n) = (cA_1, cA_2, \ldots, cA_n), \tag{4.22}$$

$$\langle A_1, A_2, \ldots, A_n | B_1, B_2, \ldots, B_n \rangle = A_1B_1 + A_2B_2 + \cdots + A_nB_n, \tag{4.23}$$

which express properties I, II, and III. This manner of defining vectors implies that we have selected a particular basis for the components, such as rectangular coordinates. On the other hand, when we define vectors through their properties I, II, III, etc., we do not single out any particular basis or coordinate system. Each viewpoint is useful, and the two are equivalent. For example, we can write physical relationships concisely with a vector equation, such as

$$\mathbf{F} = m\mathbf{a},$$

but when we want numerical results we find it easier to deal with a set of three equations relating components, such as

$$F_x = ma_x \qquad \mathbf{F} = F_x\mathbf{e}_x + F_y\mathbf{e}_y + F_z\mathbf{e}_z$$
$$F_y = ma_y \qquad \mathbf{a} = a_x\mathbf{e}_x + a_y\mathbf{e}_y + a_z\mathbf{e}_z$$
$$F_z = ma_z,$$

or perhaps

$$F_r = ma_r \qquad \mathbf{F} = F_r\mathbf{e}_r + F_\theta\mathbf{e}_\theta + F_\phi\mathbf{e}_\phi$$
$$F_\theta = ma_\theta \qquad \mathbf{a} = a_r\mathbf{e}_r + a_\theta\mathbf{e}_\theta + a_\phi\mathbf{e}_\phi$$
$$F_\phi = ma_\phi.$$

We would select as basis vectors those most appropriate to our particular problem. The problem is usually simplified if we choose perpendicular axes (or, more generally, orthogonal axes). However, this is not necessary.

REFERENCES

[1] J. von Neumann, *Mathematical Foundations of Quantum Mechanics*, Princeton University Press, Princeton, New Jersey (1955).

[2] B. Friedman, *Principles and Techniques of Applied Mathematics*, Wiley, New York (1956).

[3] V. Rojansky, *Introductory Quantum Mechanics*, Prentice-Hall, Englewood Cliffs, New Jersey (1942).

[4] G. Birkhoff and S. MacLane, *A Survey of Modern Algebra*, Macmillan, New York (1953).

[5] P. R. Halmos, *Finite Dimensional Vector Spaces*, Princeton University Press, Princeton, New Jersey (1942).

4.5 ORTHONORMAL BASIS VECTORS: EXAMPLES

Because we are at liberty to choose our basis vectors in any way, as long as they are all independent, in general our choice will result in basis vectors $\mathbf{a}_1, \mathbf{a}_2, \ldots, \mathbf{a}_n$ of various lengths and forming various angles with one another. The array of values

$$g_{ij} = \langle \mathbf{a}_i | \mathbf{a}_j \rangle,$$

called the *metric tensor* for the basis $\mathbf{a}$, describes the geometry of the space; it tells us what the gridwork of coordinates looks like. For many purposes a set of mutually orthogonal unit vectors $\mathbf{e}_1, \mathbf{e}_2, \ldots, \mathbf{e}_n$, for which

$$\langle \mathbf{e}_i | \mathbf{e}_i \rangle = 1 \quad \text{and} \quad \langle \mathbf{e}_i | \mathbf{e}_j \rangle = 0,$$

provides a more useful basis.

The Kronecker delta symbol, δ_{ij}, defined as unity when $i = j$ and zero otherwise, provides a concise statement that the $\mathbf{e}$ vectors are orthogonal and normalized (orthonormal):

$$\langle \mathbf{e}_i | \mathbf{e}_j \rangle = \delta_{ij} \qquad \begin{aligned} \delta_{ij} &= 1, \quad i = j \\ \delta_{ij} &= 0, \quad i \neq j. \end{aligned}$$

Starting with the basis $\mathbf{a}_1, \mathbf{a}_2, \ldots, \mathbf{a}_n$, we can always obtain an orthonormal basis $\mathbf{e}_1, \mathbf{e}_2, \ldots, \mathbf{e}_n$ by following the *Schmidt orthogonalization procedure* that follows. For the first vector $\mathbf{e}_1$, take any of the $\mathbf{a}$ vectors, say $\mathbf{a}_1$. We normalize it with the factor N_1:

$$\mathbf{e}_1 = N_1 \mathbf{a}_1,$$

where N_1^2 satisfies

$$\langle \mathbf{e}_1 | \mathbf{e}_1 \rangle = 1 = N_1^2 \langle \mathbf{a}_1 | \mathbf{a}_1 \rangle = N_1^2 g_{11}.$$

Only the square of N_1 is determined by normalization; we can include an arbitrary phase, $e^{i\phi}$, in the normalization, $e^{2\phi} N_1$, if we choose. For convenience we take $\phi = 0$, so that N_1 is positive and real:

$$N_1 = +\frac{1}{\sqrt{g_{11}}}.$$

Next select a second vector, say $\mathbf{a}_2$, and remove from it (*project out*) the part that lies along $\mathbf{e}_1$. The result will be orthogonal to $\mathbf{e}_1$, and we can normalize with a factor N_2:

$$\mathbf{e} = N_2(\mathbf{a}_2 - c_1 \mathbf{e}_1).$$

We determine c_1 from

$$\langle \mathbf{e}_1 | \mathbf{e}_2 \rangle = 0 = \langle \mathbf{e}_1 | \mathbf{a}_2 \rangle - c_1 \cdot 1,$$

and the normalization from

$$\langle \mathbf{e}_2 | \mathbf{e}_2 \rangle = 1 = |N_2|^2 \langle \mathbf{a}_2 - c_1 \mathbf{e}_1 | \mathbf{a}_2 - c_1 \mathbf{e}_1 \rangle$$

and the convention that N_2 be real and positive. The third vector $\mathbf{e}_3$ follows similarly by projecting out from, say, $\mathbf{a}_3$, the components along $\mathbf{e}_2$ and $\mathbf{e}_1$, and then normalizing:

$$\mathbf{e}_3 = N_3(\mathbf{a}_3 - c_1' \mathbf{e}_1 - c_2' \mathbf{e}_2).$$

The components c_1' and c_2' follow from

$$\langle \mathbf{e}_1 | \mathbf{e}_3 \rangle = 0 = \langle \mathbf{e}_1 | \mathbf{a}_3 \rangle - c_1' \cdot 1 - 0$$

$$\langle \mathbf{e}_2 | \mathbf{e}_3 \rangle = 0 = \langle \mathbf{e}_2 | \mathbf{a}_3 \rangle - 0 - c_2' \cdot 1$$

and N_2 follows from

$$\langle \mathbf{e}_3 | \mathbf{e}_3 \rangle = 1$$

and our phase convention. Proceeding in this way, we eventually obtain the basis $\mathbf{e}_1, \mathbf{e}_2, \ldots, \mathbf{e}_n$. Clearly, the ordering of these vectors is immaterial.

A few examples may illustrate how several collections of objects, though apparently quite different, all share properties I through V, and thus may be viewed as vector spaces.

A. $\mathbf{R}_3$, Euclidean Space in Three Dimensions

This is just a formal name for the familiar three-dimensional space of directed line segments and real numbers, with the basis

$$\{\mathbf{e}_i\} = \mathbf{e}_x, \mathbf{e}_y, \mathbf{e}_z$$

and a scalar product

$$\langle \mathbf{A} | \mathbf{B} \rangle = \mathbf{A} \cdot \mathbf{B} = AB \cos \theta_{AB},$$

with orthonormal basis vectors

$$\langle \mathbf{e}_i | \mathbf{e}_j \rangle = \mathbf{e}_i \cdot \mathbf{e}_j = \delta_{ij},$$

so that when we express vectors as components,

$$\mathbf{A} = A_x \mathbf{e}_x + A_y \mathbf{e}_y + A_z \mathbf{e}_z,$$

the scalar product becomes

$$\langle \mathbf{A} | \mathbf{B} \rangle = A_x B_x + A_y B_y + A_z B_z,$$

and *length*, a special case of the scalar product, becomes

$$\text{length } \mathbf{A} = + \sqrt{\langle \mathbf{A} | \mathbf{A} \rangle} = (A_x{}^2 + A_y{}^2 + A_z{}^2)^{1/2}.$$

B. Complex n-Dimensional Space

The vectors composing this space may be viewed as directed line segments in n dimensions, or as ordered n-tuples of components; scalars are complex numbers, and the basis is

$$\{\mathbf{e}_i\} = \mathbf{e}_1, \mathbf{e}_2, \ldots, \mathbf{e}_n,$$

with the scalar product defined such that

$$\langle \mathbf{e}_i | \mathbf{e}_j \rangle = \delta_{ij}.$$

The scalar product, now a complex number, must satisfy

$$\langle a\mathbf{A} | b\mathbf{B} \rangle = a^* b \langle \mathbf{A} | \mathbf{B} \rangle.$$

Since any two vectors **A** and **B** have the expansions

$$\mathbf{A} = \sum_{i=1}^{n} A_i \mathbf{e}_i$$

$$\mathbf{B} = \sum_{i=1}^{n} B_i \mathbf{e}_i,$$

we see that the scalar product will be

$$\langle \mathbf{A} | \mathbf{B} \rangle = \left\langle \sum_i A_i \mathbf{e}_i \middle| \sum_j B_j \mathbf{e}_j \right\rangle = \sum_i \sum_j A_i^* B_j^* \langle \mathbf{e}_i | \mathbf{e}_j \rangle = \sum_i A_i^* B_i.$$

Length becomes

$$\text{length } \mathbf{A} = (|A_1|^2 + |A_2|^2 + \cdots + |A_n|^2)^{1/2}.$$

We may also think of this space as a space R_n, with basis $\mathbf{e}_1, \mathbf{e}_2, \ldots, \mathbf{e}_n$ and a *dual* space R_n^* with basis $\mathbf{e}_1^*, \mathbf{e}_2^*, \ldots, \mathbf{e}_n^*$. The scalar product is then a (complex) number that depends on a vector $\mathbf{B}$ from R_n and a vector $\mathbf{A}^*$ from the dual space R_n^*:

$$\mathbf{A} = \sum_{i=1}^{n} A_i^* \mathbf{e}_i^*$$

$$\mathbf{B} = \sum_{i=1}^{n} B_i \mathbf{e}_i$$

$$\langle \mathbf{e}_i | \mathbf{e}_j \rangle = \mathbf{e}_i^* \cdot \mathbf{e}_j = \delta_{ij}$$

$$\langle \mathbf{A} | \mathbf{B} \rangle = \mathbf{A}^* \cdot \mathbf{B} = \sum_i A_i^* B_i.$$

C. Fourier Series

In a space where the vectors are well-behaved functions of x over the interval $0 \leq x \leq L$,

$$\mathbf{A} = A(x),$$

and scalars are complex numbers, we can take for a basis the normalized exponential functions $\exp(inx/L)/\sqrt{L}$,

$$\{\mathbf{e}_n\} = \frac{1}{\sqrt{L}} \exp\left(\frac{ix}{L}\right), \quad \frac{1}{\sqrt{L}} \exp\left(\frac{-ix}{L}\right), \quad \frac{1}{\sqrt{L}} \exp\left(\frac{2ix}{L}\right), \ldots$$

with n taking all positive and negative integral values. This is an example of an infinite-dimensional space (a Hilbert space), with a scalar product defined by

$$\langle \mathbf{A} | \mathbf{B} \rangle = \int_0^L A^*(x) B(x)\, dx$$

$$\langle \mathbf{e}_n | \mathbf{e}_m \rangle = \frac{1}{\sqrt{L}} \int_0^L \exp\left(\frac{-inx}{L}\right) \exp\left(\frac{+imx}{L}\right) dx = \delta_{mn}.$$

Any vector in the space (i.e., any well-behaved function) can be expanded (in a Fourier series)

$$\mathbf{A} = \sum_{n=-\infty}^{+\infty} A_n \mathbf{e}_n$$

or

$$A(x) = \sum_{n=-\infty}^{+\infty} A_n \frac{1}{\sqrt{L}} \exp\left(\frac{inx}{L}\right).$$

The expansion coefficients (Fourier components) are

$$A_n = \langle \mathbf{e}_n | \mathbf{A} \rangle = \int_0^L \frac{1}{\sqrt{L}} \exp\left(\frac{-inx}{L}\right) A(x)\, dx.$$

As with other abstract spaces, if we know the components A_n and B_n we can find the scalar product:

$$\langle \mathbf{A} | \mathbf{B} \rangle = \sum_n \sum_m A_n^* B_m \langle \mathbf{e}_n | \mathbf{e}_m \rangle = \sum_n A_n^* B_m$$

or

$$\int_0^L A^*(x) B(x)\, dx = \sum_n A_n^* B_n.$$

The length of **A** may be defined as

$$\text{length } \mathbf{A} = \left[\int |A(x)|^2\, dx\right]^{1/2} = \left(\sum_n |A_n|^2\right)^{1/2}.$$

D. Taylor Series—Legendre Polynomials

As another example of a space of functions, consider well-behaved real functions of x,

$$\mathbf{A} = A(x),$$

over the interval $-1 \le x \le +1$, with the real numbers as scalars, and take positive powers of x as a basis:

$$\{\mathbf{u}_n\} = x^0, x, x^2, \ldots, x^n, \ldots,$$

where $n \to \infty$. Define the scalar product as

$$\langle \mathbf{A} | \mathbf{B} \rangle = \int_{-1}^{+1} A(x) B(x)\, dx$$

(another example of a Hilbert space). We see that, because

$$\langle \mathbf{u}_n | \mathbf{u}_m \rangle = \int_{-1}^{+1} x^n x^m\, dx = \left.\frac{x^{n+m+1}}{n+m+1}\right|_{-1}^{+1} = 0 \qquad (n+m \text{ odd})$$

$$= \frac{2}{n+m+1} \qquad (n+m \text{ even}),$$

the basis functions are neither orthogonal (unless $n + m$ is odd) nor normalized. We can, however, apply the Schmidt process to the **u** basis and obtain a sequence of orthonormal basis functions $\mathbf{e}_1, \mathbf{e}_2, \ldots$. Each of these will be a linear combination of odd or even powers of x, that is, an odd or even polynomial $P_n(x)$ in x:

$$\{\mathbf{e}_n\} = P_0(x), P_1(x), P_2(x), \ldots.$$

(The P_n turn out to be normalized Legendre polynomials.) Any vector in the space can be expressed in the **u** basis, corresponding to a Taylor expansion:

$$\mathbf{A} = \sum_{n=0}^{\infty} a_n \mathbf{u}_n$$

or

$$A(x) = a_0 + a_1 x + a_2 x^2 + \cdots.$$

If we attempt to find the expansion coefficient, A_m, by taking the scalar product of **A** with u_m, we obtain the equation

$$\langle \mathbf{u}_m | \mathbf{A} \rangle = \sum_{n=0}^{\infty} a_n \langle \mathbf{u}_m | \mathbf{u}_n \rangle.$$

Though all the even- or odd-n terms are zero, we still have an infinite set of equations. It is far better to find the expansion coefficients in the usual way for a Taylor expansion, taking the derivative m times with respect to x, and setting $x = 0$:

$$\frac{1}{m!}\left[\frac{\partial^m}{\partial x^m} A(x)\right]_{x=0} = a_m.$$

On the other hand, when we use the orthonormal polynomials P_n as a basis, **e**, we have

$$\mathbf{A} = \sum_{n=0}^{\infty} a'_n \mathbf{e}_n$$

or

$$A(x) = \sum_{n=0}^{\infty} a'_n P_n(x)$$

and we *can* find a'_m by taking the scalar product:

$$\langle \mathbf{e}_m | \mathbf{A} \rangle = \int_{-1}^{+1} P_m(x) A(x)\, dx = a'_m.$$

In either expansion, we have

$$\text{length } \mathbf{A} = \left(\sum_n a_n^2\right)^{1/2} = \left[\sum_n (a'_n)^2\right]^{1/2}.$$

In practice, these expansions are useful primarily when only a few terms in the expansion contribute to the "length" of **A**.

4.6 TRANSFORMATIONS AND OPERATORS

In the remainder of this book we shall often deal implicitly with two notions of "space": "physical space," in which we observe atoms, particles, or some other system, and "abstract vector space," a mathematical construction representing coordinates of the physical system. A point in the abstract space represents a particular state of the physical system. Alteration of the physical system, perhaps with the passage of time, perhaps through change of temperature or other parameters, gives a new point in the abstract space. The new point represents the new state of the system. Thus any transformation or change of the physical system leads to a *transformation* of abstract space. Each point of abstract space is replaced by a new point (perhaps the same point) according to some rule. Conversely, a transformation in abstract space may correspond to a physically meaningful alteration of the physical system. In this way we can formulate the laws of nature—the rules that govern changes in physical systems—as transformations of abstract space. This procedure is a *mapping* of the abstract space onto itself.

We denote a general transformation T in abstract space by

$$\mathbf{A} \xrightarrow{T} \mathbf{A}', \tag{6.1}$$

meaning that under the rules of this particular transformation, the vector $\mathbf{A}$ is replaced by the vector $\mathbf{A}'$. We can say that the new vector $\mathbf{A}'$ was produced from the initial vector $\mathbf{A}$ by an operator $\mathcal{Q}$,

$$\mathbf{A}' = \mathcal{Q}\mathbf{A} \tag{6.2}$$

so that (6.1) becomes

$$\mathbf{A} \to \mathcal{Q}\mathbf{A}. \tag{6.3}$$

(Throughout this chapter script letters denote operators. In later sections we will not always adhere to this notation.) A special case, the *identity transformation*, replaces every vector by itself. The unit operator $\mathcal{I}$ gives this operation:

$$\mathbf{A} = \mathcal{I}\mathbf{A}.$$

A given transformation may have an *inverse* such that we can return from $\mathbf{A}'$ back to $\mathbf{A}$ by some rule. If so, the operator $\mathcal{Q}$ of (6.2) has an inverse, denoted by $\mathcal{Q}^{-1}$, which satisfies

$$\mathbf{A}' \to \mathbf{A} = \mathcal{Q}^{-1}\mathbf{A}'.$$

Thus if we transform from $\mathbf{A}$ to $\mathbf{A}'$ and back again,

$$\mathbf{A} \to \mathbf{A}' \to \mathbf{A},$$

we find the following conditions on the operator $\mathcal{Q}$ and its inverse:

$$\mathbf{A}' = \mathcal{Q}\mathbf{A}$$

$$\mathbf{A} = \mathcal{Q}^{-1}\mathbf{A}' = \mathcal{Q}^{-1}(\mathcal{Q}\mathbf{A}).$$

Because $\mathbf{A}$ is arbitrary, $\mathcal{Q}^{-1}$ must satisfy

$$\mathcal{Q}^{-1}\mathcal{Q} = \mathit{1}. \tag{6.4}$$

Similarly we could find

$$\mathcal{Q}\mathcal{Q}^{-1} = \mathit{1}.$$

Not every transformation possesses an inverse. For example, the transformation that carries all vectors into the origin,

$$\mathbf{A}' = \mathit{0}\mathbf{A} = \mathbf{0},$$

cannot be inverted to give a unique vector.

Two useful ways of constructing operators occur frequently. Consider the object A, a *dyadic*, formed by the juxtaposition two unit vectors $\mathsf{A} = \mathbf{e}_x\mathbf{e}_x$. By definition, the scalar product of this dyadic with a vector $\mathbf{B}$ is

$$\mathsf{A}\cdot\mathbf{B} = \mathbf{e}_x\mathbf{e}_x\cdot\mathbf{B} = \mathbf{e}_x\langle\mathbf{e}_x|\,\mathbf{B}\rangle = B_x\mathbf{e}_x; \tag{6.5}$$

that is, a vector of length B_x directed along $\mathbf{e}_x$. Thus a dyadic acts as an operator, transforming one vector into another. The operator $\mathcal{B}$, defined by

$$\mathbf{a} = \mathcal{B}\mathbf{b}, \tag{6.6}$$

can have the dyadic form $\mathbf{aa}/\langle\mathbf{a}|\mathbf{b}\rangle$ or $\mathbf{ab}/\langle\mathbf{b}|\mathbf{b}\rangle$. Sometimes it is suggestive to write the dyadic as $|\mathbf{a}\rangle\langle\mathbf{a}|$, to indicate that the scalar product is to be taken. When $\mathbf{a}$ and $\mathbf{b}$ are known by their components in a basis $\{\mathbf{e}\}$,

$$\mathbf{a} = \sum_n a_n\mathbf{e}_n$$

$$\mathbf{b} = \sum_n b_n\mathbf{e}_n,$$

with

$$\langle\mathbf{e}_n|\,\mathbf{e}_m\rangle = \delta_{nm},$$

then the dyadic B is

$$\mathsf{B} = \sum_n \frac{a_n}{b_n}\,\mathbf{e}_n\mathbf{e}_n,$$

since then

$$\mathcal{B}\mathbf{c} = \mathbf{B}\cdot\mathbf{c} = \sum_n \frac{a_n}{b_n}\,\mathbf{e}_n\langle\mathbf{e}_n|\sum_k b_k\mathbf{e}_k\rangle$$

$$= \sum_n \frac{a_n}{b_n}\,\mathbf{e}_n \sum_k b_k\delta_{nk}$$

$$= \sum_n \frac{a_n}{b_n}\,\mathbf{e}_n b_n = \sum_n a_n\mathbf{e}_n = \mathbf{a}.$$

The second useful form for an operator follows from consideration of the components as the basic objects. Suppose we wish to describe a transformation under which the unit basis vectors $\{\mathbf{e}_n\}$ are carried into new unit vectors $\{\mathbf{e}'_n\}$:

$$\mathbf{e}_n \rightarrow \mathbf{e}'_n = \mathcal{A}\mathbf{e}_n.$$

Any of the new vectors, say $\mathbf{e}'_k$, must be some linear combination of the original vectors, because the $\{\mathbf{e}_n\}$ form a complete set:

$$\mathbf{e}'_k = \sum_n \mathbf{e}_n\alpha_{nk} = \mathcal{A}\mathbf{e}_k. \tag{6.7}$$

Since the $\{\mathbf{e}_n\}$ are orthonormal, the scalar product of $\mathbf{e}'_k$ with $\mathbf{e}_m$ leaves only the coefficient α_{mk}:

$$\langle\mathbf{e}_m|\mathbf{e}'_k\rangle = \alpha_{mk} = \langle\mathbf{e}_m|\mathcal{A}\mathbf{e}_k\rangle.$$

The array of values of the expansion coefficients α_{mk} form a *matrix*, denoted by $\|\alpha_{mk}\|$:

$$\|\alpha_{mk}\| \equiv \begin{Bmatrix} \alpha_{11} & \alpha_{12} & \alpha_{13} & \cdots & \alpha_{1n} \\ \alpha_{21} & \alpha_{22} & \cdots & & \\ \cdot & \cdot & & & \\ \cdot & \cdot & & & \\ \cdot & \cdot & & & \\ \alpha_{n1} & \cdot & \cdots & & \alpha_{nn} \end{Bmatrix} \tag{6.8}$$

From the matrix α, expressing the effect of the transformation on the basis vectors, we readily deduce the effect on an arbitrary vector $\mathbf{A}$, where

$$\mathbf{A} = \sum_n a_n\mathbf{e}_n.$$

The transformation carries $\mathbf{A}$ into $\mathbf{A}'$ according to the operator equation

$$\mathbf{A} \rightarrow \mathbf{A}' = \mathcal{A}\mathbf{A} = \mathcal{A}\sum_n a_n\mathbf{e}_n = \sum_n a_n\mathcal{A}\mathbf{e}_n.$$

Substitution of (6.7) for $\mathcal{A}\mathbf{e}_n$ gives

$$\mathbf{A}' = \sum_n a_n \sum_k \mathbf{e}_k\alpha_{kn} = \sum_k \mathbf{e}_k\left(\sum_n \alpha_{kn}a_n\right).$$

Since $\mathbf{A}'$ is expressible as

$$\mathbf{A}' = \sum_k a'_k \mathbf{e}_k,$$

we see that the components of $\mathbf{A}'$ follow from the transformation matrix,

$$a'_k = \sum_n \alpha_{kn} a_n. \tag{6.9}$$

When dealing with vectors as components, we often find it convenient to represent vectors as columns of component values:

$$\mathbf{A} \equiv \begin{pmatrix} a_1 \\ a_2 \\ a_3 \\ \cdot \\ \cdot \\ \cdot \\ a_n \end{pmatrix}, \qquad \mathbf{A}' \equiv \begin{pmatrix} a'_1 \\ a'_2 \\ a'_3 \\ \cdot \\ \cdot \\ \cdot \\ a'_n \end{pmatrix}.$$

In this form, the equation $\mathbf{A}' = \mathcal{A}\mathbf{A}$ for two dimensions becomes

$$\begin{pmatrix} a'_1 \\ a'_2 \end{pmatrix} = \begin{pmatrix} \alpha_{11} & \alpha_{12} \\ \alpha_{21} & \alpha_{22} \end{pmatrix} \begin{pmatrix} a_1 \\ a_2 \end{pmatrix}.$$

Equation 6.9 then provides the rule for multiplying a matrix by a column vector:

$$\begin{pmatrix} \beta & \alpha \\ \delta & \varepsilon \end{pmatrix} \begin{pmatrix} x \\ y \end{pmatrix} = \begin{pmatrix} \beta x + \alpha y \\ \delta x + \varepsilon y \end{pmatrix}. \tag{6.10}$$

The operators of quantum mechanics are all *linear operators*, that is, they satisfy

$$\mathcal{Q}(a\mathbf{A} + b\mathbf{B}) = a(\mathcal{Q}\mathbf{A}) + b(\mathcal{Q}\mathbf{B}), \tag{6.11}$$

where a and b are scalars. Either dyadics or matrices can be used to represent linear operators in abstract space. Other common examples of linear operators occur in function spaces, where the abstract vectors are functions $\mathbf{A} = A(x)$. There we encounter differential operators such as

$$\mathcal{A} = \frac{d}{dx}, \qquad \mathcal{B} = \frac{d^2}{dx^2} - x,$$

leading to the operator equations

$$\mathcal{A}\mathbf{A} \equiv \frac{d}{dx} A(x), \qquad \mathcal{B}\mathbf{A} \equiv \frac{d^2}{dx^2} A(x) - xA(x).$$

The scalar product of the transformed vector $\mathcal{A}\mathbf{B}$ with a vector $\mathbf{A}$ gives a scalar, say α:

$$\langle \mathbf{A} | \mathcal{A}\mathbf{B} \rangle = \alpha. \tag{6.12}$$

We can produce this same number, α, by first transforming **A** and then projecting onto **B**. This transformation defines the *adjoint operator* (sometimes called the Hermitian adjoint) denoted by $\mathcal{A}^\dagger$:

$$\alpha = \langle \mathcal{A}^\dagger \mathbf{A} | \mathbf{B} \rangle. \tag{6.13}$$

We can therefore use the notation

$$\langle \mathbf{A} | \mathcal{A} | \mathbf{B} \rangle \equiv \langle \mathbf{A} | \mathcal{A}\mathbf{B} \rangle = \langle \mathcal{A}^\dagger \mathbf{A} | \mathbf{B} \rangle.$$

Note that since $\langle \mathbf{A} | \mathbf{C} \rangle^* = \langle \mathbf{C} | \mathbf{A} \rangle$ according to our definition of scalar product, then

$$\langle \mathbf{A} | \mathcal{A}\mathbf{B} \rangle^* = \langle \mathcal{A}^\dagger \mathbf{B} | \mathbf{A} \rangle. \tag{6.14}$$

When **A** and **B** of (6.12) are orthonormal basis vectors, the operator $\mathcal{A}$ is represented by the expansion coefficients α_{mn}:

$$\langle \mathbf{e}_n | \mathcal{A}\mathbf{e}_m \rangle = \langle \mathbf{e}_n | \sum_k \mathbf{e}_k \alpha_{km} \rangle = \alpha_{nm}, \tag{6.15}$$

but by definition

$$\alpha_{nm} = \langle \mathcal{A}^\dagger \mathbf{e}_n | \mathbf{e}_m \rangle.$$

Use of (6.14) gives

$$\alpha_{nm} = \langle \mathbf{e}_m | \mathcal{A}^\dagger \mathbf{e}_n \rangle^* = \langle \mathbf{e}_m | \sum_k \mathbf{e}_k \alpha^\dagger_{kn} \rangle^* = (\alpha^\dagger_{mn})^*,$$

or

$$(\alpha_{nm})^* = \alpha^\dagger_{mn}, \tag{6.16}$$

so that the expansion coefficients of the adjoint operator are the complex conjugates of the coefficients for the operator, with the ordering of the basis vectors reversed. The relationship between $\mathcal{A}$ and $\mathcal{A}^\dagger$ is evident in a matrix representation. We denote by $\mathcal{A}^{\mathrm{T}}$ the *transpose* of a matrix $\mathcal{A}$ (interchange of rows and columns) and denote by $\mathcal{A}^*$ the *complex conjugate* of $\mathcal{A}$ (The transpose is sometimes written $\tilde{A}$). Then the *Hermitian adjoint matrix is the complex conjugate of the transpose:* $\mathcal{A}^\dagger = (\mathcal{A}^{\mathrm{T}})^*$. For 2×2 matrices we have

$$\begin{aligned} \mathcal{A} &= \begin{pmatrix} a & b \\ c & d \end{pmatrix}, & \mathcal{A}^T &= \begin{pmatrix} a & c \\ b & d \end{pmatrix}, \\ \mathcal{A}^* &= \begin{pmatrix} a^* & b^* \\ c^* & d^* \end{pmatrix}, & \mathcal{A}^\dagger &= \begin{pmatrix} a^* & c^* \\ b^* & d^* \end{pmatrix}. \end{aligned} \tag{6.17}$$

In function spaces with a scalar product,

$$\langle \mathbf{A} | \mathbf{B} \rangle = \int A^*(x) B(x)\, dx, \tag{6.18}$$

the relation between an operator and its adjoint becomes

$$\int A^*(x)[\mathcal{A} B(x)]\, dx = \int B(x)[\mathcal{A}^\dagger A^*(x)]\, dx,$$

where we adopt the convention that all operators act on functions to their right. (Some authors prefer to let adjoint operators act on functions to their left.)

An operator equal to its adjoint is called *self-adjoint* or *Hermitian*, $\mathcal{H}^\dagger = \mathcal{H}$. The elements of the matrix representation of $\mathcal{H}$ satisfy

$$\mathfrak{h}^\dagger_{mn} = \mathfrak{h}^*_{nm} = \mathfrak{h}_{mn}, \tag{6.19}$$

so that all elements down the principal diagonal ($m = n$) are real. The matrix thus has the form

$$\begin{bmatrix} r & a + ib & c + id & \cdots \\ a - ib & s & \cdots & \cdots \\ c - id & \cdots & t & \cdots \\ \cdots & \cdots & \cdots & \cdots \end{bmatrix}, \tag{6.20}$$

where $a, b, c, \ldots, r, s, t, \ldots$ are real numbers. A Hermitian operator $\mathcal{H}$ satisfies the equation

$$\langle \mathbf{A} | \mathcal{H}\mathbf{B} \rangle = \langle \mathcal{H}\mathbf{A} | \mathbf{B} \rangle \tag{6.21}$$

so that the result is the same whether $\mathcal{H}$ acts to the right or to the left. In a function space this relation is

$$\int A^*(x)[\mathcal{H} B(x)]\, dx = \int B(x)[\mathcal{H} A^*(x)]\, dx. \tag{6.22}$$

Rotations play a special role in physical space, since these transformations preserve the distance and angle between any two points. *Unitary transformations*, preserving the value of the scalar product, play a corresponding role in abstract vector space. (These are called *orthogonal* transformations when only real scalars are allowed.) Thus a *unitary operator* $\mathcal{U}$, generating a unitary transformation, must satisfy, by definition, the relation

$$\langle \mathcal{U}\mathbf{A} | \mathcal{U}\mathbf{B} \rangle = \langle \mathbf{A} | \mathbf{B} \rangle, \tag{6.23}$$

which means

$$\langle \mathcal{U}\mathbf{A} | \mathcal{U}\mathbf{B} \rangle = \langle \mathbf{A} | \mathcal{U}^\dagger \mathcal{U}\mathbf{B} \rangle$$

or $\mathcal{U}^\dagger \mathcal{U} = 1$. However, the inverse, $\mathcal{U}^{-1}$, is defined by $\mathcal{U}^{-1}\mathcal{U} = 1$, so that for a unitary operator the adjoint and inverse are identical. In a matrix representation, $1 = \mathcal{U}^\dagger \mathcal{U}$ means

$$\delta_{mn} = \sum_k \mathcal{U}^\dagger_{mk}\mathcal{U}_{kn} = \sum_k \mathcal{U}^*_{km}\mathcal{U}_{kn}, \tag{6.24}$$

so that different columns (columns m and n here) are orthogonal. Similarly, $1 = \mathcal{U}\mathcal{U}^\dagger$ means

$$\delta_{mn} = \sum_k \mathcal{U}^*_{mk}\mathcal{U}_{nk}, \tag{6.25}$$

and rows m and $n \neq m$ are orthogonal.

Next consider successive transformations, first from $\mathbf{A}$ to $\mathbf{A}'$, then to $\mathbf{A}''$:

$$\mathbf{A} \rightarrow \mathbf{A}' \rightarrow \mathbf{A}''.$$

Suppose that $\mathbf{A}' = \mathbf{A}\mathcal{A}$ and $\mathbf{A}'' = \mathcal{B}\mathbf{A}'$. Then

$$\mathbf{A}'' = \mathcal{B}\mathbf{A}' = \mathcal{B}\mathcal{A}\mathbf{A},$$

so the result of the sequence is a transformation $\mathbf{A}'' = \mathcal{C}\mathbf{A}$, where

$$\mathcal{C} = \mathcal{B}\mathcal{A}.$$

Here $\mathcal{A}$ was applied to $\mathbf{A}$, followed by $\mathcal{B}$. In general this result differs from first applying $\mathcal{B}$ and then $\mathcal{A}$:

$$\mathcal{B}\mathcal{A} \neq \mathcal{A}\mathcal{B} \quad \text{(in general)}.$$

Using matrix representation of operators, with $\mathcal{A} = \|\alpha_{mn}\|$, $\mathcal{B} = \|\beta_{mn}\|$, and $\mathcal{C} = \|\gamma_{mn}\|$, we find the rules for multiplying two matrices together:

If

$$\mathbf{A} = \sum_n a_n \mathbf{e}_n \qquad \text{and} \qquad \mathbf{A}'' = \sum_n a''_n \mathbf{e}_n,$$

then

$$\mathbf{A}'' = \sum_n a''_n \mathbf{e}_n = \mathcal{C} \sum_n a_n \mathbf{e}_n = \sum_n a_n \mathcal{C}\mathbf{e}_n = \sum_n a_n \sum_m \mathbf{e}_m \gamma_{mn},$$

but alternatively

$$\mathbf{A}'' = \mathcal{B}\mathcal{A} \sum_n a_n \mathbf{e}_n = \mathcal{B} \sum_n a_n \sum_k \mathbf{e}_k \alpha_{kn} = \sum_n a_n \sum_k \alpha_{kn} \sum_m \mathbf{e}_n \beta_{mk}.$$

Thus

$$\sum_m \mathbf{e}_m \sum_n \gamma_{mn} a_n = \sum_m \mathbf{e}_n \sum_n \left(\sum_k \beta_{mk}\alpha_{kn} \right) a_n,$$

which gives the required rule:

$$\gamma_{mn} = \sum_k \beta_{mk}\alpha_{kn}. \tag{6.26}$$

When written for two-by-two matrices, this becomes

$$\begin{pmatrix} \alpha & \beta \\ \gamma & \delta \end{pmatrix}\begin{pmatrix} \alpha' & \beta' \\ \gamma' & \delta' \end{pmatrix} = \begin{pmatrix} (\alpha\alpha' + \beta\gamma') & (\alpha\beta' + \beta\delta') \\ (\gamma\alpha' + \delta\gamma') & (\gamma\beta' + \delta\delta') \end{pmatrix}. \tag{6.27}$$

4.7 EIGENVECTORS AND EIGENFUNCTIONS

A linear transformation $\mathcal{A}\mathbf{b} = \mathbf{c}$ alters, in general, both magnitude and direction of the vectors composing an abstract space. Vectors may be both stretched and rotated. However, it often happens that a transformation merely stretches the vectors that lie along selected directions. Such a vector, an *eigenvector* $\mathbf{a}$ of the transformation $\mathcal{A}$ (also called *proper vector* or *characteristic vector*), satisfies the equation

$$\mathcal{A}\mathbf{a} = a\mathbf{a}. \tag{7.1}$$

The scalar a is the *eigenvalue* (also called the *proper value* or *characteristic value*) of the operator $\mathcal{A}$ acting on $\mathbf{a}$. An operator may have several eigenvectors,

$$\mathcal{A}\mathbf{a}_1 = a_1\mathbf{a}_1 \qquad \mathcal{A}\mathbf{a}_2 = a_2\mathbf{a}_2 \quad \ldots \quad \mathcal{A}\mathbf{a}_n = a_n\mathbf{a}_n \tag{7.2}$$

or perhaps an infinite number of eigenvectors. The eigenvalues $a_1, a_2, \ldots$ need not be different. If n eigenvectors share the same eigenvalue, they are said to be (*n-fold*) *degenerate*. Vectors may be eigenvectors for several operators,

$$\mathcal{A}\mathbf{a} = a\mathbf{a}, \quad \mathcal{B}\mathbf{a} = b\mathbf{a}, \quad \ldots \tag{7.3}$$

Eigenvectors of Hermitian operators possess two useful attributes: *Hermitian operators have real eigenvalues and the eigenvectors are orthogonal* (or can be made orthogonal). To prove this statement, suppose $\mathcal{H}$ is a Hermitian operator possessing a sequence $\mathbf{a}_1, \mathbf{a}_2, \ldots$ of different (nondegenerate) eigenvectors with eigenvalues $h_1, h_2, \ldots$.

$$\mathcal{H}\mathbf{a}_n = h_n\mathbf{a}_n. \tag{7.4}$$

Then the eigenvectors satisfy

$$\langle \mathbf{a}_k | \mathcal{H}\mathbf{a}_n \rangle = h_n \langle \mathbf{a}_k | \mathbf{a}_n \rangle. \tag{7.5}$$

If we use the definition of Hermitian operator and the properties of scalar products, (7.5) gives the equation

$$\langle \mathbf{a}_k | \mathcal{H}\mathbf{a}_n \rangle = \langle \mathcal{H}\mathbf{a}_k | \mathbf{a}_n \rangle = \langle \mathbf{a}_n | \mathcal{H}\mathbf{a}_k \rangle^* = h_k^* \langle \mathbf{a}_n | \mathbf{a}_k \rangle^* = h_k^* \langle \mathbf{a}_k | \mathbf{a}_n \rangle.$$

Thus we obtain the result

$$(h_n - h_k^*)\langle \mathbf{a}_k | \mathbf{a}_n \rangle = 0.$$

When $n = k$, either $\mathbf{a}_k$ is the null vector or $h_n = h_n^*$. This condition proves that h_n is real. When $n \neq k$, then $h_n \neq h_k^*$ so that $\langle \mathbf{a}_k | \mathbf{a}_n \rangle = 0$. This condition proves the eigenvectors are orthogonal. The orthogonality can be extended to degenerate eigenvectors, $h_n = h_k = \ldots$, by application of the Schmidt orthogonalization process to the eigenvectors of each eigenvalue.

The Hermitian nature of an operator is not only a sufficient condition for real eigenvalues; it is also a necessary condition. To show this, note that

$$h_n = \langle \mathbf{a}_n | \mathcal{H}\mathbf{a}_n \rangle$$

and

$$h_n^* = \langle \mathbf{a}_n | \mathcal{H}\mathbf{a}_n \rangle^* = \langle \mathcal{H}\mathbf{a}_n | \mathbf{a}_n \rangle.$$

Thus the reality of h_n, as expressed by $h_n = h_n^*$, requires

$$\langle \mathbf{a}_n | \mathcal{H}\mathbf{a}_n \rangle = \langle \mathcal{H}^\dagger \mathbf{a}_n | \mathbf{a}_n \rangle = \langle \mathcal{H}\mathbf{a}_n | \mathbf{a}_n \rangle$$

or

$$\mathcal{H}^\dagger = \mathcal{H}.$$

As an example from a space of continuous real-valued functions of x, consider the exponential function e^{ax} and the differential operator d/dx. These operators satisfy the eigenvalue equation

$$\frac{d}{dx} e^{ax} = a e^{ax},$$

for all values of a. Exponential functions are also eigenvectors of the operator d^2/dx^2,

$$\frac{d^2}{dx^2} e^{ax} = a^2 e^{ax}$$

with eigenvalue a^2.

If we define the scalar product by the integral

$$\langle \mathbf{F} | \mathbf{G} \rangle \equiv \int_{-L}^{+L} F(x)G(x)\, dx,$$

then the operator d/dx is not Hermitian, since integration by parts yields the result

$$\left\langle \mathbf{F} \,\middle|\, \frac{d}{dx} \mathbf{G} \right\rangle = \int_{-L}^{L} F \frac{d}{dx} G\, dx = FG \Big|_{-L}^{L} - \int_{-L}^{L} G \frac{d}{dx} F\, dx$$

$$= FG \Big|_{-L}^{L} - \left\langle \frac{d}{dx} \mathbf{F} \,\middle|\, \mathbf{G} \right\rangle.$$

The negative sign makes the operator non-Hermitian. On the other hand, the operator d^2/dx^2 *is* Hermitian, since

$$\left\langle \mathbf{F} \middle| \frac{d^2}{dx^2} \mathbf{G} \right\rangle = \int_{-L}^{L} F \frac{d^2}{dx^2} G\, dx = F \frac{d}{dx} G \Big|_{-L}^{L} - \int_{-L}^{L} \frac{dF}{dx} \frac{dG}{dx}\, dx$$

$$= F \frac{d}{dx} G \Big|_{-L}^{L} - G \frac{dF}{dx} \Big|_{-L}^{L} + \int_{-L}^{L} G \frac{d^2}{dx^2} F\, dx.$$

If we limit the vector space to functions that vanish on the boundary $\pm L$ (or have vanishing first derivatives there), such as e^{iax} with $a = n\pi/L$, then the integrated terms vanish, and we obtain

$$\left\langle \mathbf{F} \middle| \frac{d^2}{dx^2} \mathbf{G} \right\rangle = \left\langle \frac{d^2}{dx^2} \mathbf{F} \middle| \mathbf{G} \right\rangle.$$

Hermitian operators also have the useful property that they can always be represented by a diagonal matrix, as we now show. Suppose we have a convenient set of orthonormal basis vectors, $\{\mathbf{e}_n\}$. Using this basis we calculate the matrix of the Hermitian operator $\mathcal{H}$, that is, all the elements

$$\mathcal{H}_{mn} \equiv \langle \mathbf{e}_m | \mathcal{H} \mathbf{e}_n \rangle. \tag{7.6}$$

Now, because $\mathcal{H}$ is Hermitian, there exists a set of orthonormal eigenvectors $\{\mathbf{a}_n\}$; for both the **a**'s and the **e**'s we have

$$\langle \mathbf{a}_m | \mathbf{a}_n \rangle = \delta_{mn}; \qquad \langle \mathbf{e}_m | \mathbf{e}_n \rangle = \delta_{mn}. \tag{7.7}$$

Because these two scalar products are identical, there exists a unitary transformation between the **a**'s and the **e**'s:

$$\mathbf{a} = \mathcal{U}\mathbf{e} \quad \text{or} \quad \mathbf{a}_n = \sum_k \mathbf{e}_k \mathcal{U}_{kn}.$$

With the eigenvectors, of course, $\mathcal{H}$ satisfies

$$\langle \mathbf{a}_m | \mathcal{H} \mathbf{a}_n \rangle = h_n \langle \mathbf{a}_m | \mathbf{a}_n \rangle = h_n \delta_{mn}, \tag{7.8}$$

On substituting the expansion of $\mathbf{a}_n$, we find

$$h_n \delta_{mn} = \left\langle \sum_j \mathbf{e}_j \mathcal{U}_{jm} \middle| \sum_k \mathbf{e}_k \mathcal{U}_{kn} \right\rangle = \sum_j \sum_k \mathcal{U}_{jm}^* \mathcal{U}_{kn} \langle \mathbf{e}_j | \mathcal{H} \mathbf{e}_k \rangle$$

$$= \sum_j \sum_k \mathcal{U}_{mj}^\dagger \mathcal{H}_{jk} \mathcal{U}_{kn}.$$

Thus by premultiplying the matrix of $\mathcal{H}$ by the $\mathcal{U}^\dagger$ matrix and postmultiplying by the $\mathcal{U}$ matrix, we obtain a diagonal matrix whose elements are the eigenvalues of $\mathcal{H}$. The transformation matrix has the elements

$$\mathcal{U}_{kn} = \langle \mathbf{a}_n | \mathbf{e}_k \rangle; \qquad \mathcal{U}_{kn} = \langle \mathbf{e}_k | \mathbf{a}_k \rangle. \tag{7.9}$$

That is, the successive columns of $\mathcal{U}$ are successive eigenvectors, the rows are the components of the **a**'s in the **e** coordinate system. For example, take Cartesian coordinates $\mathbf{e}_x$, $\mathbf{e}_y$, $\mathbf{e}_z$. Then $\mathcal{U}$ has the form [when $\mathbf{a}_n = \mathbf{a}(n)$]

$$\begin{pmatrix} a_x(1) & a_x(2) & \ldots \\ a_y(1) & a_y(2) & \ldots \\ a_z(1) & a_z(2) & \ldots \end{pmatrix}. \tag{7.10}$$

We have seen that the exponential functions are eigenfunctions of both d/dx and d^2/dx^2; in fact, they are eigenfunctions of any power or multiple of the operator $\mathfrak{D} \equiv d/dx$. What sort of operators share eigenvectors? If $\mathcal{A}$ and $\mathcal{B}$ have a common eigenvector **c**, then we must have

$$\mathcal{A}\mathbf{c} = A\mathbf{c} \quad \text{and} \quad \mathcal{B}\mathbf{c} = B\mathbf{c},$$

where A and B are the (usually unequal) eigenvalues. It follows that

$$\mathcal{A}(\mathcal{B}\mathbf{c}) = B\mathcal{A}\mathbf{c} = BA\mathbf{c},$$

and

$$\mathcal{B}(\mathcal{A}\mathbf{c}) = A\mathcal{B}\mathbf{c} = AB\mathbf{c}.$$

Because $AB = BA$ for scalars, we find

$$\mathcal{A}\mathcal{B} = \mathcal{B}\mathcal{A},$$

and the operators *commute*. Thus the *commutator* of $\mathcal{A}$ and $\mathcal{B}$,

$$[\mathcal{A}, \mathcal{B}] \equiv \mathcal{A}\mathcal{B} - \mathcal{B}\mathcal{A}, \tag{7.11}$$

must be zero if $\mathcal{A}$ and $\mathcal{B}$ share eigenvectors. The fact that commuting operators possess simultaneous eigenvectors leads to a very useful way of labeling degenerate eigenvectors. Suppose the particular eigenvector $\mathbf{a}_i$ is an eigenvector of $\mathcal{A}$ with eigenvalue A; several other eigenvectors share this eigenvalue. We then look for a second operator, $\mathcal{B}$, commuting with $\mathcal{A}$, whose eigenvalue B distinguishes $\mathbf{a}_i$ from other eigenvectors degenerate under $\mathcal{A}$. If there still remains an eigenvector other than $\mathbf{a}_i$ having eigenvalues A and B, we search for a third operator $\mathcal{C}$, commuting with both $\mathcal{A}$ and $\mathcal{B}$, whose eigenvalue C distinguishes the states. We could continue in this way until we found a set of commuting operators $\mathcal{A}$, $\mathcal{B}$, $\mathcal{C}$, . . . whose eigenvalues A, B, C, . . . unambiguously identify $\mathbf{a}_i$. Any other eigenvector $\mathbf{a}_j$ will differ in at least one eigenvalue, A', B', C', ... Thus we can replace the index i that labels a particular eigenvector by a list of eigenvalues of commuting operators: $\mathbf{a}(A, B, C, \ldots)$.

4.8 QUANTUM MECHANICS AS AN ABSTRACT VECTOR SPACE

With this brief background we can now begin to link atomic phenomena with abstract vector space. This abstract formulation of quantum theory came primarily from the work of P. A. M. Dirac, around 1930, whose *Principles of Quantum Mechanics* [1] still remains the classic work on the subject. Dirac began from a few key postulates connecting the "physical" notions of *state*, *observable*, and *measurement* with the mathematical framework of abstract vector space. The laws of atomic physics derive from these postulates just as the laws of planetary motion derive from Newton's laws. In both instances judgment on the basic postulates ultimately follows comparison between predictions of the theory and observations. In atomic theory, two fundamental forms of evidence suggest the postulates. First, the impossibility of a precise simultaneous determination of conjugate variables, as exemplified by the uncertainty principle. Second, the dual wave–particle property of matter suggests an interpretation based on probabilities.

To begin, we represent the state of an atomic system by a point in abstract space. This *state space* is an infinite-dimensional space of *state vectors*, each corresponding to some physically possible state. We then note that our inquiries into atomic properties, such as the motion of an electron or the response of an atom to an electric field, must always take the form of some measurement. Guided by theory, we interpret these observations as measurements of energy, of position, of angular momentum, or some other quantity. As we have seen, any observation on an atomic system generally disturbs the system and alters its characteristics. In other words, during the measurement, the state was transformed from $\mathbf{A}$ to a new state $\mathbf{A}'$. We therefore postulate that (linear Hermitian) operators in state space represent measurements. (These operators should be linear in order to preserve superpositions of several states. They should be Hermitian, as we shall see, in order to have real eigenvalues.) Only when the state vector of the system corresponds to an eigenvector of the operator does the state remain unaltered after the observation. For brevity, we say the system is in an *eigenstate*.

How are we to interpret eigenstates? According to our postulate, an eigenstate, say $\mathbf{e}_n$ (presumed normalized) of $\mathcal{P}$, represents a state for which we observe some property $\mathcal{P}$, and obtain a number, say P_n, from our measuring apparatus. The set of numbers, P_1 P_2, P_3, . . . supplies all the possible numbers we might obtain in any single measurement, each value corresponding to one or more of the eigenstates $\mathbf{e}_1$, $\mathbf{e}_2$, $\mathbf{e}_3$, ... The eigenstates of an observable form a set of *basis states.* Any arbitrary state is expressible as a linear combination of these basis states. Thus:

$$\mathbf{A} = \sum_n \mathbf{e}_n a_n \quad \text{where} \quad a_n = \langle \mathbf{e}_n | \mathbf{A} \rangle. \tag{8.1}$$

If we postulate that *the observed numbers are the eigenvalues of* $\mathcal{P}$, the measurement process is symbolized by the equations:

$$\mathcal{P}\mathbf{e}_n = P_n \mathbf{e}_n \quad \text{and} \quad \mathcal{P}\mathbf{A} = \sum_n P_n a_n \mathbf{e}_n. \tag{8.2}$$

It might be tempting to assume that the expansion coefficient a_n, being a direction cosine, indicates the relative probability of observing the value P_n. But probabilities are positive, real numbers, whereas the expansion coefficients need not be positive or even real. A more satisfactory interpretation is suggested by the following argument. Recall that the distribution of light intensity over a diffraction pattern corresponds to the probability of observing a photon, and that light intensity is the square of the wave amplitude. Wave amplitudes can, of course, be either positive or negative. They add algebraically to produce an interference pattern according to a formula analogous to (8.1). This reasoning suggests that an expansion coefficient a_n is a *probability amplitude*, whose square $|a_n|^2$ gives the relative probability that a measurement of $\mathcal{P}$ upon state $\mathbf{A}$ reveals eigenstate $\mathbf{e}_n$. More precisely, observation $\mathcal{P}$ will produce the value P_n with probability

$$\text{Probability of } P_n = |a_n|^2 = |\langle \mathbf{e}_n | \mathbf{A} \rangle|^2 = |\langle \mathbf{A} | \mathbf{e}_n \rangle|^2. \tag{8.3}$$

We adopt this proposal as our second basic postulate.

Next, we note that the scalar product of $\mathbf{A}$ with $\mathcal{P}\mathbf{A}$ yields

$$\langle \mathbf{A} | \mathcal{P}\mathbf{A} \rangle = \left\langle \sum_m \mathbf{e}_m a_n \middle| \sum_n \mathbf{e}_n a_n P_n \right\rangle = \sum_n |a_n|^2 P_n. \tag{8.4}$$

This is the sum of all the possible observable values, P_n, each multiplied by the probability $|a_n|^2$ of observing that value. In statistics, such an expression is called the *expectation value* or *average value* of the variable P_n. This same nomenclature has been carried over to quantum mechanics. We denote the expectation value for an operator $\mathcal{P}$ by $\langle \mathcal{P} \rangle$,

$$\langle \mathcal{P} \rangle \equiv \langle \mathbf{A} | \mathcal{P}\mathbf{A} \rangle. \tag{8.5}$$

(The notation $\langle \mathcal{P} \rangle$ implicitly assumes we have selected some particular state $\mathbf{A}$.)

When we observe $\mathcal{P}$ for a system in an eigenstate $\mathbf{e}_n$ we always obtain the number P_n. This procedure defines what we mean by an eigenstate. Equation 8.4 or 8.5 shows that P_n is the expectation value $\langle \mathcal{P} \rangle$ in this eigenstate. Each observation of a system in an arbitrary state **A** yields one of the values P_n, and as more observations are made, the average of our observations tends to the value $\langle \mathcal{P} \rangle$.

Any particular measurement will generally yield a result different from the expectation value, however. This remark leads in a natural way to the notion of uncertainty. The difference between $\mathcal{P}$ and its expectation value,

$$\Delta\mathcal{P} = \mathcal{P} - \langle \mathcal{P} \rangle.$$

tells us nothing because the expectation value of $\Delta\mathcal{P}$ is identically zero:

$$\Delta\mathcal{P} = \langle \mathbf{A} | (\mathcal{P} - \langle \mathcal{P} \rangle)\mathbf{A} \rangle = \langle \mathbf{A} | \mathcal{P}\mathbf{A} \rangle - \langle \mathcal{P} \rangle \cdot 1 \equiv 0.$$

However, the expectation value of $(\Delta\mathcal{P})^2$ does not, in general, vanish:

$$\begin{aligned} \langle (\Delta\mathcal{P})^2 \rangle &= \langle \mathbf{A} | (\mathcal{P} - \langle \mathcal{P} \rangle)(\mathcal{P} - \langle \mathcal{P} \rangle)\mathbf{A} \rangle \\ &= \langle \mathbf{A} | \mathcal{P}^2\mathbf{A} \rangle - 2\langle \mathcal{P} \rangle \langle \mathbf{A} | \mathcal{P}\mathbf{A} \rangle - \langle \mathcal{P} \rangle^2 \\ &= \langle \mathbf{A} | \mathcal{P}^2\mathbf{A} \rangle - \langle \mathbf{A} | \mathcal{P}\mathbf{A} \rangle^2. \end{aligned} \tag{8.6}$$

In statistics, $\langle (\Delta\mathcal{P})^2 \rangle_{\text{av}}$ is the *variance* and $\sqrt{\langle (\Delta\mathcal{P})^2 \rangle_{\text{av}}}$ the *standard deviation;* in quantum mechanics $\sqrt{\langle (\Delta\mathcal{P})^2 \rangle}$ is usually termed the *uncertainty* in $\mathcal{P}$. The uncertainty in $\mathcal{P}$ is zero when the system is in an eigenstate:

$$\langle (\Delta\mathcal{P})^2 \rangle = \mathbf{e}_n | \mathcal{P}^2\mathbf{e}_n \rangle - \langle \mathbf{e}_n | \mathcal{P}\mathbf{e}_n \rangle^2 = \mathcal{P}_n{}^2 - \mathcal{P}_n{}^2 \equiv 0,$$

For systems not in an eigenstate, $\langle (\Delta\mathcal{P})^2 \rangle$ generally has some finite value, indicative of the variability in our measurements.

Suppose we measure *two* properties, represented by operators $\mathcal{P}$ and $\mathcal{Q}$. If the system is in an eigenstate of *both* operators, the uncertainty will be zero for both measurements. As we saw, only commuting operators can share eigenstates. With noncommuting operators, one or both operators will have nonzero uncertainty. A bit of algebraic manipulation discloses the close connection between simultaneous uncertainty and the commutator.

We begin with the expectation value of $\Delta\mathcal{P}\ \Delta\mathcal{Q}$:

$$\begin{aligned} \langle \mathbf{A} | \Delta\mathcal{P}\ \Delta\mathcal{Q}\mathbf{A} \rangle &\equiv \langle \mathbf{A} | (\mathcal{P} - \langle \mathcal{P} \rangle)(\mathcal{Q} - \langle \mathcal{Q} \rangle)\mathbf{A} \rangle \\ &= \langle \mathbf{A} | \mathcal{P}\mathcal{Q}\mathbf{A} \rangle - 2\langle \mathcal{P} \rangle \langle \mathcal{Q} \rangle + \langle \mathcal{P} \rangle \langle \mathcal{Q} \rangle \\ &= \langle \mathbf{A} | \mathcal{P}\mathcal{Q}\mathbf{A} \rangle - \langle \mathcal{P} \rangle \langle \mathcal{Q} \rangle. \end{aligned}$$

The expectation value in the reverse order is

$$\langle \mathbf{A} | \Delta\mathcal{Q}\ \Delta\mathcal{P}\mathbf{A} \rangle = \langle \mathbf{A} | \mathcal{Q}\mathcal{P}\mathbf{A} \rangle - \langle \mathcal{P} \rangle \langle \mathcal{Q} \rangle.$$

Subtracting the two results, we obtain the expectation value of the commutator:

$$\langle \mathbf{A} | \Delta\mathcal{P}\ \Delta\mathcal{Q}\mathbf{A} \rangle - \langle \mathbf{A} | \Delta\mathcal{Q}\ \Delta\mathcal{P}\mathbf{A} \rangle = \langle \mathbf{A} | \mathcal{P}\mathcal{Q}\mathbf{A} \rangle - \langle \mathbf{A} | \mathcal{Q}\mathcal{P}\mathbf{A} \rangle = \langle [\mathcal{P}, \mathcal{Q}] \rangle.$$

But both $\mathcal{P}$ and $\mathcal{Q}$ are Hermitian, so that this can be written

$$\langle[\mathcal{P}, \mathcal{Q}]\rangle = \langle\Delta\mathcal{P}\mathbf{A}|\,\Delta\mathcal{Q}\mathbf{A}\rangle - \langle\Delta\mathcal{Q}\mathbf{A}|\,\Delta\mathcal{P}\mathbf{A}\rangle,$$

or, from the property of scalar products,

$$\langle[\mathcal{P}, \mathcal{Q}]\rangle = \langle\Delta\mathcal{P}\mathbf{A}|\,\Delta\mathcal{Q}\mathbf{A}\rangle - \langle\Delta\mathcal{P}\mathbf{A}|\,\Delta\mathcal{Q}\mathbf{A}\rangle^*.$$

But this is just twice the imaginary part of the number $\langle\Delta\mathcal{P}\mathbf{A}|\,\Delta\mathcal{Q}\mathbf{A}\rangle$:

$$\langle\mathbf{A}|\,\mathcal{P}, \mathcal{Q}]\mathbf{A}\rangle = 2i\,\mathrm{Im}\,\langle\Delta\mathcal{P}\mathbf{A}|\,\Delta\mathcal{Q}\mathbf{A}\rangle. \tag{8.7}$$

The i factor reveals that the expectation value of the commutator is an imaginary number (or zero). Now the square of the imaginary part of a number is less than or equal to the absolute value:

$$|\,\mathrm{Im}\,\langle\Delta\mathcal{P}\mathbf{A}|\,\Delta\mathcal{Q}\mathbf{A}\rangle|^2 \leq |\langle\Delta\mathcal{P}\mathbf{A}|\,\Delta\mathcal{Q}\mathbf{A}\rangle|^2. \tag{8.8}$$

Furthermore, the Cauchy–Schwartz inequality states that

$$|\langle\mathbf{A}|\,\mathbf{B}\rangle|^2 \leq \langle\mathbf{A}|\,\mathbf{A}\rangle\langle\mathbf{B}|\,\mathbf{B}\rangle \tag{8.9}$$

or, when applied to the right-hand side of (8.8), that

$$\begin{aligned} |\langle\Delta\mathcal{P}\mathbf{A}|\,\Delta\mathcal{Q}\mathbf{A}\rangle|^2 &\leq \langle\Delta\mathcal{P}\mathbf{A}|\,\Delta\mathcal{P}\mathbf{A}\rangle\langle\Delta\mathcal{Q}\mathbf{A}|\,\mathbf{A}\mathcal{Q}\mathbf{A}\rangle \\ &\leq \langle\mathbf{A}|\,(\Delta\mathcal{P})^2\mathbf{A}\rangle\langle\mathbf{A}|\,(\Delta\mathcal{Q})^2\mathbf{A}\rangle. \end{aligned} \tag{8.10}$$

From (8.7), (8.8), and (8.9), we obtain the inequality

$$\langle[\mathcal{P}, \mathcal{Q}]\rangle^2 \leq 4\langle\Delta\mathcal{P}^2\rangle\langle\Delta\mathcal{Q}^2\rangle. \tag{8.11}$$

Equation 8.11 is the mathematical expression of Heisenberg's uncertainty principle. For example, the simplest nonzero commutator is a constant times the unit operator. Equation 8.7 shows that the constant includes a factor i, and we set the remaining constant equal to $\hbar$:

$$[\mathcal{P}, \mathcal{Q}] = i\hbar. \tag{8.12}$$

Such operators have their simultaneous uncertainty bounded by

$$\sqrt{\langle\Delta\mathcal{P}\rangle^2}\,\sqrt{\langle\Delta\mathcal{Q}^2\rangle} \geq \tfrac{1}{4}\hbar\,. \tag{8.13}$$

The position and momentum operators introduced with the Schrödinger equation satisfy this commutation relation. For those operators, (8.10) expresses the Heisenberg uncertainty principle as

$$\Delta p\,\Delta x \geq \tfrac{1}{4}\hbar. \tag{8.14}$$

REFERENCE

[1] P. A. M. Dirac, *The Principles of Quantum Mechanics*, Oxford University Press, New York (1958), 4th ed.

4.9 REPRESENTATIONS

Let us see how this rather formal development applies to the simple hydrogen atom we studied in the last chapter. Following the postulates of the last section, we say that a hydrogen atom exists in some quantum state, represented by a vector (or point) in an abstract space. For the moment, we denote this vector by **A**. What can we say about the state **A**?

First, let us suppose the energy of the atom is sharply defined, and does not change with time. (This assumption is not necessary, of course, for a quantum-mechanical system, but in atomic structure we are primarily interested in observing states with well-defined energy.) The atom must then be in an energy eigenstate, i.e., an eigenstate of the Hamiltonian operator, $\mathcal{H}$, having energy E_n as an eigenvalue:

$$\mathcal{H}\mathbf{A} = E_n\mathbf{A}. \tag{9.1}$$

For hydrogen, the subscript n is just the principal quantum number; for more complex atoms it distinguishes various possible eigenvalues. We can thus designate state **A** by the label E_n, or simply by n.

We need additional labels to distinguish states with the same n. According to our discussion in the last section, these labels should be the eigenvalues of a complete set of commuting operators. In the present example the Hamiltonian operator may be written

$$\mathcal{H} = \frac{1}{2m}\left(\mathcal{P}_r^{\,2} + \hbar^2\frac{\mathcal{L}^2}{r^2}\right) + V(r). \tag{9.2}$$

A satisfactory set of commuting operators is $\mathcal{L}^2$ and $\mathcal{L}_z$. We have seen that these operators have eigenstates satisfying

$$\mathcal{L}^2\mathbf{A} = l(l+1)\mathbf{A}$$
$$\mathcal{L}_z\mathbf{A} = m\mathbf{A},$$

Thus, it is natural to use l and m to complete our set of labels. $\mathbf{A}(n, l, m)$ is an eigenstate of $\mathcal{H}$, $\mathcal{L}^2$, and $\mathcal{L}_z$ with eigenvalues E_n, $l(l+1)$, and m.

This way of describing the state **A** is called the *energy–angular-momentum representation*. Our choice of basis states was such that $\mathcal{H}$, $\mathcal{L}^2$, and $\mathcal{L}_z$ are represented by diagonal matrices:

$$\begin{aligned}\langle\mathbf{A}(n, l, m)|\,\mathcal{H}\,|\mathbf{A}(n', l', m')\rangle &= E_n\delta_{nn'}\delta_{ll'}\delta_{mm'}\\ \langle\mathbf{A}(n, l, m)|\,\mathcal{L}^2|\mathbf{A}(n', l', m')\rangle &= l(l+1)\delta_{nn'}\delta_{ll'}\delta_{mm'}\\ \langle\mathbf{A}(n, l, m)|\,\mathcal{L}_z|\mathbf{A}(n', l', m')\rangle &= m\delta_{nn'}\delta_{ll'}\delta_{mm'}.\end{aligned} \tag{9.3}$$

It will often prove convenient to omit the letter **A** from our notation for a matrix element, and write merely

$$\langle n, l, m | \mathcal{H} | n, l, m \rangle = E_n.$$

The operators $\mathcal{L}_x$ and $\mathcal{L}_y$ (or $\mathcal{L}_+$ and $\mathcal{L}_-$) do not commute with $\mathcal{L}_z$, so they will not have diagonal matrices in this representation. From Section 3.10 we see that

$$\mathcal{L}_x = -\frac{1}{\sqrt{2}}(\mathcal{L}_+ - \mathcal{L}_-)$$

has only the off-diagonal matrix elements

$$\langle n, l, m+1 | \mathcal{L}_x | n, l, m \rangle = \tfrac{1}{2}\sqrt{l(l+1) - m(m+1)}$$
$$\langle n, l, m-1 | \mathcal{L}_x | n, l, m \rangle = \tfrac{1}{2}\sqrt{l(l+1) - m(m-1)}.$$

Similar results hold for $\mathcal{L}_y$.

The choice of a particular set of observables specifies a set of basis states, a *representation*. For an atom, one usually deals with some form of angular-momentum representation, whereas for free particles it is usually more convenient to use a linear-momentum representation. In either case position will not be sharply defined; the position operator $\mathcal{X}$ will not have a diagonal matrix. If we wish to picture the distribution of a particle in space, we must then transform from the representation in which the energy operator has a diagonal matrix to a representation in which the basis states are well-defined positions. In one dimension we want to transform from energy states $\mathbf{A}_n$,

$$\mathcal{H}\mathbf{A}_n = E_n\mathbf{A}_n, \qquad \langle \mathbf{A}_n | \mathbf{A}'_n \rangle = \delta_{nn'}, \tag{9.4}$$

to states of position, $\mathbf{e}_n$,

$$\mathcal{X}\mathbf{e}_n = x_n\mathbf{e}_n, \qquad \langle \mathbf{e}_n | \mathbf{e}'_n \rangle = \delta_{nn'}, \tag{9.5a}$$

where, for the moment, we assume x takes only particular discrete values x_n. The transformation is

$$\mathbf{A}_n = \sum_k \mathbf{e}_k \langle \mathbf{e}_k | \mathbf{A}_n \rangle. \tag{9.6a}$$

We shall write the expansion coefficients as

$$\langle \mathbf{e}_k | \mathbf{A}_n \rangle \equiv \psi(x_k | n) \equiv \psi_n(x_k). \tag{9.7}$$

They are functions of x and the quantum number n, which we shall see are the Schrödinger wavefunctions. When the atom is in the state $\mathbf{A}_n$, the normalization condition gives

$$\langle \mathbf{A}_n | \mathbf{A}_n \rangle = 1 = \sum_k |\langle \mathbf{e}_k | \mathbf{A}_n \rangle|^2 = \sum_k |\psi(x_k | n)|^2. \tag{9.8}$$

This result shows that the eigenvalues x_k are distributed with probabilities

$|\psi|^2$. That is, the probability of being at point x_k is $|\psi(x_k|n)|^2$. We see that our interpretation of $\psi(x_k|n)$ is the same as our earlier interpretation of the Schrödinger wavefunction. We must next show that ψ satisfies the Schrödinger differential equation.

The action of an operator $\mathcal{B}$ on an energy eigenstate can be expressed in position representation:

$$\mathcal{B}\mathbf{A}_n = \mathcal{B} \sum_k \mathbf{e}_k \psi(x_k|\, n). \tag{9.9a}$$

We can write the right-hand side in two ways. First, as an operator $\mathcal{B}$ acting on abstract vectors,

$$\mathcal{B}\mathbf{e}_k = \sum_l \mathbf{e}_l \langle x_l|\, \mathcal{B}\,|\, x_k\rangle, \tag{9.10}$$

giving

$$\mathcal{B}\mathbf{A}_n = \sum_l \mathbf{e}_l \sum_k \langle x_l|\, \mathcal{B}\,|\, x_k\rangle \psi(x_k|\, n).$$

The k summation could also be obtained by a suitable operator acting upon the variable x_k in the function $\psi(x_l|n)$:

$$\mathcal{B}\psi(x_l|\, n) \equiv \sum_k \langle x_l|\, \mathcal{B}\,|\, x_k\rangle \psi(x_k|\, n),$$

so we can write (9.9) as

$$\mathcal{B}\mathbf{A}_n = \sum_l \mathbf{e}_l \mathcal{B}\psi(x_l|\, n). \tag{9.11}$$

We can therefore deal either with operators acting on abstract vectors or with operators acting on functions.

The $\mathcal{X}$ operator does not, of course, have the discrete spectrum of eigenvalues x_n we have so far assumed; x is a continuous variable. We must modify our equations somewhat, replacing x_n by the continuous variable x, and replacing summation by an integral:

$$\mathcal{X}\mathbf{e}(x) = x\mathbf{e}(x) \tag{9.5b}$$

$$\mathbf{A}_n = \int dx\, \mathbf{e}(x)\psi(x|\, n) \tag{9.6b}$$

$$\mathcal{B}\mathbf{A}_n = \int dx\, \mathbf{e}(x)\mathcal{B}\psi(x|\, n). \tag{9.9b}$$

This simple replacement is not without mathematical difficulty, and several approaches have been proposed over the years to eliminate some of the logical difficulties. The simplest approach is that of Dirac, who replaced the Kronecker delta,

$$\langle \mathbf{e}_n | \mathbf{e}_{n'} \rangle = \delta_{nn'}, \tag{9.12a}$$

by the "pathological" *Dirac delta function,*

$$\langle \mathbf{e}(x) | \mathbf{e}(x') \rangle = \delta(x - x'), \tag{9.12b}$$

defined by the requirement that

$$\int dx\, f(x)\, \delta(x - x_0) = f(x_0). \tag{9.13}$$

That is, the delta function picks out the value of $f(x)$ at the particular point x_0. The theory of such "functions" has been placed on a mathematical foundation by L. Schwartz, through the theory of distributions (cf. Lighthill [1]).

As an example of operators acting on abstract vectors and on functions, we recall that the Heisenberg uncertainty principle leads to the requirement that the operators representing position and momentum must satisfy

$$[\mathcal{X}, \mathcal{P}_x] = i\hbar.$$

This relation means that

$$[\mathcal{X}, \mathcal{P}_x]\mathbf{A}_n = \int dx\, \mathbf{e}(x)[\mathcal{X}, \mathcal{P}_x]\psi(x | n)$$

must equal

$$i\hbar\mathbf{A}_n = i\hbar \int dx\, \mathbf{e}(x)\psi(x | n).$$

The commutation relation between two differential operators,

$$[\mathcal{X}, \mathcal{P}_x]\psi(x | n) = i\hbar\psi(x | n)$$

is satisfied for any function ψ if we choose

$$\mathcal{X} = x, \qquad \mathcal{P}_x = -i\hbar \frac{d}{dx}.$$

This prescription is just the one we first used to derive the Schrödinger differential equation. Thus we see that the operator equation

$$(\mathcal{H} - E_n)\mathbf{A}_n = \int dx\, \mathbf{e}(x)[\mathcal{H} - E_n]\psi(x | n) = 0 \tag{9.14a}$$

is equivalent to the differential equation

$$\left(\frac{\mathcal{P}_x^{\ 2}}{2m} + V - E_n\right)\psi(x | n) = 0. \tag{9.14b}$$

We are at liberty, therefore, to study atoms either by solving differential equations, such as (9.14*b*), or by using the machinery of operators and abstract vectors, such as (9.14*a*). The choice is dictated by convenience and familiarity.

Note in passing that, if we consider a function of momentum, $\varphi(p|n)$, rather than the function of position, $\psi(x|n)$, the commutation relation

$$[\mathcal{X}, \mathcal{P}_x]\varphi(p|n) = i\hbar\varphi(p|n)$$

will be satisfied for

$$\mathcal{X} = i\hbar\frac{\partial}{\partial p} \qquad \mathcal{P}_x = p.$$

REFERENCE

[1] M. J. Lighthill, *Introduction to Fourier Analysis and Generalized Functions*, Cambridge University Press, New York (1958).

5. Perturbation Theory

5.1 TIME-INDEPENDENT THEORY

A. Introduction

Very few problems in quantum mechanics can be solved exactly. (The nonrelativistic hydrogen atom is one of the few exactly soluble problems.) If we alter the Coulomb potential even slightly, adding an angle-dependent potential, the equation generally ceases to be separable, and we can no longer obtain neat analytic solutions. (An exception: if the perturbation is a uniform electric field, the equation still separates in parabolic coordinates.) Even greater difficulties face us when we attempt to solve the Schrödinger equation for a collection of interacting particles, for the Hamiltonian then consists of kinetic-energy operators $\mathfrak{I}(i)$ of individual particles, plus interactions $\mathcal{V}(ij)$ between all the particles:

$$\mathcal{H} = \sum_i \mathfrak{I}(i) + \sum_{ij} \mathcal{V}(ij).$$

This last term prevents us from immediately separating the equation into a sum of single-particle equations.

Generally one must approach such a problem from some similar but *soluble* problem and try to modify or combine known solutions to fit the problem under investigation. Perturbation theory is one such method, and it proves well suited to many problems in atomic physics. In the present section, we discuss a procedure for treating stationary (i.e., time-independent) perturbations developed by Lord Rayleigh [1], and applied to quantum mechanics by E. Schrödinger [2]. The Rayleigh–Schrödinger method is widely used in atomic physics (cf. the reviews by Dalgarno [3], [4]; and Hirschfelder, Byers-Brown, and Epstein [5]), although other methods also find favor (Morse and Feshbach [6] describe several alternative approaches). Further details can be found in standard references [7]–[9].

Suppose we can solve exactly the equation

$$\mathcal{H}^0 \mathbf{A}_{nl} = \varepsilon_n \mathbf{A}_{nl}, \qquad \varepsilon_n \neq \varepsilon_{n'} \tag{1.1}$$

for both eigenvalues ε_n and eigenvectors $\mathbf{A}_{nl}$. For generality we shall assume that the eigenvectors are degenerate: the second subscript l distinguishes different eigenvectors with the same eigenvalue ε_n. (In practice, n and l both stand for *sets* of quantum numbers.) We assume that the eigenvectors form a complete orthonormal set of basis vectors:

$$\langle \mathbf{A}_{nl} | \mathbf{A}_{n'l'} \rangle = \delta_{nn'}\delta_{ll'}. \tag{1.2}$$

We now want to solve the equation

$$(\mathcal{H}^0 + \lambda \mathcal{V})\Psi_{nl} = E_{nl}\Psi_{nl}, \tag{1.3}$$

where λ is a small number, and $\mathcal{V}$ a *perturbing potential.* Since (1.3) becomes (1.1) when the perturbation disappears, we look for a solution of the form

$$\Psi_{nl} = \Psi_{nl}^{(0)} + \lambda\Psi_{nl}^{(1)} + \lambda^2\Psi_{nl}^{(2)} + \cdots \tag{1.4}$$

$$E_{nl} = E_{nl}^{(0)} + \lambda E_{nl}^{(1)} + \lambda^2 E_{nl}^{(2)} + \cdots, \tag{1.5}$$

As the superscripts suggest, we usually refer to the $\Psi_{nl}^{(0)}$ and $E_{nl}^{(0)}$ as *zero-order states and zero-order energies*, the $\Psi_{nl}^{(1)}$ and $E_{nl}^{(1)}$ as *first-order* states and energies, and so on. The zero-order solution $\Psi_{nl}^{(0)}$ and $E_{nl}^{(0)}$ must correspond to solutions of (1.1), and further terms in the two series represent corrections to these simple solutions. We shall see that it becomes increasingly complicated to determine the corrections as we proceed to higher powers of λ. In practice one can seldom proceed beyond second-order corrections. More commonly we merely take first-order corrections. For this reason we always try to start from an unperturbed solution that lies as close as possible to the true solution.

To begin, we insert the series (1.4) and (1.5) into (1.1) to obtain

$$(\mathcal{H}^0 - E_{nl}^{(0)} - \lambda E_{nl}^{(1)} - \lambda^2 E_{nl}^{(2)} + \cdots + \lambda\mathcal{V})(\Psi_{nl}^{(0)} + \lambda\Psi_{nl}^{(1)} + \cdots) = 0.$$

For this equation to hold for arbitrary λ, the coefficient of each power of λ must be zero. Collecting these coefficients, we find

$$0 = (\mathcal{H}^0 - E_{nl}^{(0)})\Psi_{nl}^{(0)}, \tag{λ^0}$$

$$0 = (\mathcal{H}^0 - E_{nl}^{(0)})\Psi_{nl}^{(1)} + (\mathcal{V} - E_{nl}^{(1)})\Psi_{nl}^{(0)}, \tag{λ^1}$$

$$0 = (\mathcal{H}^0 - E_{nl}^{(0)})\Psi_{nl}^{(2)} + (\mathcal{V} - E_{nl}^{(1)})\Psi_{nl}^{(1)} - E_{nl}^{(2)}\Psi_{nl}^{(0)}, \tag{λ^2}$$

and so on. These equations form the framework of the theory; taken with some prescription for orthogonality (below), they completely determine the approximation to Ψ_{nl} and E_{nl}.

Since the states $\mathbf{A}_{nl}$ form a basis, we can expand the approximations to Ψ_{nl} in this basis:

$$\Psi_{nl}^{(0)} = \sum_{mk} \mathbf{A}_{mk}\langle \mathbf{A}_{mk} | \Psi_{nl}^{(0)} \rangle, \tag{1.6a}$$

$$\Psi_{nl}^{(1)} = \sum_{mk} \mathbf{A}_{mk}\langle \mathbf{A}_{mk} | \Psi_{nl}^{(1)} \rangle, \tag{1.6b}$$

and so on. The expansion coefficients $\langle \mathbf{A}_{mk} | \Psi_{nl}^{(p)} \rangle$ tell us all we need to know about the exact solution Ψ_{nl}.

We could require that different states Ψ_{nl} be exactly orthogonal to all orders of λ,

$$\langle \Psi_{nl} | \Psi_{n'l'} \rangle = \delta_{nn'} \delta_{ll'}$$

but instead we find it more convenient to require that all the corrections $\Psi_{kl'}^{(p)}$ be orthogonal to the zero-order state $\Psi_{nl}^{(0)}$ with the same unperturbed energy (same n):

$$\langle \Psi_{nl}^{(0)} | \Psi_{nl'}^{(p)} \rangle = 0 \quad \text{if} \quad p \neq 0 \quad \text{and} \quad l' \neq l. \tag{1.7}$$

This is equivalent to the conditions

$$\langle \mathbf{A}_{nl} | \Psi_{nl'}^{(1)} \rangle = \langle \mathbf{A}_{nl} | \Psi_{nl'}^{(2)} \rangle = \cdots = 0, \qquad \text{for} \quad l' \neq l. \tag{1.8}$$

B. Zero-Order Energy

In the zero-order energy approximation we neglect terms in λ and higher powers of λ in all the equations. In this approximation, Ψ_{nl} is just $\Psi_{nl}^{(0)}$, and it satisfies the same equation as $\mathbf{A}_{nl}$ [(λ^0) or (1.1)]:

$$\mathcal{H}^0\Psi_{nl}^{(0)} = E_{nl}^{(0)}\Psi_{nl}^{(0)}, \qquad \mathcal{H}^0\mathbf{A}_{nl} = E_n\mathbf{A}_{nl}.$$

Therefore the eigenvalue $E_{nl}^{(0)}$ must be ε_n, and the state $\Psi_{nl}^{(0)}$ must be either a particular state $\mathbf{A}_{nl}$ or, if the states are degenerate, some linear combination of states with the same energy (same n):

$$E_{nl}^{(0)} = \varepsilon_n, \tag{1.9}$$

$$\Psi_{nl}^{(0)} = \sum_{l'} \mathbf{A}_{nl'}\langle \mathbf{A}_{nl'} | \Psi_{nl}^{(0)} \rangle. \tag{1.10}$$

That is,

$$\langle \mathbf{A}_{n'l'} | \Psi_{nl}^{(0)} \rangle = 0 \qquad \text{unless} \quad n = n'.$$

To zero order, we see that the perturbation does not mix states with different unperturbed energy. The zero-order approximation $E_{nl}^{(0)}$ to the actual energy E_{nl} is just the eigenvalue ε_n of $\mathcal{H}^0$. Just as basis states $\mathbf{A}_{nl}$ and $\mathbf{A}_{n'l'}$ with different energies are orthogonal, the zero-order states $\Psi_{nl}^{(0)}$ and $\Psi_{n'l'}^{(0)}$ with different n are orthogonal. We can make these states orthogonal for the index l as well if we wish.

C. First-Order Energy

Now we proceed to the (λ^1) equation and take the scalar product with $\mathrm{A}_{nl'}$ (same n, arbitrary l):

$$\langle \mathbf{A}_{nl'} | \mathcal{H}^0 - E_{nl}^{(0)} | \Psi_{nl}^{(1)} \rangle + \langle \mathbf{A}_{nl'} | \mathcal{V} | \Psi_{nl}^{(0)} \rangle = E_{nl}^{(1)} \langle \mathbf{A}_{nl'} | \Psi_{nl}^{(0)} \rangle. \tag{1.11}$$

Since $\mathcal{H}^0$ is Hermitian, it gives

$$\mathbf{A}_{nl'} \mathcal{H}^0 = \varepsilon_n \mathbf{A}_{nl'} = E_{nl'}^{(0)} \mathbf{A}_{nl'} = E_{nl}^{(0)} \mathbf{A}_{nl'},$$

and the first term of (1.10) vanishes identically. We have just seen that $\Psi_{nl}^{(0)}$ is some linear combination of $\mathbf{A}_{nl}$ states (with the same n):

$$\Psi_{nl}^{(0)} = \sum_{l''} \langle \mathbf{A}_{nl''} | \Psi_{nl}^{(0)} \rangle \mathbf{A}_{nl''}. \tag{1.12}$$

Therefore (1.10) can be written as

$$\sum_{l''} \langle \mathbf{A}_{nl'} | \mathcal{V} | \mathbf{A}_{nl''} \rangle \langle \mathbf{A}_{nl''} | \Psi_{nl}^{(1)} \rangle = E_{nl}^{(1)} \langle \mathbf{A}_{nl'} | \Psi_{nl}^{(0)} \rangle. \tag{1.13}$$

If N different states $\mathbf{A}_{nl}$ have the same energy, there will be N similar equations for the various values of l for a given n. Let us look, for the moment, at some fixed value of n. If we use the following abbreviations,

$$V_{ll'} \equiv \langle \mathbf{A}_{nl} | \mathcal{V} | \mathbf{A}_{nl'} \rangle,$$
$$\langle l | l' \rangle \equiv \langle \mathbf{A}_{nl} | \Psi_{nl'} \rangle,$$
$$e_l \equiv E_{nl}^{(1)},$$

the equations take the form

$$\begin{array}{ccccc}
(V_{11} - e_1)\langle 1|1\rangle + & V_{12}\langle 2|1\rangle + \cdots + & & V_{1n}\langle N|1\rangle = 0, \\
V_{21}\langle 1|2\rangle + & (V_{22} - e_2)\langle 2|2\rangle + \cdots + & & V_{2n}\langle N|2\rangle = 0, \\
\cdot & \cdot & \cdots & \cdot \\
\cdot & \cdot & \cdots & \cdot \\
\cdot & \cdot & \cdots & \cdot \\
V_{n1}\langle 1|N\rangle + & V_{n2}\langle 2|N\rangle + \cdots + & & (V_{nn} - e_n)\langle N|N\rangle = 0.
\end{array} \tag{1.14}$$

These simultaneous equations for the N unknowns $\langle l|l'\rangle$ have a solution only if the determinant of the coefficients (the *secular determinant*) vanishes:

$$\det(V_{ll'} - x\delta_{ll'}) \equiv |V_{ll'} - x\delta_{ll'}| = 0. \tag{1.15}$$

This relationship is known as the *secular equation*. The $V_{ll'}$ are known numbers (matrix elements between $\mathbf{A}_{nl}$ states), and the N possible roots x are the unknown eigenvalues $E_{nl}^{(1)}$.

When the basis states $\mathbf{A}_{nl}$ are not degenerate, the secular equation merely identifies the eigenvalue with the expectation value of $\mathcal{V}$:

$$\langle \mathbf{A}_n | \mathcal{V} | \mathbf{A}_n \rangle = E_n^{(1)} \qquad \text{(nondegenerate)}. \tag{1.16}$$

When two basis states possess the same energy the secular equation is quadratic. The two roots may be identical or different. We shall discuss examples in the next section.

When three basis states share the same unperturbed energy the secular equation becomes a cubic equation, whose explicit solution can still be found. However, for quartic (or higher) equations, closed solutions do not exist in general, and we must resort to numerical methods for solutions.

Let us look at the general equation in more detail. Multiply (1.13) by $\langle \Psi_{nk}^{(0)} | \mathbf{A}_{nl} \rangle$ and sum over l':

$$\sum_{l'l''} \langle \Psi_{nk}^{(0)} | \mathbf{A}_{nl'} \rangle \langle \mathbf{A}_{nl'} | \mathcal{V} | \mathbf{A}_{nl''} \rangle \langle \mathbf{A}_{nl''} | \Psi_{nl'}^{(0)} \rangle = E_{nl}^{(1)} \sum_{l'} \langle \Psi_{nk}^{(0)} | \mathbf{A}_{nl'} \rangle \langle \mathbf{A}_{nl'} | \Psi_{nl}^{(0)} \rangle.$$

The quantity on the left-hand side of this equation is simply

$$\langle \Psi_{nk}^{(0)} | \mathcal{V} | \Psi_{nl}^{(0)} \rangle,$$

as we can verify using (1.12). Similarly, the right-hand side becomes

$$E_{nl}^{(1)} \langle \Psi_{nk}^{(0)} | \Psi_{nl}^{(0)} \rangle.$$

The requirement that the $\Psi_{nl}^{(0)}$ be orthonormal then gives the result

$$\langle \Psi_{nl}^{(0)} | \mathcal{V} | \Psi_{nk}^{(0)} \rangle = E_{nl}^{(1)} \delta_{lk}. \tag{1.17}$$

Thus the first-order corrections to the energy are the eigenvalues of the interaction, evaluated with zero-order eigenstates. In other words *degenerate zero-order eigenstates are states that make the interaction matrix diagonal; the diagonal elements are the eigenvalues.* In matrix notation (1.16) is

$$(U^\dagger)_{ij} V_{jk} U_{kl} = E_i \delta_{il}, \tag{1.18}$$

where the matrix $U_{kl} \equiv \langle \mathbf{A}_{nk} | \Psi_{nl}^{(0)} \rangle$ transforms the interaction $V_{jk} \equiv \langle \mathbf{A}_{nj} | \mathcal{V} | \mathbf{A}_{nk} \rangle$ computed with $\mathbf{A}_{nk}$ states into a diagonal matrix. Thus, to obtain the first-order energy correction and zero-order eigenstates, we must find the transformation matrix U_{kl} that diagonalizes the V_{jk} matrix. This task is actually very simple for a digital computer. Given the V_{jk} matrix, we obtain the transformation matrix and the eigenvalues.

We can often choose our basis $\mathbf{A}_{nl}$ such that the interaction matrix is already diagonal in l:

$$\langle \mathbf{A}_{nl} | \mathcal{V} | \mathbf{A}_{nl'} \rangle = V_l \delta_{ll'}. \tag{1.19}$$

The basis states themselves now provide our zero-order approximation states:

$$\Psi_{nl}^{(0)} = \mathbf{A}_{nl}, \qquad E_{nl}^{(1)} = \langle \mathbf{A}_{nl} | \mathcal{V} | \mathbf{A}_{nl} \rangle. \tag{1.20}$$

Thus, to this order,

$$\Psi_{nl} \cong \mathbf{A}_{nl}, \qquad E_{nl} \cong \varepsilon_n + \lambda \langle \mathbf{A}_{nl} | \mathcal{V} | \mathbf{A}_{nl} \rangle.$$

We thus avoid solving a secular equation or diagonalizing a matrix for the first-order energy correction $E_{nl}^{(1)}$, which is simply a matrix element.

D. First-Order Eigenstates

Still looking at the (λ^1) equation we can next obtain the first-order correction to the eigenstates by finding the expansion coefficients for $\Psi_{nl}^{(1)}$ in terms of $\mathbf{A}_{nl}$. The scalar product of the (λ^1) equation with $\mathbf{A}_{n'l'}$ ($n \neq n'$ and $l \neq l'$) yields

$$(\varepsilon_{n'} - E_{nl}^{(0)}) \langle \mathbf{A}_{n'l'} | \Psi_{nl}^{(1)} \rangle + \langle \mathbf{A}_{n'l'} | \mathcal{V} | \Psi_{nl}^{(0)} \rangle = E_{nl}^{(1)} \langle \mathbf{A}_{n'l'} | \Psi_{nl}^{(0)} \rangle. \tag{1.21}$$

The right-hand side is zero, according to our subsidiary orthogonality condition (1.7), and we obtain the result

$$\langle \mathbf{A}_{n'l'} | \Psi_{nl}^{(1)} \rangle = \sum_{l''} \frac{\langle \mathbf{A}_{n'l'} | \mathcal{V} | \mathbf{A}_{nl''} \rangle}{\varepsilon - \varepsilon_{n'}} \langle \mathbf{A}_{nl''} | \Psi_{nl}^{(0)} \rangle. \tag{1.22}$$

Thus the first-order correction to the eigenstate mixes states with different zero-order energies. These corrections are most important when the states are close in energy; in fact, if the states are too close it may be better to consider them degenerate, relabel them, and apply the results of the last section. States differing greatly in energy will in general not mix very much, and one may often neglect their contribution to the energy correction.

If the zero-order states are the basis states, or if the basis states are not degenerate, (1.22) simplifies to

$$\langle \mathbf{A}_{n'l'} | \Psi_{nl}^{(1)} \rangle = \frac{\langle \mathbf{A}_{n'l'} | \mathcal{V} | \mathbf{A}_{nl} \rangle}{\varepsilon_n - \varepsilon_{n'}}. \tag{1.23}$$

That is, the first approximation to Ψ_{nl} is simply

$$\Psi_{nl} \cong \mathbf{A}_{nl} + \lambda \sum_{l'n' \neq n} \frac{\langle \mathbf{A}_{n'l'} | \mathcal{V} | \mathbf{A}_{nl} \rangle}{\varepsilon_n - \varepsilon_{n'}} \mathbf{A}_{n'l'}. \tag{1.24}$$

E. Second-Order Energy

Going on now to the (λ^2) equation we can obtain the second-order correction to the energy. The scalar product with $\mathbf{A}_{nl'}$ (same n, arbitrary l') gives

$$\langle \mathbf{A}_{nl'} | \mathcal{H}^0 - E_{nl}^{(0)} | \Psi_{nl}^{(2)} \rangle + \langle \mathbf{A}_{nl'} | \mathcal{V} | \Psi_{nl}^{(1)} \rangle$$
$$- E_{nl}^{(1)} \langle \mathbf{A}_{nl'} | \Psi_{nl}^{(1)} \rangle - E_{nl}^{(2)} \langle \mathbf{A}_{nl'} | \Psi_{nl}^{(0)} \rangle = 0. \quad (1.25)$$

The first and third terms we have seen are zero, so that

$$E_{nl}^{(2)} \langle \mathbf{A}_{nl'} | \Psi_{nl}^{(0)} \rangle = \langle \mathbf{A}_{nl'} | \mathcal{V} | \Psi_{nl}^{(1)} \rangle$$
$$= \sum_{n''l''} \langle \mathbf{A}_{nl'} | \mathcal{V} | \mathbf{A}_{n''l''} \rangle \langle \mathbf{A}_{n''l''} | \Psi_{nl}^{(1)} \rangle$$
$$= \sum_{n''l''k} \frac{\langle \mathbf{A}_{nl'} | \mathcal{V} | \mathbf{A}_{n''l''} \rangle \langle \mathbf{A}_{n''l''} | \mathcal{V} | \mathbf{A}_{nk} \rangle \langle \mathbf{A}_{nk} | \Psi_{nl}^{(0)} \rangle}{\varepsilon_n - \varepsilon_{n''}}. \quad (1.26)$$

This equation simplifies a little if we are able to choose a basis such that $\Psi_{nl}^{(0)} = \mathbf{A}_{nl}$. We then obtain:

$$E_{nl}^{(2)} = \sum_{n''l''}{}' \frac{\langle \mathbf{A}_{nl} | \mathcal{V} | \mathbf{A}_{n''l''} \rangle \langle \mathbf{A}_{n''l''} | \mathcal{V} | \mathbf{A}_{nl} \rangle}{\varepsilon_n - \varepsilon_{n''}}, \quad (1.27)$$

(where the sum omits terms with $n'' = n$). That is, the best approximation of the energy, to second order, is

$$E_{nl} = \varepsilon_n + \lambda \langle \mathbf{A}_{nl} | \mathcal{V} | \mathbf{A}_{nl} \rangle + \lambda^2 \sum_{n'l'}{}' \frac{\langle \mathbf{A}_{nl} | \mathcal{V} | \mathbf{A}_{n'l'} \rangle \langle \mathbf{A}_{n'l'} | \mathcal{V} | \mathbf{A}_{nl} \rangle}{\varepsilon_n - \varepsilon_{n'}}. \quad (1.28)$$

If the eigenstates $\mathbf{A}_{nl}$ are to form a complete set [as they must for (1.5) to hold], they must usually comprise both states with discrete energies (bound states) and states with continuous energies (continuum states). Thus the summation in (1.28) and (1.26), etc., must actually include an integration over the continuum energies. When a particular state lies well below any ionization limit, the energy denominator may be sufficiently large that we can neglect continuum mixing. However, numerous important effects arise from mixing bound states with continuum states. (Continuum mixing is particularly important for states whose energies, though discrete, lie above an ionization limit. This mixing gives rise to autoionization [10, 11].) We shall use the symbol S to denote summation over discrete values and integration over continuous values:

$$\mathop{\mathsf{S}}_n \rightarrow \sum_n \quad \text{or} \quad \int dn.$$

For example, if eigenstates are characterized by continuous energies $E = \hbar\omega$, and there are $\rho_\alpha(E)$ states of the discrete type α in the interval from E to $E + dE$, then we have

$$\mathop{\mathsf{S}}_n \mathop{\mathsf{S}}_\alpha \rightarrow \int \rho_\alpha(E)\, dE \sum_\alpha = \hbar \int \rho_\alpha\, d\omega \sum_\alpha \cdot$$

In (1.27) and (1.28) we used a primed summation sign, $\sum'$, to signify omission of summands for which the energy denominator $\varepsilon_n - \varepsilon_{n'}$ vanished. We continue this convention below, using the symbol S' to indicate omission of divergent summands; that is, for summation over discrete variables S' means

$$\mathsf{S}'_n \frac{f(n)}{\varepsilon_n - \varepsilon_0} \to \sum_{n \neq 0} \frac{f(n)}{\varepsilon_n - \varepsilon_0}$$

and for integration over continuous variables S' means the *Cauchy principal-value integral*

$$\mathsf{S}' \frac{f(E)}{E - \varepsilon_0} \to \mathcal{P} \int dE \frac{f(E)}{E - \varepsilon_0},$$

which is defined as

$$\mathcal{P} \int_A^B \frac{dE}{E - \varepsilon_0} = \lim_{\delta \to 0} \left[\int_A^{\varepsilon_0 - \delta} \frac{dE}{E - \varepsilon_0} + \int_{\varepsilon_0 + \delta}^B \frac{dE}{E - \varepsilon_0} \right].$$

F. The General Case

We can readily generalize the preceding results to give wavefunctions to any desired order of accuracy. The equation of order p reads

$$(\mathcal{H}^0 - E_{nl}^{(0)})\Psi_{nl}^{(p)} + (\mathcal{V} - E_{nl}^{(1)})\Psi_{nl}^{(p-1)} = E_{nl}^{(2)}\Psi_{nl}^{(p-2)} + \cdots + E_{nl}^{(p)}\Psi_{nl}^{(0)} (\lambda^p).$$

For simplicity, we assume the basis functions $\mathbf{A}_{nl}$ coincide with the zero-order functions $\Psi_{nl}^{(0)}$. We then have $\langle \mathbf{A}_{nl'} | \Psi_{nl}^{(p)} \rangle = 0$, and we need only to find the coefficients $\langle \mathbf{A}_{n'l'} | \Psi_{nl}^{(p)} \rangle$ with $n' \neq n$. Taking the scalar product of (λ^p) with $\mathbf{A}_{nl}$ we obtain

$$\langle \mathbf{A}_{n'l'} | \Psi_{nl}^{(p)} \rangle = \frac{\langle \mathbf{A}_{n'l'} | \mathcal{V} | \Psi_{nl}^{(p-1)} \rangle}{\varepsilon_n - \varepsilon_{n'}}. \tag{1.29}$$

We can now substitute $\Psi^{(p-1)}$ in terms of $\Psi^{(p-2)}$, then substitute $\Psi^{(p-2)}$ in terms of $\Psi^{(p-3)}$, and so on:

$$\begin{aligned} \langle \mathbf{A}_{n'l'} | \Psi_{nl}^{(p)} \rangle &= \mathsf{S}' \frac{\langle \mathbf{A}_{n'l'} | \mathcal{V} | \mathbf{A}_{n''l''} \rangle}{\varepsilon_n - \varepsilon_{n'}} \frac{\langle \mathbf{A}_{n''l''} | \mathcal{V} | \Psi_{nl}^{(p-2)} \rangle}{\varepsilon_n - \varepsilon_{n''}} \\ &= \underset{(p\,-\,1 \text{ sums})}{\mathsf{S}' \cdots \mathsf{S}'} \frac{\langle \mathbf{A}_{n'l'} | \mathcal{V} | \mathbf{A}_{n''l''} \rangle}{(\varepsilon_n - \varepsilon_{n'})} \cdots \frac{\langle \mathbf{A}_{n''l''} | \mathcal{V} | \mathbf{A}_{nl} \rangle}{(\varepsilon_n - \varepsilon_{n''})}. \end{aligned} \tag{1.30}$$

Thus we obtain the wavefunction

$$\Psi_{nl} = \mathbf{A}_{nl}$$
$$+ \lambda \, \mathsf{S}' \, \mathbf{A}_{n'l'} \frac{\langle n'l' | \mathcal{V} | nl \rangle}{\varepsilon_n - \varepsilon_{n'}}$$
$$+ \lambda^2 \, \mathsf{S}' \, \mathsf{S}' \, \mathbf{A}_{n'l'} \frac{\langle n'l' | \mathcal{V} | n''l'' \rangle}{(\varepsilon_n - \varepsilon_{n'})} \frac{\langle n''l'' | \mathcal{V} | nl \rangle}{(\varepsilon_n - \varepsilon_{n''})}$$
$$+ \lambda^3 \, \mathsf{S}' \, \mathsf{S}' \, \mathsf{S}' \, \mathbf{A}_{n'l'} \frac{\langle n'l' | \mathcal{V} | n''l'' \rangle}{(\varepsilon_n - \varepsilon_{n'})} \frac{\langle n''l'' | \mathcal{V} | n'''l''' \rangle}{(\varepsilon_n - \varepsilon_{n'''})} \frac{\langle n'''l''' | \mathcal{V} | nl \rangle}{(\varepsilon_n - \varepsilon_{n'''})} . \tag{1.31}$$

where $\langle n'l' | \mathcal{V} | nl \rangle \equiv \langle \mathbf{A}_{n'l'} | \mathcal{V} | \mathbf{A}_{nl} \rangle$, etc. and summations go over all primed quantum numbers. The energy follows from a similar series:

$$E_{nl} = \varepsilon_n$$
$$+ \lambda \langle nl | \mathcal{V} | nl \rangle$$
$$+ \lambda^2 \mathsf{S}' \langle nl | \mathcal{V} | n'l' \rangle \frac{\langle n'l' | \mathcal{V} | nl \rangle}{(\varepsilon_n - \varepsilon_{n'})}$$
$$+ \lambda^3 \mathsf{S}' \mathsf{S}' \langle nl | \mathcal{V} | n'l' \rangle \frac{\langle n'l' | \mathcal{V} | n''l'' \rangle}{(\varepsilon_n - \varepsilon_{n'})} \frac{\langle n''l'' | \mathcal{V} | nl \rangle}{(\varepsilon_n - \varepsilon_{n''})} . \tag{1.32}$$

The approximation Ψ_{nl} is not normalized. As we see from (1.31), the normalization differs from unity by a positive, second-order quantity, plus higher-order corrections:

$$\langle \Psi_{nl} | \Psi_{nl} \rangle = 1$$
$$+ \lambda^2 \mathsf{S}' \frac{|\langle n'l' | \mathcal{V} | nl \rangle|^2}{(\varepsilon_n - \varepsilon_{n'})^2}$$
$$+ 2\lambda^3 \mathsf{S}' \mathsf{S}' \frac{\langle nl | \mathcal{V} | n'l' \rangle \langle n'l' | \mathcal{V} | n''l'' \rangle \langle n''l'' | \mathcal{V} | nl \rangle}{(\varepsilon_n - \varepsilon_{n'})^2 (\varepsilon_n - \varepsilon_{n''})}$$
$$+ \cdots$$

We summarize these results as follows:

1. Zero-order energies are eigenvalues of $\mathcal{H}^0$.
2. Zero-order eigenstates diagonalize $\mathcal{V}$ between states that are degenerate in zero order. These states are orthogonal.
3. First-order energy corrections are the diagonal elements of $\mathcal{V}$ between zero-order states.
4. First-order eigenstates include mixtures of states with different energies.
5. Higher-order corrections involve sums over products of matrix elements, with energy difference denominators.

REFERENCES

[1] J. W. Strutt, Baron Rayleigh, *The Theory of Sound*, Dover, New York (1945), vol. 1, sec. 90.
[2] E. Schrödinger, *Ann. d Physik* **80,** 437 (1926).
[3] A. Dalgarno, *Quantum Theory*, D. R. Bates (ed.), Academic, New York (1961).
[4] A. Dalgarno, *Advan. Phys.* **11,** 281 (1962).
[5] J. O. Hirschfelder, W. Byers-Brown, and S. T. Epstein, *Advan. Quant. Chem.* **1**, 255 (1964).
[6] P. M. Morse and H. Feshbach, *Methods of Theoretical Physics*, McGraw-Hill, New York (1953), Chapter 9.
[7] P. I. Richards, *Manual of Mathematical Physics*, Pergamon, New York (1959, Chapter 19.
[8] A. Messiah, *Quantum Mechanics*, Wiley, New York (1963).
[9] J. Mathews and R. L. Walker, *Mathematical Methods of Physics*, Benjamin, New York (1965), Chapter 10.
[10] U. Fano, *Phys. Rev.* **124,** 1866 (1961); U. Fano and J. W. Cooper, *Phys. Rev.* **137,** A1364 (1965).
[11] B. W. Shore, *Rev. Mod. Phys.* **39,** 439 (1967).

5.2 EXAMPLES

To see how this perturbation theory works out in a simple case, consider two degenerate basis states $\mathbf{A}_1$ and $\mathbf{A}_2$, sharing the energy ε:

$$\begin{aligned} \mathcal{H}^0\mathbf{A}_1 &= \varepsilon\mathbf{A}_1, \\ \mathcal{H}^0\mathbf{A}_2 &= \varepsilon\mathbf{A}_2. \end{aligned} \tag{2.1}$$

Presumably we know all the properties of these basis states, that is, we can calculate any relevant matrix elements between these states. We apply a small perturbation $\mathcal{V}$ to the Hamiltonian $\mathcal{H}^0$, and then seek the two eigenstates Ψ_1 and Ψ_2 of this new Hamiltonian:

$$\begin{aligned} (\mathcal{H}^0 + \lambda\mathcal{V})\Psi_1 &= E_1\Psi_1, \\ (\mathcal{H}^0 + \lambda\mathcal{V})\Psi_2 &= E_2\Psi_2. \end{aligned} \tag{2.2}$$

Perturbation theory provides approximations in the form

$$\begin{aligned} \Psi_1 &= \Psi_1^{(0)} + \lambda\Psi_1^{(1)} + \lambda^2\Psi_1^{(2)} + \cdots \\ \Psi_2 &= \Psi_2^{(0)} + \cdots \end{aligned} \tag{2.3}$$

and

$$\begin{aligned} E_1 &= E_1^{(0)} + \lambda E_1^{(1)} + \lambda^2 E_1^{(2)} + \cdots \\ E_2 &= E_2^{(0)} + \cdots \end{aligned} \tag{2.4}$$

We now express the zero-order approximation $\Psi_i^{(0)}$ to these eigenstates as linear combinations of $\mathbf{A}_1$ and $\mathbf{A}_2$:

$$\begin{aligned}\Psi_1 &\cong \Psi_1^{(0)} = \langle 1|1\rangle \mathbf{A}_1 + \langle 2|1\rangle \mathbf{A}_2,\\ \Psi_2 &\cong \Psi_2^{(0)} = \langle 1|2\rangle \mathbf{A}_1 + \langle 2|2\rangle \mathbf{A}_2.\end{aligned} \tag{2.5}$$

As we saw in the last section, the first-order energies are the roots of the secular determinant

$$\begin{vmatrix} V_{11} - x & V_{12} \\ V_{21} & V_{22} - x \end{vmatrix} = 0,$$

where $V_{ij} \equiv \langle \mathbf{A}_i | \mathcal{V} | \mathbf{A}_j \rangle$. The secular equation reads

$$x^2 - x(V_{11} + V_{22}) + (V_{11}V_{22} - V_{12}V_{21}) = 0. \tag{2.6}$$

The two roots of this quadratic equation give the two first-order energy corrections:

$$x = E_1^{(1)} = \bar{V} - \tfrac{1}{2}\sqrt{(V_{22} - V_{11})^2 + 4V_{12}V_{21}} \tag{2.7}$$

and

$$x = E_2^{(1)} = \bar{V} + \tfrac{1}{2}\sqrt{(V_{22} - V_{11})^2 + 4V_{12}V_{21}},$$

where

$$\begin{aligned}\bar{V} &\equiv \tfrac{1}{2}(V_{11} + V_{22})\\ &= \tfrac{1}{2}\langle \mathbf{A}_1 | \mathcal{V} | \mathbf{A}_1 \rangle + \tfrac{1}{2}\langle \mathbf{A}_2 | \mathcal{V} | \mathbf{A}_2 \rangle.\end{aligned}$$

Here we have identified Ψ_1 as the state of lower energy. Armed with these roots of the secular equation we can obtain the expansion coefficients for $\Psi_1^{(0)}$ from (1.14). In the present example this reads

$$[V_{11} - E_1^{(1)}]\langle 1|1\rangle + V_{12}\langle 2|1\rangle = 0. \tag{2.8}$$

We also need the normalization condition

$$\langle 1|1\rangle^2 + \langle 2|1\rangle^2 = 1. \tag{2.9}$$

The solution of these simultaneous equations is

$$\begin{aligned}\langle 1|1\rangle^2 &= \frac{(V_{12})^2}{[V_{11} - E_1^{(1)}]^2 + (V_{12})^2},\\ \langle 2|1\rangle^2 &= \frac{(V_{11} - E_1^{(1)})^2}{[V_{11} - E_1^{(1)}]^2 + (V_{12})^2}.\end{aligned} \tag{2.10}$$

Similar equations hold for the expansion coefficients $\langle 1|2\rangle$ and $\langle 2|2\rangle$ of $\Psi_2^{(0)}$. Once we adopt a phase convention, such as requiring that $\langle 1|1\rangle$ be positive and real, the expansion coefficients are completely determined.

Two extreme cases are of particular interest: (*i*) when the diagonal elements are equal; and (*ii*) when the off-diagonal elements are small.

First consider case (*i*):

$$V_{11} = V_{22} \equiv \overline{V}.$$

We assume the operator $\mathcal{V}$ is Hermitian (so that, assuming real matrix elements for simplicity, $V_{12} = V_{21}$). Equation 2.7 then shows that

$$E_1^{(1)} = \overline{V} - V_{12}, \qquad E_2^{(1)} = \overline{V} + V_{12}. \tag{2.11}$$

Thus the off-diagonal matrix element removes the degeneracy. The expansion coefficients for $\Psi_1^{(0)}$ are, according to (2.10) (with the phase convention of real, positive $\langle 1 | 1 \rangle$):

$$\langle 1 | 1 \rangle = \frac{1}{\sqrt{2}},$$

$$\langle 2 | 1 \rangle = \frac{1}{\sqrt{2}},$$

and the coefficients for $\Psi_2^{(0)}$ are

$$\langle 2 | 1 \rangle = \frac{1}{\sqrt{2}},$$

$$\langle 2 | 2 \rangle = -\frac{1}{\sqrt{2}}.$$

We therefore obtain the results

$$\Psi_1 \simeq \frac{1}{\sqrt{2}}(\mathbf{A}_1 + \mathbf{A}_2), \qquad E_1 \cong \varepsilon + \lambda(\overline{V} - V_{12}), \tag{2.12a}$$

and

$$\Psi_2 \simeq \frac{1}{\sqrt{2}}(\mathbf{A}_1 - \mathbf{A}_2), \qquad E_2 \cong \varepsilon + \lambda(\overline{V} + V_{12}). \tag{2.12b}$$

Note that Ψ_1 is symmetric in $\mathbf{A}_1$ and $\mathbf{A}_2$ while Ψ_2 is antisymmetric. The symmetric state has the lower energy. As long as we consider only two basis states, we obtain only zero-order eigenstates and first-order energies. If we wish more accurate eigenstates and eigenvalues (i.e., higher-order corrections), we must include contributions to Ψ_1 from additional nondegenerate basis states $\mathbf{A}_3, \mathbf{A}_4, \mathbf{A}_5, \ldots$.

We now consider case (*ii*): suppose the diagonal elements are unequal, with $V_{22} > V_{11}$, and the off-diagonal elements are very small. Specifically, let

$$V_{12}V_{21} \ll V_{22} - V_{11}. \tag{2.13}$$

Then the eigenvalues are very nearly the diagonal elements of the interaction matrix, and the eigenstates are very nearly the basis states.

$$\Psi_1 \simeq \mathbf{A}_1, \qquad E_1 \cong \varepsilon + \lambda V_{11}, \tag{2.14a}$$

and

$$\Psi_2 \simeq \mathbf{A}_2, \qquad E_2 \cong \varepsilon + \lambda V_{22}. \tag{2.14b}$$

According to the prescription of the perturbation theory developed in the last chapter, we should actually diagonalize the interaction matrix to obtain the zero-order eigenstates and first-order energies. But we can note (2.13) and expand the solutions of the secular equation (2.7) as

$$\begin{aligned} E_1^{(1)} &= V_{11} - \frac{V_{12}V_{21}}{V_{22} - V_{11}} + \frac{(V_{12}V_{21})^2}{(V_{22} - V_{11})^3} - \cdots, \\ E_2^{(1)} &= V_{22} + \frac{V_{12}V_{21}}{V_{22} - V_{11}} - \frac{(V_{12}V_{21})^2}{(V_{22} - V_{11})^3} + \cdots, \end{aligned} \tag{2.15}$$

Thus when we diagonalize the interaction matrix, the separation of the diagonal elements will increase; the energy eigenvalues spread apart because of the off-diagonal matrix elements. A similar expansion of (2.10) yields the eigenstates

$$\begin{aligned} \Psi_1 &\cong \left[1 - \frac{1}{2}\left(\frac{V_{12}}{\Delta}\right)^2\right]\mathbf{A}_1 + \left(\frac{V_{12}}{\Delta}\right)^2\mathbf{A}_2, \\ \Psi_2 &\cong \left(\frac{V_{12}}{\Delta}\right)^2\mathbf{A}_1 + \left[1 - \frac{1}{2}\left(\frac{V_{12}}{\Delta}\right)^2\right]\mathbf{A}_2, \end{aligned} \tag{2.16}$$

where

$$\Delta \equiv V_{22} - V_{11}.$$

When the off-diagonal element V_{12} is much smaller than the energy difference Δ, we introduce little error by using the approximation of (2.14) in place of the exact result of (2.16). The error is roughly $(V_{12}/\Delta)^2$.

5.3 TIME-DEPENDENT PERTURBATION THEORY

A. Introduction

The time-dependent Schrödinger equation,

$$\mathcal{H}\Psi(t) = i\hbar \frac{\partial}{\partial t} \Psi(t), \tag{3.1}$$

with appropriate Hamiltonian operator $\mathcal{H}$, provides the appropriate nonrelativistic equation for electrons, for atoms, and many other quantum-mechanical systems. Only for very simple idealized cases can one obtain explicit analytic solutions to (3.1). More commonly, one proceeds by breaking the Hamiltonian operator into a part $\mathcal{H}^0$, whose eigenstates (or eigenfunctions) are well known, and the remainder, a "perturbation" $\mathcal{V}$. Often the perturbation comprises a sum of various interactions $\mathcal{V}^1$, $\mathcal{V}^2$, etc. For convenience, we shall lump these together in $\mathcal{V}$:

$$\mathcal{H} = \mathcal{H}^0 + \mathcal{V}^1 + \mathcal{V}^2 + \cdots \equiv \mathcal{H}^0 + \mathcal{V}.$$

In the preceding sections we sought *eigenstates of* $\mathcal{H}$ in terms of "unperturbed" eigenstates of $\mathcal{H}^0$. We thus required that $\Psi(t)$ have the time dependence $\exp(-iEt/\hbar)$, and we looked only at the time-independent Schrödinger equation:

$$(\mathcal{H}^0 + \mathcal{V})\psi = E\psi; \qquad \Psi(t) = \psi \exp\left(\frac{-iEt}{\hbar}\right). \tag{3.2}$$

Since $\mathcal{H}^0$ and $\mathcal{V}$ were assumed independent of time, the solution ψ gave the steady-state probability distribution $|\psi|^2$, and permissible values of E corresponded to the energy of the system in the presence of the perturbation $\mathcal{V}$.

In the present section we look for more general solutions to (3.1); solutions that are *not* eigenstates of $\mathcal{H}$. These will not be energy eigenstates, and therefore will not have the simple exponential time dependence of (3.2). This more general approach becomes necessary when the interaction depends on time, $\mathcal{V}(t)$ or when, for physical reasons, the unperturbed eigenstates of $\mathcal{H}^0$ have greater significance than the eigenstates of $\mathcal{H}$. Our treatment will follow the approach of Dirac [1]. (Bohm [2] gives a clear picture of the physics behind the mathematics.)

We shall seek solutions to

$$[\mathcal{H}^0 + \mathcal{V}(t)]\Psi(t) = i\hbar \frac{\partial}{\partial t} \Psi(t) \tag{3.3}$$

in terms of eigenstates $\mathbf{A}_{n\alpha}(t)$ of $\mathcal{H}^0$:

$$\mathcal{H}^0\mathbf{A}_{n\alpha}(t) = i\hbar \frac{\partial}{\partial t} \mathbf{A}_{n\alpha}(t) = E_n\mathbf{A}_{n\alpha}(t). \tag{3.4}$$

Since several eigenstates will generally share an eigenvalue E_n, we distinguish these degenerate states by the second index α. This index α, as well as the energies E_n, may consist of a succession of discrete values, or they may encompass a continuum of values. These states have the time dependence

$$\mathbf{A}_{n\alpha}(t) = \mathbf{a}_{n\alpha} \exp \frac{-iE_n t}{\hbar}. \tag{3.5}$$

In what follows we assume that the $\mathbf{A}_{n\alpha}(t)$ states form a complete set of orthonormal states:

$$\langle \mathbf{A}_{n\alpha}(t) \,|\, \mathbf{A}_{m\beta}(t) \rangle = \delta_{nm}\, \delta_{\alpha\beta}. \tag{3.6}$$

Therefore any state $\Psi(t)$ can be expressed as a linear combination of these basis states at any instant of time t:

$$\Psi(t) = \mathsf{S}_n \mathsf{S}_\alpha\, c_{n\alpha}(t) \mathbf{A}_{n\alpha}(t), \tag{3.7}$$

where, to preserve normalization,

$$\mathsf{S}_n \mathsf{S}_\alpha\, |c_{n\alpha}(t)|^2 = 1.$$

(Here S_n denotes summation over discrete values of n and integration over continuum values.) Unlike the previous sections, the expansion coefficients $c_{n\alpha}(t)$ must now depend on time, because $\Psi(t)$ is not an energy eigenstate. Our task is to determine all the $c_{n\alpha}(t)$ as a function of time. Then from $|c_{n\alpha}(t)|^2$ we find the probability that the system described by $\Psi(t)$ has the properties of $\mathbf{A}_{n\alpha}(t)$ at the time t.

As with the Rayleigh–Schrödinger theory in the previous sections, the Schrödinger equation provides equations for the expansion coefficients $c_{m\alpha}(t)$. We have, from (3.7),

$$[\mathcal{H}^0 + \mathcal{V}(t)]\Psi(t) = [\mathcal{H}^0 + \mathcal{V}(t)]\, \mathsf{S}_n \mathsf{S}_\alpha\, c_{n\alpha}(t) \mathbf{A}_{n\alpha}(t), \tag{3.8}$$

and from (3.4), we obtain

$$i\hbar \frac{\partial}{\partial t} \Psi(t) = i\hbar\, \mathsf{S}_n \mathsf{S}_\alpha\, \dot{c}_n(t) \mathbf{A}_{n\alpha}(t) + \mathsf{S}_n \mathsf{S}_\alpha\, c_{n\alpha}(t) \mathcal{H}^0 \mathbf{A}_{n\alpha}(t). \tag{3.9}$$

Thus the time-dependent Schrödinger equation becomes

$$\mathsf{S}_n \mathsf{S}_\alpha\, c_{n\alpha}(t) \mathcal{V}(t) \mathbf{A}_{n\alpha}(t) = i\hbar\, \mathsf{S}_n \mathsf{S}_\alpha\, \dot{c}_{n\alpha}(t) \mathbf{A}_{n\alpha}(t). \tag{3.10}$$

If we take the scalar product of (3.10) with the state $\mathbf{A}_{m\beta}(t)$ we obtain an equation for the change of any coefficient with time:

$$\mathsf{S}_n \mathsf{S}_\alpha\, c_{n\alpha}(t) \langle \mathbf{A}_{m\beta}(t) \,|\, \mathcal{V}(t) \,|\, \mathbf{A}_{n\alpha}(t) \rangle = i\hbar \dot{c}_{m\beta}(t). \tag{3.11}$$

Equation 3.11 provides the basic starting point for our perturbation technique. It is convenient to remove the sinusoidal time dependence from the matrix element of (3.11) by introducing the notation

$$\langle m\alpha|\mathcal{V}(t)|n\alpha\rangle \exp(i\omega_{mn}t) \equiv \langle \mathbf{a}_{m\alpha}|\mathcal{V}(t)|\mathbf{a}_{n\alpha}\rangle \exp\left[i(E_m - E_n)\frac{t}{\hbar}\right],$$

$$\hbar\omega_{mn} \equiv E_m - E_n.$$

The basic equation then reads:

$$i\hbar\dot{c}_{m\beta}(t) = \mathop{\mathsf{S}}_{n}\mathop{\mathsf{S}}_{\alpha} \langle m\beta|\mathcal{V}(t)|n\alpha\rangle c_{n\alpha}(t) \exp(i\omega_{mn}t). \tag{3.12}$$

Equation 3.12 provides an infinite number of equations, one for each value of m and β. In words, the growth of any eigenstate $\mathbf{A}_{m\beta}(t)$ at any time depends on the matrix elements of $\mathcal{V}$ that link this state to the eigenstates already present at that time.

The matrix elements of (3.12) are often spoken of as the *interaction picture* or *interaction representation*, to distinguish them from the *Schrödinger picture* of (3.11).

B. Direct Transitions

In what follows we shall assume that once the interaction $\mathcal{V}(t)$ is "turned on," it *remains constant in time*. We further suppose that initially, at the instant $t = 0$, we know the system is definitely in the state $\mathbf{A}_{00}(t)$:

$$\Psi(0) = \mathbf{A}_{00}(0) \quad \text{or} \quad c_{n\alpha}(0) = \delta_{n0}\,\delta_{\alpha 0}.$$

With the passage of time the initial state $\mathbf{A}_{00}$ must become depleted, while other states must become populated. In other words, the system undergoes *transitions* from the initial state to other states. As long as the initial state dominates the expansion of (3.7), the growth of other states is governed by their link to the initial state. With $c_{00}(t) = 1$, (3.12) gives the approximation

$$i\hbar\dot{c}^{(1)}_{m\beta}(t) = \langle m\beta|\mathcal{V}|00\rangle \exp(i\omega_{n0}t). \tag{3.13}$$

This will hold until times such that coefficients $c_{n\alpha}$ other than c_{00} contribute to the sum in (3.7). With the initial condition $c_{m\beta}(t) = 0$, (3.13) integrates immediately:

$$\begin{aligned} c^{(1)}_{m\beta}(t) &= \langle m\beta|\mathcal{V}|00\rangle (i\hbar)^{-1}\int_0^t d\tau \exp(i\omega_{m0}\tau) \\ &= \langle m\beta|\mathcal{V}|00\rangle \left[\frac{1 - \exp(i\omega_{m0}t)}{\hbar\omega_{m0}}\right]. \end{aligned} \tag{3.14}$$

The probability, at time t, that the system Ψ has passed from $\mathbf{A}_{00}$ to $\mathbf{A}_{m\beta}$' is therefore

$$|c_{m\beta}^{(1)}(t)|^2 = 2|\langle m\beta|\mathcal{V}|00\rangle|^2\left[\frac{1-\cos(\omega_{m0}t)}{\hbar^2\omega_{m0}{}^2}\right]. \tag{3.15}$$

With passing time this probability oscillates between a minimum of

$$|c_{m\beta}^{(1)}(t)|^2 = 0 \quad \text{whenever} \quad t = n\,\frac{2\pi\hbar}{(E_n - E_0)} \tag{3.16a}$$

(where n is an integer), and a maximum of

$$|c_{m\beta}^{(1)}(t)|^2 = 4\,\frac{|\langle m\beta|\mathcal{V}|00\rangle|^2}{(E_m - E_0)^2} \quad \text{whenever} \quad t = \frac{m}{2}\,\frac{2\pi\hbar}{(E_n - E_0)} \tag{3.16b}$$

(where m is an odd integer). We see that when the perturbing operator $\mathcal{V}$ links eigenstates with nearly the same unperturbed energy, $E_m \approx E_0$, the probability of state $\mathbf{A}_{m\beta}$ can become quite large. However, this only happens after very long times. In most physically important cases states exist with a continuum of energies very close to the energy E_0 of $\mathbf{A}_{00}$. We then wish to know the probability integrated over some small energy interval around E_0. We want to know the value of the quantity

$$\int_{E_0-\varepsilon}^{E_0+\varepsilon} dE_m|c_{m\beta}^{(1)}(t)|^2.$$

In fact, because our observations generally do not distinguish between some of the degenerate states, we need an additional summation (or integration) over the indices that are *not distinguished* in the particular observation. We want the value of the integral

$$\int_{E_0-\varepsilon}^{E_0+\varepsilon} \rho_\beta(E_m)\,dE_m|c_{m\beta}^{(1)}(t)|^2,$$

where $\rho_\beta(E_m)$ is the average number-density of undistinguished states of energy E_m:

$$\frac{1}{\Delta E}\,\underset{\beta}{\mathsf{S}}\int_{\Delta E} dE = \int_{\Delta E} \rho_\beta(E)\,dE.$$

From (3.15) we obtain

$$\int_{E_0+\varepsilon}^{E_0-\varepsilon} \rho_\beta(E_m)\,dE_m|c_{m\beta}^{(1)}(t)|^2$$
$$= 2\int_{E_0-\varepsilon}^{E_0+\varepsilon} \rho_\alpha(E_m)\,dE_m|\langle m\beta|\mathcal{V}|00\rangle|^2\left[\frac{1-\cos\omega_{m0}t}{(E_m - E_0)^2}\right]. \tag{3.17}$$

With a change of variable $x = \omega_{m0}t = (E_m - E_0)t/\hbar$ the integral on the right side becomes

$$\frac{2t}{\hbar}\int_{-\varepsilon\hbar t}^{+\varepsilon\hbar t} dx\,\frac{(1-\cos x)}{x^2}\left|\left\langle E_0 + \frac{x\hbar}{t},\ \beta\,|\mho|\,E_0,\ 0\right\rangle\right|^2 \rho_\beta\left(E_0 + \frac{\hbar x}{t}\right).$$

As we look at longer times $t \gg \hbar/E_0$ (the time scale $\hbar/E_0$ is of the order of 10^{-16} sec for atomic energy levels) we can neglect the difference between E_0 and $E_m = E_0 + x\hbar/t$ in the matrix element, and let the limits of integration tend to $+\infty$, $-\infty$. [Of course we still must have $c_{00}(t) \approx 1$; we shall see that changes in $c_{00}(t)$ occur generally on a scale of 10^{-8} sec for atomic radiative transitions, so that these two conditions are compatible.] We thus obtain, in place of (3.17), the expression

$$\frac{2t}{\hbar}\rho_\beta(E_0)\,|\langle 0\beta|\mho|00\rangle|^2\int_{-\infty}^{\infty} dx\,\frac{(1-\cos x)}{x^2}. \tag{3.18}$$

The integral has the value π. In this approximation, then, the probability of finding states within an increment ΔE of the initial energy grows linearly with time:

$$\int_{\Delta E}\rho_\beta(E_m)\,dE_m\,|c_{m\beta}^{(1)}(t)|^2 = \frac{2\pi}{\hbar}\,|\langle m\beta|\mho|00\rangle|^2\rho_\beta(E_0)t \qquad (E_m = E_0). \tag{3.19}$$

This growth rate of the probability for observing states undistinguished from $\mathbf{A}_\alpha$ defines the *transition probability per unit time* or *transition rate w:*

$$w(00 \rightarrow m\beta) = \frac{1}{t\Delta E}\,\mathsf{S}_{\beta}\,\mathsf{S}_{\Delta E}\,|c_{m\beta}^{(1)}(t)|^2 \qquad (E_m = E_0). \tag{3.20}$$

Equation 3.19 then provides *Fermi's Famous Golden Rule* [3] for transition rates:

$$w(00 \rightarrow m\beta) = \frac{2\pi}{\hbar}\rho_\beta(E_0)\,|\langle m\beta|\mho|00\rangle|^2 \qquad (E_n = E_0). \tag{3.21}$$

Keep in mind that the density of states $\rho_\beta(E_0)$ appropriate to any particular transition rate $w(00 \rightarrow m_\beta)$ depends on how many different degenerate states we choose to distinguish with the observation and how many we lump together in the summation S_β.

C. Indirect Transitions

Frequently a state of interest $\mathbf{A}_{n\alpha}$ has no matrix element $\langle n\alpha|\mho|00\rangle$ to the initial state, or this matrix element may be very small. This does not preclude the possibility of finding the system in state $\mathbf{A}_{n\alpha}$ eventually. Once the states $\mathbf{A}_{m\beta}$ become populated, transitions may occur to $\mathbf{A}_{n\alpha}$. Equation

3.12 relates (without approximation) the growth of $c_{m\beta}(t)$ to the *intermediate states* $\mathbf{A}_{n\alpha}$:

$$i\hbar c_{m\beta}^{(2)}(t) = \mathsf{S}_n \mathsf{S}_\alpha \langle m\beta|\mathcal{V}|n\alpha\rangle \int_0^t dt\, c_{n\alpha}^{(1)}(t) \exp(i\omega_{mn}t). \tag{3.22}$$

For times such that the initial state $\mathbf{A}_{00}$ remains relatively undepleted, $c_{00}(t) \simeq 1$, (3.14) provides an adequate value for $c_{n\alpha}^{(1)}(t)$. Inserting this approximation, we obtain

$$i\hbar c_{m\beta}^{(2)}(t) = \mathsf{S}_n \mathsf{S}_\alpha \langle m\beta|\mathcal{V}|n\alpha\rangle\langle n\alpha|\mathcal{V}|00\rangle \int dt \left[\frac{1-\exp(i\omega_{n0}t)}{\hbar\omega_{n0}}\right] \exp(i\omega_{mn}t). \tag{3.23}$$

When we use the initial condition $c_{m\beta}(0) = 0$, this integrates to (note that $\omega_{n0} + \omega_{mn} = \omega_{m0}$)

$$c_{m\beta}^{(2)}(t) = \mathsf{S}_n \mathsf{S}_\alpha \frac{\langle m_\beta|\mathcal{V}|n\alpha\rangle\langle n\alpha|\mathcal{V}|00\rangle}{(E_n - E_0)} \left[\frac{1-\exp(i\omega_{m0}t)}{\hbar\omega_{m0}} - \frac{1-\exp(i\omega t_{mn})}{\hbar\omega_{mn}}\right]. \tag{3.24}$$

To proceed further, it is convenient to separate the intermediate states into two types: those near a resonance frequency, for which either $E_n = E_0$ or $E_n = E_m$, and those far from resonance, for which the energy differences $|E_n - E_0|$ and $|E_n - E_m|$ are appreciable.

When matrix elements linking the initial state to states with the same energy are zero or very small, we can neglect "resonant" intermediate states (states with $\omega_{mn} = 0$).

When $|\omega_{mn}| \gg 0$, the second term in brackets contributes only an oscillatory part which averages out to zero. The first term is independent of the summation, and we can then write the nonresonant contribution (i.e., $E_n \neq E_0$) to $c_{m\beta}(t)$ as

$$c_{m\beta}^{(2)}(t) = \left[\frac{1-\exp(i\omega_{m0}t)}{\hbar\omega_{m0}}\right] \mathsf{S}'_n \mathsf{S}_\alpha \frac{\langle m\beta|\mathcal{V}|r\alpha\rangle\langle n\alpha|\mathcal{V}|00\rangle}{(E_n - E_0)}. \tag{3.25}$$

(The prime on S'_n signifies that states with $E_n = E_0$ must be omitted from the sum.)

For resonant processes ($\omega_{nm} = 0$ or $\omega_{n0} = 0$) we can proceed by using a limiting process, wherein $E_n t \to \infty$, and we replace S_n by $\int dn = \int \rho(E)\, dE$. The procedure is similar to that of (3.17)–(3.19). In performing the integration we must include both of the bracketed terms (3.24). The result is [4], [5]:

$$c_{m\beta}^{(2)}(t) = \left[\frac{1-\exp(i\omega_{m0}t)}{\hbar\omega_{m0}}\right] i\pi\, \mathsf{S}_\alpha \langle m\beta|\mathcal{V}|0\alpha\rangle\langle 0\alpha|\mathcal{V}|00\rangle. \tag{3.26}$$

Note that the time dependence is the same in both the resonant (3.26) and nonresonant (3.25) indirect transitions as it is for the direct transitions (3.14). Therefore we can collect the results for the various indirect and direct processes that can contribute to $c_{m\beta}(t)$ to second order as

$$c_{m\beta}(t) = \left[\frac{1 - \exp(i\omega_{m0}t)}{\hbar\omega_{m0}}\right] \langle m\beta|\mathfrak{T}|00\rangle, \tag{3.27}$$

where we use the symbol

$$\langle m\beta|\mathfrak{T}|00\rangle \equiv \langle m\beta|\mathcal{V}|00\rangle + \mathop{\mathsf{S}'}_{n} \mathop{\mathsf{S}}_{\alpha} \frac{\langle m\beta|\mathcal{V}|n\alpha\rangle\langle n\alpha|\mathcal{V}|00\rangle}{(E_n - E_0)} + i\pi \mathop{\mathsf{S}}_{\alpha} \langle m\beta|\mathcal{V}|0\alpha\rangle\langle 0\alpha|\mathcal{V}|00\rangle. \tag{3.28}$$

The transition rate, for second-order processes, is given by

$$w(00 \rightarrow m\beta) = \frac{2\pi}{\hbar} \rho_\beta(E_0) |\langle m\beta|\mathfrak{T}|00\rangle|^2. \tag{3.29}$$

Formula (3.29) gives a more precise form of the golden rule, in which a *transition operator* [6] $\mathfrak{T}$ replaces the less accurate operator $\mathcal{V}$. The matrix elements (3.28) are often called the *T matrix*. [To be more precise, (3.28) gives only the second-order approximation in an infinite series for the *T* matrix.] The *T* matrix is particularly useful in the modern quantum mechanical theory of collisions, as discussed by Lippmann and Schwinger [6] or Messiah [7].

D. Decay

The foregoing treatment applies only for times so short that the initial state remains almost fully populated. In many problems we want to observe the system after much longer times. We have seen that the initial state $\mathbf{A}_{00}$ gets depleted by the growth of other states. With passing time, $c_{00}(t)$ must decrease from its initial value 1. If none of the secondary states provide a return to the initial state, $c_{00}(t)$ must monotonically approach zero. Suppose then, we let the coefficient of the initial state be

$$c_{00}(t) = \exp(-\gamma t), \tag{3.30}$$

where γ is a complex quantity to be determined. Let $\frac{1}{2}\Gamma$ be the real part and $\Delta\omega$ be the complex part:

$$\gamma = \tfrac{1}{2}\Gamma + i\,\Delta\omega. \tag{3.31}$$

Then the probability of observing the initial state, given by

$$|c_{00}(t)|^2 = |\exp(-\gamma t)|^2 = \exp(-\Gamma t), \tag{3.32}$$

will decay exponentially with a *decay constant* Γ. The *half-life* of the initial state, $\tau_{1/2}$, defined as the time required for $|c_{00}(t)|^2$ to decrease by a factor of 2, is just

$$\tau_{1/2} = \frac{\ln 2}{\Gamma} = \frac{0.6932}{\Gamma}. \tag{3.33}$$

This trial solution (3.30) satisfies our requirements that

$$c_{00}(0) = 1, \qquad c_{00}(\infty) = 0.$$

With this function, the basic equation (3.12) now gives the growth rate for states growing directly from the initial state:

$$\begin{aligned} i\hbar \dot{c}_{m\beta}(t) &= \langle m\beta|\mathcal{V}|00\rangle \exp(i\omega_{m0}t - \gamma t) \\ &\equiv \langle m\beta|\mathcal{V}|00\rangle \exp(-iXt), \end{aligned} \tag{3.34}$$

where $X \equiv \omega_{0m} - i\gamma = \omega_{0m} + \Delta\omega - i\Gamma/2$. When integrated, (3.34) gives

$$c_{m\beta}(t) = \langle m\beta|\mathcal{V}|00\rangle \left[\frac{\exp(-iXt) - 1}{\hbar X}\right]. \tag{3.35}$$

In the limit $\gamma \to 0$, the initial state persists indefinitely, and (3.35) becomes simply (3.14). We can now use this estimate of $c_{m\beta}(t)$ in (3.12) to find an expression for γ. From the expression

$$i\hbar \dot{c}_{00}(t) = \mathop{\mathsf{S}}_{m} \mathop{\mathsf{S}}_{\beta} \langle 00|\mathcal{V}|m\beta\rangle c_{m\beta}(t) \exp(i\omega_{0m}t), \tag{3.36}$$

we obtain the result

$$\begin{aligned} -i\hbar\gamma &= \mathop{\mathsf{S}}_{m} \mathop{\mathsf{S}}_{\beta} \langle 00|\mathcal{V}|m\beta\rangle c_{m\beta}(t) \exp(i\omega_{0m}t + \gamma t) \\ &= \mathop{\mathsf{S}}_{m} \mathop{\mathsf{S}}_{\beta} \langle 00|\mathcal{V}|m\beta\rangle\langle m\beta|\mathcal{V}|00\rangle \exp(iXt) \left[\frac{\exp(-iXt) - 1}{\hbar X}\right], \end{aligned} \tag{3.37}$$

so that the real and imaginary parts of γ are given by the expression

$$\Delta\omega - \tfrac{1}{2}i\Gamma = \mathop{\mathsf{S}}_{m} \mathop{\mathsf{S}}_{\beta} \frac{|\langle m\beta|\mathcal{V}|00\rangle|^2}{\hbar^2} \left[\frac{1 - \exp(iXt)}{X}\right]. \tag{3.38}$$

If one examines this expression for times long with respect to the atomic periods ($\omega_{0m}t \gg 1$), then as Heitler shows [5], the imaginary part of this equation becomes very nearly

$$\Gamma = \frac{2\pi}{\hbar} \mathop{\mathsf{S}}_{m} \mathop{\mathsf{S}}_{\beta} |\langle m\beta|\mathcal{V}|00\rangle|^2 \,\delta(E_m - E_0). \tag{3.39}$$

A more accurate result obtains if we use the better approximation $\langle m\beta|\mathfrak{J}|00\rangle$ from (3.27) and (3.28) in place of $\langle m\beta|\mathcal{V}|00\rangle$:

$$\Gamma = \frac{2\pi}{\hbar} \mathop{\mathsf{S}}_{m} \mathop{\mathsf{S}}_{\beta} |\langle m\beta | \mathfrak{V} | 00 \rangle|^2 \delta(E_m - E_0). \tag{3.40}$$

Comparing this result with (3.21) or (3.29), we see that the decay constant is simply the sum of all energy-conserving transition rates from the initial state:

$$\Gamma = \mathop{\mathsf{S}}_{m} \mathop{\mathsf{S}}_{\beta} w(00 \rightarrow m\beta)\delta(E_m - E_0). \tag{3.41}$$

The real part of (3.38) gives, in this approximation, the second-order energy shift produced by the perturbation:

$$\hbar\Delta\omega = \mathop{\mathsf{S}'}_{m} \mathop{\mathsf{S}}_{\alpha} \frac{|\langle m\beta | \mathfrak{V} | 00 \rangle|^2}{E_0 - E_m}, \tag{3.42}$$

where energy conserving terms ($E_m = E_0$) are omitted from the sum. That is, the continuum integral in S'_m specifies the Cauchy principal-value of the integral over the singularity at $E_m = E_0$. (Recall section 5.1E.)

Equation 3.35 can now provide the expansion coefficients $c_{m\beta}(t)$ after the initial state has been significantly depleted. In the limit $\Gamma t \gg 1$ (that is, we ask for the state of the system after many decay times or half-lives), we find

$$|c_{m\beta}(00)|^2 = \frac{|\langle m\beta | \mathfrak{V} | 00 \rangle|^2}{|\hbar X|^2} = \frac{|\langle m\beta | \mathfrak{V} | 00 \rangle|^2}{\hbar^2(\omega_{0m} + \Delta\omega)^2 - \hbar^2(\Gamma/2)^2} \cdot \tag{3.43}$$

We see that because the lifetime of the initial state is not infinite (Γ is not zero), there is a finite probability of observing a transition to some state with slightly different *unperturbed* energy than the initial state. This does not mean that energy is not conserved between initial and final states. Rather, it means that the *unperturbed* energies which we use in (3.43) cannot be precisely determined if the lifetime is too short. The uncertainty principle

$$\Delta E \, \Delta t \geq \hbar$$

limits the energy precision to roughly

$$\Delta E \geq \hbar\Gamma$$

for a state with mean life $1/\Gamma$. But this energy spread is just what we obtain in (3.43).

REFERENCES

[1] P. A. M. Dirac, *The Principles of Quantum Mechanics*, Oxford University Press, New York (1958), 4th ed.

[2] D. Bohm, *Quantum Theory*, Prentice-Hall, Englewood Cliffs, New Jersey (1951), Part IV.
[3] E. Fermi, *Nuclear Physics*, University of Chicago Press, Chicago (1950), p. 142.
[4] L. Schiff, *Quantum Mechanics*, McGraw-Hill, New York, (1955), 2nd ed., p. 203.
[5] W. Heitler, *The Quantum Theory of Radiation*, Oxford University Press, New York (1953), 3rd ed., p. 183.
[6] B. Lippmann and J. Schwinger, *Phys. Rev.* **79,** 469 (1950).
[7] A. Messiah, *Quantum Mechanics*, Wiley, New York (1962), Chapter 19.

6. Angular-Momentum States

6.1 GENERAL ANGULAR-MOMENTUM OPERATORS AND EIGENSTATES

In elementary calculus the exponential function of x is usually introduced by defining a power series,

$$e^x = 1 + \frac{x}{1!} + \frac{x^2}{2!} + \frac{x^3}{3!} + \cdots. \tag{1.1}$$

We can define the exponential function of an operator or matrix $\mathcal{A}$ in the same way,

$$\exp(\mathcal{A}) = 1 + \frac{\mathcal{A}}{1!} + \frac{\mathcal{A}^2}{2!} + \frac{\mathcal{A}^3}{3!} + \cdots, \tag{1.2}$$

where now we must understand that the operator $\exp(\mathcal{A})$ acts on some function or, more generally, on a vector in some abstract space. The exponential operator is especially useful in altering vectors without changing their length, i.e., "rotating" them. Suppose we have an abstract vector $\mathbf{A}(\alpha)$ that depends upon some parameter α (such as time or an angle). If we increase the parameter by the amount α_1 from an initial value of α_0, the abstract vector must change from $\mathbf{A}(\alpha_0)$ to $\mathbf{A}(\alpha_0 + \alpha_1)$. To preserve probability this change must be a unitary transformation, $\mathcal{U}$. Suppose the transformation depends only on the increment α_1, not on the initial value α_0:

$$\mathbf{A}(\alpha_0) \rightarrow \mathbf{A}(\alpha_0 + \alpha_1) = \mathcal{U}(\alpha_1)\mathbf{A}(\alpha_0). \tag{1.3}$$

A further transformation will be given by

$$\begin{aligned}\mathbf{A}(\alpha_0 + \alpha_1) \rightarrow \mathbf{A}(\alpha_0 + \alpha_1 + \alpha_2) &= \mathcal{U}(\alpha_2)\mathbf{A}(\alpha_0 + \alpha_1) \\ &= \mathcal{U}(\alpha_2)\mathcal{U}(\alpha_1)\mathbf{A}(\alpha_0).\end{aligned}$$

The $\mathcal{U}$'s therefore satisfy the equation

$$\mathcal{U}(\alpha_2 + \alpha_1) = \mathcal{U}(\alpha_2)\mathcal{U}(\alpha_1),$$

which means $\mathcal{U}$ must have the form of an exponential,

$$\mathcal{U}(\alpha) = C \exp(\mathcal{B}\alpha).$$

The inverse and Hermitian adjoint of $\mathcal{U}$ are then

$$\mathcal{U}^{-1} = C^{-1} \exp(-\mathcal{B}\alpha)$$
$$\mathcal{U}^{\dagger} = C^{*} \exp(\mathcal{B}^{\dagger}\alpha).$$

Unitary $\mathcal{U}$ means $\mathcal{U}^{\dagger} = \mathcal{U}^{-1}$; thus $C = 1$ and $\mathcal{A}$ must have the form $i\mathcal{A}$, where $\mathcal{A}$ is Hermitian:

$$\mathcal{U}(\alpha) = \exp(i\mathcal{A}\alpha) \tag{1.4}$$
$$\mathbf{A}(\alpha) = \exp(i\mathcal{A}\alpha)\mathbf{A}(0). \tag{1.5}$$

We thus have the equation

$$\frac{\partial}{\partial\alpha}\mathbf{A}(\alpha) = i\mathcal{A} \exp(i\mathcal{A}\alpha)\mathbf{A}(0) = i\mathcal{A}\mathbf{A}(\alpha). \tag{1.6}$$

When α is the time t, the operator $(-\mathcal{A})$ for quantum-mechanical state vectors is the Hamiltonian, for we then have the time-dependent Schrödinger equation:

$$i\hbar \frac{\partial}{\partial t}\mathbf{A}(t) = \mathcal{H}\mathbf{A}(t).$$

Thus the Hamiltonian operator is the *generator* of time displacements of quantum-mechanical states.

A second example occurs with spatial displacements. The Taylor expansion expresses the value of a function $A(x)$ at the point $x + a$ in terms of the derivatives of A at the point x:

$$A(x + a) = A(x) + a\frac{d}{dx}A(x) + \frac{a^2}{2}\frac{d^2}{dx^2}A(x) + \cdots.$$

Using the momentum operator $\mathcal{P}_x = (\hbar/i)d/dx$, we can write this series as

$$A(x + a) = \left(1 + ia\frac{\mathcal{P}_x}{\hbar} + \frac{i^2a^2}{2}\frac{\mathcal{P}_x{}^2}{\hbar^2} + \cdots\right)A(x).$$

We recognize the series as the expansion of an exponential, so that the x displacement by amount a [the transformation $\mathcal{U}(a)$], is generated by the x component of momentum:

$$\mathcal{U}(a)\mathbf{A}(x) = \mathbf{A}(x + a) = \exp\left(\frac{ia\mathcal{P}_x}{\hbar}\right)\mathbf{A}(x).$$

Let us consider the scalar field $A(x, y, z)$ and take α to be an infinitesimal change in the orientation of the x and y axes. The transformation $\mathcal{U}$ is a physical rotation about the z axis by an amount $d\phi$, which we can write as

$$\mathcal{U}(d\phi) = \exp(-i\mathcal{J}_z\, d\phi). \tag{1.7}$$

What is the operator $\mathcal{J}_z$, the generator of this rotation? We have

$$A(x, y, z) \rightarrow A(x', y', z') = \exp(-i\,\mathcal{J}_z\, d\phi)A(x, y, z). \tag{1.8}$$

If we expand the exponential and retain only the first term in $d\phi$, we have

$$A(x', y', z') = (1 - i\mathcal{J}_z\, d\phi)A(x, y, z). \tag{1.9}$$

But the function $A(x', y', z')$ can be expanded in a Taylor series about x, y, z:

$$\begin{aligned} A(x', y', z') &= A(x + y\,d\phi, y - x\,d\phi, z) \\ &= A(x, y, z) + d\phi\left(y\frac{\partial}{\partial x} - x\frac{\partial}{\partial y}\right)A(x, y, z). \end{aligned}$$

Comparing these two results, we see that

$$i\mathcal{J}_z = x\frac{\partial}{\partial y} - y\frac{\partial}{\partial x} \equiv i\mathcal{L}_z, \tag{1.10}$$

and $\mathcal{J}_z$ is just the operator of orbital angular momentum about the rotation (z) axis. Clearly the same result applies about any axis. We therefore find that a rotation by $d\phi$ about the $\mathbf{n}$ direction corresponds to the transformation

$$\mathcal{U}(\mathbf{n}, d\phi) = \exp(-i\,\mathcal{J}\cdot\mathbf{n}\, d\phi). \tag{1.11}$$

Now consider the effect of this same transformation on a *vector* field, such as an electric field. A vector field is the collection of three quantities, $A_x(x, y, z)$, $A_y(x, y, z)$, and $A_z(x, y, z)$, defined at every point in space. Under the rotation of (1.7) these components transform into

$$\begin{aligned} A_x(x, y, z) &\rightarrow A_x(x + y\,d\phi, y - x\,d\phi, z) - d\phi\, A_x(x + y\,d\phi, y - x\,d\phi, z) \\ A_y(x, y, z) &\rightarrow d\phi\, A_x(x + y\,d\phi, y - x\,d\phi, z) + A_y(x + y\,d\phi, y - x\,d\phi, z) \\ A_z(x, y, z) &\rightarrow A_z(x + y\,d\phi, y - x\,d\phi, z). \end{aligned} \tag{1.12}$$

The vector analog of (1.9) is

$$\mathbf{A}' = (1 + i\mathcal{J}_z\, d\phi)\mathbf{A}. \tag{1.13}$$

If we write $\mathbf{A}$ as a column vector,

$$\mathbf{A} = \begin{pmatrix} A_x \\ A_y \\ A_z \end{pmatrix},$$

then we see that the matrix $\mathcal{J}_z$ is composed of two parts, which we write as

$$\mathcal{J}_z = \mathcal{L}_z + \mathcal{S}_z. \tag{1.14}$$

The first part acts to displace each component:

$$\mathcal{L}_z = -i\left(x\frac{\partial}{\partial x} - y\frac{\partial}{\partial y}\right)\begin{pmatrix} 1 & 0 & 0 \\ 0 & 1 & 0 \\ 0 & 0 & 1 \end{pmatrix}$$

and the second part acts to mix the x and y components:

$$\mathcal{S}_z = -i\begin{pmatrix} 0 & 1 & 0 \\ -1 & 0 & 0 \\ 0 & 0 & 0 \end{pmatrix}.$$

We can say that a vector field has an *intrinsic* angular momentum, or *spin*. This is true for *any* vector field—our discussion has not been restricted to a quantum-mechanical field. We can see that spin enters our discussion because the vector field has more than one component; it has three components, compared with a single component for a scalar field. Fields having *two* components or two degrees of freedom are also possible—they are called *spinor fields*—as are fields with four or more components.

Before we begin to study the properties of angular-momentum operators, we should mention what motivates this discussion. Basically, we want to take advantage of symmetry properties of atoms. Free atoms exhibit rotational symmetry about any axis—there is no preferred direction in free space. Diatomic molecules also exhibit rotational symmetry, but only along the interatomic axis. By rotational symmetry we mean that the energy does not depend on orientation, so that the Hamiltonian does not depend on angular variables. This means the Hamiltonian commutes with all angular operators, and in particular, it commutes with the rotation operator. Thus eigenstates of the rotation operator (angular momentum states) provide useful basis states (cf. Section 4.7). In this section we deduce some of the properties of angular-momentum states from rather general arguments about the rotation operators. We follow closely the discussion of Rose [1] and Dirac [2]. For a thorough systematic discussion of the results of this chapter, the reader should consult the paper by Schwinger [3]. (This reprint volume [3] also includes the fundamental papers by Racah referred to below, and it appends an extensive bibliography on angular momentum.)

The properties of angular-momentum states follow from the action of the three components of the angular-momentum operator. For the moment we take these to be $\mathcal{J}_x$, $\mathcal{J}_y$, and $\mathcal{J}_z$, corresponding to infinitesimal rotations $d\theta_x$, $d\theta_y$, and $d\theta_z$ about the x, y, and z axes. Later we use the complex spherical components $\mathcal{J}_{+1}$, $\mathcal{J}_{-1}$, and $\mathcal{J}_0$. We have seen that rotations about the x and y axes are, by definition, produced by the operators

$$\exp(-i\mathcal{J}_x\, d\theta_x) \quad \text{and} \quad \exp(-i\mathcal{J}_y\, d\theta_y).$$

That is, the angular-momentum operators are defined to be the operators that generate infinitesimal rotations. If we rotate first about the x axis, then about the y axis, the rotation operator is (neglecting terms higher than quadratic in the infinitesimals)

$$\begin{aligned}\exp(-i\mathcal{J}_y\, d\theta_y)\, &\exp(-i\mathcal{J}_x\, d\theta_x)\\ &\simeq (1 - i\mathcal{J}_y\, d\theta_y - \mathcal{J}_y^2\, d\theta_y)(1 - i\mathcal{J}_x\, d\theta_x - \mathcal{J}_x^2\, d\theta_x)\\ &\simeq 1 - i\mathcal{J}_y\, d\theta_y - i\mathcal{J}_x\, d\theta_x - \mathcal{J}_x^2 d\theta_x^2 - \mathcal{J}_y^2\, d\theta_y^2 - \mathcal{J}_y\mathcal{J}_x\, d\theta_x\, d\theta_y. \qquad (1.15)\end{aligned}$$

A rotation in the opposite order, first about y, then about x, is generated by the operator

$$\begin{aligned}\exp(-i\mathcal{J}_x\, d\theta_x)\, &\exp(-i\mathcal{J}_y\, d\theta_y)\\ &\simeq 1 - i\mathcal{J}_y\, d\theta_y - i\mathcal{J}_x\, d\theta_x - \mathcal{J}_x^2\, d\theta_x^2 - \mathcal{J}_y^2\, d\theta_y^2 - \mathcal{J}_x\mathcal{J}_y\, d\theta_x\, d\theta_y. \qquad (1.16)\end{aligned}$$

Except for the last term these expressions are equal, so that, to first order in the infinitesimals $d\theta$, the ordering of rotations is immaterial. We can see

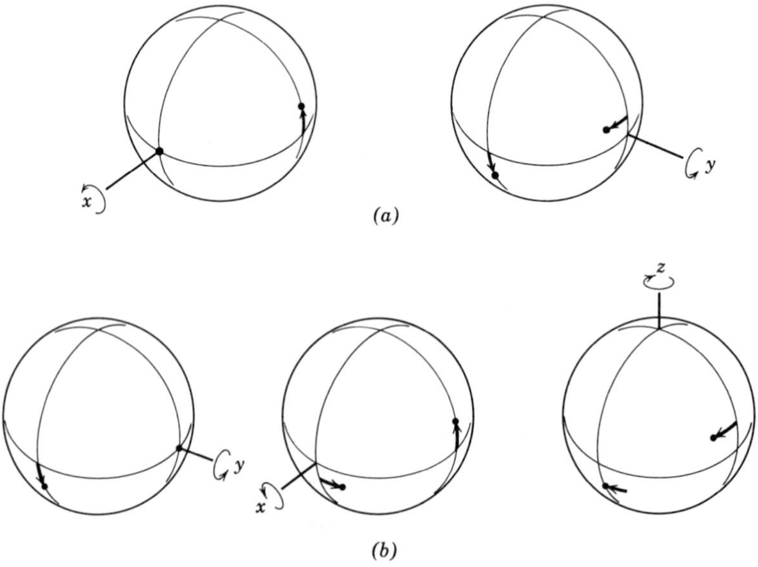

Fig. 6.1 (*a*) Rotation about *x*, then *y*; (*b*) rotation about *y*, then *x*.

from Fig. 6.1 that it is necessary to rotate the first sequence again by $d\theta_x\, d\theta_y$ about the z axis to duplicate the second sequence:

$$\exp(-i\mathcal{J}_z\, d\theta_x\, d\theta_y) \exp(-i\mathcal{J}_y\, d\theta_y) \exp(-i\mathcal{J}_x\, d\theta_x)$$
$$\simeq 1 - i\mathcal{J}_y\, d\theta_y - i\mathcal{J}_x\, d\theta_x - \mathcal{J}_x^{\,2}\, d\theta_x^{\,2} - \mathcal{J}_y^{\,2}\, d\theta_y^{\,2}$$
$$- \mathcal{J}_y\mathcal{J}_x\, d\theta_x\, d\theta_y - i\mathcal{J}_z\, d\theta_x\, d\theta_y. \qquad (1.17)$$

Equating (1.16) and (1.17) we see that

$$-\mathcal{J}_x\mathcal{J}_y\, d\theta_x\, d\theta_y = -\mathcal{J}_y\mathcal{J}_x\, d\theta_x\, d\theta_y - i\mathcal{J}_z\, d\theta_x\, d\theta_y$$

or, since $d\theta_x\, d\theta_y$ is arbitrary, we obtain the basic *commutation relation* of angular momentum operators:

$$i\mathcal{J}_z = \mathcal{J}_x\mathcal{J}_y - \mathcal{J}_y\mathcal{J}_x \equiv [\mathcal{J}_x, \mathcal{J}_y]. \qquad (1.18a)$$

Since our labeling of axes is arbitrary, (1.18*a*) holds for any cyclic permutation of x, y, and z:

$$i\mathcal{J}_x = [\mathcal{J}_y, \mathcal{J}_z] \quad \text{and} \quad i\mathcal{J}_y = [\mathcal{J}_z, \mathcal{J}_x]. \qquad (1.18b)$$

Equations 1.18 must be satisfied by the Cartesian components of any operator that generates infinitesimal rotations, and thus they serve to define angular momentum operators in a very general way.

Just as with the orbital angular momentum operators, it is easier to deal with complex spherical components once we have seen the physical significance of the definition (1.18). We define these components as we did previously for the $\mathcal{L}$ operators:

$$\mathcal{J}_{+1} = -\frac{1}{\sqrt{2}}(\mathcal{J}_x + i\mathcal{J}_y)$$
$$\mathcal{J}_{-1} = +\frac{1}{\sqrt{2}}(\mathcal{J}_x - i\mathcal{J}_y) \qquad (1.19)$$
$$\mathcal{J}_0 = \mathcal{J}_z.$$

These then satisfy the commutation relations

$$[\mathcal{J}_0, \mathcal{J}_{+1}] = \mathcal{J}_{+1}$$
$$[\mathcal{J}_0, \mathcal{J}_{-1}] = -\mathcal{J}_{-1} \qquad (1.20)$$
$$[\mathcal{J}_{+1}, \mathcal{J}_{-1}] = -\mathcal{J}_0$$

as one can see by directly substituting (1.19) into (1.20), using (1.18). Thus (1.20) and (1.18) provide equivalent *definitions* of angular-momentum operators. We define the square of the total angular momentum, $\mathcal{J}^2$, by

$$\mathcal{J}^2 = \mathcal{J}_x^{\,2} + \mathcal{J}_y^{\,2} + \mathcal{J}_z^{\,2}. \qquad (1.21)$$

This too can be written in alternative ways by using the commutation relations (1.20):

$$\mathcal{J}^2 = -\mathcal{J}_{+1}\mathcal{J}_{-1} + \mathcal{J}_0\mathcal{J}_0 - \mathcal{J}_{-1}\mathcal{J}_{+1} \tag{1.22a}$$

$$= -2\mathcal{J}_{+1}\mathcal{J}_{-1} + \mathcal{J}_0(\mathcal{J}_0 - 1) \tag{1.22b}$$

$$= -2\mathcal{J}_{-1}\mathcal{J}_{+1} + \mathcal{J}_0(\mathcal{J}_0 + 1). \tag{1.22c}$$

The commutation relations (1.20) reveal that $\mathcal{J}_{+1}$ and $\mathcal{J}_{-1}$ are ladder operators acting on the eigenvalues of $\mathcal{J}_0$. For whenever two operators satisfy the commutation relation

$$[\mathcal{A}, \mathcal{B}] = b\mathcal{B}, \tag{1.23}$$

then for an eigenstate of **A**, with

$$\mathcal{A}\mathbf{A} = a\mathbf{A}$$

we have that

$$\begin{aligned} \mathcal{A}\mathcal{B}\mathbf{A} &= \mathcal{B}\mathcal{A}\mathbf{A} + b\mathcal{B}\mathbf{A} \\ \mathcal{A}(\mathcal{B}\mathbf{A}) &= (a + b)(\mathcal{B}\mathbf{A}). \end{aligned} \tag{1.24}$$

Thus the operator $\mathcal{B}$, acting on the eigenstate of $\mathcal{A}$, alters the eigenvalue by the increment b. Comparing (1.23) with (1.20) we see that $\mathcal{J}_{+1}$ ($\mathcal{J}_{-1}$) increases (decreases) the eigenvalue of $\mathcal{J}_0$ by unity. If we have

$$\mathcal{J}_0\mathbf{A}(m) = m\mathbf{A}(m),$$

then we have

$$\begin{aligned} \mathcal{J}_{+1}\mathbf{A}(m) &= \text{factor} \times \mathbf{A}(m + 1) \\ \mathcal{J}_{-1}\mathbf{A}(m) &= \text{factor}' \times \mathbf{A}(m - 1), \end{aligned} \tag{1.25}$$

where the numerical factors will be determined below.

Next we can verify that $\mathcal{J}^2$, defined by (1.21) or (1.22) commutes with any of its components:

$$\begin{aligned} [\mathcal{J}^2, \mathcal{J}_x] = [\mathcal{J}^2, \mathcal{J}_y] = [\mathcal{J}^2, \mathcal{J}_z] = 0 \\ [\mathcal{J}^2, \mathcal{J}_{+1}] = [\mathcal{J}^2, \mathcal{J}_{-1}] = [\mathcal{J}^2, \mathcal{J}_0] = 0. \end{aligned} \tag{1.26}$$

This means a state can be an eigenstate of $\mathcal{J}^2$ and any one (but *only* one, unless the eigenvalue is zero) of the components. We can thus label a state according to its eigenvalues of $\mathcal{J}^2$ and $\mathcal{J}_0$:

$$\begin{aligned} \mathcal{J}^2\mathbf{A}(\lambda m) &= \lambda\mathbf{A}(\lambda m) \\ \mathcal{J}_0\mathbf{A}(\lambda m) &= m\mathbf{A}(\lambda m). \end{aligned} \tag{1.27}$$

Our definition of angular-momentum operators is not yet complete. If these operators are to correspond to observable quantities, the eigenvalues must be real numbers; i.e., the operators $\mathcal{J}^2$ and $\mathcal{J}_0$ must be Hermitian. The operators $\mathcal{J}_x$ and $\mathcal{J}_y$, being on an equal footing with $\mathcal{J}_z \equiv \mathcal{J}_0$ apart from our choice of coordinate directions, must also be Hermitian:

$$(\mathcal{J}^2)^\dagger = \mathcal{J}^2, \qquad \mathcal{J}_x^\dagger = \mathcal{J}_x, \qquad \mathcal{J}_y^\dagger = \mathcal{J}_y, \qquad \mathcal{J}_0^\dagger = \mathcal{J}_0. \tag{1.28}$$

The operators $\mathcal{J}_{+1}$ and $\mathcal{J}_{-1}$ are not Hermitian, however. Since for any Hermitian operator $\mathcal{H}$ we have

$$(i\mathcal{H})^\dagger = -i\mathcal{H}^\dagger = -i\mathcal{H},$$

then the Hermitian adjoints of $\mathcal{J}_{\pm 1}$ are

$$\begin{aligned}(\mathcal{J}_{+1})^\dagger &= -\frac{1}{\sqrt{2}}(\mathcal{J}_x + i\mathcal{J}_y)^\dagger = -\frac{1}{\sqrt{2}}(\mathcal{J}_x - i\mathcal{J}_y) = -\mathcal{J}_{-1} \\ (\mathcal{J}_{-1})^\dagger &= -\mathcal{J}_{+1}.\end{aligned} \tag{1.29}$$

That is,

$$\langle \mathbf{A} | \mathcal{J}_{\pm 1}\mathbf{A}\rangle = -\langle \mathcal{J}_{\mp 1}\mathbf{A} | \mathbf{A}\rangle.$$

The requirement for real eigenvalues λ and m, and the consequent adjoint properties of $\mathcal{J}_{+1}$ and $\mathcal{J}_{-1}$, provides a constraint on m. Write (1.22) as

$$[\mathcal{J}^2 - \mathcal{J}_0(\mathcal{J}_0 - 1)]\mathbf{A} = -2\mathcal{J}_{+1}\mathcal{J}_{-1}\mathbf{A} \tag{1.30a}$$

$$[\mathcal{J}^2 - \mathcal{J}_0(\mathcal{J}_0 + 1)]\mathbf{A} = -2\mathcal{J}_{-1}\mathcal{J}_{+1}\mathbf{A}. \tag{1.30b}$$

Then take the scalar product of (1.30*a*) with $\mathbf{A}(\lambda m)$ [using (1.29)]:

$$\begin{aligned}\lambda - m(m+1) &= -2\langle \mathbf{A} | \mathcal{J}_{-1}\mathcal{J}_{+1}\mathbf{A}\rangle \\ &= 2\langle \mathcal{J}_{+1}\mathbf{A} | \mathcal{J}_{+1}\mathbf{A}\rangle.\end{aligned} \tag{1.31}$$

The right-hand side, being of the form $\langle \mathbf{B} | \mathbf{B}\rangle$, cannot be negative. We thus must have

$$\lambda \geq m(m+1) \tag{1.32a}$$

and the eigenvalues m have an upper bound fixed by λ. In the same way, (1.30*b*) shows that

$$\lambda \geq m(m-1), \tag{1.32b}$$

which gives a bound on negative m. We know the ladder operators $\mathcal{J}_{\pm 1}$ alter the eigenvalues m in increments of ± 1, so the allowed values (for a given λ) must run from some lower bound $m_<$ to an upper bound $m_>$ in integral steps:

$$m_<, \; m_< + 1, \; m_< + 2, \; \ldots, \; m_>.$$

When m has its maximum (minimum) value, the operator $\mathcal{J}_{+1}$ ($\mathcal{J}_{-1}$) must give zero when applied to the state (this property *defines* the extreme-value state):

$$\mathcal{J}_{+1}\mathbf{A}(\lambda m_>) = 0, \qquad \mathcal{J}_{-1}\mathbf{A}(\lambda m_<) = 0.$$

The right-hand side of (1.30) must then be zero, and the equality sign holds in (1.32):

$$\lambda = m_<(m_< - 1) = m_>(m_> + 1). \tag{1.33}$$

This means $m_< = -m_>$. We will denote this extreme value of m by j, so that (1.33) reads

$$\lambda = j(j + 1) \tag{1.34}$$

and the eigenvalues m run

$$-j, \ -j + 1, \ -j + 2, \ \ldots, \ j - 1, \ j. \tag{1.35}$$

This succession, from $-j$ to $+j$ in steps of unity, can hold only if *j has integral or half odd-integral values.* [For example, starting with the value $m = -2.2$ we would have the sequence -2.2, -1.2, -0.2, $+0.8$, $+1.8$, $+2.8$, . . . , and the sequence in (1.35) could not be satisfied.] We have thus found that angular-momentum eigenstates satisfy the equations

$$\mathcal{J}^2\mathbf{A}(jm) = j(j + 1)\mathbf{A}(jm), \qquad j = 0, \tfrac{1}{2}, 1, \tfrac{3}{2}, \cdots \tag{1.36}$$

$$\mathcal{J}_0\mathbf{A}(jm) = m\mathbf{A}(jm), \qquad -j \le m \le j. \tag{1.37}$$

We see from (1.35) that m can take $2j + 1$ different values. We thus have $2j + 1$ different states $\mathbf{A}(jm)$ for any value of j:

$$\mathbf{A}(j, -j), \ \mathbf{A}(j, \ -j + 1), \ \ldots, \ \mathbf{A}(j, j).$$

Using just the commutation relations (1.20) we can relate all these $2j + 1$ states of differing m to any particular state, say $\mathbf{A}(j, j)$. We write the undetermined factors in (1.25) as

$$\mathcal{J}_{+1}\mathbf{A}(jm) = C_m^+\mathbf{A}(j, m + 1) \tag{1.38a}$$

$$\mathcal{J}_{-1}\mathbf{A}(jm) = C_{m-1}^-\mathbf{A}(j, m - 1). \tag{1.38b}$$

Let us assume that all the $\mathbf{A}$ states are normalized, $\langle \mathbf{A}(jm) | \mathbf{A}(jm) \rangle = 1$. For the moment we drop j from our notation, considering only states of a particular j value. Then using (1.38) and (1.29), we have

$$\begin{aligned}\langle \mathbf{A}(m) | \mathcal{J}_{-1}\mathcal{J}_{+1}\mathbf{A}(m) \rangle &= C_m^+ \langle \mathbf{A}(m) | \mathcal{J}_{-1}\mathbf{A}(m + 1) \rangle = C_m^+ C_m^- \\ &= - \ \langle \mathcal{J}_{+1}\mathbf{A}(m) | \mathcal{J}_{+1}\mathbf{A}(m) \rangle = - | C_m^+ |^2;\end{aligned}$$

but from (1.30*b*) we have

$$\begin{aligned}\langle \mathbf{A}(m) | \mathcal{J}_{-1}\mathcal{J}_{+1}\mathbf{A}(m) \rangle &= -\tfrac{1}{2}\langle \mathbf{A}(m) | \, [\mathcal{J}^2 - \mathcal{J}_0(\mathcal{J}_0 + 1)]\mathbf{A}(m) \rangle \\ &= -\tfrac{1}{2}[j(j + 1) - m(m + 1)],\end{aligned}$$

so that

$$| C_m^+ |^2 = -C_m^+ C_m^- = j(j + 1) - m(m + 1).$$

If we adopt the customary convention that C_m^+ be real and negative, then

$$C_m^+ = -C_m^- = -\left[\frac{j(j+1)-m(m+1)}{2}\right]^{1/2} = -\left[\frac{(j-m)(j+m+1)}{2}\right]^{1/2},$$

$$C_{m-1}^- = \left[\frac{j(j+1)-m(m-1)}{2}\right]^{1/2} = \left[\frac{(j+m)(j-m+1)}{2}\right]^{1/2},$$

and we have the important result

$$\mathcal{J}_{+1}\mathbf{A}(jm) = -\mathbf{A}(jm+1)\left[\frac{j(j+1)-m(m+1)}{2}\right]^{1/2}, \qquad (1.39a)$$

$$\mathcal{J}_{-1}\mathbf{A}(jm) = \mathbf{A}(jm-1)\left[\frac{j(j+1)-m(m-1)}{2}\right]^{1/2}, \qquad (1.39b)$$

where $\mathbf{A}(jm \pm 1)$ *is normalized if* $\mathbf{A}(jm)$ *is normalized.* Equations 1.39 can also be written as

$$\mathbf{A}(jm \pm 1) = \mp\mathcal{J}_{\pm 1}\mathbf{A}(jm)\left[\frac{2}{(j \mp m)(j \pm m + 1)}\right]^{1/2}, \qquad (1.40)$$

which shows that

$$\mathbf{A}(j, j-1) = \frac{1}{\sqrt{j}}\,\mathcal{J}_{-1}\mathbf{A}(j,j),$$

$$\mathbf{A}(j, j-2) = \frac{\sqrt{2^2}}{\sqrt{2\cdot 1}\sqrt{2j(2j-1)}}\,\mathcal{J}_{-1}\mathcal{J}_{-1}\mathbf{A}(j,j).$$

Thus, after $j - m$ applications, we obtain

$$\mathbf{A}(jm) = (-1)^{j-m}\left[\frac{2^{j-m}(j+m)!}{(2j)!(j-m)!}\right]^{1/2}(\mathcal{J}_{-1})^{j-m}\mathbf{A}(j,j). \qquad (1.41)$$

Angular-momentum eigenstates having different eigenvalues are orthogonal. This follows immediately from our requirement that $\mathcal{J}$ and $\mathcal{J}_0$ be Hermitian, which can be written as the identities

$$\langle\mathbf{A}(j)|\,\mathcal{J}^2\mathbf{A}(j')\rangle - \langle\mathcal{J}^2\mathbf{A}(j)|\,\mathbf{A}(j')\rangle = 0,$$
$$\langle\mathbf{A}(m)|\,\mathcal{J}_0\mathbf{A}(m')\rangle - \langle\mathcal{J}_0\mathbf{A}(m)|\,\mathbf{A}(m')\rangle = 0.$$

Substituting the eigenvalues of $\mathcal{J}^2$ and $\mathcal{J}_0$, we find

$$[j(j+1) - j'(j'+1)]\langle\mathbf{A}(j)|\mathbf{A}(j')\rangle = 0$$
$$[m - m']\langle\mathbf{A}(m)|\mathbf{A}(m')\rangle = 0.$$

Either $j = j'$ *and* $m = m'$, or else the scalar product is zero. Thus angular-momentum states, when normalized, satisfy the orthonormality condition

$$\langle\mathbf{A}(jm)|\,\mathbf{A}(j'm')\rangle = \delta_{jj'}\,\delta_{mm'}. \qquad (1.42)$$

A. Example 1—Orbital Angular Momentum

We have already seen that when angular-momentum states are taken to be *functions* of r, θ, and ϕ, the angular-momentum operators are *differential operators:*

$$\mathcal{J}_{+1} = -\frac{1}{\sqrt{2}} e^{i\phi}\left(\frac{\partial}{\partial\theta} + i\cot\theta\,\frac{\partial}{\partial\phi}\right)$$

$$\mathcal{J}_{-1} = \frac{1}{\sqrt{2}} e^{-i\phi}\left(\frac{\partial}{\partial\vartheta} - i\cot\theta\,\frac{\partial}{\partial\phi}\right)$$

$$\mathcal{J}_{0} = -i\,\frac{\partial}{\partial\phi}$$

$$\mathcal{J}^2 = -\csc^2\theta\left(\sin\theta\,\frac{\partial}{\partial\theta}\sin\theta\,\frac{\partial}{\partial\theta} + \frac{\partial^2}{\partial\phi^2}\right).$$

The eigenfunctions are, as we saw in Section 3.9, the (normalized) spherical harmonics $Y_{lm}(\theta, \phi)$:

$$\mathcal{J}^2 Y_{lm} = l(l+1)Y_{lm}, \qquad \mathcal{J}_0 Y_{lm} = mY_{lm}, \qquad \int d\Omega\; Y_{lm}(\Omega)^* Y_{l'm'}(\Omega) = \delta_{ll'}\,\delta_{mm'}.$$

B. Example 2—Pauli Spin Matrices

Suppose we define, following Pauli [4], four independent 2×2 matrices:

$$1 = \begin{pmatrix}1 & 0\\ 0 & 1\end{pmatrix}, \quad \sigma_x = \begin{pmatrix}0 & 1\\ 1 & 0\end{pmatrix}, \quad \sigma_y = \begin{pmatrix}0 & -i\\ i & 0\end{pmatrix}, \quad \sigma_z = \begin{pmatrix}1 & 0\\ 0 & -1\end{pmatrix}. \tag{1.43}$$

It is easy to check that these matrices satisfy the commutation relations

$$[\sigma_x, \sigma_y] = 2i\sigma_z, \qquad [\sigma_y, \sigma_z] = 2i\sigma_x, \qquad [\sigma_z, \sigma_x] = 2i\sigma_y,$$

so that we may identify $\mathcal{J}_x = \frac{1}{2}\sigma_x, \mathcal{J}_y = \frac{1}{2}\sigma_y, \mathcal{J}_z = \frac{1}{2}\sigma_z$. If we define matrices by

$$\begin{aligned}
\mathcal{J}_0 &= \frac{1}{2}\sigma_z &&= \frac{1}{2}\begin{pmatrix}1 & 0\\ 0 & -1\end{pmatrix}\\
\mathcal{J}_{+1} &= -\frac{1}{\sqrt{8}}(\sigma_x + i\sigma_y) &&= \frac{1}{\sqrt{2}}\begin{pmatrix}0 & -1\\ 0 & 0\end{pmatrix}\\
\mathcal{J}_{-1} &= +\frac{1}{\sqrt{8}}(\sigma_x - i\sigma_y) &&= \frac{1}{\sqrt{2}}\begin{pmatrix}0 & 0\\ 1 & 0\end{pmatrix},
\end{aligned} \tag{1.44}$$

then these satisfy the angular-momentum commutation rules (1.20). [It will be a useful exercise in matrix manipulation to verify that (1.20) follow from the definitions (1.44).] From (1.22*b*) we find that

$$\mathcal{J}^2 = -\begin{pmatrix} 0 & -1 \\ 0 & 0 \end{pmatrix}\begin{pmatrix} 0 & 0 \\ 1 & 0 \end{pmatrix} + \frac{1}{4}\begin{pmatrix} 1 & 0 \\ 0 & -1 \end{pmatrix}\begin{pmatrix} 1 & 0 \\ 0 & -1 \end{pmatrix} - \frac{1}{2}\begin{pmatrix} 1 & 0 \\ 0 & -1 \end{pmatrix}$$

$$= \frac{3}{4}\begin{pmatrix} 1 & 0 \\ 0 & 1 \end{pmatrix}. \tag{1.45}$$

Thus the eigenvalue of $\mathcal{J}^2$ is $\frac{3}{4} = j(j+1)$, from which we see $j = \frac{1}{2}$. We can readily verify that the eigenstates are the two-component column vectors (called *spinors*)

$$\alpha \equiv \begin{pmatrix} 1 \\ 0 \end{pmatrix}, \qquad \beta \equiv \begin{pmatrix} 0 \\ 1 \end{pmatrix}. \tag{1.46}$$

Using the definitions (1.44) through (1.46) we can verify by matrix multiplication that

$$\begin{aligned} \mathcal{J}^2\alpha &= \tfrac{3}{4}\alpha & \mathcal{J}^2\beta &= \tfrac{3}{4}\beta \\ \mathcal{J}_0\alpha &= +\tfrac{1}{2}\alpha & \mathcal{J}_0\beta &= -\tfrac{1}{2}\beta \\ \mathcal{J}_{+1}\alpha &= 0 & \mathcal{J}_{+1}\beta &= -\frac{\alpha}{\sqrt{2}} \\ \mathcal{J}_{-1}\alpha &= \frac{\beta}{\sqrt{2}} & \mathcal{J}_{-1}\beta &= 0, \end{aligned} \tag{1.47}$$

in agreement with the results of (1.36), (1.37), and (1.39).

The states α and β describe the internal structure or spin of an electron. They are eigenstates of angular momentum (called *spin* in this case), $j = \frac{1}{2}$. The projection of spin upon the z axis is the eigenvalue of $\mathcal{J}_z \equiv \mathcal{J}_0$, and takes the value $m = +\frac{1}{2}$ for α ("spin up") and $m = -\frac{1}{2}$ for β ("spin down").

Note that the scalar product of two arbitrary spinors or column vectors

$$\gamma \equiv \begin{pmatrix} \gamma_1 \\ \gamma_2 \end{pmatrix}, \qquad \delta \equiv \begin{pmatrix} \delta_1 \\ \delta_2 \end{pmatrix},$$

must be

$$\langle \gamma | \delta \rangle = (\gamma_1^* \gamma_2^*)\begin{pmatrix} \delta_1 \\ \delta_2 \end{pmatrix} = \gamma_1^*\delta_1 + \gamma_2^*\delta_2. \tag{1.48}$$

C. Example 3—Spin-One States

It is easy to verify that the three-dimensional matrices

$$\mathcal{S}_x \equiv \begin{pmatrix} 0 & 0 & 0 \\ 0 & 0 & -i \\ 0 & i & 0 \end{pmatrix}, \quad \mathcal{S}_y \equiv \begin{pmatrix} 0 & 0 & i \\ 0 & 0 & 0 \\ -i & 0 & 0 \end{pmatrix}, \quad \mathcal{S}_z \equiv \begin{pmatrix} 0 & -i & 0 \\ i & 0 & 0 \\ 0 & 0 & 0 \end{pmatrix}, \tag{1.49}$$

satisfy angular-momentum commutation relations, and that the operators

$$\begin{aligned} \mathcal{S}_{+1} &\equiv -\frac{1}{\sqrt{2}}(\mathcal{S}_x + i\mathcal{S}_y) = -\frac{1}{\sqrt{2}}\begin{pmatrix} 0 & 0 & -1 \\ 0 & 0 & -i \\ 1 & i & 0 \end{pmatrix} \\ \mathcal{S}_0 &\equiv \mathcal{S}_z \\ \mathcal{S}_{-1} &\equiv +\frac{1}{\sqrt{2}}(\mathcal{S}_x - i\mathcal{S}_y) = +\frac{1}{\sqrt{2}}\begin{pmatrix} 0 & 0 & 1 \\ 0 & 0 & -i \\ -1 & i & 0 \end{pmatrix} \end{aligned} \tag{1.50}$$

satisfy the appropriate equations for complex spherical components. Three-dimensional basis vectors in Cartesian coordinates are

$$\mathbf{e}_x = \begin{pmatrix} 1 \\ 0 \\ 0 \end{pmatrix}, \qquad \mathbf{e}_y = \begin{pmatrix} 0 \\ 1 \\ 0 \end{pmatrix}, \qquad \mathbf{e}_z = \begin{pmatrix} 0 \\ 0 \\ 1 \end{pmatrix}, \tag{1.51}$$

and complex spherical vectors are

$$\mathbf{e}_{+1} = -\frac{1}{\sqrt{2}}\begin{pmatrix} 1 \\ i \\ 0 \end{pmatrix}, \qquad \mathbf{e}_0 = \begin{pmatrix} 0 \\ 0 \\ 1 \end{pmatrix}, \qquad \mathbf{e}_{-1} = +\frac{1}{\sqrt{2}}\begin{pmatrix} 1 \\ -i \\ 0 \end{pmatrix}. \tag{1.52}$$

REFERENCES

[1] M. E. Rose, *Elementary Theory of Angular Momentum*, Wiley, New York (1957), Chaps. 1 and 2.

[2] P. A. M. Dirac, *The Principles of Quantum Mechanics*, Oxford University Press, New York (1958), 4th ed.

[3] J. Schwinger, On Angular Momentum, in *Quantum Theory of Angular Momentum*, a collection of reprints and original papers edited by L. C. Biedenharn and H. Van Dam, Academic, New York (1965).

[4] W. Pauli, *Z. Physik* **43**, 601 (1927).

6.2 COUPLING AND CLEBSCH–GORDAN COEFFICIENTS

In the last section we saw that the commutation relations (1.18) (or 1.20) suffice to endow Hermitian operators $\mathcal{J}_x$, $\mathcal{J}_y$, and $\mathcal{J}_z$ (or $\mathcal{J}_{+1}$, $\mathcal{J}_0$, and $\mathcal{J}_{-1}$) with the properties of angular-momentum components. For particular applications these operators might be represented by square matrices or by differential operators. The corresponding eigenstates would then be represented by column vectors or by functions. We need not use such explicit representations, of course, and it is usually just as easy to consider the $\mathcal{J}_p$ operators as simply acting on state vectors (states) of an appropriate abstract vector space.

Suppose we take two different sets of angular-momentum operators $j(a)$ and $j(b)$, acting on states of two different abstract spaces, **A** and **B**:

$$j^2(a)\mathbf{A} = a(a+1)\mathbf{A} \qquad j^2(b)\mathbf{B} = b(b+1)\mathbf{B} \tag{2.1}$$
$$j_0(a)\mathbf{A} = \alpha\mathbf{A} \qquad j_0(b)\mathbf{B} = \beta\mathbf{B}.$$

(For example, **A** might be a space of functions, **B** a space of column matrices; or **A** might be the space for particle 1, **B** the space for particle 2.) Here and in the remainder of this chapter, Greek letters as well as the letter M will denote *magnetic quantum numbers*. Just as with ordinary Cartesian vectors we can define the sum of two angular momenta through the sum of components. For ordinary vectors **a** and **b** the sum **a** + **b** is

$$(\mathbf{a} + \mathbf{b})_i = \mathbf{a}_i + \mathbf{b}_i \qquad (\text{for } i = x, y, z). \tag{2.2}$$

We therefore *define* an operator $\mathcal{J}$ by the equation

$$\mathcal{J} = j(a) + j(b) \tag{2.3a}$$

meaning the three equations,

$$\begin{aligned} \mathcal{J}_x &= j_x(a) + j_x(b) \\ \mathcal{J}_y &= j_y(a) + j_y(b) \\ \mathcal{J}_z &= j_z(a) + j_z(b) \end{aligned} \tag{2.3b}$$

or, for the more useful complex spherical components,

$$\mathcal{J}_p = j_p(a) + j_p(b) \qquad p = +1, 0, -1. \tag{2.3c}$$

Since $j(a)$ and $j(b)$ act on different coordinates (they act in different abstract spaces), we can apply them to a state in any order. They commute. Thus the components of $\mathcal{J}$ satisfy the same commutation relations as those of $j(a)$ and $j(b)$:

$$[\mathcal{J}_0, \mathcal{J}_{\pm 1}] = \pm\mathcal{J}_{\pm 1} \qquad [\mathcal{J}_{\pm 1}, \mathcal{J}_{-1}] = \mathcal{J}_0 \tag{2.4}$$

and $\mathcal{J}$ is also an angular momentum. That is, there exist eigenstates **C** which satisfy

$$\mathcal{J}^2\mathbf{C}(JM) = J(J+1)\mathbf{C}(JM), \qquad \mathcal{J}_0\mathbf{C}(JM) = M\mathbf{C}(JM),$$

where

$$\begin{aligned} \mathcal{J}^2 &= -\mathcal{J}_{+1}\mathcal{J}_{-1} + \mathcal{J}_0\mathcal{J}_0 - \mathcal{J}_{-1}\mathcal{J}_{+1} \\ &= -2\mathcal{J}_{-1}\mathcal{J}_{+1} + \mathcal{J}_0(\mathcal{J}_0 + 1). \end{aligned} \tag{2.5}$$

As with any angular momentum, we can show that J must take either integral or half-odd-integral values, and M takes values ranging from $-J$ to $+J$ in integral steps. We can write this result in terms of the $j(a)$ and $j(b)$ components using the definition (2.3c):

$$\begin{aligned}\mathcal{J}^2 = {} & [-2j_{-1}(a)j_{+1}(a) + j_0^2(a) + j_0(a)] \\ & + [-2j_{-1}(b)j_{+1}(b) + j_0^2(b) + j_0(b)] \\ & - 2j_{-1}(a)j_{+1}(b) - 2j_{-1}(b)j_{+1}(a) + 2j_0(a)j_0(b);\end{aligned}$$

but this is just

$$\mathcal{J}^2 = j^2(a) + 2j(a)\cdot j(b) + j^2(b) \tag{2.6}$$

as we should have expected from (2.2).

We can use (2.6) to relate the eigenstates $\mathbf{C}(JM)$ of $\mathcal{J}^2$ to eigenstates $\mathbf{A}(a\alpha)$ and $\mathbf{B}(b\beta)$ of $j^2(a)$ and $j^2(b)$. We begin by defining the *Kronecker product* $\mathbf{A} \otimes \mathbf{B}$ (also known as the *Cartesian product*) of the spaces $\mathbf{A}$ and $\mathbf{B}$ as the totality of pairs of states $\mathbf{A}(a\alpha)\mathbf{B}(b\beta)$:

$$\mathbf{A} \otimes \mathbf{B} \equiv \sum_a \sum_\alpha \sum_b \sum_\beta \mathbf{A}(a\alpha)\mathbf{B}(b\beta). \tag{2.7}$$

It should be clear from the definition (2.3), that eigenstates of $\mathcal{J}^2$ must be expressible in terms of such pairs. We can immediately check that a state of this product space is an eigenstate of the (commuting) operators $j^2(a)$, $j_0(a)$, $j^2(b)$, and $j_0(b)$:

$$\begin{aligned} j^2(a)\mathbf{A}(a\alpha)\mathbf{B} &= a(a+1)\mathbf{A}(a\alpha)\mathbf{B} \\ j_0(a)\mathbf{A}(a\alpha)\mathbf{B} &= \alpha\mathbf{A}(a\alpha)\mathbf{B}\end{aligned} \tag{2.8}$$

with similar expressions for $j^2(b)$, $j_0(b)$. From the definitions of $\mathcal{J}_0$, the state $\mathbf{AB}$ is also an eigenstate of $\mathcal{J}_0$, with eigenvalue $\alpha + \beta$. However, this state is *not* an eigenstate of $\mathcal{J}^2$, for according to (2.6) we have

$$\begin{aligned}\mathcal{J}^2\mathbf{A}(a\alpha)\mathbf{B}(b\beta) = {} & [a(a+1) + b(b+1) + 2\alpha\beta]\mathbf{AB} \\ & - 2j_{+1}(a)\mathbf{A}j_{-1}(b)\mathbf{B} \\ & - 2j_{-1}(a)\mathbf{A}j_{+1}(b)\mathbf{B}.\end{aligned}$$

The last two terms give, according to (1.39), terms of the sort

$$\sqrt{a(a+1) - \alpha(\alpha \pm 1)}\ \sqrt{b(b+1) - \beta(\beta \mp 1)}\ \mathbf{A}(a, \alpha \pm 1)\mathbf{B}(b, \beta \mp 1),$$

so $\mathcal{J}^2$ acts to mix states with different values of α and β although it does not mix values of a and b. The eigenstates of $\mathcal{J}^2$ can therefore be chosen as eigenstates of the four (commuting) operators $\mathcal{J}^2$, $\mathcal{J}_0$, $j^2(a)$, and $j^2(b)$.

Since the eigenstates $\mathbf{A}$ and $\mathbf{B}$ form complete spaces for the operators $j(a)$ and $j(b)$, the product space $\mathbf{A} \otimes \mathbf{B}$ is a complete space for combinations of these operators such as $\mathcal{J}$. An eigenstate of $\mathcal{J}^2$ can therefore be expressed as some linear combination of states from $\mathbf{A} \otimes \mathbf{B}$. If $\mathbf{C}(JM)$ is a normalized eigenstate of $\mathcal{J}^2$ and $\mathcal{J}_0$,

$$\begin{aligned} \mathcal{J}^2\mathbf{C}(JM) &= J(J+1)\mathbf{C}(JM) \\ \mathcal{J}_0\mathbf{C}(JM) &= M\mathbf{C}(JM), \end{aligned} \tag{2.9}$$

then we can write this linear combination as

$$\mathbf{C}(JM) = \sum_{\alpha}\sum_{\beta} (a\alpha, b\beta \,|\, JM)\mathbf{A}(a\alpha)\mathbf{B}(b\beta). \tag{2.10}$$

This is a particular example of a unitary transformation. The expansion coefficients here defined,

$$(a\alpha, b\beta \,|\, JM) \equiv \langle \mathbf{AB} \,|\, \mathbf{C} \rangle, \tag{2.11}$$

are known as *Clebsch–Gordan* (CG) or *vector-coupling* (VC) coefficients. Our notation, that of Condon and Shortley [1], emphasizes the definition (2.11) and exhibits the six arguments (not independent) upon which the coefficients depend. We often say these coefficients relate *uncoupled* eigenstates of $j^2(a)$, $j_0(a)$, $j^2(b)$, $j_0(b)$ to the *coupled* eigenstates of $j^2(a)$, $j^2(b)$, $\mathcal{J}^2$ $\mathcal{J}_0$. We shall see that the CG coefficients can be chosen real, so that

$$(a\alpha, b\beta \,|\, JM) = (JM \,|\, b\beta, a\alpha) \tag{2.12}$$

(note the ordering of a and b). Just as we showed that different eigenstates $\mathbf{A}(a\alpha)$ were orthogonal because $j^2(a)$ and $j_0(a)$ are Hermitian (1.42), we must also show the eigenstates $\mathbf{C}(JM)$ to be orthogonal if $\mathcal{J}^2$ and $\mathcal{J}_0$ are Hermitian. We assume, in what follows, that all angular-momentum eigenstates have been normalized, so that we have

$$\langle \mathbf{C}(JM) \,|\, \mathbf{C}(J'M') \rangle = \delta_{JJ'}\,\delta_{MM'}. \tag{2.13}$$

Since the CG coefficients are coefficients of a unitary transformation, they satisfy the orthogonality relation

$$\sum_{\alpha\beta} (JM \,|\, b\beta, a\alpha)(a\alpha, b\beta) \,|\, J'M') = \delta_{JJ'}\delta_{MM'}. \tag{2.14}$$

[This result follows directly from (2.13) and the similar orthogonality of the $\mathbf{A}$ and $\mathbf{B}$ states.] The inverse expansion is also possible:

$$\mathbf{A}(a\alpha)\mathbf{B}(b\beta) = \sum_{JM} (a\alpha, b\beta) \,|\, JM)\mathbf{C}(JM). \tag{2.15}$$

This leads in turn to the orthogonality relation

$$\sum_{JM} (a\alpha, b\beta \,|\, JM)(JM \,|\, b\beta', a\alpha') = \delta_{\alpha\alpha'}\,\delta_{\beta\beta'}. \tag{2.16}$$

Let us now determine some properties of these important coefficients.

First, notice that (2.10) is actually only a sum over one quantum number, say α. To prove this statement, act on the left-hand side with $\mathcal{J}_0$ and on the right-hand side with the equivalent $j_0(a) + j_0(b)$, to obtain

$$M\mathbf{C}(JM) = \sum_{\alpha} \sum_{\beta} (\alpha + \beta)(JM \mid b\beta, a\alpha)\mathbf{A}(a\alpha)\mathbf{B}(b\beta).$$

Comparison with (2.10) for $\mathbf{C}(JM)$ shows that for each term of the sum, we must have

$$\alpha + \beta = M. \tag{2.17}$$

Thus for a given M and α, the second summation index β is fixed. The CG coefficients therefore satisfy

$$(a\alpha, b\beta \mid JM) = 0 \quad \text{unless} \quad \alpha + \beta = M. \tag{2.18}$$

Nevertheless we will often write (2.10) as a double sum to emphasize the symmetry.

Next we note that when M takes the maximum permissible value J, the CG coefficient in expansion (2.10) having $\alpha = a$ is

$$(a\alpha, b\beta \mid JM) \rightarrow (aa, bJ - a \mid JJ).$$

In this case the condition $-b \leq \beta \leq b$ becomes

$$-b \leq J - a \leq b \quad \text{or} \quad a - b \leq J \leq a + b.$$

Similarly, the coefficient having $\beta = b$ requires

$$b - a \leq J \leq a + b.$$

The combination of these two restrictions is just the vector-model *triangle rule*,

$$|a - b| \leq J \leq a + b, \tag{2.19}$$

that the numbers a, b, and J form the sides of a triangle. We can also verify the *integer perimeter* rule,

$$a + b + J = \text{an integer} \tag{2.20}$$

by applying the condition $\alpha + \beta = M$ to the case $\alpha = a$, $\beta = b$, $M = J$.

We can use the properties of ladder operators to obtain a recursion relation for the CG coefficients: operate on the left-hand side of (2.10) with, say $\mathcal{J}_{+1}$ and on the right-hand side use the equivalent operator $j_{+1}(a) + j_{+1}(b)$. Then take the scalar product with the state $\mathbf{A}(a\alpha)\,\mathbf{B}(b\beta)$:

$$\langle \mathbf{AB} \mid \mathcal{J}_{+1} \mid \mathbf{C} \rangle = \sum_{\alpha'\beta'} (JM \mid b\beta', a\alpha') \times \langle \mathbf{AB} \mid j_{+1}(a) + j_{+1}(b) \mid \mathbf{A}(\alpha')\mathbf{B}(\beta') \rangle.$$

Using the result (1.39) of the last section and the orthogonality of the **A** and **B** states, we obtain the recursion relation

$$\sqrt{J(J+1) - M(M+1)}\,(JM+1\,|\,b\beta, a\alpha)$$
$$= \sqrt{a(a+1) - \alpha(\alpha-1)}\,(JM\,|\,b\beta, a\alpha-1)$$
$$+ \sqrt{b(b+1) - \beta(\beta-1)}\,(JM\,|\,b\beta-1, a\alpha) \tag{2.21}$$

with a similar result for $\mathcal{J}_{-1}$. The two recursion relations are usually combined ([1], p. 74) as:

$$\sqrt{(J \pm M)(J \mp M + 1)}\,(JM \mp 1\,|\,b\beta, a\alpha)$$
$$= \sqrt{(a \mp \alpha)(a \pm \alpha + 1)}\,(JM\,|\,b\beta, a\alpha \pm 1)$$
$$+ \sqrt{(b \mp \beta)(b \pm \beta + 1)}\,(JM\,|\,b\beta \pm 1, a\alpha). \tag{2.22}$$

The state $\mathbf{C}(JJ)$ with $J = a + b$ (called the "stretched" case, since the triangle of a, b, and J degenerates into a straight line) corresponds uniquely (except for phase) to the state $\mathbf{A}(aa)\,\mathbf{B}(bb)$. The sum in (2.10) for this case reads, since only $\alpha = a$, and $\beta = b$ are permitted,

$$\mathbf{C}(JJ) = (JJ\,|\,bb, aa)\mathbf{A}(aa)\mathbf{B}(bb).$$

If we choose this CG coefficient as real and positive, then normalization requires

$$(JJ\,|\,bb, aa) = 1. \tag{2.23}$$

This choice is known as the *Condon and Shortley phase convention*. Using the recursion relations we can obtain, for any set of values a, b, and J, all of the CG coefficients in terms of the particular one with $M = J$, $\alpha = a$, and $\beta = J - a$. This starting coefficient is in turn fixed by normalizing and a phase convention. (Examples are worked out by Rose [2].)

Closed forms for the CG coefficients have been obtained by Wigner [3] (by means of group-theoretical methods) and Racah [4] (with the aid of an additional recursion relation). *Racah's formula* is

$$(JM\,|\,b\beta, a\alpha) = \delta_{\alpha+\beta,M}\sqrt{2J+1}\,\sqrt{\Delta(abJ)}$$
$$\times \sum_z \frac{(-1)^z}{(z!)} \frac{[(a-\alpha)!(a+\alpha)!(b-\beta)!(b+\beta)!(J-M)!(J+M)!]^{1/2}}{\left\{\begin{matrix}(a+b-J-z)!(a-\alpha-z)!(b+\beta-z)!\\ \times (J-b+\alpha+z)!(J-a-\beta-z)!\end{matrix}\right\}} \tag{2.24}$$

where the *triangle coefficient* is

$$\Delta(abJ) \equiv \frac{(a+b-J)!(a-b+J)!(-a+b+J)!}{(a+b+J+1)!}. \tag{2.25}$$

In the summation z takes on all integral values such that none of the factorials become zero. Special cases of this formula appear in Condon

Table 6.1 Selected Values of Clebsch-Gordan Coefficients

j_1	j_2	J	m_1	m_2	M	$(j_1m_1\ j_2m_2\|JM)$
$\frac{1}{2}$	$\frac{1}{2}$	1	$\frac{1}{2}$	$-\frac{1}{2}$	0	$\sqrt{\frac{1}{2}} = 0.70711$
			$-\frac{1}{2}$	$\frac{1}{2}$	0	$\sqrt{\frac{1}{2}} = 0.70711$
			$\frac{1}{2}$	$\frac{1}{2}$	1	1
$\frac{1}{2}$	1	$\frac{3}{2}$	$\frac{1}{2}$	0	$\frac{1}{2}$	$\sqrt{\frac{2}{3}} = 0.81650$
			$-\frac{1}{2}$	1	$\frac{1}{2}$	$\sqrt{\frac{1}{3}} = 0.57735$
			$\frac{1}{2}$	1	$\frac{3}{2}$	1
1	1	1	1	-1	0	$\sqrt{\frac{1}{2}} = 0.70711$
			0	0	0	0
			-1	1	0	$-\sqrt{\frac{1}{2}}$
			1	0	1	$\sqrt{\frac{1}{2}}$
			0	1	1	$-\sqrt{\frac{1}{2}}$
1	1	2	1	-1	0	$\sqrt{\frac{1}{6}} = 0.40825$
			0	0	0	$\sqrt{\frac{2}{6}} = 0.81650$
			-1	1	0	$\sqrt{\frac{1}{6}} = 0.40825$
			1	0	1	$\sqrt{\frac{1}{2}} = 0.70711$
			0	1	1	$\sqrt{\frac{1}{2}}$
			1	1	2	1
			1	-1	0	$\sqrt{\frac{1}{6}} = 0.40825$

and Shortley [1], pp. 76–77 or the *Handbook of Mathematical Functions* [5], pp. 1006–1010. Table 6.1 gives several useful examples.

From the explicit formula (2.24) we can obtain some useful symmetry properties of the CG coefficients:

$$\begin{aligned}(a\alpha;\, b\beta\,|\,JM) &= (-1)^{a+b-J}(b\beta;\, a\alpha\,|\,JM)\\ &= (-1)^{a+b-J}(a,\, -\alpha;\, b,\, -\beta\,|\,J,\, -M)\\ &= (-1)^{a-\alpha}\sqrt{\frac{2J+1}{2b+1}}\,(a\alpha;\, J,\, -M\,|\,b,\, -\beta)\\ &= (-1)^{b-\beta}\sqrt{\frac{2J+1}{2a+1}}\,(J,\, -M;\, b\beta\,|\,a,\, -\alpha). \qquad (2.26)\end{aligned}$$

The CG coefficient $(a\alpha\,|\,\alpha a, 00)$ describes the coupling of no angular momentum at all. We have

$$(a\alpha\,|\,b\beta, 00) = (a\alpha\,|\,00, b\beta) = \delta_{ab}\,\delta_{\alpha\beta}. \tag{2.27}$$

Application of the symmetry relations gives

$$(00\,|\,a\alpha, a\beta) = \frac{(-1)^{a-\alpha}}{\sqrt{2a+1}}\,\delta_{\alpha+\beta,0}. \tag{2.28}$$

For some applications, the CG symmetry properties of (2.26) become cumbersome, and the more symmetrical *three-j symbols* (or *Wigner coefficients*) are frequently used:

$$\begin{pmatrix} a & b & J \\ \alpha & \beta & -M \end{pmatrix} \equiv \frac{(-1)^{a+b+M}}{\sqrt{2J+1}}\,(a\alpha, b\beta\,|\,JM). \tag{2.29}$$

Table 6.2 Some 3-j Symbols

$J = 0 \qquad M = 0$

$$\begin{pmatrix} l & l & 0 \\ m & -m & 0 \end{pmatrix} = \frac{(-1)^{l-m}}{\sqrt{2l+1}}$$

$J = a + b \qquad M = \alpha + \beta$

$$\begin{pmatrix} a & b & J \\ \alpha & \beta & M \end{pmatrix} = \frac{(-1)^{a-b+M}}{(2J+1)!}\;\frac{\sqrt{(2a)!(2b)!(J+M)!(J-M)!}}{(a+\alpha)!(a-\alpha)!(b+\beta)!(b-\beta)!}$$

$\alpha = a \qquad \beta = -\alpha - M$

$$\begin{pmatrix} a & b & J \\ a & \beta & M \end{pmatrix} = \frac{(-1)^{b-a+M}\sqrt{(2a)!(-a+b+J)!(b-\beta)!(J-M)!}}{(a+b+J)!(a-b+J)!(a+b-J)!(b+\beta)!(J+M)!}$$

$2g = a + b + J$

$$\begin{pmatrix} a & b & J \\ 0 & 0 & 0 \end{pmatrix} = \begin{cases} 0 & \text{if } g = \text{odd} \\ (-1)^g \dfrac{g!\sqrt{\Delta(abJ)}}{(g-a)!(g-b)!(g-J)!} & \text{if } g = \text{even} \end{cases}$$

$$\Delta(abJ) \equiv \frac{(a+b-J)!(a-b-J)!(-a+b+J)!}{(a+b+J+1)!}$$

$$\begin{pmatrix} a & b & J \\ \alpha & \beta & M \end{pmatrix} = \begin{pmatrix} J & a & b \\ M & \alpha & \beta \end{pmatrix} = \begin{pmatrix} b & J & a \\ \beta & M & \alpha \end{pmatrix}$$

$$= (-1)^{a+b+J}\begin{pmatrix} a & J & b \\ \alpha & M & \beta \end{pmatrix} = (-1)^{a+b+J}\begin{pmatrix} a & b & J \\ -\alpha & -\beta & -M \end{pmatrix}$$

$$\begin{pmatrix} a & b & J \\ \alpha & \beta & M \end{pmatrix} = \frac{(-1)^{\alpha+\beta+M}}{\sqrt{2J+1}}\,(a\alpha, b\beta\,|\,JM)$$

The 3-j symbols take the same value for any *even* interchange of columns

$$\begin{pmatrix} a & b & J \\ \alpha & \beta & M \end{pmatrix} = \begin{pmatrix} J & a & b \\ M & \alpha & \beta \end{pmatrix} = \begin{pmatrix} b & J & a \\ \beta & M & \alpha \end{pmatrix}, \tag{2.30}$$

whereas an *odd* permutation merely introduces the phase $(-1)^{a+b+c}$

$$\begin{pmatrix} a & b & J \\ \alpha & \beta & M \end{pmatrix} = (-1)^{a+b+J} \begin{pmatrix} b & a & J \\ \beta & \alpha & M \end{pmatrix}, \text{ etc.} \tag{2.31}$$

The symbols also satisfy the condition

$$\begin{pmatrix} a & b & J \\ \alpha & \beta & M \end{pmatrix} = (-1)^{a+b+J} \begin{pmatrix} a & b & J \\ -\alpha & -\beta & -M \end{pmatrix}. \tag{2.32}$$

Using the 3-j symbols, we can write the orthogonality relations as

$$\sum_{\alpha\beta} \begin{pmatrix} a & b & J \\ \alpha & \beta & M \end{pmatrix} \begin{pmatrix} a & b & J' \\ \alpha & \beta & M' \end{pmatrix} = \frac{\delta_{JJ'}\, \delta_{MM'}}{(2J+1)}, \tag{2.33}$$

$$\sum_{JM} (2J+1) \begin{pmatrix} a & b & J \\ \alpha & \beta & M \end{pmatrix} \begin{pmatrix} a & b & J \\ \alpha' & \beta' & M \end{pmatrix} = \delta_{\alpha\alpha'}\, \delta_{\alpha\alpha'}. \tag{2.34}$$

As a general rule, the CG coefficients are useful when we are actually constructing a "coupled" state, whereas the 3-j symbols are more useful when we are performing sums over various quantum numbers. Brief tables of 3-j symbols occur in the books by Edmonds [6], Messiah [7], de Shalit and Talmi [8], and Wigner [9], and extended tables are given by Metropolis et al. [10]. Table 6.2 gives a few important special cases.

REFERENCES

[1] E. U. Condon and G. H. Shortley, *The Theory of Atomic Spectra*, Cambridge University Press, Cambridge, England (1935).

[2] M. E. Rose, *Elementary Theory of Angular Momentum*, Wiley, New York (1957), Chap. IV.

[3] E. P. Wigner, *Group Theory and its Application to the Quantum Mechanics of Atomic Spectra*, Academic, New York (1959).

[4] G. Racah, *Phys. Rev.* **62**, 438 (1942).

[5] M. Abramowitz and I. A. Stegun, *Handbook of Mathematical Functions*, Natl. Bur. Stds. Applied Mathematics Series 55 (1964).

[6] A. R. Edmonds, *Angular Momentum in Quantum Mechanics*, Princeton University Press, Princeton, New Jersey (1957).

[7] A. Messiah, *Quantum Mechanics*, Wiley, New York (1962).

[8] A. de Shalit and I. Talmi, *Nuclear Shell Theory*, Academic, New York (1963).

[9] E. P. Wigner, *Group Theory and its Application to the Quantum Mechanics of Atomic Spectra*, Academic, New York (1959).

[10] M. Rotenberg, R. Bivens, N. Metropolis, and J. K. Wooten, Jr., *The 3-j and 6-j Symbols*, MIT Technology Press, Cambridge, Mass. (1959).

6.3 MULTIPLE COUPLING AND RACAH COEFFICIENTS

Although the preceding discussion of adding (coupling) *two* angular momenta suffices to treat many important problems in physics, one often deals with *three* or more angular momenta. This occurs when treating atoms comprising several electrons, each with an orbital and a spin angular momentum. It also occurs, as we shall see, in the evaluation of certain matrix elements.

If we have three angular momenta $\mathfrak{a}$, $\mathfrak{b}$, and $\mathfrak{c}$ [i.e., operators $\mathfrak{a}_{+1}$, $\mathfrak{a}_0$, $\mathfrak{a}_{-1}$, etc. satisfying the defining commutation rules (1.20)] having eigenstates $\mathbf{A}(a\alpha)$, $\mathbf{B}(b\beta)$, and $\mathbf{C}(c\gamma)$, we can form linear combinations of the states from the Kronecker-product space $\mathbf{A} \otimes \mathbf{B} \otimes \mathbf{C}$ which are eigenstates of $\mathcal{J}^2 = (\mathfrak{a} + \mathfrak{b} + \mathfrak{c})^2$ and $\mathcal{J}_0 = \mathfrak{a}_0 + \mathfrak{b}_0 + \mathfrak{c}_0$. In what follows we shall always assume that these angular momenta refer to different distinguishable particles or to different types of angular momenta. We use different symbols **A**, **B**, and **C** to emphasize that these abstract state vectors refer to different abstract spaces. A more common notation, due to Dirac, is $|a\alpha\rangle$, $|b\beta\rangle$, $|c\gamma\rangle$. The case of identical particles will be taken up later. As with two angular momenta, we define the *total angular momentum* $\mathcal{J}$ by defining its components:

$$\mathcal{J}_p = \mathfrak{a}_p + \mathfrak{b}_p + \mathfrak{c}_p \qquad (p = +1, 0, -1), \tag{3.1}$$

$$\mathcal{J}^2 = -\mathcal{J}_{+1}\mathcal{J}_{-1} + \mathcal{J}_0\mathcal{J}_0 - \mathcal{J}_{-1}\mathcal{J}_{+1}. \tag{3.2}$$

We can readily extend the discussion of the last section to construct eigenstates $\Psi(JM)$ of $\mathcal{J}^2$ and $\mathcal{J}_0$. For example, we could first couple the states **A** and **B** to an intermediate state **D**:

$$\mathbf{D}(D\delta) = \sum_{\alpha\beta} (D\delta \,|\, b\beta, a\alpha)\mathbf{A}(a\alpha)\mathbf{B}(b\beta), \tag{3.3}$$

then couple the third state **C** onto **D**:

$$\begin{aligned}\Psi(ab(D)cJM) &= \sum_{\gamma M\sigma} (JM \,|\, c\gamma, D\delta)\mathbf{D}(D\delta)\mathbf{C}(c\gamma)\\ &= \sum (JM \,|\, c\gamma, D\delta)(D\delta \,|\, b\beta, a\alpha)\mathbf{ABC}.\end{aligned} \tag{3.4}$$

In Dirac notation, this reads

$$|ab(D)cJM\rangle = \sum (JM \,|\, c\gamma, D\delta)(D\delta \,|\, b\beta, a\alpha)\,|c\gamma\rangle\,|b\beta\rangle\,|a\alpha\rangle.$$

The sum goes over all permissible values for α, β, γ, and δ. In our notation for Ψ, we have introduced explicit mention of the intermediate state $\mathbf{D}(D\delta)$.

This is because the state Ψ, as constructed in (3.4), is an eigenstate of the five operators a^2, b^2, c^2, $\mathcal{J}^2$, $\mathcal{J}_0$, and the operator $\mathcal{D}^2$ defined by

$$\mathcal{D}_p = a_p + b_p, \qquad (p = +1, 0, -1), \tag{3.5}$$
$$\mathcal{D}^2 = -\mathcal{D}_{-1}\mathcal{D}_{+1} + \mathcal{D}_0\mathcal{D}_0 - \mathcal{D}_{+1}\mathcal{D}_{-1},$$

as we readily confirm from the first line of (3.4). We have, in fact, replaced the six labels a, α, b, β, c, γ of the uncoupled states in the product space $\mathbf{A} \otimes \mathbf{B} \otimes \mathbf{C}$ by the six labels a, b, c, D, J, M for the coupled states. The operator $\mathcal{D}^2$ acts only in the subspace $\mathbf{A} \otimes \mathbf{B}$; that is, on states $\mathbf{A}(a\alpha)$ and $\mathbf{B}(b\beta)$. Since different states $\mathbf{D}(D\delta)$ of (3.3) are orthogonal (see the discussion in Section 6.2), we have the following orthogonality rule on Ψ:

$$\langle\Psi(ab(D)cJM)\,|\,\Psi(a'b'(D')c'J'M')\rangle = \delta_{aa'}\,\delta_{bb'}\,\delta_{cc}\,\delta_{DD'}\,\delta_{JJ'}\,\delta_{MM'}. \tag{3.6}$$

This coupling procedure could just as well be done in a different order: couple the states $\mathbf{A}$ and $\mathbf{C}$ to an intermediate state $\mathbf{E}$:

$$\mathbf{E}(E\epsilon) = \sum_{\alpha\gamma} (E\epsilon\,|\,c\gamma,\, a\alpha)\mathbf{A}(a\alpha)\mathbf{C}(c\gamma);$$

then couple $\mathbf{B}$:

$$\Psi(bc(E)aJM) = \sum_{\epsilon\beta} (JM\,|\,b\beta,\, E\epsilon)\mathbf{E}(E\epsilon)\mathbf{B}(b\beta) \tag{3.7}$$
$$= (JM\,|\,b\beta,\, E\epsilon)(E\epsilon\,|\,c\gamma,\, a\alpha)\mathbf{A}(a\alpha)\mathbf{B}(b\beta)\mathbf{C}(c\gamma).$$

The written ordering of states in (3.7) is immaterial, $\mathbf{ABC} = \mathbf{BCA}$, etc., since this simply stands for a collection of three states taken from three different spaces. However, the arguments of the CG coefficients define a definite order in which the vectors are coupled:

$$\Psi(ba(E)cJM) \neq \Psi(bc(E)aJM), \text{ etc.}$$

The state Ψ defined by (3.7) is an eigenstate of a^2, b^2, c^2, $\mathcal{J}^2$, $\mathcal{J}_0$, and the operator $\mathcal{E}^2$, where

$$\mathcal{E}_p = b_p + c_p \qquad (p = +1, 0, -1)$$

acts only within the subspace $\mathbf{B} \otimes \mathbf{C}$.

The states produced in these two coupling schemes, say $\Psi(DJM)$ for (3.4) and $\Psi(EJM)$ for (3.5), are not orthogonal. Denoting their scalar product by

$$\langle\Psi(DJM)\,|\,\Psi(EJM)\rangle \equiv (ab(D)c, JM\,|\,ac(E)b, JM), \tag{3.8}$$

we find the requirement

$$\Psi(DJM) = \sum_{EJ'M'} (ab(D)c, JM\,|\,ac(E)b, J'M')\Psi(EJ'M'). \tag{3.9a}$$

But both $\Psi(DJM)$ and $\Psi(EJM)$ are eigenstates of $\mathcal{J}_0$ with eigenvalue M;

therefore $M' = M$. The transformation coefficients, (3.8), are in fact independent of M, as we can see by applying $\mathcal{J}_{+1}$:

$$\mathcal{J}_{+1}\Psi(DJM) = \sum_{EJ'} (ab(D)c, JM|ac(E)b, J'M)\mathcal{J}_{+1}\Psi(EJ'M),$$

but

$$\mathcal{J}_{+1}\Psi(DJM) = \frac{\sqrt{J(J+1) - M(M+1)}}{\sqrt{2}}\Psi(DJ\,M+1),$$

$$\mathcal{J}_{+1}\Psi(EJM) = \frac{\sqrt{J(J+1) - M(M+1)}}{\sqrt{2}}\Psi(EJ\,M+1),$$

so that

$$\Psi(DJ\,M+1) = \sum_{EJ'} (ab(D)c, JM|ac(E)b, JM)\Psi(EJ\,M+1) \quad (3.9b)$$

and therefore the coefficients cannot depend on M.

For these coupling coefficients, Racah [1] introduced the function $W(abcd; ef)$ of six variables now known as the *Racah coefficient*

$$(ab(D), cJ|ac(E), bJ) = \sqrt{2D+1}\,\sqrt{2E+1}\,W(EcbD; Ja). \quad (3.10)$$

Later Wigner [2] introduced the 6-*j symbol:*

$$(ab(D)c, J|ac(E)b, J) = (-1)^{b+c+D+E}\sqrt{2D+1}\,\sqrt{2E+1}\begin{Bmatrix} a & b & E \\ J & c & D \end{Bmatrix}, \quad (3.11)$$

possessing greater symmetry amongst the arguments. Using (3.4) and (3.7) we can relate these coefficients to a sum of the product of four CG coefficients:

$$W(EcbD; Ja) = \sqrt{(2E+1)(2D+1)} \times \sum (JM|c\gamma, D\delta)(D\delta|b\beta, a\alpha)(JM|b\beta, E\epsilon)(E\epsilon|c\gamma, a\alpha).. \quad (3.12)$$

The summation indices are *any two m* values; rule (2.16) fixes the other four. Using (2.22) for the CG coefficients, Racah [1] derived an equation for $W(abcd; ef)$ that consists of a single sum

$$\begin{aligned}(-1)^{a+b+c+d}W(abcd; ef) &= \begin{Bmatrix} a & b & e \\ d & c & f \end{Bmatrix} = \Delta(abe)\,\Delta(acf)\,\Delta(dbf)\,\Delta(dce) \\ &\times \sum_z (-1)^z(z+1)!\{[z-(a+b+e)]![z-(a+c+f)]! \\ &\times (z-d+b+f)]![z-(d+c+e)]![a+b+d+c-z]! \\ &\times [b+c+e+f-z]![a+d+e+f+z]!\}^{-1}, \end{aligned} \quad (3.13)$$

where $\Delta(abc)$ is given by (2.25) and z takes all values such that none of the factorials in the sum become negative. The Racah coefficient $W(abcd; ef)$ is defined for integral and half-odd-integral values of the six arguments, with the restriction that the triads

$$(abe), \quad (acf), \quad (dbf), \quad (dce)$$

must have integral sums. Further, from the condition on z, these triads *must form triangles*. These four triads [the arguments of the triangle coefficients $\Delta(abc)$ in (3.13)] are just the triads from the four CG coefficients in (3.12). These triangles are easily marked on the six-j symbol:

$$\begin{Bmatrix} x & x & x \\ \cdot & \cdot & \cdot \end{Bmatrix} \quad \begin{Bmatrix} x & \cdot & \cdot \\ \cdot & x & x \end{Bmatrix} \quad \begin{Bmatrix} \cdot & x & \cdot \\ x & \cdot & x \end{Bmatrix} \quad \begin{Bmatrix} \cdot & \cdot & x \\ x & x & \cdot \end{Bmatrix} \tag{3.14a}$$

or on the Racah coefficient

$$\begin{matrix} W(xx\cdot\cdot;\, x\cdot) & W(x\cdot x\cdot;\, \cdot x) \\ W(\cdot x\cdot x;\, \cdot x) & W(\cdot\cdot xx;\, \cdot x). \end{matrix} \tag{3.14b}$$

The Racah coefficients vanish unless the integer and triangle rules hold, but not every Racah coefficient satisfying these selection rules is nonzero.

The symmetry properties of these functions follow from (3.13). The arguments of the 6-j symbols may be interchanged in pairs without alteration of the value of the symbol:

$$\begin{Bmatrix} a & b & c \\ d & e & f \end{Bmatrix} = \begin{Bmatrix} a & c & b \\ d & f & e \end{Bmatrix} = \begin{Bmatrix} b & c & a \\ e & f & d \end{Bmatrix}, \quad \text{etc.} \tag{3.15a}$$

The Racah coefficients satisfy the relations

$$\begin{aligned} W(abcd, ef) &= W(badc; ef) = W(cdab; ef) \\ &= W(acbd; fe) = W(dcba; fe) \end{aligned} \tag{3.15b}$$

and

$$\begin{aligned} W(abcd; ef) &= (-1)^{e+f-a-d} W(abcf; ad) \\ &= (-1)^{e+f-b-c} W(aefd; bc). \end{aligned}$$

When one of the arguments is zero, the coefficients become simply

$$\begin{Bmatrix} a & b & c \\ b & a & 0 \end{Bmatrix} = \frac{(-1)^{a+b+c}}{\sqrt{(2a+1)(2b+1)}} \tag{3.16}$$

$$W(abab; c0) = W(aabb; 0c) = \frac{(-)^{a+b+c}}{\sqrt{(2a+1)(2b+1)}}$$

(unless the arguments fit this pattern, or a pattern obtained by suitable pair interchange, the coefficient has the value zero.) Formulas for important coefficients appear in the books by Edmonds, Messiah, and de Shalit and

Talmi (cited in the previous section) and numerical values are tabulated by Rotenberg et al [3]. Table 6.3 gives some important special cases of the 6-j coefficient, taken from Edmonds.

Proceeding next to the coupling of *four* angular momenta we can define a total angular momentum $\mathcal{J}$ by the sums of four components:

$$\mathcal{J}_p = \mathfrak{a}_p + \mathfrak{b}_p + \mathfrak{c}_p + \mathfrak{d}_p \qquad (p = -1, 0, +1).$$

Table 6.3 Some 6-j Symbols

$$\begin{Bmatrix} J & a & b \\ 0 & b & a \end{Bmatrix} = \frac{(-1)^{a+b+J}}{\sqrt{(2a+1)(2b+1)}}$$

$$\begin{Bmatrix} J & a & b \\ 1 & b & a \end{Bmatrix} = \frac{(-1)^{a+b+J}[J(J+1) - a(a+1) - b(b+1)]}{\sqrt{(2a+1)(2b+1)}\sqrt{a(a+1)}\sqrt{b(b+1)}}$$

$$\begin{Bmatrix} J & a & b \\ 2 & b & a \end{Bmatrix} = \frac{(-1)^{a+b+J}}{\sqrt{(2a+1)(2b+1)}} \times \frac{[3C(C+1) - 4a(a+1)b(b+1)]}{\sqrt{a(a+1)(2a+3)(2a-1)}\sqrt{b(b+1)(2b+3)(2b-1)}}$$

where $C \equiv J(J+1) - a(a+1) - b(b+1)$

$$\begin{Bmatrix} a & b & c \\ A & B & C \end{Bmatrix} = \begin{Bmatrix} b & a & c \\ B & A & C \end{Bmatrix} = \begin{Bmatrix} b & c & a \\ B & C & A \end{Bmatrix} = \begin{Bmatrix} A & B & c \\ a & b & C \end{Bmatrix} \quad \text{etc.}$$

As with three angular momenta, when we go from the *uncoupled scheme*, specified by eigenvalues of the eight operators $\mathfrak{a}^2$, $\mathfrak{a}_0$, $\mathfrak{b}^2$, $\mathfrak{b}_0$, $\mathfrak{c}^2$, $\mathfrak{c}_0$, $\mathfrak{d}^2$, $\mathfrak{d}_0$, to the *coupled scheme*, specified by the six eigenvalues of $\mathfrak{a}^2$, $\mathfrak{b}^2$, $\mathfrak{c}^2$, $\mathfrak{d}^2$, $\mathcal{J}^2$, $\mathcal{J}_0$, we must specify two intermediate quantum numbers as well. One way of specifying these is to take the angular momenta in pairs, and then couple these pairs:

$$\begin{aligned} \mathcal{G} &= \mathfrak{a} + \mathfrak{b} \\ \mathcal{H} &= \mathfrak{c} + \mathfrak{d} \\ \mathcal{J} &= \mathcal{G} + \mathcal{H} = (\mathfrak{a} + \mathfrak{b}) + (\mathfrak{c} + \mathfrak{d}) \end{aligned}$$

(where, as usual, each vector equation stands for three equations for components). But we could have chosen the pairs in a different way:

$$\begin{aligned} \mathfrak{L} &= \mathfrak{a} + \mathfrak{c} \\ \mathcal{K} &= \mathfrak{b} + \mathfrak{d} \\ \mathcal{J} &= \mathfrak{L} + \mathcal{K} = (\mathfrak{a} + \mathfrak{c}) + (\mathfrak{b} + \mathfrak{d}). \end{aligned}$$

Table 6.4 Some 9-j Symbols

$$\begin{Bmatrix} a & b & C \\ d & e & F \\ G & H & J \end{Bmatrix} = \sum_x (-1)^{2x}(2x+1) \begin{Bmatrix} a & b & C \\ F & J & x \end{Bmatrix} \begin{Bmatrix} d & e & F \\ b & x & H \end{Bmatrix} \begin{Bmatrix} G & H & J \\ x & a & d \end{Bmatrix}$$

$$\begin{Bmatrix} a & b & J \\ c & d & J \\ K & K & 0 \end{Bmatrix} = \frac{(-1)^{b+c+J+K}}{\sqrt{2J+1}\,\sqrt{2K+1}} \begin{Bmatrix} a & b & J \\ d & c & K \end{Bmatrix}$$

$$\begin{Bmatrix} S & S & 1 \\ L & L & 2 \\ J & J & 1 \end{Bmatrix} = \frac{\begin{Bmatrix} S & L & J \\ L & S & 1 \end{Bmatrix} \begin{Bmatrix} J & L & S \\ L & J & 1 \end{Bmatrix} + \dfrac{(-1)^{S+L+J+1}}{3(2L+1)} \begin{Bmatrix} S & J & L \\ J & S & 1 \end{Bmatrix}}{5 \begin{Bmatrix} 2 & L & L \\ L & 1 & 1 \end{Bmatrix}}$$

$$\begin{Bmatrix} a & b & C \\ d & e & F \\ G & H & I \end{Bmatrix} = (-1)^S \underbrace{\begin{Bmatrix} a & c & b \\ d & f & e \\ G & I & H \end{Bmatrix}}_{\text{Interchange columns}} = (-1)^S \underbrace{\begin{Bmatrix} d & e & F \\ a & b & C \\ G & H & I \end{Bmatrix}}_{\text{Interchange rows}}$$

$$S = a + b + C + d + e + F + G + H + I$$

For a given choice of pairings, states with different intermediate quantum numbers are orthogonal. However, the two pairing schemes (*coupling schemes*) relate by a unitary transformation. The transformation does not depend on the eigenvalue of J_0 [the argument of (3.9) applies here too], and Wigner introduced the 9-*j symbol* for this coefficient:

$$(ab(G)cd(H)J\,|\,ac(L)bd(K)J) = \sqrt{(2G+1)(2H+1)(2K+1)(2L+1)} \begin{Bmatrix} a & b & G \\ c & d & H \\ L & K & J \end{Bmatrix}. \quad (3.17)$$

The 9-*j* symbol can be written as a sum over the product of *six* CG coefficients or as the sum over the product of *three* Racah coefficients. Written in terms of the more symmetrical 6-*j* symbols, this sum is

$$\sum_x (-1)^{2x}(2x+1) \begin{Bmatrix} a & b & G \\ H & J & x \end{Bmatrix} \begin{Bmatrix} a & c & L \\ K & J & x \end{Bmatrix} \begin{Bmatrix} c & H & d \\ b & K & x \end{Bmatrix} = \begin{Bmatrix} a & b & G \\ c & d & H \\ L & K & J \end{Bmatrix}, \quad (3.18)$$

and the definition in terms of 3-*j* symbols reads

$$\sum\begin{pmatrix} a & b & G \\ \cdot & \cdot & \cdot \end{pmatrix}\begin{pmatrix} c & d & H \\ \cdot & \cdot & \cdot \end{pmatrix}\begin{pmatrix} G & H & J \\ \cdot & \cdot & \cdot \end{pmatrix}$$

$$\times\begin{pmatrix} a & c & L \\ \cdot & \cdot & \cdot \end{pmatrix}\begin{pmatrix} b & d & K \\ \cdot & \cdot & \cdot \end{pmatrix}\begin{pmatrix} L & K & J \\ \cdot & \cdot & \cdot \end{pmatrix} = \begin{pmatrix} a & b & G \\ c & d & H \\ L & K & J \end{pmatrix}, \quad (3.19)$$

where the dots signify dummy indices to be summed over.

The 9-j symbol has the following symmetry under interchange of rows or columns: if

$$R = a + b + c + d + G + H + J + K + L$$

is the sum of all the arguments, then *interchange of two adjacent rows or two adjacent columns multiplies the symbol by* $(-1)^R$.

From (3.18) we can show that when one of the arguments is zero, the 9-j symbol reduces to a 6-j symbol or Racah coefficient:

$$\begin{Bmatrix} a & b & K \\ c & d & K \\ L & L & 0 \end{Bmatrix} = \frac{(-1)^{b+c+K+L}}{\sqrt{2K+1}\sqrt{2L+1}}\begin{Bmatrix} a & b & K \\ d & c & L \end{Bmatrix}$$

$$= \frac{1}{\sqrt{2K+1}\sqrt{2L+1}} W(bKLc; ad).$$

Table 6.5 6-j Sum Rules

$$\sum_x (-1)^{2x}(2x+1)\begin{Bmatrix} a & b & x \\ a & b & F \end{Bmatrix} = 1$$

$$\sum_x (-1)^{a+b+x}(2x+1)\begin{Bmatrix} a & b & x \\ b & a & F \end{Bmatrix} = \delta_{F0}\sqrt{(2a+1)(2b+1)}$$

$$\sum_x (2x+1)\begin{Bmatrix} a & b & x \\ c & d & F \end{Bmatrix}\begin{Bmatrix} c & d & x \\ a & b & G \end{Bmatrix} = \frac{\delta_{FG}}{(2F+1)}$$

$$\sum_x (-1)^{F+G+x}(2x+1)\begin{Bmatrix} a & b & x \\ c & d & F \end{Bmatrix}\begin{Bmatrix} c & d & x \\ b & a & C \end{Bmatrix} = \begin{Bmatrix} a & d & F \\ b & c & G \end{Bmatrix}$$

$$\sum_x (-1)^{S}(2x+1)\begin{Bmatrix} a & b & x \\ c & d & G \end{Bmatrix}\begin{Bmatrix} c & d & x \\ e & f & H \end{Bmatrix}\begin{Bmatrix} e & f & x \\ a & b & J \end{Bmatrix} = \begin{Bmatrix} a & d & G \\ f & H & c \\ J & e & b \end{Bmatrix}$$

$$S = a + b + c + d + e + f + G + H + J + x$$

$$\sum_x (-1)^{2x}(2x+1)\begin{Bmatrix} a & b & x \\ c & d & G \end{Bmatrix}\begin{Bmatrix} c & d & x \\ e & f & H \end{Bmatrix}\begin{Bmatrix} e & f & x \\ a & b & J \end{Bmatrix} = \begin{Bmatrix} a & d & G \\ f & H & c \\ J & e & b \end{Bmatrix}$$

(Other cases can be derived by an interchange of rows and columns.) Table 6.4 gives expressions for some 9-j symbols.

Table 6.6 Recoupling Coefficients

$$\langle ab(E), c, J | a, bc(F), J\rangle = (-1)^{a+b+c+J}\sqrt{2E+1}\,\sqrt{2F+1}\begin{Bmatrix} b & a & E \\ J & c & F \end{Bmatrix}$$

$$\langle ab(E), c, J | ac(G), b, J\rangle = (-1)^{E+c+b+G}\sqrt{2E+1}\,\sqrt{2F+1}\begin{Bmatrix} E & c & J \\ G & b & a \end{Bmatrix}$$

$$\langle ab(E), b, 0 | a, bb(0), a\rangle = (-1)^{a+b-E}\frac{\sqrt{2E+1}}{\sqrt{2a+1}\,\sqrt{2b+1}}$$

$$\langle abJ | baJ\rangle = (-1)^{a+b-J}$$

$$\langle ab(E), cd(F), J | ac(G), bd(H), J\rangle$$

$$= \sqrt{(2E+1)(2F+1)(2G+1)(2H+1)}\begin{Bmatrix} a & b & E \\ c & d & F \\ G & H & J \end{Bmatrix}$$

For convenience, Table 6.5 collects some of the formulas connecting recoupling coefficients with n-j symbols. Table 6.6 shows some of the important summation properties of the 6-j symbols. A lengthier discussion of n-j symbols will be found in the papers of reference [4] or the book by Yutsis, Levinson, and Vanagas [5].

REFERENCES

[1] G. Racah, *Phys. Rev.* **62,** 438 (1942).
[2] E. P. Wigner, *Group Theory and its Application to the Quantum Mechanics of Atomic Spectra*, Academic Press, New York (1959).
[3] M. Rotenberg, R. Bivens, N. Metropolis, and J. K. Wooten, Jr., *The 3-j and 6-j Symbols*, M.I.T. Technology Press, Cambridge, Mass. (1959).
[4] L. C. Biedenharn and H. Van Dam, eds., *Quantum Theory of Angular Momentum*, Academic, New York (1965).
[5] A. P. Yutsis, I. B. Levinson, and V. V. Vanagas, *The Theory of Angular Momentum*, transl. from Russian by A. Sen and A. R. Sen. Available from Office of Technical Services, U.S. Dept. of Commerce, Washington, D.C. (1962).

6.4 TENSOR OPERATORS AND THE WIGNER–ECKART THEOREM

A. Definition

We have seen that the study of any quantum-mechanical system ultimately reduces to the calculation of matrix elements for appropriate operators between various basis states. In this section we see how to calculate matrix elements in the angular-momentum representation—when the basis states are chosen to be eigenstates of various angular-momentum operators. As we note in Appendix A, all states of angular momentum J, whether they be represented by functions, by matrices, or simply by abstract state vectors, share the property that when the coordinate system is rotated, the states in the new coordinate system are

$$\mathbf{A}(JM)_{\text{new}} = \sum_{M'} \mathfrak{D}^{(J)}_{M'M}\, \mathbf{A}(JM')_{\text{old}}, \tag{4.1a}$$

where $\mathfrak{D}^{(J)}$ is the *rotation matrix* of order J. Thus angular-momentum states possess well-defined rotational properties.

In the present section we study the properties of various *operators* that possess well-defined rotational properties. These include angular-momentum operators (the generators of infinitesimal rotations), the functions Y_{lm} viewed as operators, and appropriate linear combinations of these operators. In particular, we are interested in operators that possess the rotational properties of (4.1). Following the work of Wigner [1] we can define an *irreducible tensorial set* $\mathbf{T}^{(k)}$ (the name proposed by Fano and Racah [2]) of order k as a collection of $2k + 1$ elements or components

$$T^{(k)}_k, \quad T^{(k)}_{k-1}, \quad \cdots \quad T^{(k)}_m \quad \cdots \quad T^{(k)}_{-k},$$

which transform under rotations according to the equation

$$T^{(k)}_m\,(\text{new}) = \sum_{n.'} \mathfrak{D}^{(k)}_{m'm} T^{(k)}_{m'}\,(\text{old}). \tag{4.1b}$$

Although (4.1b) provides a definition of a *tensor operator* $\mathbf{T}^{(k)}$ in terms of rotational symmetry, we shall find it more convenient to deal with operator commutation relations. Recall that angular-momentum operators $\mathcal{J}_p$ satisfy, by definition (1.20) the relations:

$$\begin{aligned} [\mathcal{J}_0, \mathcal{J}_{+1}] &= \mathcal{J}_{+1} \\ [\mathcal{J}_0, \mathcal{J}_{-1}] &= -\mathcal{J}_{-1} \\ [\mathcal{J}_{+1}, \mathcal{J}_{-1}] &= -\mathcal{J}_0. \end{aligned} \tag{4.2}$$

With the aid of a CG coefficient these equations can be written

$$[\mathcal{J}_p, \mathcal{J}_q] = \sqrt{2}\,(1p, 1q|1p+q)\mathcal{J}_{p+q}. \tag{4.3}$$

We next note that the action of $\mathcal{J}_p$ upon the angular-momentum state $\mathbf{A}(JM)$,

$$\mathcal{J}_{\pm 1}\mathbf{A}(JM) = \mp\left[\frac{J(J+1) - M(M\pm 1)}{2}\right]^{1/2}\mathbf{A}(JM\pm 1), \tag{4.4a}$$
$$\mathcal{J}_0\mathbf{A}(JM) = M\mathbf{A}(JM),$$

which follows directly from (4.2), can also be written in terms of a CG coefficient:

$$\mathcal{J}_p\mathbf{A}(JM) = \sqrt{J(J+1)}\,(1p, JM|JM+p)\mathbf{A}(J, M+p). \tag{4.4b}$$

If we now regard $\mathbf{A}(JM)$ as an operator, then the commutator of $\mathcal{J}_p$ and $\mathbf{A}(JM)$, defined by the operator equation on an arbitrary state $\mathbf{B}$,

$$[\mathcal{J}_p, \mathbf{A}(JM)]\mathbf{B} = \mathcal{J}_p\{\mathbf{A}(JM)\mathbf{B}\} - \mathbf{A}(JM)\mathcal{J}_p\mathbf{B},$$

can be written:

$$[\mathcal{J}_p, \mathbf{A}(JM)] = \sqrt{J(J+1)}\,(1p, JM|JM+p)\mathbf{A}(J, M+p). \tag{4.5a}$$

In a classic paper Racah [3] suggested that one could take (4.5*a*) as the definition of a tensor operator $\mathbf{T}^{(k)}$. That is, we define $\mathbf{T}^{(k)}$ by equations for $2k+1$ components $T_q^{(k)}$,

$$[\mathcal{J}_p, T_q^{(k)}] = \sqrt{k(k+1)}\,(1p, kq|k\,p+q)T_{p+q}^{(k)}. \tag{4.5b}$$

In more detail, Racah's definition reads

$$[\mathcal{J}_{\pm 1}, T_q^{(k)}] = \mp\left[\frac{k(k+1) - q(q\pm 1)}{2}\right]^{1/2} T_{q\pm 1}^{(k)} \tag{4.5c}$$
$$[\mathcal{J}_0, T_q^{(k)}] = qT_q^{(k)}.$$

With this definition we see that all angular-momentum operators (orbital, spin, etc.) are tensor operators of order 1, having three components:

$$\{\mathcal{J}_p\} = J_{+1}^{(1)},\quad J_0^{(1)},\quad J_{-1}^{(1)}.$$

The Racah tensor $\mathbf{C}^{(l)}$, with components

$$C_m^{(l)} = \left(\frac{4\pi}{2l+1}\right)^{1/2} Y_{lm} \tag{4.6}$$

is a tensor of order l. In particular, the position vector $\mathbf{r}$ is a tensor of order 1,

$$\mathbf{r} = r\mathbf{C}^{(1)}, \tag{4.7a}$$

having the components

$$r_{+1}^{(1)} = -\frac{(x+iy)}{\sqrt{2}}, \quad r_0^{(1)} = z, \quad r_{-1}^{(1)} = \frac{(x-iy)}{\sqrt{2}}. \tag{4.7b}$$

The usefulness of Racah's definition appears when we calculate the matrix element of $T_q^{(k)}$ between two angular-momentum states. Suppose we take the matrix element of $[\mathcal{J}_{+1}, T_q^{(k)}]$ between states specified by the eigenvalues J, M, and any other necessary quantum numbers α. From (4.5) we find:

$$\langle \alpha JM | \mathcal{J}_{+1} T_q^{(k)} | \alpha' J' M' \rangle - \langle \alpha JM | T_q^{(k)} \mathcal{J}_{+1} | \alpha' J' M' \rangle$$
$$= -\left[\frac{k(k+1) - q(q+1)}{2}\right]^{1/2} \langle \alpha JM | T_{q+1}^{(k)} | \alpha' J' M' \rangle. \tag{4.8}$$

Now use the property $(\mathcal{J}_{+1})^\dagger = -\mathcal{J}_{-1}$ and (4.4) to find

$$\begin{aligned} 0 = &-\sqrt{J(J+1) - M(M-1)}\,\langle \alpha JM - 1 | T_q^{(k)} | \alpha' J' M' \rangle \\ &+\sqrt{J'(J'+1) - M'(M'+1)}\,\langle \alpha JM | T_q^{(k)} | \alpha' J' M' + 1 \rangle \\ &+\sqrt{k(k+1) - q(q+1)}\,\langle \alpha JM | T_{q+1}^{(k)} | \alpha' J' M' \rangle. \end{aligned} \tag{4.9}$$

Now compare (4.7) with the recursion relation for CG coefficients (2.22):

$$\begin{aligned} 0 = &-\sqrt{J(J+1) - M(M-1)}\,(J'M', kq | JM+1) \\ &+\sqrt{J'(J'+1) - M'(M'+1)}\,(J'M'+1, kq | JM) \\ &+\sqrt{k(k+1) - q(q+1)}\,(J'M', kq+1 | JM). \end{aligned} \tag{4.10}$$

Similar relations hold for the commutator of $T_q^{(k)}$ with $\mathcal{J}_{-1}$. Equations 4.9 and 4.10 show that the matrix element

$$\langle \alpha JM | T_q^{(k)} | \alpha' J' M' \rangle$$

possesses the same dependence on M, M', and q as does the CG coefficient

$$(J'M', kq | JM).$$

Thus we can write the matrix element as proportional to the CG coefficient. The proportionality constant depends on αJ, $\alpha' J'$, and on the tensor operator $\mathbf{T}^{(k)}$. Following Racah, we write the proportionality as

$$\langle \alpha JM | T_q^{(k)} | \alpha' J' M' \rangle = (J'M', kq | JM) \frac{\langle \alpha J \| \mathbf{T}^{(k)} \| \alpha' J' \rangle}{\sqrt{2J+1}}$$
$$= (-1)^{J-M} \begin{pmatrix} J & k & J' \\ -M & q & M' \end{pmatrix} \langle \alpha J \| \mathbf{T}^{(k)} \| \alpha' J' \rangle. \tag{4.11}$$

This result, commonly referred to as the *Wigner–Eckart theorem* [4], breaks the matrix element of a tensor operator into two parts: the CG coefficient contains "the geometry," for it depends on components along some arbitrary direction; the *reduced matrix element*,

$$\langle \alpha J \| \mathbf{T}^{(k)} \| \alpha' J' \rangle,$$

contains "the physics" of the matrix element, for it is independent of our choice of coordinate orientation.

As we shall now see, the "geometrical" factor is responsible for several important rules of atomic physics.

B. Selection Rules

As a consequence of the Wigner–Eckart theorem, the numbers J and J' must satisfy a triangle relation with k or the CG coefficient vanishes. Thus J and J' can differ by no more than k. If $J = J' = 0$, then k must be zero. We therefore have the selection rules:

$$\langle \alpha JM | T_0^{(0)} | \alpha' J' M' \rangle = 0 \quad \text{unless} \quad J' = J \quad \text{and} \quad M' = M \tag{4.12a}$$

$$\langle \alpha JM | T_q^{(1)} | \alpha' J' M' \rangle = 0 \quad \text{unless} \quad J' = J \quad \text{or} \quad J \pm 1 \quad \text{(but not} \quad J' = J = 0) \tag{4.12b}$$

$$\langle \alpha JM | T_q^{(2)} | \alpha' J' M' \rangle = 0 \quad \text{unless} \quad J' = J \quad \text{or} \quad J \pm 1 \quad \text{or} \quad J \pm 2 \quad \text{(but not} \quad J' = J = 0) \tag{4.12c}$$

$$\langle \alpha 00 | T_q^{(k)} | \alpha' 00 \rangle = 0 \quad \text{unless} \quad k = 0. \tag{4.12d}$$

In every case we must have

$$q = M - M' \tag{4.13}$$

or the CG coefficient vanishes. If a particular problem specifies the component q, then M and M' must satisfy (4.13). If instead we specify the levels M and M', then q is fixed.

C. Sum Rules

The probabilities of physical interest relate to the square of an appropriate matrix element,

$$P(M, M', q) \equiv |\langle \alpha JM | T_q^{(k)} | \alpha' J' M' \rangle|^2. \tag{4.14}$$

Frequently we do not distinguish the states of a given J, and we then wish to sum $P(M, M', q)$ over various possible values of M, M', or q. By the Wigner–Eckart theorem we have

$$P(M, M', q) = \frac{|\langle \alpha J \| \mathbf{T}^{(k)} \| \alpha' J' \rangle|^2}{(2J + 1)} (J'M', kq | JM)^2. \tag{4.15}$$

Of course M, M', and q are not independent; summation of $P(M, M', q)$ over q simply picks out the value $q = M' - M$:

$$\sum_q P(M, M', q) = P(M, M', M' - M). \tag{4.16}$$

We can use the normalization property of CG coefficients to sum $P(M, M', q)$ over M':

$$\sum_{M'} (J'M', kq|JM)^2 = 1 \qquad (q = M - M').$$

We then obtain

$$\sum_{M'q} P(M, M', q) = \frac{|\langle \alpha J \| \mathbf{T}^{(k)} \| \alpha' J' \rangle|^2}{(2J + 1)}. \tag{4.17}$$

We can also sum over the final index M, using

$$\sum_{M=-J}^{J} 1 = (2J + 1).$$

We then obtain

$$\sum_{MM'q} P(M, M', q) = |\langle \alpha J \| \mathbf{T}^{(k)} \| \alpha' J' \rangle|^2. \tag{4.18}$$

Equation 4.18 shows the physical significance of reduced matrix elements: these quantities squared correspond to transition probabilities summed over magnetic quantum numbers.

D. Example: $\langle \alpha J \| 1 \| \alpha' J' \rangle$

Now let us see how to evaluate the reduced matrix element in some simple cases. As the simplest example, let $T_q^{(k)}$ be a scalar, $T_0^{(0)}$. For convenience, take the scalar $1 \equiv 1_0^{(0)}$. The Wigner–Eckart theorem gives

$$\langle \alpha JM | 1_0^{(0)} | \alpha' J' M' \rangle = \delta_{MM'} \delta_{JJ'} \frac{\langle \alpha J \| 1 \| \alpha' J' \rangle}{\sqrt{2J + 1}}. \tag{4.19}$$

However, this matrix element is simply the orthogonality integral:

$$\langle \alpha JM | 1 | \alpha' J' M' \rangle = (\alpha JM | \alpha' J' M') = \delta_{\alpha\alpha'} \delta_{JJ'} \delta_{MM'}. \tag{4.20}$$

Thus, comparing (4.19) and (4.20), we obtain:

$$\langle \alpha J \| 1 \| \alpha' J' \rangle = \delta_{JJ'} \delta_{\alpha\alpha'} \sqrt{2J + 1}. \tag{4.21}$$

E. Example: $\langle \alpha J \| \mathbf{J} \| \alpha' J' \rangle$

Now let $T_q^{(k)}$ be a component of angular momentum, $T_q^{(k)} = \mathcal{J}_q \equiv J_q$. The Wigner–Eckart theorem gives

$$\langle \alpha JM | \mathcal{J}_q | \alpha' J' M' \rangle = (JM, 1q | J'M') \frac{\langle \alpha J \| \mathbf{J} \| \alpha' J' \rangle}{\sqrt{2J+1}}. \tag{4.22}$$

If we take the component $\mathcal{J}_0$ and use the expression from Table 6.1 for the CG coefficient we find

$$\langle \alpha JM | \mathcal{J}_0 | \alpha' J' M' \rangle = \delta_{MM'} \frac{M}{\sqrt{J(J+1)}} \frac{\langle \alpha J \| \mathbf{J} \| \alpha' J' \rangle}{\sqrt{2J+1}}. \tag{4.23}$$

But we have already seen that the matrix element of $\mathcal{J}_0$ is just

$$\langle \alpha JM | \mathcal{J}_0 | \alpha' J' M' \rangle = \delta_{MM'} \delta_{JJ'} \delta_{\alpha\alpha'} M. \tag{4.24}$$

Thus, comparing (4.21) and (4.22), we find

$$\langle \alpha J \| \mathbf{J} \| \alpha' J' \rangle = \delta_{\alpha\alpha'} \delta_{JJ'} \sqrt{J(J+1)}. \tag{4.25}$$

Therefore

$$\langle \alpha JM | \mathcal{J}_q | \alpha' J' M' \rangle = \delta_{\alpha\alpha'} \delta_{JJ'} (JM, 1q | JM') \left[\frac{J(J+1)}{2J+1} \right]^{1/2}. \tag{4.26}$$

We might note that, by solving (4.26) for $(JM, 1q | JM')$, we can write the matrix elements of any vector operator $\mathcal{V}$ (i.e., tensor operator of order 1) as

$$\langle \alpha JM | \mathcal{V}_q | \alpha JM' \rangle = \langle \alpha JM | \mathcal{J}_q | \alpha JM' \rangle \frac{\langle \alpha J \| \mathbf{V}^{(1)} \| \alpha J \rangle}{\sqrt{J(J+1)}}. \tag{4.27}$$

However, (4.27) cannot be applied to off-diagonal elements of $\mathcal{V}$ (between αJ and $\alpha' J' \neq \alpha J$).

F. Example: $\langle l \| \mathbf{C}^{(k)} \| l' \rangle$

For a final example, we consider matrix elements of the tensor operator $\mathbf{C}^{(k)}$. We begin by examining the product of a spherical harmonic $Y_{lm}(\theta_A \phi_A) \equiv Y_{lm}(\Omega_A)$ in the direction A and a spherical harmonic $Y^*_{lm}(\Omega_B)$ in the direction B. If we sum this product over m, the resulting quantity must not depend on how we chose the orientation of the z axis (i.e., the result is a *scalar* quantity)

$$\sum_m Y_{lm}(\Omega_A) Y^*_{lm}(\Omega_B) = \sum_m Y_{lm}(\Omega_{A'}) Y^*_{lm}(\Omega_{B'}). \tag{4.28}$$

Here Ω_A and Ω_B refer to one coordinate system, $\Omega_{A'}$ and $\Omega_{B'}$ refer to a rotated coordinate system. If we choose the z' axis to coincide with the B direction ($\theta_{B'} \phi_{B'} = 0, 0$) we can use the relations

$$Y_{lm}(0, \phi) = \delta_{m0}\left(\frac{2l+1}{4\pi}\right)^{1/2}, \tag{4.29}$$

$$Y_{l0}(\theta, \phi) = \left(\frac{2l+1}{4\pi}\right)^{1/2} P_l(\cos\theta) = \left(\frac{2l+1}{4\pi}\right)^{1/2} C_0^{(l)}, \tag{4.30}$$

to obtain the *addition theorem* for spherical harmonics:

$$\begin{aligned}\left(\frac{2l+1}{4\pi}\right)^{1/2} Y_{l0}(\Omega_{AB}) &= \frac{2l+1}{4\pi} P_l(\cos\theta_{AB}) \\ &= \sum_m Y_{lm}(\Omega_A) Y^*_{lm}(\Omega_B) \\ &= \sum_m (-1)^m Y_{lm}(\Omega_A) Y_{l-m}(\Omega_B).\end{aligned} \tag{4.31}$$

Here we have used the result $Y^*_{lm} = (-)^m Y_{l-m}$. The addition theorem may also be written as

$$C_0^{(l)}(\Omega_{AB}) = \mathbf{C}^{(l)}(\Omega_A)\cdot\mathbf{C}^{(l)}(\Omega_B). \tag{4.32}$$

Note that, since $P_l(1) = 1$, (4.31) gives the useful result

$$\sum_m |C_m^{(l)}|^2 = \frac{4\pi}{2l+1}\sum_m |Y_{lm}|^2 = 1. \tag{4.33}$$

Now let us consider the integral

$$\begin{aligned}c^k(lm, l'm') &\equiv \langle lm|C_q^{(k)}|l'm'\rangle \\ &= \int Y^*_{lm}(\Omega) C_q^{(k)}(\Omega) Y_{l'm'}(\Omega)\, d\Omega \\ &= \left(\frac{4\pi}{2k+1}\right)^{1/2} \int Y^*_{lm}(\Omega) Y_{kq}(\Omega) Y_{l'm'}(\Omega)\, d\Omega.\end{aligned} \tag{4.34}$$

If we take the particular case $m = m' = 0$ we have, according to the Wigner–Eckart theorem,

$$\begin{aligned}\langle l0|C_0^{(k)}|l'0\rangle &= \frac{(l'0, k0|l0)}{\sqrt{2l+1}} \langle l\|\mathbf{C}^{(k)}\|l'\rangle \\ &= \int Y^*_{l0} C_0^{(k)} Y_{l'0}\, d\Omega \\ &= \frac{\sqrt{2l+1}\sqrt{2l'+1}}{2} \int P_l(x) P_k(x) P_{l'}(x)\, dx.\end{aligned} \tag{4.35}$$

Let us now apply the addition theorem. We obtain

Table 6.7 Properties of Racah Tensors

Values

$$C_0^{(0)} = 1 \qquad C_0^{(1)} = \cos\theta \qquad C_0^{(2)} = \frac{3\cos^2\theta - 1}{2}$$

$$C_{\pm1}^{(1)} = \mp \frac{\sin\theta}{\sqrt{2}} e^{\pm i\phi} \qquad C_{\pm1}^{(2)} = \mp \sqrt{\frac{3}{2}} \cos\theta \sin\theta \, e^{\pm i\phi}$$

$$C_{\pm2}^{(2)} = \sqrt{\frac{3}{8}} \sin^2\theta \, e^{\pm 2i\phi}$$

General relations

$$C_q^{(k)} = (-1)^q C_{-q}^{(k)*} = \left(\frac{4\pi}{2k+1}\right)^{1/2} Y_{kq} = (-1)^q \left(\frac{(k-q)!}{(k+q)!}\right)^{1/2} P_k{}^q(\cos\theta)\, e^{iq\phi}$$

Summation properties

$$\sum_q |C_q^{(k)}|^2 = 1$$

$$\sum_k (2k+1) C_0^{(k)} = 2\delta(\cos\theta - 1)$$

$$\sum_q C_q^{(k)}(\Omega) C_q^{(k)}(\Omega')^* = P_k(\cos\omega)$$

Integration properties

$$\int d\Omega\, C_q^{(k)}(\Omega) C_{q'}^{(k')}(\Omega) = \delta_{kk'}\delta_{qq'} \frac{4\pi}{2k+1}$$

$$\int d\Omega\, C_q^{(k)}(\Omega) C_{q'}^{(k')}(\Omega) C_{q''}^{(k'')}(\Omega) = 4\pi \begin{pmatrix} k & k' & k'' \\ 0 & 0 & 0 \end{pmatrix} \begin{pmatrix} k & k' & k'' \\ q & q' & q'' \end{pmatrix}$$

Addition theorem

$$C_q^{(k)}(\Omega) C_{q'}^{(k')}(\Omega) = \sum_{k''} C_{q''}^{(k'')}(\Omega)(2k''+1)(-1)^{q''} \begin{pmatrix} k & k' & k'' \\ q & q' & -q'' \end{pmatrix} \begin{pmatrix} k & k' & k'' \\ 0 & 0 & 0 \end{pmatrix}$$

$$\int d\Omega' \langle l0|\, C_0^{(k)} \,|l'0\rangle$$

$$= 4\pi \langle l0|\, C_0^{(k)} \,|l'0\rangle = \sum_{mm'q} (-1)^{m+m'+q} \frac{4\pi}{\sqrt{2l+1}\,\sqrt{2l'+1}}$$

$$\times \int Y_{lm}^*(\Omega') C_q^{(k)}(\Omega') Y_{l'm'}(\Omega')\, d\Omega' \int Y_{l-m}^*(\Omega) C_{-q}^{(k)}(\Omega) Y_{l-m}(\Omega)\, d\Omega$$

$$= \frac{4\pi}{\sqrt{2l+1}\,\sqrt{2l'+1}} \sum_{mmq'} \langle lm|\, C_q^{(k)} \,|l'm'\rangle \langle l-m|\, C_{-q}^{(k)} |\, l'-m'\rangle. \quad (4.36)$$

Table 6.8 Matrix Elements of Racah Tensors

Values of $\langle l \,\|\mathbf{C}^{(k)}\|\, l'\rangle$

$\langle s\|\mathbf{C}^{(0)}\|s\rangle = 1$	$\langle s\|\mathbf{C}^{(1)}\|p\rangle = -1$
	$\langle s\|\mathbf{C}^{(2)}\|d\rangle = 1$
	$\langle s\|\mathbf{C}^{(3)}\|f\rangle = -1$
$\langle p\|\mathbf{C}^{(0)}\|p\rangle = \sqrt{3}$	
$\langle p\|\mathbf{C}^{(2)}\|p\rangle = -\sqrt{2\cdot 3/5}$	
	$\langle p\|\mathbf{C}^{(1)}\|d\rangle = -\sqrt{2}$
$\langle d\|\mathbf{C}^{(0)}\|d\rangle = \sqrt{5}$	$\langle p\|\mathbf{C}^{(3)}\|d\rangle = \sqrt{9/7}$
$\langle d\|\mathbf{C}^{(2)}\|d\rangle = -\sqrt{2\cdot 5/7}$	$\langle p\|\mathbf{C}^{(2)}\|f\rangle = \sqrt{9/5}$
$\langle d\|\mathbf{C}^{(4)}\|d\rangle = \sqrt{2\cdot 5/7}$	$\langle p\|\mathbf{C}^{(4)}\|f\rangle = -\sqrt{4/3}$
$\langle f\|\mathbf{C}^{(0)}\|f\rangle = \sqrt{7}$	$\langle d\|\mathbf{C}^{(1)}\|f\rangle = -\sqrt{3}$
$\langle f\|\mathbf{C}^{(2)}\|f\rangle = -\sqrt{4\cdot 7/5}$	$\langle d\|\mathbf{C}^{(3)}\|f\rangle = \sqrt{4/3}$
$\langle f\|\mathbf{C}^{(4)}\|f\rangle = \sqrt{2\cdot 7/11}$	$\langle d\|\mathbf{C}^{(5)}\|f\rangle = -\sqrt{2\cdot 25/3\cdot 11}$
$\langle f\|\mathbf{C}^{(6)}\|f\rangle = +\sqrt{2\cdot 5\cdot 7/3\cdot 11\cdot 13}$	

Notes

$$\langle l\|\mathbf{C}^{(k)}\|l'\rangle = \sqrt{2l+1}\,\sqrt{2l'+1}\begin{pmatrix} l' & k & l \\ 0 & 0 & 0\end{pmatrix}$$

$$= (-1)^k\langle l'\|\mathbf{C}^{(k)}\|l\rangle = (-1)^k\left(\frac{2l+1}{2k+1}\right)^{1/2}\langle k\|\mathbf{C}^{(l)}\|l'\rangle$$

$$= (-1)^k\left(\frac{2l'+1}{2k+1}\right)^{1/2}\langle l\|\mathbf{C}^{(l')}\|k\rangle = \left(\frac{2l'+1}{2k+1}\right)^{1/2}\langle k\|\mathbf{C}^{(l')}\|l\rangle$$

$$\langle l\|\mathbf{C}^{(0)}\|l\rangle = \sqrt{2l+1}$$

$$\langle l\|\mathbf{C}^{(1)}\|l'\rangle = (-1)^{l_>-l}\sqrt{l_>}$$

$$\langle l\|\mathbf{C}^{(k)}\|l'\rangle^2 = (-1)^k\langle l\|\mathbf{C}^{(k)}\|l'\rangle\langle l'\|\mathbf{C}^{(k)}\|l\rangle = \frac{(2l+1)(2l'+1)}{2}\int P_l(x)P_k(x)P_{l'}(x)\,dx$$

Now apply the Wigner–Eckart theorem and use the normalization property of the CG coefficients:

$$\langle l0|\,C_0^{(k)}|\,l'0\rangle = \frac{|\langle l\|\mathbf{C}^{(k)}\|l'\rangle|^2}{\sqrt{(2l+1)^3}\,\sqrt{2l'+1}}\,(-1)^{l+k-l'}\sum_{mm'q}(l'm',kq|lm)$$

$$= \frac{(-1)^{l+k-l'}}{\sqrt{2l+1}\,\sqrt{2l'+1}}\,|\langle l\|\mathbf{C}^{(k)}\|l'\rangle|^2. \tag{4.37}$$

Comparing this result with (4.35), we obtain

$$\begin{aligned}\langle l\|\mathbf{C}^{(k)}\|l'\rangle &= (-1)^{l+k-l'}\sqrt{2l'+1}\,(l'0, k0\,|\,l0)\\ &= \sqrt{2l'+1}\,(l'0, k0\,|\,l0)\\ &= (-1)^k\sqrt{2l+1}\,(l0, k0\,|\,l'0),\end{aligned} \tag{4.38}$$

since $k + l + l'$ must be an even integer. Note that

$$\langle l\|\mathbf{C}^{(k)}\|l'\rangle = (-1)^k\langle l'\|\mathbf{C}^{(k)}\|l\rangle.$$

Thus we can write

$$\begin{aligned}\langle lm\,|\,C_q^{(k)}\,|\,l'm'\rangle &= (-1)^k(l'm', kq\,|\,lm)(l0, k0\,|\,l'0)\\ &\equiv c^k(lm, l'm').\end{aligned} \tag{4.39}$$

Condon and Shortley [5] and Slater [6] provide tables of these c^k coefficients.

A useful expression for the product of two Racah tensors or two spherical harmonics follows from (4.34). We note that the product $C_q^{(k)}Y_{lm'}$ as a well-behaved function, can be expanded in spherical harmonics:

$$C_q^{(k)}(\Omega)\,Y_{lm}(\Omega) = \sum_{l'm'} Y_{l'm'}(\Omega)\int Y^*_{l'm'}(\Omega')C_q^{(k)}(\Omega')\,Y_{lm}(\Omega')\,d\Omega'.$$

This can be written, by use of (4.39) and the CG symmetry property, as

$$C_m^{(l)}C_{m'}^{(l')} = \sum_{kq}(lm, l'm'\,|\,kq)(l0, l'0\,|\,k0)C_q^{(k)}. \tag{4.40}$$

(Here each Racah tensor has the same argument, Ω.)

The Racah tensors occur frequently in atomic-structure problems. For reference, Table 6.7 records some of their properties. Table 6.8 gives values of the reduced matrix elements of these operators.

REFERENCES

[1] E. P. Wigner, *Group Theory and its Application to the Quantum Mechanics of Atomic Spectra*, Academic, New York (1959).

[2] U. Fano and G. Racah, *Irreducible Tensorial Sets*, Academic, New York (1959).

[3] G. Racah, *Phys. Rev.* **62,** 438 (1942).

[4] E. P. Wigner, *Z. Physik* **43,** 624 (1927); C. Eckart, *Rev. Mod. Phys.* **2,** 305 (1930).

[5] E. U. Condon and G. H. Shortley, *The Theory of Atomic Spectra*, Cambridge University Press, Cambridge, England (1935), p. 178.

[6] J. C. Slater, *Quantum Theory of Atomic Structure*, McGraw-Hill, New York (1960), vol. 1, p. 489.

6.5 COUPLING TENSOR OPERATORS

We are now in a position to extend the notion of coupling, introduced for eigenstates in abstract space, to arbitrary irreducible tensorial sets. We are primarily interested in operators here, and for brevity we refer to these irreducible tensor operators as simply tensor operators or tensors. If we have an operator $T_q^{(k)}$ and another operator $U_{q'}^{(k')}$ we take all possible pairs $T_q^{(k)}U_{q'}^{(k')}$ (the ordering is usually important) to form the Kronecker product $\mathbf{T}^{(k)} \otimes \mathbf{U}^{(k')}$. Not every pair or linear combination of pairs has the property of a tensor operator [i.e., property (4.5*c*)] but certain linear combinations do have this property. The *tensor product*

$$V_Q^{(K)} \equiv [\mathbf{T}^{(k)} \times \mathbf{U}^{(k')}]_Q^{(K)} \equiv \sum_{qq'} (kqk'q' | KQ) T_q^{(k)} U_{q'}^{(k')} \tag{5.1}$$

is an irreducible tensor operator of order K, whose components are labeled by Q. From the triangle rule for CG coefficients we see that from two tensors of order k and k' we can form a total of $2k + 1$ or $2k' + 1$ (whichever is smaller) different tensors:

$$|k - k'| \leq K \leq k + k'.$$

As an example, if the two coupled tensors are of equal order we can form a tensor of order zero. Using the fact that $(kq, k - q|00) = (-1)^{k-q}/\sqrt{2k+1}$, we have

$$[\mathbf{T}^{(k)} \times \mathbf{U}^{(k)}]_0{}^0 = \frac{(-1)^k}{\sqrt{2k+1}} \sum_q (-1)^q T_q^{(k)} U_{-q}^{(k)}. \tag{5.2}$$

Apart from a numerical factor, this expression coincides with the scalar product:

$$\begin{aligned} \mathbf{T}^{(k)} \cdot \mathbf{U}^{(k)} &\equiv \sum_a (-1)^q T_q^{(k)} U_{-q}^{(k)} \\ &= (-1)^k \sqrt{2k+1}\, [\mathbf{T}^{(k)} \times \mathbf{U}^{(k)}]_0^{(0)}. \end{aligned} \tag{5.3}$$

Let us see how this applies to ordinary "physical" vectors, such as the position vector or angular-momentum vector. The three complex spherical components of a vector **A** form the components of a spherical tensor of order 1, and we have already used (5.3) several times in previous chapters:

$$\mathbf{A} \cdot \mathbf{B} = -A_{-1}B_{+1} + A_0 B_0 - A_{+1}B_{-1} = -\sqrt{3}\, [\mathbf{A}^{(1)} \times \mathbf{B}^{(1)}]_0^{(0)}. \tag{5.4}$$

The tensor of order 0 formed from two vectors is the scalar product.

The tensor of order 1 formed from two vectors has the components

$$[\mathbf{A}^{(1)} \times \mathbf{B}^{(1)}]_Q^{(1)} = \sum_{qq'} (1q1q' | 1Q) A_q B_{q'}. \tag{5.5}$$

Specifically,

$$[\mathbf{A}^{(1)} \times \mathbf{B}^{(1)}]^{(1)}_{+1} = \frac{1}{\sqrt{2}}(A_{+1}B_0 - A_0B_{+1}),$$

$$[\mathbf{A}^{(1)} \times \mathbf{B}^{(1)}]^{(1)}_{0} = \frac{1}{\sqrt{2}}(A_{+1}B_{-1} - A_{-1}B_{+1}), \tag{5.6}$$

$$[\mathbf{A}^{(1)} \times \mathbf{B}^{(1)}]^{(1)}_{-1} = \frac{1}{\sqrt{2}}(A_0B_{-1} - A_{-1}B_0).$$

Apart from a numerical factor $\sqrt{2}$, this is the cross product or *vector product* of ordinary vector analysis. For if we write

$$\mathbf{C} = \mathbf{A} \times \mathbf{B},$$

meaning

$$C_x = A_yB_z - A_zB_y, \qquad C_y = A_zB_x - A_xB_z, \qquad C_z = A_xB_y - A_yB_x,$$

then in complex spherical coordinates we have

$$C_Q = (\mathbf{A} \times \mathbf{B})_Q = i\sqrt{2}\,[\mathbf{A}^{(1)} \times \mathbf{B}^{(1)}]^{(1)}_{Q}. \tag{5.7}$$

The tensor of order one formed from two vectors is the cross product.

The cross products of the unit vectors $\mathbf{e}_{+1}$, $\mathbf{e}_0$, $\mathbf{e}_{-1}$ satisfy a similar equation,

$$\mathbf{e}_p \times \mathbf{e}_q = i\sqrt{2}\,(1p, 1q\,|\,1p + q)\mathbf{e}_{p+q}. \tag{5.8}$$

Specifically, these products are

$$\mathbf{e}_{+1} \times \mathbf{e}_{+1} = \mathbf{e}_0 \times \mathbf{e}_0 = \mathbf{e}_{-1} \times \mathbf{e}_{-1} = 0,$$

$$\mathbf{e}_{+1} \times \mathbf{e}_0 = i\mathbf{e}_{+1}, \quad \mathbf{e}_{-1} \times \mathbf{e}_0 = -i\mathbf{e}_{-1},$$

$$\mathbf{e}_{+1} \times \mathbf{e}_{-1} = i\mathbf{e}_0.$$

(These relationships are discussed by Rose [1], p. 122.)

The third possible combination of two vectors produces a tensor of order 2:

$$[\mathbf{A}^{(1)} \times \mathbf{B}^{(1)}]^{(2)}_{Q} = \sum_{qq'} (1q, 1q'\,|\,2Q)A^{(1)}_q B^{(1)}_{q'}. \tag{5.9}$$

The components are

$$[\mathbf{A}^{(1)} \times \mathbf{B}^{(1)}]^{(2)}_{\pm 2} = A_{\pm 1}B_{\pm 1},$$

$$[\mathbf{A}^{(1)} \times \mathbf{B}^{(1)}]^{(2)}_{\pm 1} = -\frac{1}{\sqrt{2}}(A_0B_{\pm 1} + A_{\pm 1}B_0), \tag{5.10}$$

$$[\mathbf{A}^{(1)} \times \mathbf{B}^{(1)}]^{(2)}_{0} = \frac{1}{\sqrt{6}}(A_{+1}B_{-1} + 2A_0B_0 + A_{-1}B_{+1}).$$

If we specialize **A** and **B** to the position vector $\mathbf{r} = r\mathbf{C}^{(1)}$ {where $C_m^{(l)} = [4\pi/(2l+1)]^{1/2} Y_{lm}$ is the Racah tensor of order l} we obtain

$$\begin{aligned}
[\mathbf{r}^{(1)} \times \mathbf{r}^{(1)}]^{(2)}_{\pm 2} &= \qquad r_{+1}r_{+1} &&= \sqrt{\tfrac{2}{3}}\, r^2 C^{(2)}_{\pm 2}, \\
[\mathbf{r}^{(1)} \times \mathbf{r}^{(1)}]^{(2)}_{\pm 1} &= \quad -\sqrt{2}\, r_0 r_{\pm 1} &&= \sqrt{\tfrac{2}{3}}\, r^2 C^{(2)}_{\pm 1}, \qquad (5.11)\\
[\mathbf{r}^{(1)} \times \mathbf{r}^{(1)}]^{(2)}_{0} &= \sqrt{\tfrac{2}{3}}\,(r_0 r_0 + r_{+1} r_{-1}) &&= \sqrt{\tfrac{2}{3}}\, r^2 C^{(2)}_{0} \\
&= \sqrt{\tfrac{1}{6}}\,(3z^2 - r^2).
\end{aligned}$$

If we take **A** and **B** to be unit (complex) vectors, (5.8) gives the elements of a spherical dyadic, $\mathsf{I}^{(2)}$:

$$\begin{aligned}
\mathsf{I}^{(2)} \equiv [\mathbf{e}^{(1)} \times \mathbf{e}^{(1)}]^{(2)} &= \mathbf{e}_{+1}\mathbf{e}_{+1} - \sqrt{\tfrac{1}{2}}\,\mathbf{e}_{+1}\mathbf{e}_0 + \sqrt{\tfrac{1}{6}}\,\mathbf{e}_{+1}\mathbf{e}_{-1} \\
&\quad - \sqrt{\tfrac{1}{2}}\,\mathbf{e}_0\mathbf{e}_{+1} + \sqrt{\tfrac{2}{3}}\,\mathbf{e}_0\mathbf{e}_0 - \sqrt{\tfrac{1}{2}}\,\mathbf{e}_0\mathbf{e}_{-1} \\
&\quad + \sqrt{\tfrac{1}{6}}\,\mathbf{e}_{-1}\mathbf{e}_{+1} - \sqrt{\tfrac{1}{2}}\,\mathbf{e}_{-1}\mathbf{e}_0 + \mathbf{e}_{-1}\mathbf{e}_{-1}. \qquad (5.12)
\end{aligned}$$

Comparing the quadrupole dyadic of Section 6.10, we see that

$$\begin{aligned}
\mathsf{Q} &= \sqrt{\tfrac{2}{3}} \sum_m (-1)^m C^{(2)}_{-m} \mathsf{I}^{(2)}_{+m} = \sqrt{\tfrac{2}{3}}\, \mathbf{C}^{(2)} \cdot \mathsf{I}^{(2)} \\
&= \sqrt{\tfrac{10}{3}}\, [[\mathbf{e}^{(1)} \times \mathbf{e}^{(1)}]^{(2)} \times \mathbf{C}^{(2)}]^{(0)}_0. \qquad (5.13)
\end{aligned}$$

The tensor of order 2 formed from two vectors is a dyadic. This illustrates the coupling of spherical harmonics, for (4.40) gives

$$\sum_m (lm, l'm' \mid kq) C^{(l)}_m C^{(l')}_{m'} = (l0, l'0 \mid k0) C^{(k)}_q \qquad (5.14a)$$

or

$$[\mathbf{C}^{(l)} \times \mathbf{C}^{(l')}]^{(k)}_q = (l0, l'0 \mid k0) C^{(k)}_q. \qquad (5.14b)$$

In the present instance this reads

$$[\mathbf{C}^{(1)} \times \mathbf{C}^{(1)}]^{(2)}_q = \sqrt{\tfrac{2}{3}}\, \mathbf{C}^{(2)}_q. \qquad (5.15)$$

With this digression we now come to the key formula for evaluating reduced matrix elements of tensor operators. Suppose the tensor operator of order k, $\mathbf{A}^{(k)}$, acts on angular-momentum states $\Psi(a\alpha)$ and the tensor operator $\mathbf{B}^{(k')}$ acts on angular-momentum states $\Psi(b\beta)$. Then

$$\langle abJ \| [\mathbf{A}^{(k)} \times \mathbf{B}^{(k')}]^{(K)} \| a'b'J' \rangle = \sqrt{(2J+1)(2J'+1)(2K+1)} \times \begin{Bmatrix} a & b & J \\ a' & b' & J' \\ k' & k & K \end{Bmatrix} \langle a \| \mathbf{A}^{(k)} \| a' \rangle \langle b \| \mathbf{B}^{(k')} \| b' \rangle. \qquad (5.16)$$

This important formula follows directly from the definition of a reduced

Table 6.9 Tensor Matrix Elements

Matrix Elements

$$\langle JM|\,T_q^{(k)}\,|J'M'\rangle = (-1)^{J-M}\begin{pmatrix} J' & k & J \\ -M' & q & M \end{pmatrix}\langle J\|\mathbf{T}^{(k)}\|J'\rangle = \frac{(J'M', kq\,|\,JM)}{\sqrt{2J+1}}\langle J\|\mathbf{T}^{(k)}\|J'\rangle$$

$$\langle abJM|\,\mathbf{A}^{(k)}\cdot\mathbf{B}^{(k)}\,|a'b'J'M'\rangle = \delta_{JJ'}\delta_{MM'}\,(-1)^{J+b+a'}\begin{Bmatrix} J & b & a \\ k & a' & b' \end{Bmatrix}\langle a\|\mathbf{A}^{(k)}\|a'\rangle\langle b\|\mathbf{B}^{(k)}\|b'\rangle$$

$$\langle abJM|\,\mathbf{A}^{(0)}\cdot\mathbf{B}^{(0)}\,|a'b'J'M'\rangle = \delta_{JJ'}\delta_{MM'}\,\frac{\langle a\|\mathbf{A}^{(0)}\|a'\rangle}{\sqrt{2a+1}}\,\frac{\langle b\|\mathbf{B}^{(0)}\|b'\rangle}{\sqrt{2b+1}}$$

$$\langle lm|\,C_q^k\,|l'm'\rangle \equiv c^k(lm, l'm') = (-1)^m\sqrt{(2l+1)(2l'+1)}\begin{pmatrix} l & k & l' \\ -m & q & m' \end{pmatrix}\begin{pmatrix} l & k & l' \\ 0 & 0 & 0 \end{pmatrix} = (-1)^k(l'm', kq\,|\,lm)(l0, k0\,|\,l'0)$$

Reduced matrix elements

$$\langle abJ\|[\mathbf{A}^{(\alpha)}\times\mathbf{B}^{(\beta)}]^{(k)}\|a'b'J'\rangle = \sqrt{(2K+1)(2J+1)(2J'+1)}\begin{Bmatrix} a & b & J \\ a' & b' & J' \\ \alpha & \beta & k \end{Bmatrix}\langle a\|\mathbf{A}^{(\alpha)}\|a'\rangle\langle b\|\mathbf{B}^{(\beta)}\|b'\rangle$$

$$\langle abJ\|\mathbf{A}^{(k)}\cdot\mathbf{B}^{(k)}\|a'b'J'\rangle = \delta_{JJ'}\sqrt{2J+1}\,(-1)^{J+b+a'}\begin{Bmatrix} J & b & a \\ k & a' & b' \end{Bmatrix}\langle a\|\mathbf{A}^{(k)}\|a'\rangle\langle b\|\mathbf{B}^{(k)}\|b'\rangle$$

$$\langle abJ\|\mathbf{A}^{(0)}\cdot\mathbf{B}^{(0)}\|a'b'J'\rangle = \delta_{JJ'}\sqrt{2J+1}\,\frac{\langle a\|\mathbf{A}^{(0)}\|a'\rangle}{\sqrt{2a+1}}\,\frac{\langle b\|\mathbf{B}^{(0)}\|b'\rangle}{\sqrt{2b+1}}$$

$$\langle abJ\|\mathbf{A}^{(k)}\|a'b'J'\rangle = \delta_{bb'}\sqrt{2J+1}\,\sqrt{2J'+1}\,(-1)^{a+b+J'+k}\begin{Bmatrix} b & a & J \\ k & J' & a' \end{Bmatrix}\langle a\|\mathbf{A}^{(k)}\|a'\rangle$$

$$\langle baJ\|\mathbf{A}^{(k)}\|b'a'J'\rangle = \delta_{bb'}\sqrt{2J+1}\,\sqrt{2J'+1}\,(-1)^{a'+b+J+k}\begin{Bmatrix} b & a & J \\ k & J' & a' \end{Bmatrix}\langle a\|\mathbf{A}^{(k)}\|a'\rangle$$

$$\langle\alpha J\|\mathbf{J}\|\alpha'J'\rangle = \delta_{\alpha\alpha'}\delta_{JJ'}\sqrt{J(J+1)}\,\sqrt{2J+1}$$

$$\langle\alpha J\|1\|\alpha'J'\rangle = \delta_{\alpha\alpha'}\delta_{JJ'}\sqrt{2J+1}$$

$$\langle l\|\mathbf{C}^{(k)}\|l'\rangle = \sqrt{2l'+1}\,(l'0, k0\,|\,l0) = \sqrt{2l'+1}\,\sqrt{2l+1}\begin{pmatrix} l' & k & l \\ 0 & 0 & 0 \end{pmatrix}$$

$$\langle l\|\mathbf{C}^{(1)}\|l'\rangle = (-1)^{l_>-l}\sqrt{l_>}\quad \text{if}\quad l = l' \pm 1$$

matrix element, the definition of the 9-j symbol, and the completeness relation of 3-j symbols.

From the properties of the 6-j symbol we now can obtain a number of important special cases of (5.11). First, suppose $\mathbf{B}^{(k')}$ is just the unit tensor of order zero, $1^{(0)}$. We then obtain the matrix element of an operator $\mathbf{A}^{(k)}$ acting on the $\Psi(a)$ part of a coupled state:

$$\begin{aligned}\langle abJ\|\mathbf{A}^{(k)}\|a'b'J'\rangle &\\ &= \delta_{bb'}\sqrt{(2J+1)(2J'+1)}\; W(akbJ';a'J)\;\langle a\|\mathbf{A}^{(k)}\|a'\rangle \\ &= \delta_{bb'}\sqrt{2J+1}\;\sqrt{2J'+1}\;(-1)^{a+k+b+J'}\begin{Bmatrix} b & a & J \\ k & J' & a'\end{Bmatrix}\langle a\|\mathbf{A}^{(k)}\|a'\rangle. \qquad (5.17)\end{aligned}$$

A similar result holds if we take $\mathbf{A}^{(k)} = 1^{(0)}$, or, what is the same thing, couple $\Psi(a)$ and $\Psi(b)$ in the opposite order:

$$\begin{aligned}\langle baJ\|\mathbf{A}^{(k)}\|b'a'J'\rangle &\\ &= \delta_{bb'}\sqrt{(2J+1)(2J'+1)}\; W(a'kbJ;aJ')\langle a\|\mathbf{A}^{(k)}\|a'\rangle \\ &= \delta_{bb'}\sqrt{2J+1}\;\sqrt{2J'+1}\;(-1)^{a'+k+b+J}\begin{Bmatrix} b & a & J \\ k & J' & a'\end{Bmatrix}\langle a\|\mathbf{A}^{(k)}\|a'\rangle. \\ & \qquad (5.18)\end{aligned}$$

These two matrix elements, (5.17) and (5.18), differ by the phase $(-1)^{a-a'+J'-J}$. We also obtain the useful formula for the scalar product of two tensors $\mathbf{A}^{(k)}\cdot\mathbf{B}^{(k)}$ using (5.3):

$$\begin{aligned}\langle abJ\|\mathbf{A}^{(k)}\cdot\mathbf{B}^{(k)}\|a'b'J'\rangle = \delta_{JJ'}(-1)^k W(a'kJb;ab') &\\ \times\langle a\|\mathbf{A}^{(k)}\|a'\rangle \times \langle b\|\mathbf{B}^{(k)}\|b'\rangle. &\qquad (5.19)\end{aligned}$$

By applying these last few formulas, we can work out the matrix elements for any tensor operator. For convenience, Table 6.9 summarizes the basic formulas of this so-called *Racah algebra*.

APPENDIX A: THE ROTATION MATRIX

In this chapter we have defined angular-momentum states $\mathbf{A}(JM)$ as eigenstates of $\mathcal{J}^2$ and $\mathcal{J}_0$. Our definition thus relates to the action of the operators $\mathcal{J}_x$, $\mathcal{J}_y$, and $\mathcal{J}_z$ which are defined as the generators of infinitesimal rotations in three-dimensional space. Let us now investigate the connection between these angular-momentum eigenstates and finite rotations.

As we have seen, the operator corresponding to a rotation ϕ about the x axis is

$$\mathcal{U}_x(\phi) = \exp(-i\phi\mathcal{J}_x) = 1 - i\phi\mathcal{J}_x = \tfrac{1}{2}(i\phi)^2\mathcal{J}_x{}^2 - \cdots. \qquad (A.1)$$

and similar operators of rotations about the y and z axes. Now since the

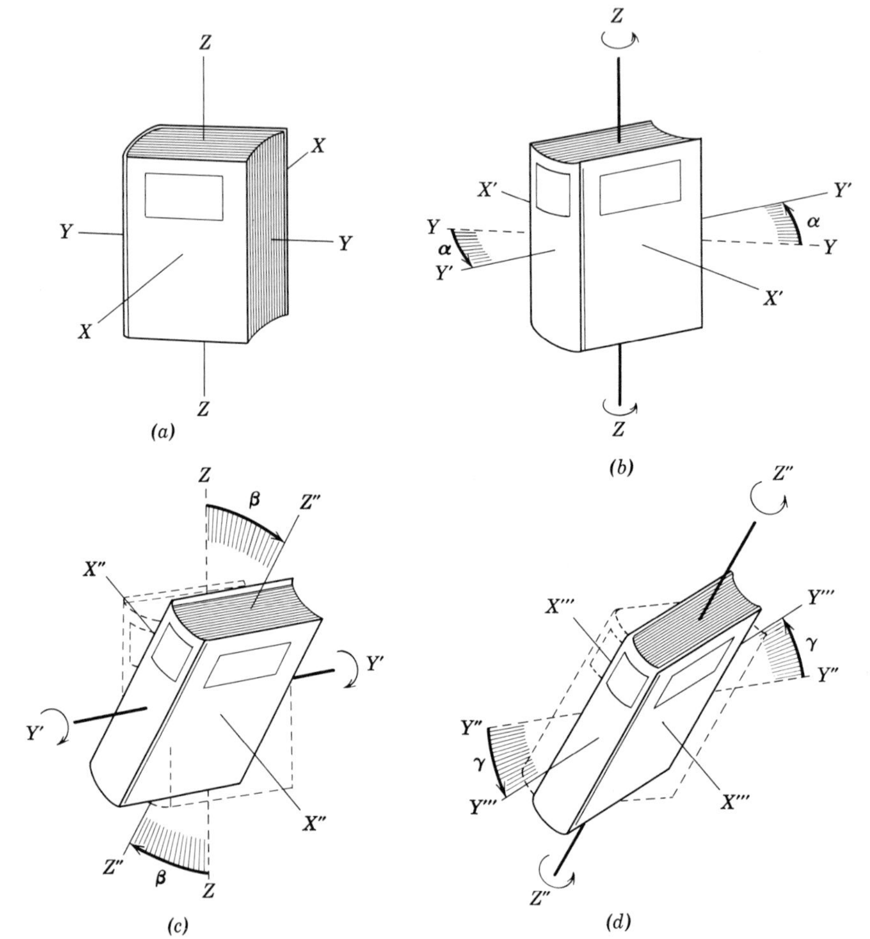

Fig. 6.2 Definition of Euler angles α, β, γ: (*a*) unrotated axes X, Y, Z; (*b*) axes X', Y', $Z' = Z$ after rotation α about Z; (*c*) axes X'', $Y'' = Y'$, Z'' after rotation β about Y'; (*d*) axes X''', Y''', $Z''' = Z''$ after rotation γ about Z''.

total angular-momentum operator $\mathcal{J}^2$ commutes with $\mathcal{J}_x$, $\mathcal{J}_y$, and $\mathcal{J}_z$, then it also commutes with any power $(\mathcal{J}_x)^n$, $(\mathcal{J}_y)^n$, $(\mathcal{J}_z)^n$. Thus $\mathcal{J}^2$ commutes with the exponential operator:

$$[\mathcal{J}^2, \mathcal{U}_i(\phi)] = 0 \qquad (i = x, y, z). \tag{A.2}$$

This equation means that an eigenstate that has been rotated about *any* axis remains an eigenstate of $\mathcal{J}^2$:

$$\mathcal{J}^2[\mathcal{U}(\phi)\mathbf{A}(JM)] = J(J + 1)[\mathcal{U}(\phi)A(JM)]. \tag{A.3}$$

However, since $\mathcal{J}_0 \equiv \mathcal{J}_z$ does not commute with $\mathcal{J}_x$ or $\mathcal{J}_y$, a rotated state $\mathcal{U}_x(\phi)\mathbf{A}(JM)$ or $\mathcal{U}_y(\phi)\mathbf{A}(JM)$ will no longer be an eigenstate of $\mathcal{J}_0$. Thus an arbitrary rotation merely mixes states with different M values:

$$\mathcal{U}\mathbf{A}(JM) = \sum_{M'} \mathbf{A}(JM') \times \mathcal{D}^{(J)}_{M'M}(\mathcal{U}). \tag{A.4}$$

The expansion coefficients here are just the matrix elements of $\mathcal{U}$ between eigenstate $\mathbf{A}(JM)$ and $\mathbf{A}(JM')$:

$$\mathcal{D}^{(J)}_{M'M}(\mathcal{U}) = \langle \mathbf{A}(JM') | \mathcal{U} | \mathbf{A}(JM) \rangle \equiv \langle JM' | \mathcal{U} | JM \rangle. \tag{A.5}$$

Sometimes it is convenient to write (A.4) in the form

$$\mathbf{A}(JM)_{\text{new}} = \sum_{M'} \mathcal{D}^{(J)}_{M'M}(\mathcal{U}) \mathbf{A}(JM')_{\text{old}} \tag{A.6}$$

in order to emphasize the transformation from an "old" coordinate system to a "new" system by the operator $\mathcal{U}$. Equation A.6 expresses an eigenfunction (for example $\cos\theta$) in one coordinate system in terms of a set of functions of *rotated* coordinates (such as $\cos\theta'$ and $\sin\theta'$): the arguments of the functions differ.

The most convenient way to describe an arbitrary rotation is in terms of the three Euler angles. To define these angles, we break up an arbitrary rotation into three steps (see Fig. 6.2): first, rotate about the z (vertical) axis by an angle α; then rotate by an angle β about the new y' axis (the *line of nodes*); finally rotate about the new z'' axis (the *figure axis*) by an angle γ. The resulting over-all rotation is

$$\mathcal{U}(\alpha, \beta, \gamma) = \mathcal{U}_{z''}(\gamma)\mathcal{U}_{y'}(\beta)\mathcal{U}_z(\alpha). \tag{A.7}$$

Note that the angles α, β are just the usual spherical angles θ, ϕ for the orientation of the figure axis of a rigid body, and γ is the rotation of a rigid body about its figure axis. The rotation $\mathcal{U}(\alpha, \beta, \gamma)$ can also be produced by rotations in the opposite order. In this case the various rotation axes refer to the *same* coordinate system [rather than rotated coordinates y' and z'' of (A.7)]:

$$\begin{aligned}\mathcal{U}(\alpha, \beta, \gamma) &= \mathcal{U}_z(\alpha)\mathcal{U}_y(\beta)\mathcal{U}_z(\gamma) \\ &= \exp(i\alpha\mathcal{J}_z)\exp(i\beta\mathcal{J}_y)\exp(-i\alpha\mathcal{J}_z).\end{aligned} \tag{A.8}$$

Expression (A.8) for $\mathcal{U}$ gives the result for the rotation matrix:

$$\begin{aligned}\mathcal{D}^{(J)}_{M'M}(\alpha, \beta, \gamma) &= \langle JM' | \mathcal{U}_z(\alpha)\mathcal{U}_y(\beta)\mathcal{U}_z(\gamma) | JM \rangle \\ &= \exp[-i(\alpha M' + \gamma M)]\, d^{(J)}_{M'M}(\beta),\end{aligned} \tag{A.9}$$

where

$$d^{(J)}_{M'M}(\beta) = \langle JM' | \exp(-i\beta\mathcal{J}_y) | JM \rangle. \tag{A.10}$$

Wigner [2] obtained the following expression:

Table 6.10 Properties of the Rotation Matrices

General relations

$$\mathcal{D}^{(j)}_{m'm}(\alpha\beta\gamma) = \langle jm' | e^{i\alpha J_z} e^{i\beta J_y} e^{i\gamma J_z} | jm \rangle = e^{im'\alpha} d^{(j)}_{m'm}(\beta) e^{im\alpha}$$

$$\mathcal{D}^{(j)}_{m'm}(\alpha\beta\gamma)^* = \mathcal{D}^{(j)}_{m'm}(-\alpha, \beta, -\gamma) = (-1)^{m'-m} \mathcal{D}^{(j)}_{-m'-m}(\alpha\beta\gamma)$$

Special values

$$\mathcal{D}^{(l)}_{m0}(\alpha\beta\gamma) = (-1)^m \left(\frac{4\pi}{2l+1}\right)^{½} Y_{lm}(\beta\alpha) = (-1)^m C^{(l)}_m$$

$$\mathcal{D}^{(l)}_{0m}(\alpha\beta\gamma) = \left(\frac{4\pi}{2l+1}\right)^{½} Y_{lm}(\beta\alpha) = C^{(l)}_m$$

$$\mathcal{D}^{(l)}_{00}(\alpha\beta\gamma) = P_l(\cos\beta)$$

$$\mathcal{D}^{(j)}_{m'm}(0\beta 0) = d^{(j)}_{m'm}(\beta)$$

Summation properties

$$\sum_{m_1'm_2'm_1'} \begin{pmatrix} j_1 & j_2 & j_3 \\ m_1' & m_2' & m_3' \end{pmatrix} \mathcal{D}^{(j_1)}_{m_1'm_1}(\Omega) \mathcal{D}^{(j_2)}_{m_2'm_2}(\Omega) \mathcal{D}^{(j_3)}_{m_3'm_3}(\Omega) = \begin{pmatrix} j_1 & j_2 & j_3 \\ m_1 & m_2 & m_3 \end{pmatrix}$$

$$\sum_{m_1m_2m_1'm_2'} \begin{pmatrix} j_1 & j_2 & J' \\ m_1' & m_2' & M' \end{pmatrix} \mathcal{D}^{(j_1)}_{m_1'm_1}(\Omega) \mathcal{D}^{(j_2)}_{m_2'm_2}(\Omega) \begin{pmatrix} j_1 & j_2 & J \\ m_1 & m_2 & M \end{pmatrix} = \frac{\delta_{JJ'}}{(2J+1)} \mathcal{D}^{(J)*}_{M'M}(\Omega)$$

$$\sum_{JMM'} (2J+1) \begin{pmatrix} j_1 & j_2 & J \\ m_1' & m_2' & M' \end{pmatrix} \mathcal{D}^{(J)*}_{M'M}(\Omega) \begin{pmatrix} j_1 & j_2 & J \\ m_1 & m_2 & M \end{pmatrix} = \mathcal{D}^{(j_1)}_{m_1'm_1}(\Omega) \mathcal{D}^{(j_2)}_{m_2'm_2}(\Omega)$$

$$\sum_{m''} \mathcal{D}^{(j)}_{m'm''}(\alpha_2\beta_2\gamma_2) \mathcal{D}^{(j)}_{m''m}(\alpha_1\beta_1\gamma_1) = \mathcal{D}^{(j)}_{m'm}(\alpha\beta\gamma)$$

Integration properties

$$\frac{1}{8\pi^2} \int_0^{2\pi} d\alpha \int_0^{2\pi} d\gamma \int_0^{\pi} \sin\beta \, d\beta \, \mathcal{D}^{(j_1)}_{m_1'M_1}(\alpha\beta\gamma)^* \mathcal{D}^{(j_2)}_{m_2'm_2}(\alpha\beta\gamma) = \frac{\delta_{m_1m_2} \delta_{m_1'm_2'} \delta_{j_1j_2}}{(2j_1+1)}$$

$$\frac{1}{8\pi^2} \int_0^{2\pi} d\alpha \int_0^{2\pi} d\gamma \int_0^{\pi} \sin\beta \, d\beta \, \mathcal{D}^{(j_1)}_{m_2'm_1}(\alpha\beta\gamma) \mathcal{D}^{(j_2)}_{m_2'm_2}(\alpha\beta\gamma) \mathcal{D}^{(j_1)}_{m_3'm_3}(\alpha\beta\gamma) = \begin{pmatrix} j_1 & j_2 & j_3 \\ m_1' & m_2' & m_3' \end{pmatrix} \begin{pmatrix} j_1 & j_2 & j_3 \\ m_1 & m_2 & m_3 \end{pmatrix}$$

Table 6.11 The Rotation Matrices $d^{(1/2)}$ and $d^{(1)}$

		$m = \frac{1}{2}$	$m = -\frac{1}{2}$
$d^{(1/2)}_{m'm}(\beta)$	$m' = \frac{1}{2}$	$\cos\frac{\beta}{2}$	$\sin\frac{\beta}{2}$
	$-\frac{1}{2}$	$-\sin\frac{\beta}{2}$	$\cos\frac{\beta}{2}$

		$m = 1$	$m = 0$	$m = -1$
$d^{(1)}_{m'm}(\beta)$	$m' = 1$	$\frac{1}{2}(1+\cos\beta)$	$\frac{1}{\sqrt{2}}\sin\beta$	$\frac{1}{2}(1-\cos\beta)$
	0	$-\frac{1}{\sqrt{2}}\sin\beta$	$\cos\beta$	$\frac{1}{\sqrt{2}}\sin\beta$
	-1	$\frac{1}{2}(1-\cos\beta)$	$-\frac{1}{\sqrt{2}}\sin\beta$	$\frac{1}{2}(1+\cos)\beta$

$$d^{(J)}_{M'M}(\beta) = \left[\frac{(J-M)!(J+M')!}{(J+M)!(J-M')!}\right]^{1/2} \frac{(-x)^{M-M'}}{(1+x^2)^J} \frac{1}{(M'-M)!} \times {}_2F_1(M'-J, -M-J; M'-M+1; -x^2), \quad \text{(A.11)}$$

where

$$x = \tan\frac{\beta}{2}.$$

Table 6.10 collects some of the properties of the rotation matrices. Table 6.11 gives some specific examples of the d matrices. The text by Gottfried [3] contains an excellent discussion of the rotation matrices, their properties, and their application to quantum mechanics.

REFERENCES

[1] M. E. Rose, *Elementary Theory of Angular Momentum*, Wiley, New York (1957).
[2] E. P. Wigner, *Group Theory and its Application to the Quantum Mechanics of Atomic Spectra*, Academic, New York (1959).
[3] K. Gottfried, *Quantum Mechanics*, Benjamin, New York (1966) vol. 1.

7. The Many-Electron Hamiltonian

7.1 ELECTROSTATIC INTERACTIONS

In the next two chapters we shall put to use the tools of perturbation theory and angular momentum. Our objective will be to understand some of the properties of many-electron atoms. At the same time, we shall take note of some important corrections to the nonrelativistic model of the hydrogen atom treated in Chapter 3.

Our first task will be to write down the many-electron Hamiltonian, proceeding from "large" terms to fine corrections on the energy, in the form

$$\mathcal{H} = \mathcal{H}^1 + \mathcal{H}^2 + \cdots .$$

As our basic atomic model, we consider N electrons surrounding a very small, dense nucleus of Z protons and $(A - Z)$ neutrons (a total of A *nucleons*). Here Z is the nuclear charge or atomic number and A is the atomic weight, except for the binding energy. Since nuclear radii are typically found to be about $1.5 \times A^{1/3} \times 10^{-13}$ cm, compared with atomic dimensions of a few angstroms, we may consider the nucleus to be a fixed point-charge at the origin, for a first approximation. (In Section 7.4 we shall consider the effects of finite nuclear mass, size, shape, and spin.)

The kinetic energy of the electrons provides the first term in the Hamiltonian,

$$\frac{1}{2m} \sum_i p^2(i). \tag{1.1}$$

In the present approximation the nucleus remains stationary.

Next, the attraction between the point nucleus and each electron contributes a Coulomb energy,

$$-Ze^2 \sum_i \frac{1}{r_i}, \tag{1.2}$$

and the electrostatic repulsion between electrons contributes

$$+e^2 \sum_{i<j} \frac{1}{r_{ij}}, \tag{1.3}$$

where $r_{ij} \equiv |\mathbf{r}_i - \mathbf{r}_j|$ is the distance between electrons i and j. This summation runs over all distinct pairs of electrons: the index j runs from 2 through N and, for a given j, the index i takes values 1 through $j - 1$.

We shall find it convenient to express the interelectron repulsion in terms of Racah tensors, using the expansion discussed in Chapter 3:

$$e^2 \sum_{i<j} \frac{1}{|\mathbf{r}_i - \mathbf{r}_j|} = e^2 \sum_{i<j} \sum_{k=0}^{\infty} \frac{r_<^k}{r_>^{k+1}} \mathbf{C}^{(k)}(i) \cdot \mathbf{C}^{(k)}(j). \tag{1.4}$$

In this way we factor the interaction into a radial part and an angular part. Equally important, the interaction has been separated into factors that depend only on the coordinates of the individual electrons, rather than the distance or angle between them.

Combining the preceding energies, we obtain the largest part of the nonrelativistic Hamiltonian for a free atom:

$$\mathcal{H}_{\text{free}} = \sum_i \left[\frac{p^2(i)}{2m} - \frac{Ze^2}{r_i}\right] + \sum_{i<j} \frac{e^2}{r_{ij}}. \tag{1.5}$$

7.2 EXTERNAL ELECTRIC FIELDS

When external charges surround an atom the Hamiltonian must include Coulomb interactions between the charges and atomic electrons. If the charges $q_1, q_2, \ldots$ are located at the positions $\rho_1, \rho_2, \ldots,$ then the interaction energy is

$$-\sum_i^{\text{electrons}} \sum_j^{\text{charges}} \frac{eq_j}{|\mathbf{r}_i - \boldsymbol{\rho}_j|}. \tag{2.1}$$

We can treat this interaction more conveniently if we express it as a multipole expansion. Since the perturbing charges are all outside the atom $(\rho_i > r_j)$ we can write the expansion as

$$-\sum_i^{\text{electrons}} \sum_j^{\text{charges}} \sum_k eq_j \frac{r_i^k}{\rho_j^{k+1}} \mathbf{C}^{(k)}(i) \cdot \mathbf{C}^{(k)}(j). \tag{2.2}$$

To this expression we add the electrostatic interaction between external charges and the point-charge nucleus,

$$\sum_j^{\text{charges}} \frac{Zeq_j}{\rho_j}. \tag{2.3}$$

The $k = 0$ term in the electron energy, added to the nuclear electrostatic energy, (2.3), gives a net electrostatic energy if the atom is ionized:

$$-\sum_i \sum_j \frac{eq_j}{\rho_j} + \sum_j \frac{Zeq_j}{\rho_j} = (Z - N)e\varphi(0). \tag{2.4}$$

Here the quantity

$$\varphi(0) = \sum_j \frac{q_j}{\rho_j} \tag{2.5}$$

is the electrostatic potential at the coordinate origin (at the nucleus) resulting from external charges.

The $k = 1$ term in the electron interaction, (2.2), gives the interaction of the net atomic dipole moment $\mathbf{D}$ with the external electric field $\mathbf{E}(0)$ at the origin:

$$-\sum_i er_i\mathbf{C}^{(1)}(i) \cdot \sum_j q_j \frac{\mathbf{C}^{(1)}(j)}{(\rho_j)^2} \equiv \mathbf{D}\cdot\mathbf{E}(0). \tag{2.6}$$

The electron dipole-moment operator is a tensor operator of order 1,

$$\mathbf{D} \equiv \mathbf{D}^{(1)} \equiv -\sum_i e\mathbf{r}_i = -\sum_i er_i\mathbf{C}^{(1)}(i). \tag{2.7}$$

The electric field vector is also a tensor of order 1,

$$\mathbf{E}(0) \equiv \mathbf{E}^{(1)}(0) \equiv \sum_j q_j \frac{\boldsymbol{\rho}_j}{(\rho_j)^3}. \tag{2.8}$$

Of course this dipole interaction also occurs when we place the atom in *any* external electric field, whether or not we wish to compute the field from a charge distribution. If the charge is distributed continuously, then (2.8) becomes

$$\mathbf{E}(0) = \int dq\, \frac{\boldsymbol{\rho}}{\rho^3}. \tag{2.9}$$

If the external charges are paired off as dipoles, we should express the interaction in terms of external dipole moments. The electrostatic potential at $\mathbf{r}$ of a dipole moment $\boldsymbol{\mu}$ located at the origin is

$$\varphi(\mathbf{r}) = -\boldsymbol{\mu}\cdot\nabla\frac{1}{r}. \tag{2.10}$$

The field at r from this dipole is

$$\mathbf{E}(\mathbf{r}) = -\nabla\varphi(\mathbf{r}) = \nabla(\boldsymbol{\mu}\cdot\nabla)\frac{1}{r} = -\frac{1}{r^3}\left[\boldsymbol{\mu} - 3\mathbf{r}\frac{(\boldsymbol{\mu}\cdot\mathbf{r})}{r^2}\right]. \tag{2.11}$$

Using tensor operators, we can write this (cf. Judd [1]) as

$$\mathbf{E}(\mathbf{r}) = \frac{\sqrt{10}}{r^3}\,[\boldsymbol{\mu}^{(1)} \times \mathbf{C}^{(2)}]^{(1)}. \tag{2.12}$$

Thus we can write the interaction of interest as

$$\sqrt{10}\sum_i^{\text{electrons}} er_i\mathbf{C}^{(1)}(i)\cdot\sum_j^{\text{dipoles}}\frac{1}{(\rho_j)^3}\,[\boldsymbol{\mu}^{(1)} \times \mathbf{C}^{(2)}(j)]^{(1)}. \tag{2.13}$$

The $k = 2$ term gives the interaction of an atomic quadrupole tensor, $\mathbf{Q}^{(2)}$, with an external field-gradient tensor, $\mathbf{U}^{(2)}$, evaluated at the origin:

$$-\sum_i^{\text{electrons}} er_i^2\mathbf{C}^{(2)}(i)\cdot\sum_j^{\text{charges}} q_j\frac{\mathbf{C}^{(2)}(j)}{(\rho_j)^3} \equiv -\mathbf{Q}^{(2)}\cdot\mathbf{U}^{(2)}. \tag{2.14}$$

Here the operators are tensors of order 2,

$$\mathbf{Q}^{(2)} \equiv \sum_i er_i^2\mathbf{C}^{(2)}(i), \tag{2.15}$$

$$\mathbf{U}^{(2)} = \sum_j q_j\frac{\mathbf{C}^{(2)}(j)}{(\rho_j)^3}\,. \tag{2.16}$$

We can write the tensor component $U_0^{(2)}(0)$ as:

$$\mathbf{U}_0^{(2)} = \sum_j q_j\frac{(3Z_j - \rho_j^2)}{(\rho_j)^5} = \frac{1}{2}\sum_j\frac{\partial}{\partial Z_j}E_z(j) = -\frac{1}{2}\sum_j\frac{\partial^2}{\partial Z_j^2}\frac{q_j}{\rho_j}, \tag{2.17}$$

where Z_j is the z coordinate of the jth charge. The component $Q_0^{(2)}$ of the quadrupole tensor can be written:

$$Q_0^{(2)} = e\sum_i(3z_i^2 - r_i^2), \tag{2.18}$$

where z_i is the ith electron z coordinate. The Wigner–Eckart theorem permits us to write a matrix element of $\mathbf{U}^{(2)}\cdot\mathbf{Q}^{(2)}$ in terms of matrix elements of $U_0^{(2)}$ and $Q_0^{(2)}$, along with appropriate CG coefficients.

We could calculate additional terms in the multipole expansion if necessary. For an atom embedded in a crystal, the electrostatic interactions alter the atomic energy levels significantly from those of a free atom. Even atoms of a gas encounter fields caused by passing molecules, atoms, ions, and electrons.

To summarize this discussion: external charges and fields contribute the Hamiltonian terms

$$\mathcal{H}_{\text{ext}} = (Z - N)e\varphi(0) - e\mathbf{E}(0)\cdot\sum_i\mathbf{r}_i - e\mathbf{U}^{(2)}\cdot\sum_i r_i^2\mathbf{C}^{(2)}(i). \tag{2.19}$$

When the perturbing field arises from a distant molecule, it may prove convenient to express the energy in terms of multipole moments of the perturber. Suppose we have two collections of charges, I and II. The charges e_i of collection I are located at positions $\mathbf{r}_i$, measured from an origin 0_{I}, whereas the charges q_j of collection II are located at positions ρ_j measured from an origin 0_{II}. If the coordinate origin 0_{II} is located at $\mathbf{R}$ in the 0_{I} reference frame, the distance between charge e_i and charge q_j is $|\mathbf{r}_i - \rho_j - \mathbf{R}|$. The multipole moments of the two collections of charge are

$$\text{system I:}\quad Q_m^{(l)}(\text{I}) = \sum_i e_i (r_i)^l C_m^{(l)}(i), \tag{2.20a}$$

$$\text{system II:}\quad Q_m^{(l)}(\text{II}) = \sum_j e_j (\rho_j)^l C_m^{(l)}(j), \tag{2.20b}$$

as evaluated in reference frames I and II, respectively. The Coulomb interaction between the charges of the two systems can be expanded in powers of R. When the two systems of charge are well separated, so that $R > r_i$ and $R > \rho_j$, the interaction is

$$\begin{aligned}\mathcal{H}_{\text{coul}} &= \sum_i \sum_j \frac{e_i q_j}{|\mathbf{r}_i - \rho_j - \mathbf{R}|} \\ &= \sum_L \frac{1}{R^{L+1}} \mathbf{C}^{(L)}(\hat{\mathbf{R}}) \cdot \mathbf{B}^{(L)},\end{aligned} \tag{2.21}$$

where $\mathbf{C}^{(L)}$ is a Racah tensor, $\hat{\mathbf{R}}$ is the direction of the vector $\mathbf{R}$, and the tensor $\mathbf{B}^{(L)}$ is given by the expression

$$B_M^{(L)} = \sum_{l'+l=L} (-1)^{l'} \left[\frac{(2L)!}{(2l)!(2l')!}\right]^{1/2} [\mathbf{Q}^{(l)}(\text{I}) \times \mathbf{Q}^{(l')}(\text{II})]_M^{(L)}. \tag{2.22}$$

The sum over l and l' goes over those values for which $l' + l = L$ and the brackets denote the coupling of angular momentum:

$$[\mathbf{Q}^{(l)} \times \mathbf{Q}^{(l')}]_M^{(L)} \equiv \sum_{mm'} (lm, l'm' | LM)\, Q_m^{(l)}\, Q_{m'}^{(l')}.$$

When we take the z axis along $\mathbf{R}$, (2.21)–(2.22) become

$$\mathcal{H}_{\text{coul}} = \sum_L \frac{1}{R^{L+1}} B_0^{(L)}, \tag{2.23}$$

$$\begin{aligned}B_0^{(L)} &= \sum_{l'+l=L} (-1)^{l'} \left[\frac{(2L)!}{(2l)!(2l')!}\right]^{1/2} \sum_m (lm, l' - m | L0) Q_m^{(l)}(\text{I})\, Q_{-m}^{(l')}(\text{II}) \\ &= \sum_{l'+l=L} \sum_m \frac{(-1)^{l'} L!}{[(l-m)!(l+m)!(l'-m)!(l'+m)!]^{1/2}} Q_m^{(l)}(\text{I})\, Q_{-m}^{(l')}(\text{II}).\end{aligned} \tag{2.24}$$

Equations 2.21–2.24 express the Coulomb interaction in terms of multipole-multipole interactions; for example, if the net charges of collections I and II are Z_{I} and Z_{II},

$$Q_0^{(0)}(\mathrm{I}) = Z_{\mathrm{I}}, \qquad Q_0^{(0)}(\mathrm{II}) = Z_{\mathrm{II}}, \tag{2.25}$$

the first few terms of V are

$$\begin{aligned}\mathcal{H}_{\text{coul}} &= \frac{1}{R}[Z_{\mathrm{II}}Z_{\mathrm{I}}] \\ &+ \frac{1}{R^2}[Z_{\mathrm{II}}Q_0^{(1)}(\mathrm{I}) - Z_{\mathrm{I}}Q_0^{(1)}(\mathrm{II})] \\ &+ \frac{1}{R^3}[Z_{\mathrm{II}}Q_0^{(2)}(\mathrm{I}) + Z_{\mathrm{I}}Q_0^{(2)}(\mathrm{II}) \\ &- Q_{-1}^{(1)}(\mathrm{I})\,Q_1^{(1)}(\mathrm{II}) - 2Q_0^{(1)}(\mathrm{I})\,Q_0^{(1)}(\mathrm{II}) - Q_1^{(1)}(\mathrm{I})\,Q_{-1}^{(1)}(\mathrm{II})].\end{aligned} \tag{2.26}$$

The final three terms of (2.26) comprise a dipole-dipole interaction. Higher terms include dipole-quadrupole, quadrupole-quadrupole, etc.

Equations 2.21–2.24 can be derived with the aid of an addition theorem for solid harmonics given by Rose [2]:

$$Q_M^{(L)}(\mathbf{r}_1 + \mathbf{r}_2) = \sum_{l+l'=L} (-1)^{l'}\left[\frac{(2L)!}{(2l)!(2l')!}\right]^{1/2}[\mathbf{Q}^{(l)}(\mathbf{r}_1) \times \mathbf{Q}^{(l')}(\mathbf{r}_2)]_M^{(L)}, \tag{2.27}$$

$$V_M^{(L)}(\mathbf{r}_1 - \mathbf{r}_2) = \sum_{l-l'=L} (-1)^{l'}\left[\frac{(2l'+1)!}{(2l)!(2L+1)!}\right]^{1/2}[\mathbf{Q}^{(l)}(\mathbf{r}_1) \times \mathbf{V}^{(l')}(\mathbf{r}_2)]_M^{(L)}. \tag{2.28}$$

Here $Q_m^{(l)}$ and $V_m^{(l)}$ are solid harmonics:

$$Q_m^{(l)}(\mathbf{r}) = r^l C_m^{(l)}(\hat{\mathbf{r}}) \equiv r^l\left(\frac{4\pi}{2l+1}\right)^{1/2} Y_{lm}, \tag{2.29}$$

$$V_m^{(l)}(\mathbf{r}) = \frac{1}{r^{l+1}}\, C_m^{(l)}(\hat{\mathbf{r}}) \equiv \frac{1}{r^{l+1}}\left(\frac{4\pi}{2l+1}\right)^{1/2} Y_{lm}. \tag{2.30}$$

By iterating (2.28) we obtain a generalization of (2.21):

$$\begin{aligned}V_M^{(L)}(\mathbf{r} - \rho - \mathbf{R}) = \sum_{l,l',l''} (-1)^{l'}\left[\frac{(2l''+1)!}{(2l)!(2l')!(2L+1)!}\right]^{1/2} \\ \times [\mathbf{Q}^{(l)}(\mathbf{r}) \times [\mathbf{Q}^{(l')}(\rho) \times \mathbf{V}^{(l'')}(\mathbf{R})]^{(l'-l'')}]_M^{(L)}.\end{aligned}$$

[Note that $V_m^{(l)}(-\mathbf{R}) = (-1)^l V_m^{(l)}(\mathbf{R})$]. Equation 2.21 corresponds to the case $L = 0$:

$$\mathcal{H}_{\text{coul}} = V_0^{(0)}(\mathbf{r} - \rho - \mathbf{R}) = \frac{1}{|\mathbf{r} - \rho - \mathbf{R}|}.$$

The preceding expansions, as well as other similar relationships, have been derived by Carlson and Rushbrooke [3], Buehler and Hirschfelder [4],

Fontana [5], and Chiu [6]. Our discussion followed the review by Dalgarno and Davison [7].

REFERENCES

[1] B. R. Judd, *Operator Techniques in Atomic Spectroscopy*, McGraw-Hill, New York (1963).
[2] M. E. Rose, *Elementary Theory of Angular Momentum*, Wiley, New York (1957), pp. 60–61; *J. Math. and Phys.* **37**, 215 (1958).
[3] B. C. Carlson and G. S. Rushbrooke, *Proc. Cambr. Phil. Soc.* **46**, 626 (1950).
[4] R. J. Buehler and J. O. Hirschfelder, *Phys. Rev.* **83**, 628 (1951).
[5] P. S. Fontana, *J. Math. Phys.* **2**, 825 (1961).
[6] Y-N Chiu, *J. Math. Phys.* **5**, 283 (1964).
[7] A. Dalgarno and W. D. Davison, The Calculation of Van der Waals Interactions, in *Advances in Atomic and Molecular Physics*, **2**, 1, edited by D. R. Bates and I. Estermann, Academic, New York (1966).

7.3 RELATIVISTIC CORRECTIONS

The Hamiltonian of the preceding sections suffices to predict the gross, qualitative structure of simple atoms. Indeed, even the simple Bohr theory predicts reasonably correct energy levels and radii for hydrogen. However, close examination of the hydrogen spectrum reveals details of atomic structure that these simple approximations cannot explain. The major inadequacy of this Hamiltonian can be traced to our nonrelativistic approximation: we assumed electron velocities to be much smaller than the velocity of light, which is certainly not correct for electron motion close to the nucleus.

If we wish to describe particles moving with high velocities, we can no longer ignore requirements imposed by the theory of relativity. Basically, a relativistic equation must treat the time coordinate on an equal footing with the three spatial coordinates. The Schrödinger equation, by contrast, involves the first derivative with respect to time and the second derivative with respect to spatial coordinates.

In 1928 P. A. M. Dirac proposed [1] a wave equation that was linear in all derivatives. The Dirac equation has been well established as the appropriate relativistic equation for electrons and protons. When one includes necessary corrections for the interaction with the radiation field, the predictions of the Dirac theory are in excellent agreement with observations.

The Dirac equation introduces some important qualitative changes in our picture of the electron. Most importantly, it endows an electron with an additional degree of freedom, an intrinsic angular momentum, and an intrinsic magnetic moment. In short, a Dirac electron has spin $\frac{1}{2}$.

In the limit of low electron velocities, the Dirac equation can be written in the form of a Schrödinger equation, with additional terms from the electron spin and other relativistic effects. We discuss some of the terms of this *Pauli approximation* [2] below.

To begin our discussion, the electron mass does not remain constant as the electron velocity approaches the velocity of light. Rather, the mass increases without limit as $v \to c$. (Experiments by Kauffmann [3] from 1901 to 1906 provided the first evidence for this remarkable mass increase.) The mass of the moving electron becomes

$$m = \frac{m_0}{\sqrt{1 - (v/c)^2}}, \tag{3.1}$$

with m_0 the electron rest mass. The kinetic energy of an electron becomes

$$\begin{aligned} T = \frac{p^2}{2m} &= \frac{p^2}{2m_0}\left[1 - \left(\frac{v}{c}\right)^2\right]^{-1/2} \\ &= \frac{p^2}{2m_0}\left[1 - \frac{1}{2}\left(\frac{v}{c}\right)^2 - \frac{1}{8}\left(\frac{v}{c}\right)^4 - \cdots\right]. \end{aligned} \tag{3.2}$$

With the approximation $(m_0 v)^2 = p^2$, (3.2) can be written

$$\frac{p^2}{2m} = \frac{p^2}{2m_0} - \frac{cp^4}{(2m_0 c)^3} - \cdots \simeq \frac{p^2}{2m_0}\left[1 - \frac{T}{2m_0 c^2}\right]. \tag{3.3}$$

Thus we find that, for a many-electron atom, the kinetic energy is

$$T \simeq \sum_i \left[\frac{p^2(i)}{2m_0} - \frac{cp^4(i)}{(2m_0 c)^3}\right]. \tag{3.4}$$

Next, Dirac's theory provides a spin magnetic moment $\boldsymbol{\mu} = -g_s \beta \mathbf{S}$, where $\beta \equiv e\hbar/2mc$ is the Bohr magneton. Radiative corrections raise g_s from the value of exactly 2 in the Dirac theory to the observed value 2.002:

$$g_s \simeq 2\left(1 + \frac{\alpha}{2\pi} - 2.973\,\frac{\alpha^2}{\pi^2} + \cdots\right) \simeq 2(1 + 1.145 \times 10^{-3}).$$

In the absence of externally imposed fields, an electron is still influenced by other moving electrons and the nucleus. The electric fields of these charges appear as magnetic fields to a moving observer. If the total electric field is $\mathbf{E}$, the Dirac theory gives a Hamiltonian term,

$$-\mathbf{H}\cdot\boldsymbol{\mu} = \frac{(\mathbf{E} \times \mathbf{v})}{2c} \cdot (g_s \beta \mathbf{S}), \tag{3.5}$$

for each electron. (The factor $\frac{1}{2}$ is the Thomas factor [4].) The velocity is very nearly $\mathbf{p}/m$ (although in the presence of a magnetic field, the momentum includes a small additional term from the momentum of the radiation field), so that we obtain

$$-\mathbf{H}\cdot\boldsymbol{\mu} = \left(\frac{g_s\beta}{2m_0c}\right)(\mathbf{E} \times \mathbf{p})\cdot\mathbf{S}. \tag{3.6}$$

For a hydrogen-like atom, the electric field is

$$\mathbf{E} = -\text{grad}\,\frac{Ze}{r} \equiv -\boldsymbol{\nabla}\frac{Ze}{r} = Ze\frac{\mathbf{r}}{r^3}, \tag{3.7}$$

so that the energy increment in the Hamiltonian is

$$\frac{g_s\beta}{2mc}\,\frac{Ze}{r^3}\,(\mathbf{r} \times \mathbf{p})\cdot\mathbf{S} = \frac{g_sZ\beta^2}{r^3}\,\mathbf{L}\cdot\mathbf{S}. \tag{3.8}$$

where $\mathbf{L} = \hbar(\mathbf{r} \times \mathbf{p})$. For an atom with several electrons the electric field is commonly taken as a central field, the nuclear attraction screened by the average motion of the other electrons. With such an approximation, the electric field is radial, with magnitude

$$E_r = -(\text{grad}\,\bar{\varphi}(r))_r = -\frac{1}{r}\frac{\partial\bar{\varphi}(r)}{\partial r} = \frac{e\mathcal{Z}(r)}{r^3} \tag{3.9}$$

where $\bar{\varphi}$ denotes the average electrostatic potential, and $\mathcal{Z}(r)$ is the charge inside a sphere of radius r. The interaction can then be written as

$$-\mathbf{H}\cdot\boldsymbol{\mu} = \xi(r)\mathbf{L}\cdot\mathbf{S}, \tag{3.10}$$

where

$$\xi(r) = -\frac{\hbar^2}{2m^2c^2}\,\frac{1}{r}\,\frac{\partial\bar{\varphi}}{\partial r} = g_s\beta^2\,\frac{\mathcal{Z}(r)}{r^3}. \tag{3.11}$$

We thereby obtain the *spin-orbit interaction*

$$\mathcal{H}_{\text{spin-orbit}} = \xi(r)\mathbf{L}\cdot\mathbf{S} \tag{3.12}$$

responsible for the atomic fine-structure discussed in Section 2.8. For a many-electron atom, (3.12) becomes

$$\mathcal{H}_{\text{spin-orbit}} = \sum_i \xi(r_i)\mathbf{L}(i)\cdot\mathbf{S}(i). \tag{3.13}$$

REFERENCES

[1] P. A. M. Dirac, *Proc. Roy. Soc. A* **117**, 610 (1928); *The Principles of Quantum Mechanics*, Oxford University Press, New York (1957), 4th ed., Chap. 11.
[2] W. Pauli, *Z. Physik* **43**, 601 (1927).
[3] W. Kaufmann, *Ann. d. Physik* **19**, 487 (1906).
[4] L. H. Thomas, *Nature* **117**, 514 (1926); *Phil. Mag.* **3**, 1 (1927).

7.4 NUCLEAR EFFECTS

The structure of an atomic nucleus—its shape and finite mass, volume, and spin—produces small but discernible effects on atomic energy levels. A study of these effects can provide valuable knowledge of nuclear structure as well as atomic structure. Detailed discussions of nuclear influence appear in the books by Kopfermann [1] and Ramsey [2]. For more recent results, consult Kuhn [3]. Here we simply indicate the nature of various nuclear effects.

A. Mass

In Chapter 2 we saw that in a one-electron atom with nuclear mass AM the free electron mass m_0 must be replaced by the reduced mass m,

$$m = m_0\left(1 - \frac{m_0}{AM} + \cdots\right). \tag{4.1}$$

Calculations then proceed as if the nucleus were fixed in space. Two isotopes having masses AM and $(A + 1)M$ therefore have slightly different Rydberg constants,

$$R_{A+1} - R_A \simeq R_\infty \left(\frac{m_0}{m}\right)\frac{1}{A(A+1)} \simeq \frac{R_\infty}{1836A^2}. \tag{4.2}$$

This produces a *mass-dependent isotope shift* of spectral lines. For an atom with several electrons the problem is more complicated. With the center of mass as the coordinate origin, the electrons at $\mathbf{r}_1, \ldots, \mathbf{r}_n$ have kinetic energy

$$\frac{p_1^2}{2m_0} + \cdots + \frac{p_n^2}{2m_0}. \tag{4.3}$$

To this energy we must add the kinetic energy of the nucleus of mass AM at R. However, if the center of mass is at rest, the momentum of the nucleus, $\mathbf{p}$, plus all the electronic moments must add to zero. Thus the nuclear kinetic energy can be written

$$\frac{p^2}{2AM} = \frac{(-\mathbf{p}_1 - \cdots - \mathbf{p}_n)^2}{2AM}$$

$$= \frac{1}{2AM}(p_1^2 + \cdots + p_n^2 + 2\mathbf{p}_1\cdot\mathbf{p}_2 + \cdots + 2\mathbf{p}_1\cdot\mathbf{p}_n + \cdots). \tag{4.4}$$

Adding this to (4.3) gives the kinetic energy

$$\frac{p_1^2}{2m} + \cdots + \frac{p_n^2}{2m} + \frac{1}{AM}\left(\sum_{i<j} \mathbf{p}_i\cdot\mathbf{p}_j\right), \tag{4.5}$$

where m is the usual reduced mass (4.1). The presence of the cross terms $\mathbf{p}_i \cdot \mathbf{p}_j$ in (4.5) reflects the possibility of correlated motion of the electrons, and produces a different shift for different energy levels. For light atoms this correlation shift can be comparable to the simple reduced-mass shift of (4.2) (cf. Kopfermann [1], p. 161).

B. Volume

The nucleus actually occupies a finite volume, and it is possible for an electron to move *inside* the nucleus; high-energy electrons are commonly used to probe the structure of the nucleus. Bound electrons tend to avoid the nucleus simply because of the angular-momentum barrier in the effective potential. For "s" electrons, no such barrier exists; the s wavefunction is not zero at the origin. Thus there is a finite probability that s electrons may be found inside the nucleus. As an electron penetrates further into the nucleus, the electrostatic potential drops toward zero from its high value $\varphi = Ze/r_0$ at the nuclear surface (at $r = r_0$). The actual field inside the nucleus depends on the detailed structure of the nucleus (on the wavefunctions of the protons and neutrons). For our purposes we need merely note that the potential energy $V = -e\varphi$ for s orbitals is shifted upward by the Coulomb attraction at small distances. The s energy levels are, accordingly, shifted upward. This shift is approximately proportional to the overlap of the nuclear volume and the probability density $|\psi(0)|^2$ of the electron at the nucleus. Since this shift varies with nuclear size for a given nuclear charge, it can be detected as a *volume-dependent isotope shift* of spectral lines. This shift becomes more pronounced in heavier elements. Thus the observed isotope shift in light elements is predominantly a mass effect, whereas the isotope shift in heavy elements is a volume effect.

C. Shape

The electrostatic potential outside the nucleus may differ perceptibly from a simple Coulomb potential if the protons are not distributed with spherical symmetry inside the nucleus. More precisely, the motion of the nucleons within the nucleus may exhibit deviations from spherical symmetry. To see how this phenomenon affects the electrons, we write out in detail the electrostatic attraction between each electron, $\mathbf{r}_i$, and each proton, $\mathbf{R}_j$, and then use the multipole expansion. Since the electrons are, on the average, far outside the nucleus ($r_i \gg R_j$), the expansion reads

$$-\sum_i^{\text{electrons}} \sum_j^{\text{protons}} \frac{e^2}{|\mathbf{r}_i - \mathbf{R}_j|} = -e^2 \sum_k \sum_i^{\text{electrons}} \sum_j^{\text{protons}} \frac{R_j^k}{r_i^{k+1}} \mathbf{C}^{(k)}(i) \cdot \mathbf{C}^{(k)}(j). \quad (4.6)$$

For each value of k, the expansion represents the product of a *nuclear-multipole tensor* $\mathbf{Q}^{(k)}$, a tensor operator of order k,

$$\mathbf{Q}^{(k)} = e \sum_j (R_j)^k \mathbf{C}^{(k)}(j), \tag{4.7}$$

with an electronic *charge-distribution tensor*,

$$\mathbf{U}^{(k)} = -e \sum_i \frac{\mathbf{C}^{(k)}(i)}{(r_i)^{k+1}}. \tag{4.8}$$

The $k = 0$ multipole term is simply the interaction of the electrons with a point charge:

$$-\sum_i^{\text{electrons}} \frac{e}{r_i} \sum_j^{\text{protons}} e = -\sum_i \frac{Ze^2}{r_i}. \tag{4.9}$$

The $k = 1$ term of (4.8) gives the interaction between a nuclear electric dipole moment and the electron field. However, no static "odd" electric moments (i.e., k = an odd integer) have been observed for nuclei. The following argument shows why the odd nuclear moments should be unobserved. The parity of the operator $C_m^{(k)}$ is $(-1)^k$. Nuclear states, as well as nondegenerate atomic states for free atoms, have been found to have well-defined parity. If we take the expectation value of an operator $C_m^{(k)}$, as we do in evaluating the energy to first order in a perturbation theory, we require the matrix element between two states of the same parity. The matrix element of an odd operator $\mathcal{O}$ (i.e., k = odd integer) between two even or two odd states satisfies the relation

$$\langle \psi(\mathbf{r}) | \mathcal{O}(\mathbf{r}) | \psi(\mathbf{r}) \rangle = -\langle \psi(-\mathbf{r}) | \mathcal{O}(-\mathbf{r}) | \psi(-\mathbf{r}) \rangle. \tag{4.10}$$

In the absence of external fields giving a preferred direction, this matrix element cannot depend on our choice of coordinate axes. That is, we obtain the same result in a "mirror image" coordinate system:

$$\langle \psi(\mathbf{r}) | \mathcal{O}(\mathbf{r}) | \psi(\mathbf{r}) \rangle = +\langle \psi(-\mathbf{r}) | \mathcal{O}(-\mathbf{r}) | \psi(-\mathbf{r}) \rangle. \tag{4.11}$$

Therefore the expectation value for *odd* operators will be zero. This argument holds only for a free unperturbed system. An electric field will destroy the coordinate symmetry, and the states will no longer have well-defined parity. The field produces an *induced moment*. Such induced nuclear moments will be quite small, but may be observable (cf. Gunther-Mohr, Geschwind, and Townes [4], and references in Ramsey [2]).

The $k = 2$ term of (4.8) provides an interaction between a nuclear quadrupole tensor, $\mathbf{Q}^{(2)}$, and the gradient of the electric field of the electrons, $\mathbf{U}^{(2)}$:

$$\mathcal{H}_{\text{nuclear quad}} = -\sum_i^{\text{electrons}} e \frac{\mathbf{C}^{(2)}(i)}{(r_i)^3} \cdot \sum_j^{\text{protons}} e(R_j)^2 \mathbf{C}^{(2)}(j) = \mathbf{Q}^{(2)} \cdot \mathbf{U}^{(2)}. \tag{4.12}$$

To calculate the energy shift from this interaction we take the expectation value of this operator in a state characterized by electronic angular momentum **J** and nuclear angular momentum **I**. Let the state be further characterized by the total angular momentum $\mathbf{F} = \mathbf{I} + \mathbf{J}$. Then the expectation value is

$$\Delta E_{\text{quad}} = \langle \mathcal{H}_{\text{nuclear quad}} \rangle = \langle (IJ)FM_F | \mathbf{U}^{(2)} \cdot \mathbf{Q}^{(2)} | (IJ)FM_F \rangle. \tag{4.13}$$

This expression reduces to a convenient form when we apply tensor-operator theory:

$$\Delta E_{\text{quad}} = (-1)^{J+I+F} \begin{Bmatrix} J & I & F \\ I & J & 2 \end{Bmatrix} \langle J \| \mathbf{U}^{(2)} \| J \rangle \langle I \| \mathbf{Q}^{(2)} \| I \rangle. \tag{4.14}$$

The reduced matrix elements of (4.14) can be evaluated in terms of any particular tensor components, most conveniently the $U_0^{(2)}$ and $Q_0^{(2)}$ components, through application of the Wigner–Eckart theorem:

$$\langle J \| \mathbf{U}^{(2)} \| J \rangle = \frac{eq_J}{\begin{pmatrix} J & 2 & J \\ -J & 0 & J \end{pmatrix}}, \tag{4.15}$$

$$\langle I \| \mathbf{Q}^{(2)} \| I \rangle = \frac{eQ}{\begin{pmatrix} I & 2 & I \\ -I & 0 & I \end{pmatrix}}. \tag{4.16}$$

Here the atomic matrix element is

$$\begin{aligned} eq_J \equiv \Phi_{JJ}(0) &\equiv \langle J, M_J = J | \sum_i^{\text{electrons}} \frac{\partial^2}{\partial z_i^2} \frac{e}{r_i} | J, M_J = J \rangle \\ &\equiv \langle J, M_J = J | \sum_i \frac{C_0^{(2)}(i)}{r^3} | J, M_J = J \rangle, \end{aligned} \tag{4.17}$$

and the nuclear matrix element (conventionally called the *nuclear quadrupole moment*) is

$$eQ \equiv \langle IM_I = I | \sum_j^{\text{protons}} e(3z_j^2 - R_j^2) | IM_I = I \rangle. \tag{4.18}$$

The energy shift can then be written as

$$\Delta E_{\text{quad}} = (-1)^{J+I+F} \frac{\begin{Bmatrix} J & I & F \\ I & J & 2 \end{Bmatrix}}{\begin{pmatrix} J & 2 & J \\ -J & 0 & J \end{pmatrix} \begin{pmatrix} I & 2 & I \\ -I & 0 & I \end{pmatrix}} (e^2 Q q_J). \tag{4.19}$$

By inserting expressions for the angular-momentum coefficients, we obtain *Casimir's Formula* [5]:

$$\Delta E_{\text{quad}} = B\left[\frac{3C(C-1) - 4J(J+1)I(I+1)}{2J(2J-1)I(2I-1)}\right],$$
$$C \equiv J(J+1) + I(I+1) - F(F+1), \tag{4.20}$$
$$B \equiv eQ\Phi_{JJ}(0) \equiv eQeq_J.$$

Here B is conventionally called the *quadrupole coupling constant.* The quadrupole interaction (4.12) is the alignment energy of a nucleus having a nonspherical charge distribution, in a nonuniform electric field. A positive quadrupole moment, $Q > 0$, corresponds to an elongated (cigar-shaped) nucleus; a negative quadrupole moment, $Q < 0$, means a flattened (pie-plate) nucleus. The alignment axis is the direction of the field gradient at the nucleus. Quantized orientations of a nuclear quadrupole moment give a hyperfine splitting to the atomic energy levels.

D. Spin

Many, though not all, nuclei possess an intrinsic angular momentum or nuclear spin, customarily denoted **I**. As a result, these nuclei also possess magnetic moments $\boldsymbol{\mu}$ proportional to the angular momentum, conventionally written in one of two ways,

$$\boldsymbol{\mu} = \gamma_N \hbar \mathbf{I} \equiv \frac{\mu_I}{I}\mathbf{I}. \tag{4.21}$$

The nuclear *gyromagnetic ratio* γ_N is often written in terms of the nuclear magneton β_N and a dimensionless g factor,

$$\gamma_N \hbar = g\beta_N = g\,\frac{e\hbar}{2M_p c}, \tag{4.22}$$

where M_p is the proton mass.

The nuclear magneton is smaller than the Bohr magneton β by the ratio of electron to proton mass, 1/1836:

$$\beta = 0.9273 \times 10^{-20} \text{ erg/gauss},$$
$$\beta_N = \frac{\beta}{1836} = 0.5050 + 10^{-23} \text{ erg/gauss}.$$

Both the proton and the neutron have spin $\frac{1}{2}$, with g factors

$$g = 5.58 \text{ for protons},$$
$$g = -3.83 \text{ for neutrons}.$$

Nuclear g factors are observed to vary between -3.8 and $+5.6$. The value of g for a particular nucleus provides important information for determining nuclear structure (cf. Evans [6]).

A nuclear magnetic moment $\boldsymbol{\mu}$ gives rise to an alignment energy in the magnetic field $\mathbf{H}_{\text{elec}}$ created by moving electrons. As long as the electrons remain outside the nuclear volume, the energy operator is simply:

$$\mathcal{H}_{\text{nuclear spin}} = -\boldsymbol{\mu}\cdot\mathbf{H}_{\text{elec}} = -\boldsymbol{\mu}\cdot(\mathbf{H}_{\text{orb}} + \mathbf{H}_{\text{spin}}). \tag{4.23}$$

Here $\mathbf{H}_{\text{orb}}$ is the field due to the motion of point charges, calculated in Chapter 3:

$$\mathbf{H}_{\text{orb}} = -\frac{e}{c}\,\frac{\mathbf{r}\times\mathbf{v}}{r^3} = -2\beta\,\frac{\mathbf{L}}{r^3}\,. \tag{4.24}$$

The field $\mathbf{H}_{\text{spin}}$ originating with the electron (spin) magnetic moments, $-2\beta\mathbf{S}$, can be calculated from a magnetostatic potential φ_{spin} (cf. Smythe [7], p. 7)

$$\mathbf{H}_{\text{spin}} = -\nabla\varphi_{\text{spin}} = -\nabla\left(2\beta\mathbf{S}\cdot\nabla\frac{1}{r}\right), \tag{4.25}$$

or using a magnetic vector-potential $\mathbf{A}_{\text{spin}}$:

$$\mathbf{H}_{\text{spin}} = \nabla\times\mathbf{A}_{\text{spin}} = -\nabla\times\left(\frac{2\beta\mathbf{S}\times\mathbf{r}}{r}\right). \tag{4.26}$$

Performing the differentiation and using $\mathbf{r} = r\mathbf{C}^{(1)}$ we obtain

$$\mathbf{H}_{\text{spin}} = \frac{2\beta}{r^3}\,[\mathbf{S} - 3\mathbf{C}^{(1)}(\mathbf{S}\cdot\mathbf{C}^{(1)})]. \tag{4.27}$$

As we have noted, an s electron has a finite probability of being inside the nuclear volume. To include this possibility, we need to express the energy in terms of a point electron dipole moment at the origin interacting with the field $\mathbf{H}_{\text{nucl}}$ generated by a nuclear current loop. The result (cf. Slichter [8], p. 86) provides the *Fermi contact interaction* [9]:

$$+2\beta\mathbf{S}\cdot\mathbf{H}_{\text{nucl}} = \frac{8\pi}{3}\,\beta\mathbf{S}\cdot\boldsymbol{\mu}\,\delta(\mathbf{r}), \tag{4.28}$$

where $\delta(\mathbf{r})$ is the three-dimensional Dirac delta function. Putting together these magnetic effects, with the nuclear moment written $\boldsymbol{\mu} = g_N\beta_N\mathbf{I}$, we obtain the contribution to the Hamiltonian:

$$\mathcal{H}_{\text{nuclear spin}} = -2\left(\frac{g_N\beta_N\beta}{r^3}\right)[\mathbf{I}\cdot\mathbf{L} - \mathbf{I}\cdot\mathbf{S} + 3(\mathbf{I}\cdot\mathbf{C}^{(1)})(\mathbf{S}\cdot\mathbf{C}^{(1)})] + (g_N\beta_N\beta)\,\frac{8\pi}{3}\,\delta(\mathbf{r})\mathbf{I}\cdot\mathbf{S}. \tag{4.29}$$

This interaction can be written as

$$\mathcal{H}_{\text{nuclear spin}} = -(2g_N\beta_N\beta)\left[\frac{\mathbf{I}\cdot\mathbf{N}}{r^3} - \frac{4\pi}{3}\,\delta(\mathbf{r})\mathbf{I}\cdot\mathbf{S}\right], \tag{4.30}$$

where the electron operator is

$$\mathbf{N} = \mathbf{L} - \mathbf{S} + 3\mathbf{C}^{(1)}(\mathbf{S}\cdot\mathbf{C}^{(1)}), \tag{4.31}$$
$$= \mathbf{L}^{(1)} - \sqrt{10}\,[\mathbf{S}^{(1)} \times \mathbf{C}^{(2)}]^{(1)}.$$

The last expression follows by the techniques of Chapter 4 (cf. Judd [10], p. 86). The nuclear spin interaction (4.29)–(4.30) is responsible for additional hyperfine splitting.

REFERENCES

[1] H. Kopfermann, *Nuclear Moments*, Academic, New York (1958).
[2] N. F. Ramsey, *Nuclear Moments*, Wiley, New York (1953).
[3] H. G. Kuhn, *Atomic Spectra*, Academic, New York (1961).
[4] G. R. Gunther-Mohr, S. Geschwind, and C. H. Townes, *Phys. Rev.* **81**, 289 (1951).
[5] H. Casimir, *Physica* **7**, 169 (1940).
H. B. G. Casimir, *On the Interaction Between Atomic Nuclei and Electrons*, reprinted by W. H. Freeman, San Francisco (1963).
[6] R. D. Evans, *The Atomic Nucleus*, McGraw-Hill, New York (1955).
[7] H. D. Smythe, *Static and Dynamic Electricity*, McGraw-Hill, New York (1950), 2nd ed.
[8] C. P. Slichter, *Principles of Magnetic Resonance*, Harper and Row, New York (1963).
[9] E. Fermi, *Z. Physik* **60**, 320 (1930).
[10] B. R. Judd, *Operator Techniques in Atomic Spectroscopy*, McGraw-Hill, New York (1963).

8. The Hydrogen Atom

8.1 NONRELATIVISTIC WAVEFUNCTIONS

The Schrödinger equation for a point charge moving in a Coulomb field (Chapter 3),

$$\mathcal{H}^0\psi \equiv \left(\frac{p^2}{2m} + \frac{Ze^2}{r}\right)\psi = E^0\psi, \tag{1.1}$$

has the great advantage of being exactly soluble; we can obtain exact analytic solutions for the eigenfunctions and the eigenvalues (Sections 3.8–3.11). These solutions correctly provide quantized atomic radii and series of spectral lines. They do not, however, account for the observed finer details of the hydrogen spectrum. To explain this fine structure, we must add two corrections to the Hamiltonian $\mathcal{H}^0$: the relativistic mass increase and the magnetic moment (Chapter 7). We shall treat these terms as small perturbations, and write the corrected Hamiltonian as

$$\mathcal{H} = \mathcal{H}^0 + \mathcal{V} = \left(\frac{p^2}{2m_0} - \frac{Ze^2}{r}\right) - \frac{cp^4}{(2m_0c)^3} + \xi(r)\mathbf{S}\cdot\mathbf{L}, \tag{1.2}$$

The last two terms provide the perturbation $\mathcal{V}$. (Here, as in the following chapters, we refrain from emphasizing the operator character of **p**, **S**, and **L** by script typography.)

As we saw in Chapter 2, the eigenfunctions of $\mathcal{H}^0$,

$$\mathcal{H}^0\psi(nlm|\mathbf{r}) = E_n{}^0\psi(nlm|\mathbf{r}), \tag{1.3}$$

can be factored into a radial function $R_{nl}(r) = P_{nl}^{(r)}/r$ and a spherical harmonic $Y_{lm}(\theta, \phi)$:

$$\psi(nlm|\mathbf{r}) = R_{nl}(r)Y_{lm}(\theta, \phi). \tag{1.4}$$

The unperturbed eigenvalues consist of negative discrete energies for $n =$ integer (bound states),

$$E_n^{\,0} = -(hcR)\frac{Z^2}{n^2} \equiv -\left(\frac{e^2}{2a_0}\right)\frac{Z^2}{n^2} \equiv -\left(\frac{\alpha^2 mc^2}{2}\right)\frac{Z^2}{n^2}, \tag{1.5}$$

and a continuum of positive energies for $n = i\kappa$ (hyperbolic orbits).

Because $\mathcal{H}$ involves the spin operator $\mathbf{S}$, we must include a spin function as a factor in the solution. We shall take this function to be an eigenfunction of $\mathbf{S}^2$ and S_z for spin $\frac{1}{2}$; these spin functions χ_+ and χ_- are defined by the equations

$$\begin{aligned} \mathbf{S}^2\chi_\mu &= \tfrac{3}{4}\chi_\mu \\ S_z\chi_\mu &= \tfrac{1}{2}\mu\chi_\mu, \end{aligned} \tag{1.6}$$

where $\mu = +1, -1$ or simply $+, -$. Thus we express the eigenfunctions of $\mathcal{H}$ as a linear combination of the basis states

$$\varphi(nlm\mu\,|\,\mathbf{rs}) = R_{nl}(r)Y_l^m(\theta, \phi)\chi_\mu(\mathbf{s}), \tag{1.7}$$

which we will refer to as *hydrogenic orbitals*. They satisfy the same equation as $\psi(nlm\,|\,\mathbf{r})$:

$$\mathcal{H}^0\varphi(nlm\mu\,|\,\mathbf{rs}) = E_n^{\,0}\varphi(nlm\mu\,|\,\mathbf{rs}). \tag{1.8}$$

At times it is convenient to represent the spin functions as two-component column vectors,

$$\chi_+ = \begin{pmatrix}1\\0\end{pmatrix}, \qquad \chi_- = \begin{pmatrix}0\\1\end{pmatrix}, \tag{1.9}$$

and represent the spin operators S_x, S_y, S_z by the 2×2 Pauli matrices (Section 6.1). The eigenfunctions of $\mathbf{S}$ will then be two-component spinors,

$$\psi = \begin{pmatrix}\psi_a\\ \psi_b\end{pmatrix}. \tag{1.10}$$

However, we shall not require this explicit representation of the χ_μ in our treatment here.

The hydrogenic orbitals are degenerate wavefunctions, since the energy $E_n^{\,0}$ depends only on the principal quantum number n. For each value of n, the orbital angular-momentum quantum number l can take integral values ranging from zero to $n - 1$, a total of $n - 1$ possibilities. In turn, the magnetic quantum number m takes $2l + 1$ values for a given l, and finally, the spin projection μ takes two values for every m. The total degeneracy or statistical weight ϖ_n of an orbital is thus:

$$\varpi_n = \sum_l 2(2l + 1) = 2n^2. \tag{1.11}$$

The spin–orbit interaction removes part of this degeneracy. In fact we can see that the operator

$$\mathbf{S}\cdot\mathbf{L} = -S_{+1}L_{-1} + S_0L_0 - L_{-1}S_{+1} = \mathbf{L}\cdot\mathbf{S} \qquad (1.12)$$

transforms the orbital $\varphi(nlm\mu|\mathbf{rs})$, which is an eigenfunction of

$$\mathbf{L}^2,\ L_z,\ \mathbf{S}^2,\ S_z,$$

into a linear combination of eigenfunctions of $\mathbf{L}^2$ and $\mathbf{S}^2$ with different eigenvalues of L_z and S_z. The $\mathbf{S}\cdot\mathbf{L}$ operator does not commute with $L_z \equiv L_0$ and $S_z \equiv S_0$ although it does commute with $\mathbf{L}^2$ and $\mathbf{S}^2$. Thus it mixes states of different m and μ for the same l and s.

We can easily construct a linear combination of these degenerate orbitals for which $\mathbf{S}\cdot\mathbf{L}$ is diagonal. We first note that $\mathbf{S}\cdot\mathbf{L}$ commutes with the total angular momentum $\mathbf{J}$, defined as

$$\mathbf{J} = \mathbf{L} + \mathbf{S}. \qquad (1.13)$$

This vector equation is simply an abbreviation for three equations for components:

$$\begin{aligned} J_{+1} &= L_{+1} + S_{+1} \quad &\text{or} \quad J_x &= L_x + S_x, \\ J_0 &= L_0 + S_0 \quad &\text{or} \quad J_y &= L_y + S_y, \\ J_{-1} &= L_{-1} + S_{-1} \quad &\text{or} \quad J_z &= L_z + S_z. \end{aligned}$$

The asserted commutation property of $\mathbf{J}$ follows from the proof that

$$(S_xL_x + S_yL_y + S_zL_z)(L_x + S_x) = (L_x + S_x)(S_xL_x + S_yL_y + S_zL_z).$$

Both $\mathbf{J}^2$ and $J_z \equiv J_0$ as well as $\mathbf{L}^2$ and $\mathbf{S}^2$ commute with $\mathcal{H}^0$ and with the perturbation $\mathcal{V}$. Thus if we construct eigenfunctions of

$$\mathbf{L}^2,\ \mathbf{S}^2,\ \mathbf{J}^2,\ J_z,$$

with eigenvalues

$$l(l+1),\ \tfrac{3}{4},\ j(j+1),\ M,$$

then the perturbation $\mathcal{V}$ will be diagonal in l, j, and M. We can readily construct such a normalized eigenfunction, $\Phi(nljM|\mathbf{rs})$, by using the CG coefficients to couple $\mathbf{L}$ and $\mathbf{S}$:

$$\Phi(nljM|\mathbf{rs}) = \sum_{m\mu} (jM|lm, \tfrac{1}{2}\mu)\varphi(nlm\mu|\mathbf{rs}). \qquad (1.14)$$

Using the explicit form for these coefficients, we find, for $j = l + \frac{1}{2}$:

$$\Phi(nljM) = \left(\frac{l + M + \frac{1}{2}}{2l+1}\right)^{1/2} \varphi(nl, M - \tfrac{1}{2}, \tfrac{1}{2}) + \left(\frac{l - M + \frac{1}{2}}{2l+1}\right)^{1/2} \varphi(nl, M + \tfrac{1}{2} - \tfrac{1}{2}), \qquad (1.15)$$

and for $j = l - \frac{1}{2}$,

$$\Phi(nljM) = -\left(\frac{l - M + \frac{1}{2}}{2l + 1}\right)^{1/2} \varphi(nl, M - \tfrac{1}{2}, \tfrac{1}{2}) + \left(\frac{l + M + \frac{1}{2}}{2l + 1}\right)^{1/2} \varphi(nl, M + \tfrac{1}{2}, -\tfrac{1}{2}). \quad (1.16)$$

For example, the two $2p$ orbitals with $M = \frac{1}{2}$ are:

$$\Phi(2p\,\tfrac{3}{2}\,\tfrac{1}{2}) = R_{2p}\,\{\sqrt{\tfrac{2}{3}}\,Y_{10}\chi_+ + \sqrt{\tfrac{1}{3}}\,Y_{11}\chi_-\},$$

$$\Phi(2p\,\tfrac{1}{2}\,\tfrac{1}{2}) = R_{2p}\,\{-\sqrt{\tfrac{1}{3}}\,Y_{00}\chi_+ + \sqrt{\tfrac{2}{3}}\,Y_{11}\chi_-\},$$

The single $2s$ orbital with $M = \frac{1}{2}$ is

$$\Phi(2s\,\tfrac{1}{2}\,\tfrac{1}{2}) = R_{2s}\{Y_{00}\chi_+\}.$$

8.2 FINE STRUCTURE

Using the coupled $\Phi(nljM)$ functions, we can calculate the energy correction using first-order perturbation theory. Since $\mathcal{H}$ now has no matrix elements between degenerate functions, the first-order energy correction is simply the expectation value of the perturbation:

$$\begin{aligned} E(nljM) &\simeq E_n^{\,0} + \langle nljM|\mathcal{V}|nljM\rangle \\ &= E_n^{\,0} - \frac{c}{(2mc)^3}\langle p^4\rangle + g_s Z\beta^2 \left\langle\frac{\mathbf{S}\cdot\mathbf{L}}{r^3}\right\rangle \\ &\equiv E_n^{\,0} + \Delta E_{\text{rel}} + \Delta E_{\text{spin}}. \end{aligned} \quad (2.1)$$

To calculate the diagonal elements of the spin–orbit matrix it is easiest to express $\mathbf{S}\cdot\mathbf{L}$ in terms of $\mathbf{L}^2$ and $\mathbf{S}^2$, with

$$\mathbf{J}^2 = (\mathbf{S} + \mathbf{L})^2 = \mathbf{S}^2 + 2\mathbf{S}\cdot\mathbf{L} + \mathbf{L}^2. \quad (2.2)$$

The spin–orbit operator becomes

$$2\mathbf{S}\cdot\mathbf{L} = \mathbf{J}^2 - \mathbf{S}^2 - \mathbf{L}^2, \quad (2.3)$$

and the matrix elements are then (with $g_s = 2$):

$$\begin{aligned} \Delta E_{\text{spin}} &\equiv g_s Z\beta^2 \left\langle nljM\left|\frac{\mathbf{S}\cdot\mathbf{L}}{r^3}\right|nljM\right\rangle \\ &= Z\beta^2[j(j+1) - \tfrac{3}{4} - l(l+1)]\left\langle\frac{1}{r^3}\right\rangle. \end{aligned} \quad (2.4)$$

Specifically, we have

$$\begin{aligned} 2\langle\mathbf{S}\cdot\mathbf{L}\rangle &= -(l+1) \quad \text{for} \quad j = l - \tfrac{1}{2}, \\ 2\langle\mathbf{S}\cdot\mathbf{L}\rangle &= l \qquad\qquad \text{for} \quad j = l + \tfrac{1}{2}. \end{aligned} \quad (2.5)$$

Using the results of Chapter 3, we find

$$\left\langle \frac{1}{r^3} \right\rangle \equiv \int P_{nl} P_{nl} \frac{dr}{r^3} = \frac{Z^3}{a_0{}^3 n^3} \frac{1}{l(l+1)(l+\frac{1}{2})} . \tag{2.6}$$

Thus the energy shift that is caused by the spin–orbit interaction is, since $\beta = \frac{1}{2} e\alpha a_0$,

$$\begin{aligned} \Delta E_{\text{spin}} &= -\frac{\beta^2 Z^4}{a_0{}^3 n^3} \frac{\langle 2\mathbf{S}\cdot\mathbf{L}\rangle}{l(l+1)(l+\frac{1}{2})} \\ &= -E_n{}^0 \frac{\alpha^2 Z^2}{n} \begin{cases} +\dfrac{1}{l(2l+1)} & \text{for } j = l - \frac{1}{2} \\ +\dfrac{1}{(l+1)(2l+1)} & \text{for } j = l + \frac{1}{2}. \end{cases} \end{aligned} \tag{2.7}$$

(This energy shift is zero for s electrons, since $\langle \mathbf{S}\cdot\mathbf{L}\rangle = 0$ when $l = 0$.)

To find the relativistic mass correction we use (1.1) to write

$$\begin{aligned} -\frac{cp^4}{(2m_0c)^3} &= -\frac{1}{2m_0c^2}\left(\frac{p^2}{2m_0}\right)^2 = -\frac{1}{2m_0c^2}\left(\mathcal{H}^0 + \frac{Ze^2}{r}\right)^2 \\ &= -\frac{1}{2m_0c^2}(\mathcal{H}^0)^2 - \left(\frac{Ze^2}{m_0c^2}\right)\frac{\mathcal{H}^0}{r} - \left(\frac{Z^2e^4}{2m_0c^2}\right)\frac{1}{r^2} . \end{aligned} \tag{2.8}$$

The expectation value of this operator thus provides the correction

$$\begin{aligned} \Delta E_{\text{rel}} &\equiv -\left\langle nljm \left| \frac{cp^4}{(2mc)^3} \right| nljm \right\rangle \\ &= +\frac{(E_n{}^0)^2}{2mc^2} + \frac{Ze^2}{mc^2} E_n{}^0 \left\langle \frac{1}{r} \right\rangle + \frac{Z^2e^4}{2mc^2} \left\langle \frac{1}{r^2} \right\rangle . \end{aligned} \tag{2.9}$$

The expectation values are:

$$\left\langle \frac{1}{r} \right\rangle \equiv \int P_{nl} P_{nl} \frac{dr}{r} = \frac{Z}{a_0} \frac{1}{n^2} , \tag{2.10}$$

$$\left\langle \frac{1}{r^2} \right\rangle \equiv \int P_{nl} P_{nl} \frac{dr}{r^2} = \frac{Z^2}{a_0{}^2} \frac{1}{n^3(l+\frac{1}{2})} . \tag{2.11}$$

Thus the relativistic mass correction becomes, since $e^2/a_0mc^2 = \alpha^2$,

$$\Delta E_{\text{rel}} = E_n{}^0(\alpha^2 Z^2)\left[-\frac{1}{4n^2} + \frac{1}{n^2} - \frac{1}{n(l+\frac{1}{2})} \right] . \tag{2.12}$$

Combining (2.7) and (2.12) and ignoring the small anomalous magnetic moment, we obtain

$$\Delta E_{\text{spin}} + \Delta E_{\text{rel}}$$
$$= E_n{}^0 \frac{\alpha^2 Z^2}{n} \left\{ \frac{1}{(l+\frac{1}{2})} - \frac{3}{4n} + \frac{1}{(2l+1)} \right\} \qquad \text{for} \quad j = l - \tfrac{1}{2}$$
$$= E_n{}^0 \frac{\alpha^2 Z^2}{n} \left\{ \frac{1}{(l+\frac{1}{2})} - \frac{3}{4n} - \frac{1}{(l+1)(2l+1)} \right\} \qquad \text{for} \quad j = l + \tfrac{1}{2}, \quad (2.13)$$

or, in terms of the j value,

$$\Delta E_{\text{spin}} + \Delta E_{\text{rel}} = E_n{}^0 \frac{\alpha^2 Z^2}{n} \left\{ \frac{1}{j+\frac{1}{2}} - \frac{3}{4n} \right\}. \qquad (2.14)$$

Adding these corrections to the unperturbed energy $E_n{}^0$, we obtain finally the approximate energy of the hydrogen atom,

$$E(nj) = E_n{}^0 + \Delta E_{\text{spin}} + \Delta E_{\text{rel}}$$
$$= -(hcR)\frac{Z^2}{n^2}\left[1 + \frac{\alpha^2 Z^2}{n}\left(\frac{1}{j+\frac{1}{2}} - \frac{3}{4n}\right)\right]. \qquad (2.15)$$

We see that the corrections to $E_n{}^0$ are smaller than $E_n{}^0$ by roughly $\alpha^2 = 5.32 \times 10^{-5}$, so that we may expect the perturbation-theory approach to be fairly accurate. Equation (2.15) was first obtained by Sommerfeld in 1916 [1] from an examination of relativistic motion in the Bohr atom. Sommerfeld employed a quantum number $k = j + \frac{1}{2}$. However, his derivation omitted the electron spin, and so his result must be considered fortuitous.

To the present approximation, the energy depends on n and j but not on l (or M): the $2p_{1/2}$ orbital has the same energy as the $2s_{1/2}$ orbital. For a given n, the level with smallest j value lies lowest in energy. The interval between adjacent levels with the same n is:

$$E(nj+1) - E(nj) = (hcR)\alpha^2 \frac{Z^4}{n^3} \frac{1}{(j+\frac{1}{2})(j+\frac{3}{2})} = \frac{|E_n{}^0|\alpha^2 Z^2}{n(j+\frac{1}{2})(j+\frac{3}{2})}. \qquad (2.16)$$

The spacing therefore diminishes rapidly as one proceeds to higher principal quantum numbers.

A comment on units may be helpful. The preceding equations employ the Rydberg unit hcR, or an energy of 13.6054 eV. A common alternative, the atomic or Hartree units, expresses hcR as $e^2/2a_0$. With e the unit of charge ($e = 1$) a_0 the unit of length ($a_0 = 1$), the unit of energy is then 27.211 eV.

REFERENCE

[1] A. Sommerfeld, *Ann. d. Physik* **51,** 1 (1916).

8.3 X-RAY AND ALKALI TERMS

As we have seen in Chapters 1 and 2, the energy structure of alkali atoms, as well as x-ray terms, exhibit a marked similarity to the energy levels of hydrogen. We have interpreted this similarity as an implication that the energy diagrams gave the energy levels of a single active electron. We can now make that interpretation more precise with the aid of (2.15). Suppose that an electron moves in the Coulomb field of an effective charge Z^*,

$$Z^* = Z - \sigma.$$

The effective charge is less than the actual nuclear charge Z by an amount σ, the *screening parameter*. This screening arises from the presence of additional electrons, whose motion acts to shield any given electron from the full charge of the nucleus. We shall assume that this screening is the only effect of the inactive (or *spectator*) electrons on the motion of the active electron. Since low angular-momentum orbitals penetrate more deeply, they are screened less fully than higher angular-momentum orbitals. The screening parameters will therefore vary with l:

$$\sigma_s < \sigma_p < \sigma_d < \sigma_f \cdots \sigma_e \cdots.$$

Equation 2.15 provides a description of such single-particle motion if we introduce Z^* in place of Z:

$$E(nlj) = -(hcR)\left[\frac{(Z - \sigma_l)^2}{n^2} + \alpha^2 \frac{(Z - \sigma_l)^4}{n^3}\left(\frac{1}{j + \frac{1}{2}} - \frac{3}{4n}\right)\right]. \quad (3.1)$$

For example, this equation gives the energy levels for $n = 2$ as

$$E(2s_{1/2}) = -\tfrac{1}{4}(hcR)[(Z - \sigma_s)^2 + \tfrac{5}{16}\alpha^2(Z - \sigma_s)^4],$$
$$E(2p_{1/2}) = -\tfrac{1}{4}(hcR)[(Z - \sigma_p)^2 + \tfrac{5}{16}\alpha^2(Z - \sigma_p)^4],$$
$$E(2p_{1/2}) = -\tfrac{1}{4}(hcR)[(Z - \sigma_p)^2 + \tfrac{1}{16}\alpha^2(Z - \sigma_p)^4].$$

For hydrogen, the screening parameters are all zero, and the energies are:

$$E(2s_{1/2}) = -\tfrac{1}{4}(hcR)(1 + \tfrac{5}{16}\alpha^2),$$
$$E(2p_{1/2}) = -\tfrac{1}{4}(hcR)(1 + \tfrac{5}{16}\alpha^2),$$
$$E(2p_{3/2}) = -\tfrac{1}{4}(hcR)(1 + \tfrac{1}{16}\alpha^2).$$

Thus the $2s_{1/2}$ and $2p_{1/2}$ are degenerate, and the $2p_{3/2}$ lies higher.

A similar result applies if Z is very large and σ_l is small, as for the x-ray spectra of heavy elements. Then one has the approximations

$$E(2s_{1/2}) \simeq -\tfrac{1}{4}(hcR)Z^2(1 - 2Z\sigma_s + \tfrac{5}{16}\alpha^2Z^2),$$
$$E(2p_{1/2}) \simeq -\tfrac{1}{4}(hcR)Z^2(1 - 2Z\sigma_p + \tfrac{5}{16}\alpha^2Z^2),$$
$$E(2p_{3/2}) \simeq -\tfrac{1}{4}(hcR)Z^2(1 - 2Z\sigma_p + \tfrac{1}{16}\alpha^2Z^2).$$

With large Z, the spacing between $2s_{1/2}$ and $2p_{1/2}$ is much less than the spacing between $2p_{1/2}$ and $2p_{3/2}$, and the energy structure resembles that of hydrogen.

On the other hand, for light elements, $(Z - \sigma_l)$ is small, and the $2p_{1/2}$ and $2p_{3/2}$ levels lie close together:

$$E(2s_{1/2}) \simeq -\tfrac{1}{4}(hcR)(Z - \sigma_s)^2,$$
$$E(2p_{1/2}) \simeq -\tfrac{1}{4}(hcR)(Z - \sigma_p)^2[1 + \tfrac{5}{16}\alpha^2(Z - \sigma_p)^2],$$
$$E(2p_{3/2}) \simeq -\tfrac{1}{4}(hcR)(Z - \sigma_p)^2[1 + \tfrac{1}{16}\alpha^2(Z - \sigma_p)^2].$$

As one traces the spacings of these three levels through the periodic system, a gradual change can indeed be observed, in agreement with these simple calculations. Figure 8.1 illustrates this effect.

If we take the difference between $E(nlj)$ and $E(nl'j)$ (the x-ray *screening doublets*), we obtain

$$E(nlj) - E(nl'j) \simeq -(hcR)\left[\frac{(Z - \sigma_l)^2}{n^2} - \frac{(Z - \sigma_l')^2}{n^2}\right]$$
$$= -\frac{(hcR)}{n^2}[2Z(\sigma_l - \sigma_l') + (\sigma_l)^2 - (\sigma_l')^2]. \qquad (3.2)$$

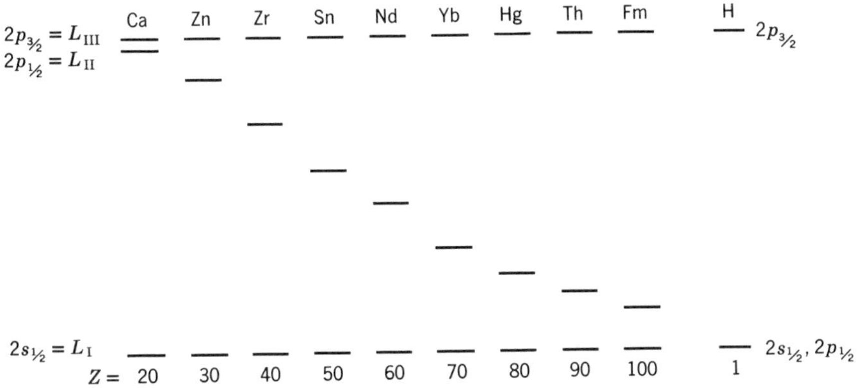

Fig. 8.1 Relative spacing of $2s$ and $2p$ levels, showing the change from screening doublets (Ca) to spin doublets (Fm) with increasing nuclear charge Z.

This formula describes the splitting of $2s_{1/2}$ and $2p_{1/2}$, for example. A simpler expression is obtained from the square root of (4.1):

$$\left(\frac{E(nlj)}{hcR}\right)^{1/2} - \left(\frac{E(nl'j)}{hcR}\right)^{1/2} \simeq \frac{\sigma_l - \sigma_l'}{n}. \tag{3.3}$$

Equation 3.3 is a statement of the fact that on a Bohr–Coster diagram, the spacing between screening doublets remains constant.

If, on the other hand, we take the difference between $E(nlj)$ and $E(nlj')$ (the *spin doublets* or *relativity doublets*) we obtain:

$$\begin{aligned} E(nlj) - E(nlj') &= -(hcR)\frac{\alpha^2(Z-\sigma_l)^4}{n^3}\left[\frac{1}{l-\frac{1}{2}+\frac{1}{2}} - \frac{1}{l+\frac{1}{2}+\frac{1}{2}}\right] \\ &= -(hcR)\frac{\alpha^2(Z-\sigma_l)^4}{n^3 l(l+1)}. \end{aligned} \tag{3.4}$$

This expression describes the splitting of $2p_{1/2}$ and $2p_{3/2}$, for example.

8.4 RADIATIVE CORRECTIONS

Equation 3.15 gives a description of the energy levels of hydrogen to an accuracy of roughly $\alpha^2 Z^2$. However, further details appear as one examines the structure more closely. The theory then must include dependence on higher powers of αZ. For example, if we retain the anomalous magnetic moment in computing $\Delta E_{\text{rel}} + \Delta E_{\text{spin}}$, we obtain an energy shift that depends upon l as well as upon j:

$$\begin{aligned} E(nlj) &= E_n^0\left\{1 + \frac{\alpha^2 Z^2}{n}\left(\frac{1}{j+\frac{1}{2}} - \frac{3}{4n} - \delta\frac{C_{lj}}{2l+1}\right)\right\}, \quad l \neq 0, \\ g_s &= 2(1+\delta) \\ C_{lj} &= -l^{-1} \qquad \text{for} \quad j = l + \tfrac{1}{2}, \\ C_{lj} &= (l+1)^{-1} \quad \text{for} \quad j = l + \tfrac{1}{2}. \end{aligned} \tag{4.1}$$

Thus the larger l level lies slightly lower in energy than the smaller l level (the $l = 0$ levels are not affected by this shift). The splitting of these levels is roughly 0.2% the spacing between adjacent j levels.

A slightly larger shift occurs because of the interaction of the electron with the electromagnetic field. The influence of such interactions is discussed in several texts on quantum electrodynamics, which the reader should consult for details. (E.g., Power [1], Akhiezer and Berestetskii [2], or Bethe and Salpeter [3].) In the first approximation this interaction can be written as

$$\mathcal{V}_{\text{rad}} = +\frac{\alpha^3 a_0{}^2}{3\pi} C\,\nabla^2\left(\frac{Ze^2}{r}\right) = \frac{\alpha^3}{3\pi}\frac{Ze^2}{a_0} C4\pi\delta(\mathbf{r}), \tag{4.2}$$

where

$$C \equiv \left(\ln\frac{mc^2}{2k_0} + \frac{19}{30}\right),$$

and k_0 is an average excitation energy. Because the interaction occurs only at the nucleus [the three-dimensional delta function $\delta(\mathbf{r})$ picks out this region], and only the $l = 0$ wavefunctions are nonzero there (because $R_{nl} \to r_l$ as $r \to 0$), the interaction affects only the $l = 0$ energy levels. Then, since

$$R_{n0}(0)\,Y_{00}(\theta, \phi) = \frac{4Z^3}{n^3}\frac{1}{\sqrt{4\pi}},$$

the energy shift caused by this interaction is

$$\begin{aligned}\Delta E_{\text{rad}} &= \frac{\alpha^3}{3\pi} C\frac{Ze^2}{a_0}\langle 4\pi\delta(\mathbf{r})\rangle,\\ &= \frac{\alpha^3}{3\pi} C\frac{Ze^2}{a_0} 4\pi\,|\psi_{l=0}(r = 0)|^2,\\ &= \frac{\alpha^3}{3\pi} C\frac{4Z^4e^2}{a_0 n^3} = -\frac{Z^4}{n}\frac{8\alpha^3 C}{3\pi}E_n{}^0.\end{aligned} \tag{4.3}$$

Thus the radiative correction raises the s levels relative to the p levels. This energy shift was first measured by Lamb and Retherford [4] in 1947, and has become known as the *Lamb shift*. For hydrogen, the observed splitting [4] of the $2^2s_{1/2}$ levels and $2^2p_{1/2}$ levels is 1057.77 Mc/sec $= \Delta E_{\text{Lamb}}/h$.

The preceding approach is based on perturbations of the nonrelativistic Hamiltonian. The proper relativistic approach, based on the Dirac equation, is discussed in detail by Dirac [5] and Bethe and Salpeter [3]. The Dirac equation has the eigenvalues (with $2hcR_\infty = \alpha^2 mc^2$)

$$E^{\text{D}}(nj) = \frac{2}{\alpha^2} hcR_\infty\left(\frac{M}{M + m}\right) \times\left\{\left[\frac{(\alpha Z)}{n - j - \frac{1}{2} + \sqrt{(j + \frac{1}{2})^2 - (\alpha Z)^2}} + 1\right]^{-1/2} - 1\right\}. \tag{4.4}$$

For precise calculations this energy must still be corrected for numerous slight effects, such as the anomalous magnetic moment, the interaction with the radiation field, and the size, shape, and motion of the nucleus:

$$E(nlj) = E^{\text{D}}(nj) + \Delta E(nlj).$$

The corrections, $\Delta E(nlj)$, take the form of a power series in (αZ) and $\log(1/\alpha Z)$. J. D. Garcia and J. E. Mack [6] have collected the correction terms [7] through $(\alpha Z)^6$ and computed energy levels and wavelengths for hydrogen-like spectra through Ca XX. Their formula may be written, for $l = 0$, as

$$\begin{aligned}\Delta E(n0j) = \frac{2hcR_\infty}{\alpha^2}\frac{(\alpha Z)^4}{n^3}\Bigg\{&-\frac{1}{8n}\left(\frac{m}{M}\right)+\frac{2}{3}\frac{(r_{\text{nucl}})^2}{(\alpha a_0)^2}\\ &+\frac{4\alpha}{3\pi}\left(1-\frac{m}{M}\right)^3\left[A_0+\ln\left(\frac{Z^2}{K_0}\right)+\ln\left(\frac{1}{\alpha Z}\right)^2\right]\\ &+\frac{(\alpha Z)}{3\pi}\left(\frac{m}{M}\right)\left[A_1+8\ln\left(\frac{Z^2}{K_0}\right)+\ln\left(\frac{1}{\alpha Z}\right)^2\right]\\ &+\frac{(\alpha Z)^2}{3\pi}\left(1-\frac{m}{M}\right)^3\left[A_2+A_4\ln\left(\frac{1}{\alpha Z}\right)^2-3\ln^2\left(\frac{1}{\alpha Z}\right)^2\right]\Bigg\},\end{aligned} \tag{4.5a}$$

and for $l \neq 0$ their formula may be written as

$$\begin{aligned}\Delta E(nlj) = \frac{2hcR_\infty}{\alpha^2}\frac{(\alpha Z)^4}{n^3}\Bigg\{&-\frac{1}{8n}\left(\frac{m}{M}\right)\\ &+\frac{4\alpha}{3\pi}\left(1-\frac{m}{M}\right)^3\left[B_1-\ln\left(\frac{Z^2}{K_0}\right)\right]\\ &+\frac{(\alpha Z)}{3\pi}\left(\frac{m}{M}\right)\left[B_2-8\ln\left(\frac{Z^2}{K_0}\right)\right]\\ &+\frac{(\alpha Z)^2}{3\pi}\left(1-\frac{m}{M}\right)^3\left[B_3\ln\left(\frac{1}{\alpha Z}\right)^2\right]\Bigg\}.\end{aligned} \tag{4.5b}$$

Garcia and Mack discuss the parameters A_0, A_1, A_2, A_4, B_1, B_2, B_3, K_0, and r_{nucl}. Edlén [8] has used these formulas to compute wavelengths of the Lyman series, in the form

$$\lambda = \lambda_0 - \Delta\lambda_{\text{Dirac}} + \Delta\lambda_{\text{Lamb}}, \tag{4.6}$$

where

$$\lambda_0 = \left[R_M Z^2\left(1-\frac{1}{n^2}\right)\right]^{-1}, \tag{4.7}$$

$$\Delta\lambda_{\text{Dirac}} = \frac{\alpha^2}{4R_M}\frac{n^4-8n/3+3}{(n^2-1)^2}, \tag{4.8}$$

$$\begin{aligned}\Delta\lambda_{\text{Lamb}} = {}&\frac{8\alpha^3}{3\pi R_\infty}\frac{n^4}{(n^2-1)^2}\left(1-\frac{m}{M}\right)\\ &\times[7.489-2\ln Z+0.0526Z-(\alpha Z)^2(3\ln^2 Z-21.6\ln Z+52.7)].\end{aligned} \tag{4.9}$$

8.5 PARITY

It is often useful to classify wavefunctions according to their inversion symmetry or *parity*. More precisely, the parity operator $\mathcal{P}$ replaces x, y, z by $-x, -y, -z$ (or r, θ, ϕ by $r, \theta - \pi, \phi - \pi$). Since two operations by $\mathcal{P}$ restore the arguments, the operator $\mathcal{P}$ must have eigenvalues $+1$ and -1, corresponding to *even* (F_e) or *odd* functions (F_0):

$$\mathcal{P}F_e(x, y, z) = F_e(-x, -y, -z) = +F_e(x, y, z), \qquad \mathcal{P}^2F_e = F_e, \tag{5.1a}$$

$$\mathcal{P}F_0(x, y, z) = F_0(-x, -y, -z) = -F_0(x, y, z), \qquad \mathcal{P}^2F_0 = F_0. \tag{5.1b}$$

That is, an eigenstate Ψ of the operator $\mathcal{P}$ satisfies the eigenvalue equation:

$$\mathcal{P}\Psi = \pi\Psi. \tag{5.2}$$

We shall refer to the eigenvalue π as the parity of Ψ, with the convention that:

for $\pi = +1$, Ψ has even parity;

for $\pi = -1$, Ψ has odd parity.

Not all functions have well-defined parities, but we can always split a function F into a part F_e with even-parity and a part F_0 with odd-parity,

$$F = F_e + F_0, \tag{5.3}$$

by setting

$$F_e(x, y, z) = \tfrac{1}{2}[F(x, y, z) + F(-x, -y, -z)], \tag{5.4a}$$

$$F_0(x, y, z) = \tfrac{1}{2}[F(x, y, z) - F(-x, -y, -z)]. \tag{5.4b}$$

The parity of a product function is the product of the individual parities,

$$\mathcal{P}F_1F_2 = \pi_1\pi_2F_1F_2, \tag{5.5}$$

since the parity operator inverts all coordinates:

$$\mathcal{P}F_1(x_1, y_1, z_1)F_2(x_2, y_2, z_2) = F_1(-x_1, -y_1, -z_1)F_2(-x_2, -y_2, -z_2). \tag{5.6}$$

The spherical harmonics have well-defined parity, as we saw in Section 3.9:

$$\mathcal{P}Y_{lm}(\theta, \phi) = Y_{lm}(\theta - \pi, \phi - \pi) = (-1)^l Y_{lm}(\theta, \phi). \tag{5.7}$$

The spherical harmonics are eigenstates of parity. Y_{lm} has even parity if l is an even integer; it has odd parity if l is an odd integer.

The radial factor of a wavefunction is unaffected by coordinate inversion,

$$\mathcal{P}F(r) = F(r). \tag{5.8}$$

However, it is useful to abbreviate the coordinates r, θ, ϕ as simply $\mathbf{r}$; the action of $\mathcal{P}$ is then written:

$$\mathcal{P}F(\mathbf{r}) = F(-\mathbf{r}). \tag{5.9}$$

The parity operator has no effect on spin variables:

$$\mathcal{P}F(\mathbf{s}) = F(\mathbf{s}). \tag{5.10}$$

Thus electron orbitals have well-defined parity, fixed by the quantum number l:

$$\mathcal{P}\varphi(nlm\mu|\,\mathbf{rs}) = (-1)^l\varphi(nlm\mu|\,\mathbf{rs}). \tag{5.11}$$

When the Hamiltonian $\mathcal{H}$ depends only on scalar quantities—quantities unchanged by inversion—$\mathcal{H}$ commutes with $\mathcal{P}$:

$$[\mathcal{H}, \mathcal{P}] = 0. \tag{5.12}$$

More generally, an operator $\mathcal{B}$ that depends on position, momentum, angular momentum, and spin satisfies the equation

$$\mathcal{P}\mathcal{B}(\mathbf{r}, \mathbf{p}, \mathbf{L}, \mathbf{s}) = \mathcal{B}(-\mathbf{r}, -\mathbf{p}, \mathbf{L}, \mathbf{s}). \tag{5.13}$$

Therefore operators of the form

$$\mathcal{B} = \mathbf{r}\cdot\mathbf{r}, \qquad \mathcal{B} = \mathbf{r}\times\mathbf{p}, \qquad \mathcal{B} = \mathbf{L}\cdot\mathbf{s}, \qquad \mathcal{B} = \mathbf{L}\cdot\mathbf{L}, \qquad \text{etc.},$$

will commute with the parity operator. Perturbations of this form will not mix states having different parity.

REFERENCES

[1] E. A. Power, *Introductory Quantum Electrodynamics*, Longmans, Green, London (1964).

[2] A. I. Akhiezer and V. B. Berestetskii, *Quantum Electrodynamics*, Interscience, New York (1965).

[3] H. Bethe and E. Salpeter, *Quantum Mechanics of One- and Two-Electron Atoms*, Academic, New York (1957).

[4] W. E. Lamb, Jr., and R. C. Retherford, *Phys. Rev.* **79,** 549 (1950); **81,** 222 (1951); **86,** 1014 (1952); W. E. Lamb, Jr., *ibid.* **85,** 259 (1952); S. Triebwasser, E. S. Dayhoff, and W. E. Lamb, Jr., *ibid.* **89,** 98 (1953); E. S. Dayhoff, S. Triebwasser, and W. E. Lamb, Jr., *ibid.*, p. 106.

[5] P. A. M. Dirac, *The Principles of Quantum Mechanics*, Oxford University Press, New York (1958), 4th ed.

[6] J. D. Garcia and J. E. Mack, *J. Opt. Soc. Am.* **55,** 654 (1965).

[7] A. J. Layzer, *J. Math. Phys.* **2,** 292 and 308 (1961).
G. W. Erickson and D. R. Yennie, *Ann. Phys.* (*N.Y.*) **35,** 271 (1965).

[8] B. Edlén, *Arkiv Fysik* **31,** 509 (1966); B. Edlén and L. A. Svensson, *ibid.* **28,** 427 (1964).

9. Complex Atoms

9.1 THE INDEPENDENT-PARTICLE MODEL

The electronic structure of isolated atoms (ideally, atoms free from the influence of neighboring atoms or external fields) is largely determined by electrostatic interactions. The Hamiltonian for an N-electron atom in this approximation,

$$\mathcal{H}^1 = \mathcal{H}^0 + \mathcal{V}^0, \tag{1.1}$$

is a sum of single-particle operators,

$$\mathcal{H}^0 \equiv \sum_{i=1}^{N}\left[\frac{p^2(i)}{2m} - \frac{Ze^2}{r_i}\right] \equiv \sum_i \mathfrak{h}(i), \tag{1.2}$$

for the motion of each electron in the Coulomb field of the nucleus, plus a sum of two-electron operators,

$$\mathcal{V}^0 = \sum_{i=1}^{j}\sum_{j=2}^{N}\frac{e^2}{|r_i - r_j|} \equiv \sum_{i<j}\frac{e^2}{r_{ij}}, \tag{1.3}$$

for the electrostatic repulsion between the electrons. Our goal is to obtain approximate eigenfunctions of $\mathcal{H}^1$; that is, functions for which the matrix of $\mathcal{H}^1$ is approximately diagonal.

Since $\mathcal{H}^0$ is simply the sum of N identical single-particle terms $\mathfrak{h}(i)$, we can easily construct eigenfunctions of $\mathcal{H}^0$ from eigenfunctions of $\mathfrak{h}(i)$. For suppose $\varphi(a|1)$, $\varphi(b|1)$, . . . are a set of eigenfunctions of $\mathfrak{h}(1)$:

$$\mathfrak{h}(1)\varphi(a|1) = \varepsilon_a\varphi(a|1) \tag{1.4}$$

(here a stands for some appropriate set of four quantum numbers, and 1 denotes the position and spin of the first electron). Then a *simple product function*

$$\Phi(ab\cdots k|12\cdots N) \equiv \phi(a|1)\phi(b|2)\cdots\phi(k|N) \tag{1.5}$$

is an eigenfunction of $\mathcal{H}^0$,

$$\mathcal{H}^0\Phi(ab\cdots k|12\cdots N) = [\varepsilon_a + \varepsilon_b + \cdots + \varepsilon_k]\Phi(ab\cdots k|12\cdots N), \tag{1.6}$$

with the eigenvalue

$$E^0 = \varepsilon_a + \varepsilon_b + \cdots + \varepsilon_k. \tag{1.7}$$

The operator $h(1)$ defined by (1.2) is just the nonrelativistic Hamiltonian for a hydrogen electron. The normalized eigenfunctions of $h(1)$ are

$$\varphi^{\mathrm{H}}(a|1) \equiv \varphi^{\mathrm{H}}(nlm\mu|\mathbf{r}_1\mathbf{s}_1) = R_{nl}{}^{\mathrm{H}}(r_1)Y_{lm}(\theta_1\phi_1)\chi_\mu(\mathbf{s}_1), \tag{1.8}$$

corresponding to the eigenvalues

$$\varepsilon_n = -\left(\frac{e^2}{2a_0}\right)\frac{Z^2}{n^2} \equiv -\left(\frac{\alpha^2mc^2}{2}\right)\frac{Z^2}{n^2} = -(hcR_\infty)\frac{Z^2}{n^2}. \tag{1.9}$$

(The superscript H signifies a hydrogenic orbital.)

Physically, a product function corresponds to an atom in which each electron moves in a well-defined orbital. The position of one electron is not correlated with the position of any other electron. More precisely, the probability of finding a given electron in a volume element depends only on the location of the volume element, not on the other electron orbitals.

Because of the interelectron Coulomb repulsion $\mathcal{V}^0$, the simple product eigenfunctions (1.5) will not be eigenfunctions of the approximate Hamiltonian $\mathcal{H}^1$; the operator $\mathcal{V}^0$ will mix the product functions. However, most conventional approaches to the theory of complex atoms presume that one can approximate any N-electron wavefunction ψ satisfactorily by some suitably chosen linear combination of simple product functions (though not necessarily hydrogenic functions). That is, we assume that we can write an approximate wavefunction ψ as

$$\psi = \sum c(ab\cdots k, 12\cdots N)\Phi(ab\cdots k|12\cdots N), \tag{1.10}$$

using the products defined by (1.5). Our task is then to determine the expansion coefficients $c(ab\cdots k, 12\cdots N)$ and the orbitals $\varphi(a|1)$, etc. This is not, in general, a simple job, because the interaction $\mathcal{V}^0$ is by no means a small perturbation on $\mathcal{H}^0$.

From our examination of the energy structure of simple atoms in Chapter 2, we inferred that electrons often seem to move in well-defined orbitals. This implies that the electrons move independently to some extent. But the field in which they move is not simply the Coulomb field of the nucleus. Each electron must also move under the average influence of all the other electrons.

One simple way to approach this problem is to introduce a new length scale R,

$$r = \frac{R}{Z}, \tag{1.11}$$

where Z is the nuclear charge. That is, we measure distances in units $a_0/Z \sim (0.5/Z) \times 10^{-8}$ cm. The momentum is similarly replaced by $p = P/Z$, and the Hamiltonian of (1.1)–(1.3) reads

$$\begin{aligned} \mathcal{H} &= Z^2\left\{\sum_i\left[\frac{P^2(i)}{2m} - \frac{e^2}{R(i)}\right] + \frac{1}{Z}\sum_{i<j}\frac{e^2}{R_{ij}}\right\}. \\ &= Z^2\left\{\mathcal{H}^0 + \frac{1}{Z}\mathcal{V}^0\right\} \end{aligned} \tag{1.12}$$

If Z is reasonably large, (1.12) offers the possibility of using perturbation theory: we express the energy and the wavefunction as a power series in the small parameter Z^{-1}. In this approach, commonly called the *Z expansion*, we deal with N-electron functions that are products of hydrogenic orbitals, and zero-order energies that are sums of N hydrogenic energies:

$$E^0 = \left(\frac{e^2}{2a_0}\right)Z^2\left[\frac{1}{n_a^{\,2}} + \frac{1}{n_b^{\,2}} + \cdots + \frac{1}{n_k^{\,2}}\right]. \tag{1.13}$$

The Z expansion has been developed extensively by D. Layzer and his co-workers [1]. Horák [2] has written a recent review which provides reference to numerous other contributors.

Another approach accounts for the influence of the other electrons on the ith electron by introducing an effective potential $u(i)$ and a single-particle Hamiltonian,

$$\mathfrak{h}_{\text{eff}}(i) = \frac{p^2(i)}{2m} + u(i), \tag{1.14}$$

for each electron. Using the effective Hamiltonian

$$\mathcal{H}^0_{\text{eff}} = \sum \mathfrak{h}_{\text{eff}}(i),$$

we can write the Hamiltonian of (1.1)–(1.3) as

$$\begin{aligned} \mathcal{H} &= \mathcal{H}^0_{\text{eff}} + \sum_i\left\{\sum_j\frac{e^2}{r_{ij}} - \left[u(i) + \frac{Ze^2}{r_i}\right]\right\} \\ &\equiv \mathcal{H}^0_{\text{eff}} + \mathcal{V}^0_{\text{eff}}. \end{aligned} \tag{1.15}$$

We want the effective potentials to make $\mathcal{V}^0_{\text{eff}}$ a small perturbation on $\mathcal{H}^0_{\text{eff}}$. Knowing the $u(i)$, we can then, in principle, obtain a set of eigenfunctions of $\mathfrak{h}_{\text{eff}}(i)$, and so construct simple product eigenfunctions of $\mathcal{H}^0_{\text{eff}}$. The most common approach has been to assume that $u(i)$ is a function of r_i alone.

This leads to the *central field approximation* [3, 4]. Under this assumption, $\mathfrak{h}_{\text{eff}}(i)$ has eigenfunctions of the form

$$\varphi(a|i) \equiv \varphi(nlm\mu|\mathbf{r}_i\mathbf{s}_i) = R_{nl}(r_i)Y_{lm}(\theta_i\phi_i)\chi_\mu(\mathbf{s}_i) \equiv r_i^{-1}P_{nl}(r_i)Y_{lm}(\theta_i\phi_i)\chi_\mu(\mathbf{s}_i) \tag{1.16}$$

with eigenvalues

$$\varepsilon_a \equiv \varepsilon_{nl}. \tag{1.17}$$

These differ from hydrogenic orbitals only in the radial factor $R_{nl}(r)$ and in the significance of the quantum number n. The zero-order energies have the form

$$E^0 = \varepsilon_{n_a l_a} + \varepsilon_{n_b l_b} + \cdots + \varepsilon_{n_k l_k}. \tag{1.18}$$

We should remark that product functions of the type given by (1.16) are not the only useful basis functions. For example, Hylleraas [5] introduced the variables

$$s = r_1 + r_2 \qquad t = -r_1 + r_2 \qquad u = r_{12} \equiv |\mathbf{r}_1 - \mathbf{r}_2|$$

and Pekeris [6] used the variables

$$\begin{aligned} x &= \tfrac{1}{2}(u - t) = \tfrac{1}{2}(r_{12} + r_1 - r_2) \\ y &= \tfrac{1}{2}(u + t) = \tfrac{1}{2}(r_{12} - r_1 + r_2) \\ z &= r_1 + r_2 - r_{12}. \end{aligned}$$

Wavefunctions involving these variables have given excellent results for two-electron atoms, and they offer promise for complex atoms, since they explicitly include the correlation of electrons. However, for simplicity we confine our discussion to separable functions. (Primas [7] discusses non-separable functions.)

The independent-particle model [8,9,10] underlies most theoretical studies of complex atoms, and we use this model exclusively in this book. The appellation "independent-particle" does not mean that the theory does not permit correlations between electrons. It simply means that the basic building blocks for all wavefunctions are product functions,

$$\Phi(ab\cdots k|12\cdots n) \equiv \varphi(a|1)\varphi(b|2)\cdots\varphi(k|N).$$

The orbitals are taken as separable functions,

$$\varphi(nlm\mu|i) = r_i^{-1}P_{nl}(r_i)Y_{lm}(\Omega_i)\chi_\mu(\mathbf{s}_i),$$

but the radial functions $P_{nl}(r)$ need not be specified at the outset of an investigation. One of the tasks of any theory of complex atoms is to specify the $P_{nl}(r)$, or at least to provide an algorithm for calculating them.

REFERENCES

[1] D. Layzer, *Monthly Notices, Roy. Astron. Soc.* **114,** 692 (1954); *Astrophys. J.* **121,** 771 (1955); *ibid.* **122,** 351 (1955); *Ann. Phys.* **8,** 27 (1959); D. Layzer and J. Bahcall, *Ann. Phys.* **17,** 177 (1962); D. Layzer, *Phys. Rev.* **132,** 735 (1963); D. Layzer, Z. Horák, M. N. Lewis, and D. P. Thompson, *Ann. Phys.* **20,** 101 (1964).
[2] Z. Horák, in *Modern Quantum Chemistry*, O. Sinanoğlu, ed., Academic, New York (1965), vol. 2, p. 7.
[3] D. R. Hartree, *Proc. Camb. Phil. Soc.* **24,** 89 (1928).
[4] E. U. Condon and G. H. Shortley, *The Theory of Atomic Spectra,* Cambridge University Press, Cambridge, England (1935), chap. 14.
[5] E. A. Hylleraas, *Z. Physik* **54,** 347 (1929); *Advances in Quantum Chemistry* **1,** 1 (1964).
[6] C. L. Pekeris, *Phys. Rev.* **112,** 1649 (1958); **115,** 1216 (1959); **126,** 143 (1962); **126,** 1470 (1962).
[7] H. Primas, *Advances in Quantum Chemistry* **1,** 45 (1964).
[8] N. Bohr, *Proc. Phys. Soc.* **35,** 296 (1963).
[9] C. K. Jørgensen, *Orbitals in Atoms and Molecules,* Academic, New York (1962).
[10] A. de Shalit and I. Talmi, *Nuclear Shell Theory,* Academic, New York (1962).

9.2 PRODUCT-FUNCTION MATRIX ELEMENTS

Matrix elements between product functions readily reduce to definite integrals. For example, a single-electron operator $f(1)$, acting on the coordinates of the first electron, has the matrix element

$$\begin{aligned}&\langle\Phi(ab\cdots k\,|\,12\cdots N)\,|\,f(1)\,|\,\Phi(a'b'\cdots k'\,|\,12\cdots N)\rangle\\&=\langle\varphi(a\,|\,1)\,|\,f(1)\,|\,\varphi(a'\,|\,1)\rangle\times\langle\varphi(b\,|\,2)\,|\,\varphi(b'\,|\,2)\rangle\times\cdots\times\langle\varphi(k\,|\,N)\,|\,\varphi(k'\,|\,N)\rangle.\end{aligned}\tag{2.1}$$

On the right-hand side of (2.1) we see the definite integral

$$\begin{aligned}&\langle\varphi(nlm\mu\,|\,1)\,|\,f(1)\,|\,\varphi(n'l'm'\mu'\,|\,1)\rangle\\&\equiv\sum_{s_1}\int dv_1\;R_{nl}(r_1)Y^*_{lm}(\Omega_1)\chi^*_\mu(\mathbf{s}_1)f(1)R_{n'l'}(r_1)Y_{l'm'}(\Omega_1)\chi_\mu(\mathbf{s}_1),\end{aligned}\tag{2.2}$$

with the volume element

$$dv_1\equiv r_1^{\,2}\,dr_1\sin\theta_1\,d\theta_1\,d\phi_1\equiv r_1^{\,2}\,dr_1\,d\Omega_1.$$

We also see that the *overlap integral* is

$$\begin{aligned}&\langle\varphi(nlm\mu\,|\,1)\,|\,\varphi(n'l'm'\mu'\,|\,1)\rangle\\&\equiv\int_0^\infty r_1^{\,2}\,dr_1\;R_{nl}(r_1)R_{n'l'}(r_2)\int_0^{4\pi}d\Omega_1\;Y_{lm}(\Omega_1)Y_{l'm'}(\Omega_1)\langle\chi_\mu(\mathbf{s}_1)\,|\,\chi_{\mu'}(\mathbf{s}_1)\rangle\\&=\delta_{ll'}\,\delta_{mm'}\,\delta_{\mu\mu'}\int_0^\infty dr_1\;P_{nl}(r_1)P_{n'l}(r_1).\end{aligned}\tag{2.3}$$

Since the integrals do not depend on what we call the integration variables—we could call them $r_1\Omega_1\mathbf{s}_1$ or $r_2\Omega_2\mathbf{s}_2$ or $r_i\Omega_i\mathbf{s}_i$—it will simplify our formulas to introduce the abbreviations

$$<\varphi(a|1)|f(1)|\varphi(a'|1)> \equiv \langle a|f|a'\rangle, \tag{2.4}$$

$$<\varphi(a|1)|\varphi(a'|1)> \equiv \langle a|a'\rangle. \tag{2.5}$$

If we use orthonormal radial functions,

$$\int_0^\infty dr\; P_{nl}(r)P_{n'l}(r) = \int_0^\infty dr\; r^2\, R_{nl}(r)\, R_{n'l}(r) = \delta_{nn'}, \tag{2.6}$$

then the overlap integral is the Kronecker delta:

$$\langle a|a'\rangle = \delta_{aa'}. \tag{2.7}$$

Similarly, we can reduce the matrix element of a two-electron operator $g(12)$, acting on the coordinates of the first two electrons, to a definite integral:

$$<\Phi(abc\cdots k|12\cdots N)|g(12)|\Phi(a'b'c'k'|12\cdots N)> = \langle ab|g|a'b'\rangle\langle c|c'\rangle\cdots\langle k|k'\rangle, \tag{2.8}$$

where

$$\langle ab|g|a'b'\rangle \equiv <\varphi(a|1)\varphi(b|2)|g(12)|\varphi(a'|1)\varphi(b'|2)>. \tag{2.9}$$

All the operators we will deal with can be factored into radial, angular, and spin factors. If we write this factoring as

$$f(r\theta\phi\mathbf{s}) = f_r(r)f_\Omega(\theta\phi)f_s(\mathbf{s}), \tag{2.10}$$

then the integral of (2.2) becomes

$$\begin{aligned}\langle nlm\mu|f|n'l'm'\mu'\rangle &= \int_0^\infty dr\; P_{nl}(r)f_r(r)P_{n'l'}(r)\\ &\quad\times\int_0^{4\pi} d\Omega\; Y^*_{lm}(\Omega)f_\Omega(\Omega)\,Y_{l'm'}(\Omega)\\ &\quad\times <\chi_\mu(\mathbf{s})|f_s(\mathbf{s})|\chi_{\mu'}(\mathbf{s})>\\ &\equiv \langle nl|f_r|n'l'\rangle\langle lm|f_\Omega|l'm'\rangle\langle\mu|f_s|\mu'\rangle.\end{aligned} \tag{2.11}$$

This equation defines the radial integral $\langle nl|f_r|n'l'\rangle$, the angular integral $\langle lm|f_\Omega|l'm'\rangle$, and the spin matrix-element $\langle\mu|f_s|\mu'\rangle$.

As an example, the hydrogenic operator $\mathfrak{h}$ of (1.2),

$$\mathfrak{h} \equiv \frac{p^2}{2m} - \frac{Ze^2}{r} = \frac{p_r^2}{2m} + \frac{\hbar^2\mathbf{L}^2}{2mr^2} - \frac{Ze^2}{r}, \tag{2.12}$$

when acting on the function $\varphi(nlm|1)$ (not necessarily a hydrogenic orbital) gives

$$\left[\frac{p_r^2}{2m}+\frac{\hbar^2\mathbf{L}^2}{2mr^2}-\frac{Ze^2}{r}\right]\frac{P_{nl}(r)}{r}\,Y_{lm}(\Omega)\chi_\mu(\mathbf{s})$$
$$=\frac{1}{r}\left(\frac{e^2a_0}{2}\right)\left[-\frac{\partial^2}{\partial r^2}+\frac{l(l+1)}{r^2}-\frac{2(Z/a_0)}{r}\right]P_{nl}(r)\,Y_{lm}(\Omega)\chi_\mu(\mathbf{s}). \quad (2.13)$$

We have used $\hbar^2/2m = e^2a_0/2$ and

$$p_r^2\psi = -\hbar^2\frac{1}{r}\frac{\partial^2}{\partial r^2}r\psi. \quad (2.14)$$

(We could also have used $\hbar^2/2m = hcR$, as in Chapter 8.) Thus we obtain

$$\langle nlm\mu|\mathfrak{h}|n'l'm'\mu'\rangle = \delta_{ll'}\,\delta_{mm'}\,\delta_{\mu\mu'}\left(\frac{e^2a_0}{2}\right)$$
$$\times\int dr\,P_{nl}(r)\left[-\frac{d^2}{dr^2}+\frac{l(l+1)}{r^2}-\frac{2Z/a_0}{r}\right]P_{n'l}(r). \quad (2.15)$$

The particular case with $n = n'$ is often denoted by $I(nl)$:

$$I(nl) \equiv \frac{1}{a_0^2}\int dr\,P_{nl}(r)\left[-\frac{d^2}{dr^2}+\frac{l(l+1)}{r^2}-\frac{2Z/a_0}{r}\right]P_{n'l}(r). \quad (2.16)$$

If the radial functions $P_{nl}(r)$ are hydrogenic, we obtain the hydrogenic eigenvalue for this integral:

$$I(nl) = -\left(\frac{e^2}{2a_0}\right)\frac{Z^2}{n^2}. \quad (2.17)$$

Another important operator is the position operator, which we can write, using the Racah tensor $\mathbf{C}^{(1)}$, as

$$\mathbf{r} = r\mathbf{C}^{(1)} \equiv r(-C^{(1)}_{-1}\mathbf{e}_1 + C^{(1)}_0\mathbf{e}_0 - C^{(1)}_1\mathbf{e}_{-1}). \quad (2.18)$$

Equation 2.11 now gives

$$\langle nlm\mu|\mathbf{r}|n'l'm'\mu'\rangle = \int_0^\infty dr\,P_{nl}(r)rP_{n'l'}(r)\times\langle lm|\mathbf{C}^{(1)}_q|l'm'\rangle\times\delta_{\mu\mu'}. \quad (2.19)$$

The angular integral can be obtained by application of the Wigner–Eckart theorem:

$$\langle lm|C^{(k)}_q|l'm'\rangle \equiv c^k(lm, l'm') = \frac{(l'm', kq|lm)}{\sqrt{2l+1}}\langle l\|\mathbf{C}^{(k)}\|l'\rangle. \quad (2.20)$$

Because of the triangle rule of CG coefficients (Section 6.2), the only nonzero element has $q = m' - m$. The even perimeter rule ($l + k + l' =$ even integer) restricts us in this instance to $l = l \pm 1$. Thus

$$\langle lm|\mathbf{C}^{(1)}|l'm'\rangle = (-1)^{m-m'}\mathbf{e}_{m-m'}(l'm', km - m'|lm)(-1)^{l-l_>}\sqrt{l_>} \quad \text{for} \quad l = l \pm 1, \tag{2.21}$$

and we obtain the result

$$\langle nlm\mu|\mathbf{r}|n'l'm'\mu'\rangle = \mathbf{e}_{m-m'}(-1)^{\phi}(l'm', 1m - m'|lm)\sqrt{l_>} \times \int_0^\infty dr\, P_{nl}(r)\, r\, P_{n'l'}(r), \tag{2.22}$$

where the phase is

$$\phi \equiv l - l_> + m - m'.$$

The most important example of a two-electron operator is the interelectron repulsion e^2/r_{12}. In order to evaluate the integral, we separate the angular part from the spin part, using the expansion

$$\frac{1}{r_{12}} = \sum_{k=1}^{\infty} \frac{(r_<)^k}{(r_>)^{k+1}} \sum_{q=-k}^{k} (-1)^q C_q^{(k)}(1) C_{-q}^{(k)}(2). \tag{2.23}$$

We then obtain

$$\begin{aligned}
\left\langle ab\left|\frac{e^2}{r_{12}}\right|cd\right\rangle
&= e^2 \sum_{kq} (-1)^q \left\langle \varphi(a|1)\varphi(b|2) \left| \frac{(r_<)^k}{(r_>)^{k+1}}\, C_q^{(k)}(1) C_q^{(k)}(2) \right| \varphi(a|1)\varphi(d|2) \right\rangle \\
&= e^2 \langle \mu_a|\mu_c\rangle\langle\mu_b|\mu_d\rangle \\
&\quad \times \sum_{kq} (-1)^q \langle l_a m_a| C_q^{(k)}|l_c m_c\rangle\langle l_b m_b| C_{-q}^{(k)}|l_d m_d\rangle R^k(ab, cd) \\
&= e^2(-1)^{m_d - m_b}\, \delta(\mu_a, \mu_c)\, \delta(\mu_b, \mu_d)\, \delta(m_a - m_c, m_d - m_b) \\
&\quad \times \sum_k c^k(l_a m_a, l_c m_c) c^k(l_b m_b, l_d m_d) R^k(ab, cd).
\end{aligned} \tag{2.24}$$

(For clarity, we here write $\delta(a, b)$ for the Kronecker delta δ_{ab}.) The radial integral here, sometimes called a *generalized Slater integral*, is

$$\begin{aligned}
R^k(ab, cd) &\equiv \int_0^\infty dr_1 \int_0^\infty dr_2\, P_a(r_1) P_b(r_2)\, \frac{(r_<)^k}{(r_>)^{k+1}}\, P_c(r_1) P_d(r_2) \\
&\equiv \int_0^\infty dr_1\, \frac{P_a(r_1)P_c(r_1)}{(r_1)^{k+1}} \int_0^{r_1} dr_2 (r_2)^k P_b(r_2) P_d(r_2) \\
&\quad + \int_0^\infty dr_2\, \frac{P_b(r_2)P_d(r_2)}{(r_2)^{k+1}} \int_0^{r_2} dr_1\, (r_1)^k P_a(r_1) P_c(r_1).
\end{aligned} \tag{2.25}$$

Because of the triangle rule of CG coefficients, the sum over k will terminate after a few terms. An upper bound on k is $2l_>$, where $l_>$ is the largest l value.

9.3 THE PAULI PRINCIPLE: ANTISYMMETRY

So far we have talked as if we could somehow tag each electron and follow its motion. In fact, such an operation is impossible. Electrons are all alike and indistinguishable. There is no physical way to distinguish the two-electron wavefunction

$$\Phi(ab|12) \equiv \varphi(a|1)\varphi(b|2) \tag{3.1a}$$

(in which electron number 1 has quantum numbers a, electron number 2 has quantum numbers b) from the wavefunction

$$\Phi(ab|21) \equiv \varphi(a|2)\varphi(b|1) \tag{3.1b}$$

(in which electron number 2 now has quantum numbers a, etc.). Similarly, no conceivable physical experiment could distinguish the six three-electron wavefunctions:

$$\begin{matrix} \Phi(abc|123) & \Phi(abc|312) & \Phi(abc|231) \\ \Phi(abc|213) & \Phi(abc|321) & \Phi(abc|132). \end{matrix}$$

Although we might determine that an atom had one electron in orbital a, another in orbital b, and a third in orbital c, we certainly could *not* say that a *particular* electron (say the first electron) was in orbital a, etc.

More generally, for an N-electron product function there are $N!$ physically indistinguishable ways of labeling the electrons. We can place any one of the N electrons into the first orbital, then place any of $N - 1$ remaining electrons into the second orbital, and so on. Each of these $N!$ mathematically distinct functions,

$$\Phi(ab\cdots k|12\cdots N), \quad \Phi(ab\cdots k|21\cdots N), \quad \text{etc.,}$$

has the same eigenvalue of $\mathcal{H}^0$

$$E^0 = \varepsilon_a + \varepsilon_b + \cdots + \varepsilon_k. \tag{3.2}$$

Indeed, any linear combination of such product functions that differ only in the electron labels will have the same eigenvalue as any one of the product functions.

At first glance, this large *exchange degeneracy* might seem to introduce formidable practical difficulties. In fact, however, the Pauli exclusion principle brings order out of this potential chaos. Recall that the Pauli principle may be stated as follows:

No two electrons can occupy the same orbital. (A)

In other words, no two electrons can have the same quantum numbers. Now consider the two functions

$$A(ab, 12) \equiv \varphi(a|1)\varphi(b|2) - \varphi(a|2)\varphi(b|1) \equiv \Phi(ab|12) - \Phi(ab|21), \quad (3.3)$$
$$S(ab, 12) \equiv \varphi(a|1)\varphi(b|2) + \varphi(a|2)\varphi(b|1) \equiv \Phi(ab|12) + \Phi(ab|21). \quad (3.4)$$

The function $S(ab, 12)$ is symmetric with respect to interchange of electron labels,

$$S(ab, 12) = -S(ab, 21),$$

and the function $A(ab, 12)$ is antisymmetric:

$$A(ab, 12) = -A(ab, 21).$$

When orbital a is identical to orbital b, then the antisymmetric function is identically zero:

$$A(aa, 12) \equiv 0,$$

and the symmetric function becomes

$$S(aa, 12) \equiv 2\varphi(a|1)\varphi(a|2).$$

Thus the antisymmetric function *automatically* satisfies the Pauli principle. Similarly, the three-electron function

$$\begin{aligned} A(abc, 123) \equiv \quad & \Phi(abc|123) - \Phi(abc|213) \\ & + \Phi(abc|312) - \Phi(abc|132) \\ & + \Phi(abc|231) - \Phi(abc|321), \end{aligned} \quad (3.5)$$

which is antisymmetric with respect to the interchange of the labels on any two electrons,

$$A(abc, 123) = -A(abc, 213) = -A(abc, 321) = -A(abc, 132),$$

will also satisfy the Pauli principle:

$$A(aac, 123) \equiv 0 \equiv A(aba, 123), \text{ etc.}$$

It is easy to see, more generally, that an antisymmetric N-electron function will satisfy the Pauli principle identically. Thus the Pauli principle is equivalent to this statement:

An N-electron wavefunction must be antisymmetric with respect to the interchange of the labels on any two electrons. (B)

For mathematical convenience, let us define an operator $\mathcal{P}(i,j)$ that interchanges the labels of electrons i and j in an N-electron product function:

$$\mathcal{P}(i,j)\Phi(a\cdots k\,|\,1\cdots i\cdots j\cdots N) = \Phi(a\cdots k\,|\,1\cdots j\cdots i\cdots N). \quad (3.6)$$

Since two successive interchanges of the same two numbers restores the original ordering,

$$\mathcal{P}(i,j)\mathcal{P}(i,j)\Phi(a\cdots k\,|\,1\cdots i\cdots j\cdots N) = \Phi(a\cdots k\,|\,1\cdots i\cdots j\cdots N), \quad (3.7)$$

it is clear that the operator $\mathcal{P}^2(i,j)$ has the eigenvalue 1. In turn the operator $\mathcal{P}(i,j)$ has eigenvalues $+1$ (for a totally symmetric function):

$$\mathcal{P}(i,j)S(a\cdots k, 1\cdots N) = +S(a\cdots k, 1\cdots N) \quad (3.8)$$

and -1 (for a totally antisymmetric function):

$$\mathcal{P}(i,j)A(a\cdots k, 1\cdots N) = -A(a\cdots k, 1\cdots N). \quad (3.9)$$

Because of the Pauli principle, only the antisymmetric functions provide physically meaningful wavefunctions.

The interchange operator $\mathcal{P}$ commutes with $\mathcal{H}^0$ and $\mathcal{V}^0$ and also with all other physically significant operators. This commutivity is the mathematical expression for the fact that we cannot distinguish electrons.

To construct the totally antisymmetric linear combination of N product functions, we start with the particular product function,

$$\Phi(ab\cdots k\,|\,12\cdots N) \equiv \varphi(a\,|\,1)\cdots\varphi(k\,|\,N), \quad (3.10)$$

in which electrons have been assigned to the orbitals in the *standard ordering* 1, 2, 3, . . . N. (This labeling is simply a mathematical device to define a conventional phase.) The orbital labels $ab\ldots k$ must also appear in some conventional standard ordering. The usual convention ranks orbitals first by n value, then by l value, then $m_l \equiv m$, and finally $m_s = \mu$. Thus with the notation nl_m^{μ}, $1s_0^+$ precedes $2p_0^+$, and $2p_0^+$ precedes $2p_1^+$. The desired antisymmetric function with the set of quantum numbers $ab\cdots k$ consists of a sum of product functions like (3.10) but with the electrons in different orderings. If an ordering can be obtained from the standard ordering by an *even* number of electron interchanges, that product function carries a *plus* sign (e.g., the ordering $231\cdots N$). If the number of interchanges is *odd*, the sign is *minus* (e.g., $132\cdots N$).

To preserve the normalization of the basic orbitals, we must divide the linear combination of product functions by the square root of the number of terms in the linear combination. This number is just the exchange degeneracy, ($N!$). We shall denote such a normalized antisymmetric function by a tilde, $\tilde{\Phi}$, or by writing an antisymmetrizing operator $\mathcal{A}$:

$$\tilde{\Phi}(a\cdots k) = \mathcal{A}\Phi(a\cdots k\,|\,1\cdots N) \equiv \mathcal{A}\phi(a\,|\,1)\cdots\phi(k\,|\,N). \quad (3.11)$$

The preceding prescription for constructing an antisymmetric function is just the definition of a determinant,

$$\tilde{\Phi}(ab\cdots k) = \frac{1}{\sqrt{N!}}\begin{vmatrix} \phi(a|1) & \phi(b|1) & \phi(k|1) \\ \phi(a|2) & \cdots & \cdot \\ \cdot & \cdots & \cdot \\ \cdot & \cdots & \cdot \\ \cdot & \cdots & \cdot \\ \phi(a|N) & \cdots & \phi(k|N) \end{vmatrix}. \tag{3.12}$$

For this reason such functions are commonly called *determinantal wavefunctions* or DWF's. The determinant of orbitals is known as a *Slater determinant*, after J. C. Slater who pointed out [1] in 1929 that a DWF will automatically satisfy the Pauli principle because a determinant vanishes if two columns are the same.

Sometimes it is convenient to write the antisymmetrizer $\mathcal{A}$ as the sum of permutation operators for one-, two-, three-, $\cdots$ electron permutations p:

$$\mathcal{A}\Phi(a\cdots k|1\cdots N) = \frac{1}{\sqrt{N!}}\sum_p (-)^p \mathcal{P}(p)\Phi(a\cdots k|1\cdots N). \tag{3.13}$$

Obviously the results are the same whether we permute electron labels or orbital labels. Conceptually it may be simpler to think of permuting electrons. However, computations are often easier when we permute orbitals.

We remark in passing that the Pauli principle and the concomitant antisymmetry of wavefunctions apply only to particles such as electrons, protons, and neutrons which have spin $\frac{1}{2}$. Photons (spin 1), and pions (spin 0) do not obey the exclusion principle. Their wavefunctions must be *symmetric*.

REFERENCE

[1] J. C. Slater, *Phys. Rev.* **34,** 1293 (1929); *The Quantum Theory of Atomic Structure,* McGraw-Hill, New York (1960).

9.4 ANTISYMMETRIZED MATRIX ELEMENTS

Let us see how antisymmetrization affects the calculation of matrix elements between wavefunctions. Typically, we wish to calculate the matrix element of some operator $\mathcal{U}$ between two antisymmetric functions:

$$\begin{aligned} <\tilde{\Phi}(a\cdots b)|\mathcal{U}|\tilde{\Phi}(a'\cdots b')> \\ &\equiv <\tilde{\Phi}(a\cdots b|1\cdots N)|\mathcal{A}^\dagger\mathcal{U}\mathcal{A}|\Phi(a'\cdots b'|1\cdots N)> \\ &\equiv <\phi(a|1)\cdots\phi(b|N)|\mathcal{A}^\dagger\mathcal{U}\mathcal{A}|\phi(a'|1)\cdots\phi(b'|N)>. \end{aligned} \tag{4.1}$$

Here the antisymmetrizer $\mathcal{A}^\dagger$ acts to the left (*sinistrally*) and $\mathcal{A}$ acts to the right (*dextrally*). The operator $\mathfrak{U}$ will usually be either the sum of single-electron operators (commonly denoted $\mathfrak{F}$) or the sum of two-electron operators (commonly denoted $\mathfrak{G}$):

$$\mathfrak{F} \equiv \sum_{i=1}^{N} f(i), \tag{4.2}$$

$$\mathfrak{G} \equiv \sum_{i=j}^{N} \sum_{j=1}^{N-1} g(ij) \quad \text{with} \quad g(ij) = g(ji). \tag{4.3}$$

Such operators obviously treat all the electrons on an equal footing.

For a two-electron function, we can easily write out explicitly the action of the antisymmetrizers of (4.1):

$$\begin{aligned}
&<\tilde{\Phi}(ab)|\mathfrak{U}|\tilde{\Phi}(a'b')> \\
&\quad = <\Phi(ab|12) - \Phi(ab|21)\left|\frac{1}{\sqrt{2}}\mathfrak{U}\frac{1}{\sqrt{2}}\right|\Phi(a'b'|12) - \Phi(a'b|21)> \\
&\quad = +\tfrac{1}{2}<\Phi(ab|12)|\mathfrak{U}|\Phi(a'b'|12)> + \tfrac{1}{2}<\Phi(ab|21)|\mathfrak{U}|\Phi(a'b'|21)> \\
&\qquad -\tfrac{1}{2}<\Phi(ab|12)|\mathfrak{U}|\Phi(a'b'|21)> - \tfrac{1}{2}<\Phi(ab|21)|\mathfrak{U}|\Phi(a'b'|12]>.
\end{aligned} \tag{4.4}$$

Clearly, the first two (and last two) terms in this sum have the same value. We can call the integration variable r_1 or r_2 or even r_5, whatever we please. Thus

$$\begin{aligned}
&<\tilde{\Phi}(ab)|\mathfrak{U}|\tilde{\Phi}(a'b')> \\
&\quad = <\Phi(ab|12)|\mathfrak{U}|\Phi(a'b'|12)> - <\Phi(ab|12)|\mathfrak{U}|\Phi(a'b'|21)>.
\end{aligned} \tag{4.5a}$$

For ease of computation, it is more convenient to write all matrix elements between simple product functions with the electrons in the standard ordering:

$$\begin{aligned}
&<\tilde{\Phi}(ab)|\mathfrak{U}|\tilde{\Phi}(a'b')> \\
&\quad = <\Phi(ab|12)|\mathfrak{U}|\Phi(a'b'|12)> - <\Phi(ab|12)|\mathfrak{U}|\Phi(b'a'|12)>.
\end{aligned} \tag{4.5b}$$

When $\mathfrak{U}$ is the $\mathfrak{F}$-type operator $f(1) + f(2)$, and the orbitals are orthonormal, then (4.5) reads

$$\begin{aligned}
<\tilde{\Phi}(ab)|\mathfrak{F}|\tilde{\Phi}(a'b')> &= \langle a|f|a'\rangle\delta(b, b') + \langle b|f|b'\rangle\delta(a, a') \\
&\quad - \langle a|f|b'\rangle\delta(b, a') - \langle b|f|a'\rangle\delta(a, b').
\end{aligned} \tag{4.6}$$

For a $\mathfrak{G}$-type operator $g(12)$, we obtain

$$<\tilde{\Phi}(ab)|\mathfrak{G}|\tilde{\Phi}(a'b')> = \langle ab|g|a'b'\rangle - \langle ab|g|b'a'\rangle. \tag{4.7}$$

The first term on the right-hand side of (4.7) is known as the *direct inter-*

action. The second term, a consequence of antisymmetrization, is the *exchange interaction.*

In the more general case of N electrons, each antisymmetrizer in (4.1) introduces a normalization factor $(N!)^{-1/2}$. The *sinistral antisymmetrizer* $\mathcal{A}^\dagger$ produces $N!$ distinct electron orderings. Since each ordering will yield the same numerical result, we can pick one ordering (say the standard ordering), for our calculation and multiply that matrix element by $(N!)$. That is, we have

$$<\tilde{\Phi}(a\cdots k)|\mathfrak{U}|\tilde{\Phi}(a'\cdots k')> = (N!)<\Phi(a\cdots k|1\cdots N)|\,\frac{1}{\sqrt{N!}}\mathfrak{U}\mathcal{A}|\Phi(a'\cdots k'|1\cdots N)>. \quad (4.8)$$

The *dextral antisymmetrizer* $\mathcal{A}$ produces all possible permutations of the electron labels $1\cdots N$, or, what amounts to the same thing mathematically, it produces all possible permutations of the orbital labels $a\cdots k$. We thus find

$$\begin{aligned}<\tilde{\Phi}(a\cdots k)|\mathfrak{U}|\tilde{\Phi}(a'\cdots k')> &= <\Phi(a\cdots k|1\cdots N)|\mathfrak{U}|\Phi(a'b'\cdots k'|1\cdots N)> \\ &- <\Phi(a\cdots k|1\cdots N)|\mathfrak{U}|\Phi(b'a'\cdots k'|1\cdots N)> \\ &+ \cdots \\ &= \sum_p (-1)^p<\Phi(a\cdots k|1\cdots N)|\mathfrak{U}\mathcal{P}(p)|\Phi(a'\cdots k'|1\cdots N)>. \quad (4.9)\end{aligned}$$

For $\mathfrak{F}$-type operators, (4.9) becomes

$$\begin{aligned}<\tilde{\Phi}(ab\cdots k)|\mathfrak{F}|\tilde{\Phi}(a'b'c'\cdots k')> &= <a|f|a'>\bar{\delta}(a, a') + <b|f|b'>\bar{\delta}(b, b') + \cdots \\ &- <a|f|b'>\bar{\delta}(a, b) + <a|f|c'>\bar{\delta}(a, c') - \cdots, \quad (4.10)\end{aligned}$$

where, for orthonormal orbitals, the symbol $\bar{\delta}(a, a')$ is *unity* if *all* orbitals are identical *except* a and a', and is *zero otherwise.* The sign preceding a term $\langle c|f|d'\rangle$ is *positive* if the sum of the ordinal numbers of orbitals c and d' is an even integer; the sign is *negative* for odd integers. For example, between the second and third orbitals the sign is negative. Between the second and fourth orbitals the sign is positive.

For $\mathfrak{G}$-type operators, we obtain

$$\begin{aligned}<\tilde{\Phi}(abc\cdots k)|\mathfrak{G}|\tilde{\Phi}(a'b'c'\cdots k')> &= [\langle ab|g|a'b'\rangle - \langle ab|g|b'a'\rangle]\bar{\delta}(ab, a'b') \\ &+ [\langle ac|g|a'c'\rangle - \langle ac|g|c'a'\rangle]\bar{\delta}(ab, a'c') \\ &+ \cdots \\ &- [\langle ab|g|b'c\rangle - \langle ab|g|b'c'] \rangle\bar{\delta}(ab, b'c') \\ &- \cdots \quad (4.11)\end{aligned}$$

Again, the sign preceding a given term depends upon the number of interchanges needed to bring the orbitals to a standard ordering. [Recall the discussion following (3.10).]

As an example, let us calculate the *expectation value* for the operator $\mathcal{H}^1$ of (1.1) between two determinantal wavefunctions:

$$<\tilde{\Phi}(ab\cdots k)|\mathcal{H}^1|\tilde{\Phi}(ab\cdots k)> = <\tilde{\Phi}(ab\cdots k)\Big|\sum_i \mathfrak{h}(i)\Big|\tilde{\Phi}(ab\cdots k)> + \Big\langle\tilde{\Phi}(ab\cdots k)\Big|\sum_{i<j}\frac{e^2}{r_{ij}}\Big|\tilde{\Phi}(ab\cdots k)\Big\rangle. \tag{4.12}$$

The first term on the right-hand side is an $\mathfrak{F}$-type operator, with the value

$$\langle a|\mathfrak{h}|a\rangle + \langle b|\mathfrak{h}|b\rangle + \cdots + \langle k|\mathfrak{h}|k\rangle.$$

These are just the $I(nl)$ integrals of (2.17). The second term is a $\mathfrak{G}$-type operator, with the value

$$\Big\langle ab\Big|\frac{e^2}{r_{12}}\Big|ab\Big\rangle - \Big\langle ab\Big|\frac{e^2}{r_{12}}\Big|ba\Big\rangle + \Big\langle ac\Big|\frac{e^2}{r_{12}}\Big|ac\Big\rangle - \Big\langle ac\Big|\frac{e^2}{r_{12}}\Big|ca\Big\rangle + \cdots.$$

According to (2.24), each of these integrals has the form

$$e^2\sum_k [\delta(\cdots)c^k(a,a)c^k(b,b)R^k(ab,ab) - \delta(\cdots)c^k(a,b)c^k(a,b)R^k(aa,bb)] \equiv \frac{e^2}{a_0}\sum_k [f_k(a,b)R^k(ab,ab) - g_k(a,b)R^k(aa,bb)].$$

The *direct integrals* $R^k(ab, ab)$ are sometimes denoted by $F^k(a, b)$, while the *exchange integrals* $R^k(aa, bb)$ are denoted $G^k(a, b)$. Thus we find

$$<\tilde{\Phi}(ab\cdots k)|\mathcal{H}^1|\tilde{\Phi}(ab\cdots k)> = I(a) + I(b) + \cdots + \sum_k [f_k(a,b)F^k(a,b) - g_k(ab)G^k(ab)] + \cdots. \tag{4.13}$$

In this expression the quantities f_k and g_k may be found from a table of values for $c^k(lm, l'm')$; they are fixed by the properties of angular momentum functions. The integrals $I(a)$, $I(b)$, ... and the *Slater integrals* F^k and G^k depend on our choice of radial functions; these must be prescribed somehow. We shall postpone discussion of the radial functions and consider the parts of the matrix elements that depend on angular momentum.

9.5 TWO ELECTRONS: INTRODUCTION

With the tools of the preceding sections, we begin the study of atoms more complicated than hydrogen. Let us start with a simplified study of a two-electron atom, of nuclear charge Z. The major parts of the Hamiltonian come from the single-particle motion in the field of a fixed nucleus,

$$\mathcal{H}^0 = \mathfrak{h}(1) + \mathfrak{h}(2) \tag{5.1}$$

plus the electronic static repulsion,

$$\mathcal{V}^0 = \frac{e^2}{r_{12}}. \tag{5.2}$$

Here, as in Section 9.1, $\mathfrak{h}(i)$ is

$$\mathfrak{h}(i) = \frac{p^2(i)}{2m} - \frac{Ze^2}{r_i}.$$

In addition we should include a spin–orbit interaction,

$$\mathcal{V}^1 = \xi(1)\mathbf{S}(1)\cdot\mathbf{L}(1) + \xi(2)\mathbf{S}(2)\cdot\mathbf{L}(2). \tag{5.3}$$

Here the radial factors $\xi(i)$ depend on the electrostatic potential $\varphi(r_i)$ felt by each electron,

$$\xi(i) = -\frac{\hbar^2}{2m^2c^2}\frac{1}{r_i}\frac{\partial\varphi(r_i)}{\partial r_i} \equiv -\frac{(\alpha a_0)^2}{2}\frac{1}{r_i}\frac{\partial\varphi(r_i)}{\partial r_i} = \beta^2\frac{Z(r_i)}{r_i^3}.$$

Thus we consider the approximate Hamiltonian,

$$\mathcal{H} = \mathcal{H}^0 + \mathcal{V}^0 + \mathcal{V}^1 \equiv \mathcal{H}^1 + \mathcal{V}^1. \tag{5.4}$$

Following the independent-particle approach, we try to express the eigenfunctions of $\mathcal{H}$ in terms of simple product functions:

$$\Phi(ab\,|\,12) \equiv \Phi(n_al_am_a\mu_a, n_bl_bm_b\mu_b\,|\,12) \equiv \phi(a\,|\,1)\phi(b\,|\,2). \tag{5.5}$$

That is, we want to find the linear combinations of these product functions, such as

$$\Psi(\gamma\,|\,12) = \sum_{ab} c(\gamma\,|\,ab)\Phi(ab\,|\,12), \tag{5.6}$$

that satisfy the equation

$$\langle\Psi(\gamma\,|\,12)\,|\mathcal{A}^\dagger\mathcal{H}\mathcal{A}\,|\,\Psi(\gamma'\,|\,12)\rangle = E_\gamma\delta_{\gamma\gamma'}. \tag{5.7}$$

The label γ stands for whatever indices or quantum numbers we use to label the eigenfunctions of $\mathcal{H}$. These functions are eigenstates of the eight operators

$$\mathbf{L}^2(a),\ L_0(a), \mathbf{S}^2(a),\ S_0(a),\ \mathbf{L}^2(b),\ L_0(b),\ \mathbf{S}^2(b),\ S_0(b), \tag{5.8}$$

corresponding to the eigenvalues

$$l_a(l_a+1),\ m_a,\ \tfrac{3}{4},\ \mu_a,\ l_b(l_b+1),\ m_b,\ \tfrac{3}{4},\ \mu_b. \tag{5.9}$$

We could, of course, deal with explicitly antisymmetrized DWF's,

$$\tilde{\Phi}(ab) \equiv \frac{1}{\sqrt{2}}\,[\Phi(ab\,|\,12) - \Phi(ab\,|\,21)],$$

and the corresponding equations,

$$\tilde{\Psi}(\gamma) = \sum_{ab} D(\gamma\,|\,ab)\tilde{\Phi}(ab),$$

$$\langle\tilde{\Psi}(\gamma)\,|\,\mathcal{H}\,|\,\tilde{\Psi}(\gamma')\rangle = E_\gamma \delta_{\gamma\gamma'}.$$

However we shall find it more convenient to work with simple product functions in the following.

The matrix elements of $\mathcal{H}^0$ between product functions (or DWF's) are examples of $\mathcal{F}$-type operators considered in the preceding sections. Those results give

$$\begin{aligned}\langle ab\,|\,\mathcal{A}^\dagger\mathcal{H}^0\mathcal{A}\,|\,a'b'\rangle &= \langle a\,|\,a'\rangle\langle b\,|\,\mathfrak{h}\,|\,b'\rangle + \langle b\,|\,b'\rangle\langle a\,|\,\mathfrak{h}\,|\,a'\rangle \\ &\quad - [\langle a\,|\,b'\rangle\langle b\,|\,\mathfrak{h}\,|\,a'\rangle + \langle b\,|\,a'\rangle\langle a\,|\,\mathfrak{h}\,|\,b'\rangle].\end{aligned} \tag{5.10}$$

For simplicity, we assume the radial functions are orthogonal, as are the angle and spin functions. Then

$$\langle nlm\mu\,|\,n'l'm'\mu\rangle = \delta_{nn'}\delta_{ll'}\delta_{mm'}\delta_{\mu\mu'}, \tag{5.11}$$

$$\begin{aligned}\langle nlm\mu\,|\,\mathfrak{h}\,|\,n'l'm'\mu'\rangle &= \delta_{ll'}\delta_{mm'}\delta_{\mu\mu'} \\ &\times \left(\frac{e^2a_0}{2}\right)\int_0^\infty P_{nl}(r)\left[-\frac{d^2}{dr^2} - \frac{2Z/a_0}{r} + \frac{l(l+1)}{r^2}\right]P_{n'l}(r)\,dr.\end{aligned} \tag{5.12}$$

This assumption means we drop the last two terms of (5.10), the terms arising from antisymmetrization:

$$\langle ab\,|\,\mathcal{A}^\dagger\mathcal{H}^0\mathcal{A}\,|\,a'b'\rangle = \langle ab\,|\,\mathcal{H}^0\,|\,a'b'\rangle. \tag{5.13}$$

The resulting matrix is diagonal in the quantum numbers $l_a m_a \mu_a$ and $l_b m_b \mu_b$, although it is not necessarily diagonal in n:

$$\begin{aligned}&\langle ab\,|\,\mathcal{H}^0\,|\,a'b'\rangle \\ &= \bar{\delta}(n_a, n_b)\{\delta(n_b, n_b')\langle n_a l_a\,|\,\mathfrak{h}\,|\,n_a' l_a\rangle + \delta(n_a, n_a')\langle n_b l_b\,|\,\mathfrak{h}\,|\,n_b' l_b\rangle\}.\end{aligned} \tag{5.14}$$

[The symbol $\bar{\delta}(n_a, n_b)$ is *unity* if *all* quantum numbers *except possibly* n_a and

n_b are the same on both sides of the matrix element. If *any other* quantum numbers differ, then $\bar{\delta}(n_a, n_b)$ is zero.]

Note that $\mathcal{H}^0$ will have these same matrix elements between *any* two linear combinations of products functions that have the same radial factors (i.e., the same values of $n_a l_a$ and $n_b l_b$).

Now let us look at the contributions of $\mathcal{V}^0$ and $\mathcal{V}^1$ to the matrix of $\mathcal{H}$. Unlike $\mathcal{H}^0$, these operators must have matrix elements between different product functions. In particular, $\mathcal{V}^0$ and $\mathcal{V}^1$ mix functions that differ only in their values of $m_a m_b \mu_a$ and μ_b. This mixing shows up in expression (5.6) for $\Psi(\gamma|12)$. We can say that the individual quantum numbers

$$\begin{matrix} n_a\ l_a\ m_a\ \mu_a \\ n_b\ l_b\ m_b\ \mu_b \end{matrix} \tag{5.15}$$

are *not good quantum numbers*, meaning that the matrix of our Hamiltonian is not diagonal in these labels, and that the eigenfunctions of $\mathcal{H}$ do not, in general, have definite well-defined values for these quantum numbers. In more classical terms, we say the operators of (5.8) do not correspond to constants of the motion (e.g., the z component of orbital angular momentum of electron number one is not conserved).

What operators *will* provide good quantum numbers? Or, in the language of classical mechanics, what quantities (apart from the total energy) are constant during the motion? First we may note that $\mathcal{H}$ is unchanged if we replace all spatial coordinates $(x_1 y_1 \cdots z_2)$ by their inverses $(-x_1 \cdots -z_2)$. Since $\mathcal{H}$ is thus invariant under the operation of spatial inversion, the eigenstates of $\mathcal{H}$ can have well-defined *parity*. As we have seen, the parity of an orbital function $\phi(nlm\mu|1)$ is just $(-1)^l$. Therefore the parity of the product function of (5.5) is

$$\pi = (-1)^{l_a + l_b}. \tag{5.16}$$

Product functions (and DWF's) *have well-defined parity*. The mixture of (5.6) will consist either of *odd* parity functions (such as $1s\ 2p$ or $3p\ 4d$) or *even* parity functions (such as $2s\ 3s$ or $2p\ 2p$). Part of the label γ on $\Psi(\gamma|12)$ should indicate parity. Often one uses a superscript ° to denote odd parity.

We remark in passing that the parity of our atomic wavefunction will no longer be a good quantum number if the Hamiltonian contains a term such as $\mathbf{A}\cdot(\mathbf{r}_1 + \mathbf{r}_2)$, where $\mathbf{A}$ is a vector independent of the electron positions. This situation occurs in the presence of a static electric field, or a radiation field, for example. The parity of $\Psi(\gamma|12)$ will then no longer be a good quantum number.

We next observe that $\mathcal{H}$ does not single out any preferred direction in space: $\mathcal{H}$ is *rotationally invariant*. This condition means we can choose the eigenstates of $\mathcal{H}$ to be unchanged by the action of a rotation operator.

That is, they can be eigenstates of *total angular momentum*. In the present example the total angular momentum $\mathbf{J}$ comprises both spin and orbital angular momentum. The three defining equations for the components of $\mathbf{J}$ (say J_{-1}, J_0, and J_{+1}) can be written as the single vector equation

$$\mathbf{J} = \mathbf{L}(a) + \mathbf{L}(b) + \mathbf{S}(a) + \mathbf{S}(b). \tag{5.17}$$

[N.B.: because this notation is simply an abbreviation for three component equations, the ordering of the vectors $\mathbf{L}(a)$, $\mathbf{L}(b)$, etc., is immaterial.] Eigenstates of total angular momentum satisfy the familiar equations

$$\begin{aligned} \mathbf{J}^2\Psi(JM|12) &= J(J+1)\Psi(JM|12), \\ \mathbf{J}^0\Psi(JM|12) &= M\Psi(JM|12). \end{aligned} \tag{5.18}$$

Thus we know that we should be able to obtain eigenfunctions of $\mathcal{H}$ that are labeled with the good quantum numbers J and M.

This result will no longer be true if the Hamiltonian contains a term such as $\mathbf{H}\cdot(\mathbf{L} + 2\mathbf{S})$, which picks out a preferred direction (the direction of $\mathbf{H}$, the magnetic field). Such perturbations occur in the presence of an external magnetic field. This perturbation mixes functions with different J. If $\mathbf{H}$ is taken as the Z direction, then M will still be a good quantum number.

If we neglect, for the moment, the spin–orbit interaction $\mathcal{V}^1$ then the simplified Hamiltonian $\mathcal{H}^1$ contains no reference to spin. Thus we know there are eigenstates of $\mathcal{H}^1$ that are also eigenstates of the total spin operator $\mathbf{S}$:

$$\mathbf{S} = \mathbf{S}(a) + \mathbf{S}(b). \tag{5.19}$$

Such functions,

$$\begin{aligned} \mathbf{S}^2\Psi(SM_S|12) &= S(S+1)\Psi(SM_S|12), \\ S^0\Psi(SM_S|12) &= M_S\Psi(SM_S|12), \end{aligned} \tag{5.20}$$

will be labeled by the good quantum numbers S and M_S.

Furthermore, $\mathcal{H}^1$ commutes with the orbital angular-momentum operator $\mathbf{L}$,

$$\mathbf{L} \equiv \mathbf{L}(a) + \mathbf{L}(b) \tag{5.21}$$

and so we may look for eigenfunctions of $\mathcal{H}^1$ that satisfy the equations

$$\begin{aligned} \mathbf{L}^2\Psi(LM_L|12) &= L(L+1)\Psi(LM_L|12), \\ L_0\Psi(LM_L|12) &= M_L\Psi(LM_L|12). \end{aligned} \tag{5.22}$$

Because the four operators

$$\mathbf{L}^2,\ L_0,\ \mathbf{S}^2,\ S_0 \tag{5.23}$$

commute with one another and with the parity operator, we know we can find eigenfunctions of $\mathcal{H}^1$,

$$\Psi(LM_LSM_S\pi\,|\,12), \tag{5.24}$$

that are labeled, at least partly, by the good quantum numbers LM_LSM_S and parity. However, L_0 and S_0 do not commute with $\mathbf{J}^2$, so the functions of (5.24) cannot also be eigenstates of $\mathbf{J}^2$. But since $\mathbf{L}^2$ and $\mathbf{S}^2$ do commute with $\mathbf{J}^2$, we can find eigenstates of the four operators

$$\mathbf{L}^2, \mathbf{S}^2, \mathbf{J}^2, J_0. \tag{5.25}$$

These eigenfunctions of $\mathcal{H}^1$,

$$\Psi(LSJM\pi\,|\,12), \tag{5.26}$$

are labeled by the good quantum numbers $LSJM$ and parity.

Suppose that, instead of neglecting $\mathcal{V}^1$, we neglect the Coulomb interaction $\mathcal{V}^0$. The operator $\mathcal{V}^1$ does not commute with $\mathbf{S}$ or $\mathbf{L}$. However, both $\mathcal{H}^0$ and $\mathcal{V}^1$ do commute with the operators $\mathbf{J}^2(a)$, $\mathbf{J}^2(b)$:

$$\begin{aligned} \mathbf{J}(a) &= \mathbf{S}(a) + \mathbf{L}(a), \\ \mathbf{J}(b) &= \mathbf{S}(b) + \mathbf{L}(b), \\ \mathbf{J} &= \mathbf{J}(a) + \mathbf{J}(b). \end{aligned} \tag{5.27}$$

Thus we can find eigenfunctions of $\mathcal{H}^0 + \mathcal{V}^1$,

$$\Psi(j_aj_bJM\pi\,|\,12), \tag{5.28}$$

that are labeled by the eigenvalues of

$$\mathbf{J}^2(a), \mathbf{J}^2(b), \mathbf{J}^2, J_0. \tag{5.29}$$

That is,

$$\mathbf{J}^2(a)\Psi(j_aj_bJM\pi\,|\,12) = j_a(j_a + 1)\Psi(j_aj_bJM\pi\,|\,12) \tag{5.30}$$

with a similar equation for $\mathbf{J}^2(b)$.

We see that there are several possible ways to choose sets of commuting operators with which to label wavefunctions. As we shall now see, the choice in any given example is primarily suggested by our judgement on which terms dominate the Hamiltonian.

9.6 RUSSELL-SAUNDERS (LS) COUPLING

With the coupling procedures for angular momentum developed in Chapter 6, we can easily construct eigenfunctions of collective angular momenta from simple product functions. For example, the equation

$$\begin{aligned}\Psi(n_al_an_bl_bLM_LSM_S|12) &\equiv \Psi(\alpha LM_LSM_S|12)\\ &\equiv \sum (l_a\bar{m}'_a, l_b\bar{m}_b|LM_L) \times (\tfrac{1}{2}\bar{\mu}'_a, \tfrac{1}{2}\bar{\mu}_b|SM_S)\\ &\quad\times \Phi(n_al_a\bar{m}_a\bar{\mu}'_a, n_bl_b\bar{m}_b\ \bar{\mu}_b|12) \qquad (6.1)\end{aligned}$$

(sum over all barred quantum numbers: $\bar{m}_a\bar{m}_b\bar{\mu}_a\bar{\mu}_b$), defines an LSM-scheme function; Ψ is an eigenstate of the eight operators

$$\mathbf{L}^2(a),\ \mathbf{L}^2(b),\ \mathbf{L}^2,\ L_0,\ \mathbf{S}^2(a),\ \mathbf{S}^2(b),\ \mathbf{S}^2,\ S_0, \qquad (6.2)$$

as well as parity. The collective operators $\mathbf{L}$ and $\mathbf{S}$ here are defined by

$$\mathbf{L} = \mathbf{L}(a) + \mathbf{L}(b),$$
$$\mathbf{S} = \mathbf{S}(a) + \mathbf{S}(b).$$

Alternatively, we can construct LSJ-scheme functions, defined by

$$\begin{aligned}\Psi(n_al_an_bl_bLSJM|12) &\equiv \Psi(\alpha LSJM|12)\\ &\equiv \sum (l_a\bar{m}'_a, l_b\bar{m}_b|L\bar{M}_L) \times (\tfrac{1}{2}\bar{\mu}'_a, \tfrac{1}{2}\bar{\mu}_b|S\bar{M}_S)\\ &\quad\times (L\bar{M}_L, S\bar{M}_S|JM)\\ &\quad\times \Phi(n_al_a\bar{m}_a\bar{\mu}'_a, n_bl_b\bar{m}_b\bar{\mu}_b|12). \qquad (6.3)\end{aligned}$$

These are eigenstates of parity and

$$\mathbf{L}^2(a),\ \mathbf{L}^2(b),\ \mathbf{S}^2(a),\ \mathbf{S}^2(b),\ \mathbf{L}^2,\ \mathbf{S}^2,\ \mathbf{J}^2,\ J_0,$$

with the collective operators

$$\mathbf{L} = \mathbf{L}(a) + \mathbf{L}(b),$$
$$\mathbf{S} = \mathbf{S}(a) + \mathbf{S}(b),$$
$$\mathbf{J} = \mathbf{L}(a) + \mathbf{L}(b) + \mathbf{S}(a) + \mathbf{S}(b) = \mathbf{L} + \mathbf{S}.$$

Linear combinations of product functions or of DWF's such as (6.1) or (6.3), in which the expansion coefficients are CG coefficients, occur quite often. We shall speak of these as *coupled functions*, and the prescriptions for constructing them as *coupling schemes*. The LSJ scheme, (6.3), is also known as the *Russell–Saunders coupling-scheme*.

The notion of coupling angular momentum was first introduced with the idea that the vectors representing individual angular-momentum quantities should be added vectorially to give resultant vectors. According to this picture, which was stressed in early texts on atomic physics, atomic angular momenta share many similarities with the angular momenta of gyroscopes and spinning tops. Although the language of angular-momentum theory reflects this physical foundation, it is not necessary to develop a picture of physical vectors linked together in order to understand the structure of atoms.

The transformations of (6.1) and (6.3) from a set of product functions (sometimes called *m-scheme* functions) to a set of "coupled" functions is an example of a unitary transformation. (More specifically, the transformation is orthogonal, since the coefficients are real.) Thus we can view the coupled functions as basis functions in an *LSM* or *LSJ* scheme. As we shall now see, the task of calculating matrix elements is frequently simplified when we use such "coupled" basis functions.

Let us calculate the matrix of $\mathcal{H}$ in the *LSJ* scheme of functions. We first observe from (6.1) or (6.3) that the coupled functions are combinations of product functions with the same values of n_al_a, n_bl_b. Therefore the matrix elements of $\mathcal{H}^0$ between coupled functions are given by (5.14), viz.:

$$\begin{aligned}\langle n_al_an_bl_bLSJM|\mathcal{H}^0|n_{a'}l_{a'}n_{b'}l_{b'}L'S'J'M'\rangle &= \langle n_al_an_bl_bLM_LSM_S|\mathcal{H}^0|n_{a'}l_{a'}n_{b'}l_{b'}L'M_{L'}S'M_{S'}\rangle \\ &= \delta(S,S')\delta(M_S,M_{S'})\delta(L,L')\delta(M_L,M_{L'})\delta(l_a,l_{a'})\delta(l_b,l_{b'}) \\ &\times\{\delta(n_b,n_{b'})\langle n_al_a|\mathfrak{h}|n_{a'}l_a\rangle + \delta(n_a,n_{a'})\langle n_bl_b|\mathfrak{h}|n_{b'}l_b\rangle\}. \qquad (6.4)\end{aligned}$$

(Again the assumption of orthonormal radial functions allows us to drop the antisymmetrizing operators.)

The matrix of $\mathcal{V}^0$ has the form

$$\langle\Psi(\gamma|12)|\mathcal{A}^\dagger\mathcal{V}^0\mathcal{A}|\Psi(\gamma'|12)\rangle = \left\langle\Psi(\gamma|12)\left|\frac{e^2}{r_{12}}\right|\Psi(\gamma|12)\right\rangle - \left\langle\Psi(\gamma|12)\left|\frac{e^2}{r_{12}}\right|\Psi(\gamma|21)\right\rangle. \qquad (6.5)$$

We can evaluate these elements directly, using the method of tensor algebra and the expansion

$$\frac{1}{r_{12}} = \sum_k \frac{(r_<)^k}{(r_>)^{k+1}}\mathbf{C}^{(k)}(1)\cdot\mathbf{C}^{(k)}(2).$$

The direct matrix element is

$$\begin{aligned}&\left\langle\Psi(\gamma|12)\left|\frac{e^2}{r_{12}}\right|\Psi(\gamma|12)\right\rangle \\ &= e^2\sum_k\left\langle\Psi(n_al_an_bl_bLSJM|12)\left|\frac{r_<^k}{r_>^k}\mathbf{C}^{(k)}\cdot\mathbf{C}^{(k)}\right|\Psi(n_a'l_a'n_b'l_b'L'S'J'M'|12)\right\rangle \\ &= e^2\sum_k R^k(n_al_an_bl_b, n_a'l_a'n_b'l_b')\langle l_al_bLSJM|\mathbf{C}^{(k)}\cdot\mathbf{C}^{(k)}|l_a'l_b'L'S'J'M'\rangle. \qquad (6.6)\end{aligned}$$

There is no spin dependence to the operator

$$\mathbf{C}^{(k)}\cdot\mathbf{C}^{(k)} \equiv T_0^{(0)}.$$

Thus we require a matrix element of the type

$$\langle \alpha LSJM | \mathbf{T}^{(0)} \cdot \mathbf{1}^{(0)} | \alpha' L' S' J' M' \rangle.$$

According to the results of Chapter 6 (Table 6.1), this matrix element is simply

$$\delta_{MM'}\delta_{JJ'}\delta_{SS'}\delta_{LL'} \frac{\langle \alpha L \| \mathbf{T}^{(0)} \| \alpha' L \rangle}{\sqrt{2L+1}} \frac{\langle S \| 1 \| S' \rangle}{\sqrt{2S+1}}.$$

Further, we find from that chapter:

$$\langle l_a l_b L \| \mathbf{C}^{(k)} \cdot \mathbf{C}^{(k)} \| l_a' l_b' L \rangle$$
$$= \sqrt{2L+1}\,(-1)^{L+l_b+l_a'} \begin{Bmatrix} L & l_b & l_a \\ k & l_a' & l_b' \end{Bmatrix} \langle l_a \| \mathbf{C}^{(k)} \| l_b \rangle \langle l_a' \| \mathbf{C}^{(k)} \| l_b' \rangle. \qquad (6.7)$$

Thus the coefficient of R^k in the direct interaction is

$$\delta_{MM'}\delta_{JJ'}\delta_{LL'}\delta_{SS'}\,(-1)^{L+l_b+l_a'} \begin{Bmatrix} L & l_b & l_a \\ k & l_a' & l_b' \end{Bmatrix} \langle l_a \| \mathbf{C}^{(k)} \| l_b \rangle \langle l_a' \| \mathbf{C}^{(k)} \| l_b' \rangle. \qquad (6.8)$$

We cannot immediately treat the exchange interaction in the same way, because the formulas of tensor operators apply only to matrix elements of the form

$$<\Psi(j_a j_b JM | 12) | [\mathbf{A}^{(k)}(a) \times \mathbf{B}^{(k')}(b)]^{(K)} | \Psi(j_a' j_b' JM | 12)>, \qquad (6.9)$$

in which operator $\mathbf{A}^{(k)}$ acts on the *first* orbital on *both* sides of the matrix element and $\mathbf{B}^{(k')}$ acts on the *second* orbital. To bring the exchange interaction into this form we must recouple the two electrons. We start with the function

$$\Psi(n_a l_a n_b l_b LSJM | 21) = \sum (L\overline{M}_L, S\overline{M}_S | JM)$$
$$\times (l_a \overline{m}_a, l_b \overline{m}_b | L M_L) \times (\tfrac{1}{2}\bar{\mu}_a, \tfrac{1}{2}\bar{\mu}_b | SM_S) \phi(\bar{a}|2)\phi(\bar{b}|1). \qquad (6.10)$$

Using the interchange properties of CG coefficients, we can rewrite this as

$$(-1)^{l_a+l_b-L}(-1)^{½+½-S} \sum (L\overline{M}_L, S\overline{M}_S | JM)$$
$$\times (l_b \overline{m}_b, l_a \overline{m}_a | L\overline{M}_L) \times (\tfrac{1}{2}\bar{\mu}_b, \tfrac{1}{2}\bar{\mu}_a | S\overline{M}_S) \phi(\bar{a}|2)\phi(\bar{b}|1). \qquad (6.11)$$

Electron 2 is still in the a orbital, but the coupling ordering is now $l_b l_a$ instead of $l_a l_b$. Comparing (6.11) with (6.3), we find that

$$\Psi(n_a l_a n_b l_b LSJM | 21) = (-1)^{l_a+l_b-L+1-S}\Psi(n_b l_b n_a l_a LM_L SM_S | 12). \qquad (6.12)$$

We can now apply the algebra of tensor operators to the matrix element to obtain

$$- \left\langle (\Psi\gamma|12) \left| \frac{e^2}{r_{12}} \right| \Psi(\gamma'|21) \right\rangle$$

$$= -(-1)^{l_a'+l_b'-L+1-S'} e^2 \sum_k \left\langle \Psi(n_a l_a n_b l_b LSJM|12) \left| \frac{r_<^k}{r_>^k} \mathbf{C}^{(k)} \cdot \mathbf{C}^{(k)} \right| \right.$$

$$\left. \times\, \Psi(n_b' l_b' n_a' l_a' L'S'J'M'\ 12) \right\rangle$$

$$= (-1)^{l_a'+l_b'-L'-S'} e^2 \sum_k \langle l_a l_b LSJM | \mathbf{C}^{(k)} \cdot \mathbf{C}^{(k)} | l_b' l_a' L'S'J'M' \rangle$$

$$\times\, R^k(n_a l_a n_b l_b, n_b' l_b' n_a' l_a')$$

$$= (-)^{l_a'+l_b'-L-S} \delta_{MM'} \delta_{JJ'} \delta_{LL'} \delta_{SS'} e^2 \sum_k (-1)^{L+l_b+l_b'} \begin{Bmatrix} L & l_a & l_b \\ k & l_a' & l_b' \end{Bmatrix} \langle l_a \| \mathbf{C}^{(k)} \| l_b' \rangle$$

$$\times\, \langle l_b \| \mathbf{C}^{(k)} \| l_a' \rangle R^k(ab, b'a'). \tag{6.13}$$

Combining the direct interaction (6.8), with the exchange interaction (6.13), we obtain the matrix element

$$\langle n_a l_a n_b l_b LSJM | \mathcal{A}^\dagger \mathcal{V}^0 \mathcal{A} | n_a' l_a' n_b' l_b' L'S'J'M' \rangle$$

$$= \delta_{MM'}\, \delta_{JJ'}\, \delta_{LL'}\, \delta_{SS'}\, e^2 \sum_k \left[(-1)^{L+a+b'} \begin{Bmatrix} l_a & l_b & L \\ l_b' & l_a' & k \end{Bmatrix} \langle l_a \| \mathbf{C}^{(k)} \| l_a' \rangle \right.$$

$$\times\, \langle l_b \| \mathbf{C}^{(k)} \| l_a' \rangle R^k(ab, a'b') + (-1)^{S+L} (-1)^{L+l_b+l_a} \begin{Bmatrix} l_a & l_b & L \\ l_a' & l_b' & k \end{Bmatrix}$$

$$\left. \times\, \langle l_a \| \mathbf{C}^{(k)} \| l_b' \rangle \langle l_b \| \mathbf{C}^{(k)} \| l_a' \rangle R^k(ab, b'a') \right], \tag{6.14}$$

(we have used the fact that $l + k + l'$ is an even integer if $\langle l \| \mathbf{C}^{(k)} \| l' \rangle$ is not zero).

Equation 6.13 gives the Coulomb interaction between two-electron Russell–Saunders functions in all generality, and it contains several particularly noteworthy results. First of all the matrix is diagonal in $LSJM$ and parity. Next, we note that the values are independent of J and M; the LSJ functions have a degeneracy:

$$\sum_{J=|L-S|}^{L+S} \sum_{M=-J}^{+J} 1 = (2L+1)(2S+1).$$

In fact this degeneracy and the matrix-element values are the same that we would get by using LSM-scheme functions:

$$\left\langle \alpha LSJM | \mathcal{A}^\dagger \frac{e^2}{r_{12}} \mathcal{A} | \alpha' L'S'J'M' \right\rangle$$

$$= \left\langle \alpha L M_L S M_S | \mathcal{A}^\dagger \frac{e^2}{r_{12}} \mathcal{A} | \alpha' L' M_L' S' M_S' \right\rangle. \tag{6.15}$$

Thus as long as we are interested only in the Hamiltonian $\mathcal{H}^1$ we can ignore the quantum numbers JM or $M_L M_S$ in our labels.

For many purposes the diagonal matrix elements of $\mathcal{H}^0 + \mathcal{V}^0$ provide useful estimates of the energy. From (6.4) and (6.14), we have:

$$\langle n_a l_a n_b l_b LSJM | \mathcal{A}^\dagger(\mathcal{H}^0 + \mathcal{V}^0)\mathcal{A} | n_a l_a n_b LSJM \rangle$$
$$= I(a) + I(b) + \sum_k f_k(l_a l_b L) F^k(a, b) + (-1)^S g_k(l_a l_b L) G^k(a, b)$$
$$\equiv E(abSL), \tag{6.16}$$

where

$$f_k(l_a l_b L) \equiv (-1)^{L+l_a+l_b} \begin{Bmatrix} l_a & l_b & L \\ l_b & l_a & k \end{Bmatrix} \langle l_a \| C^{(k)} \| l_a \rangle \langle l_b \| C^{(k)} \| l_b \rangle,$$

$$g_k(l_a l_b L) \equiv (-1)^{k+l_a+b} \begin{Bmatrix} l_a & l_b & L \\ l_a & l_b & k \end{Bmatrix} \langle l_a \| C^{(k)} \| l_b \rangle^2. \tag{6.17}$$

In particular,

$$f_0(l_a l_b L) = 1,$$
$$g_0(l_a l_b L) = (-1)^L \delta(l_a, l_b),$$

so that only the F^0 term is independent of S and L.

Equation 6.16 reveals the remarkable fact that even though the Coulomb interaction is not explicitly spin dependent, the matrix element (6.14) *does* depend on spin. The spin dependence enters as a phase factor preceding the exchange integral. This phase produces different matrix elements for singlets and for triplets. For example, the diagonal elements for the configuration ls (i.e., $l_b = l_b' = 0$) are

$$\langle lsLS | \mathcal{A}^\dagger \mathcal{V}^0 \mathcal{A} | lsLS \rangle = \begin{Bmatrix} l & 0 & l \\ 0 & l & 0 \end{Bmatrix} \langle l \| C^{(0)} \| l \rangle \langle 0 \| C^{(0)} \| 0 \rangle F^0(ls)$$
$$+ (-1)^S \begin{Bmatrix} l & 0 & l \\ l & 0 & l \end{Bmatrix} \langle l \| C^{(l)} \| 0 \rangle^2 G^l(ls)$$
$$= F^0(ls) + \frac{G^l(ls)}{(2l+1)} \quad \text{for singlets,}$$
$$= F^0(ls) - \frac{G^l(ls)}{(2l+1)} \quad \text{for triplets.} \tag{6.18}$$

Thus the triplet term lies lower in energy (Hund's rule) by the amount $[2/(2l + 1)]G^l(ls)$.

Physically this energy difference is simply a manifestation of the Pauli principle. The triplet function has a symmetric spin dependence, since

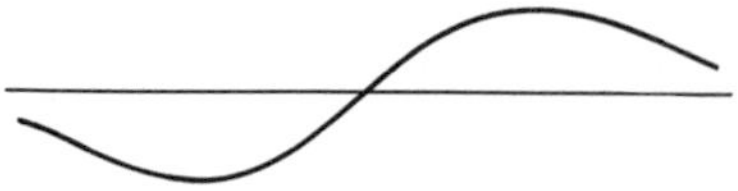

Fig. 9.1 A function that is antisymmetric in the spatial variable relative separation.

Fig. 9.2 A function that is symmetric in the spatial variable relative separation.

$$(\tfrac{1}{2}\mu, \tfrac{1}{2}\mu' \,|\, 1M_s) = (\tfrac{1}{2}\mu', \tfrac{1}{2}\mu \,|\, 1M_s),$$

hence it must have an antisymmetric spatial dependence. This result means the electrons cannot be too close to one another, because the wavefunction must be zero when the relative separation of the two electrons is zero (see Fig. 9.1). Thus in the triplet state the electrons tend to avoid each other. On the other hand, the singlet spin function is antisymmetric,

$$(\tfrac{1}{2}\mu, \tfrac{1}{2}\mu' \,|\, 00) = -(\tfrac{1}{2}\mu', \tfrac{1}{2}\mu \,|\, 00),$$

so that the singlet spatial function is symmetric. This condition results in a sizable probability that the electrons will be found quite close together (see Fig. 9.2). Since the electrons repel one another with a Coulomb force, they attain their lowest energy when they avoid each other, as in the triplet state.

Interestingly, these same arguments applied to two particles subject to *attractive* forces (such as an electron and a positron, or a proton and a neutron), predict that the *singlet* state will have the lower energy. Experiments confirm this prediction.

Equation 6.14 shows that l is not strictly a good quantum number. For example, the matrix element between the $L = 1$ terms of the configuration $3p\ 3s$ and the configuration $3p\ 3d$ is

$$\begin{aligned}\langle 3p\ 3s\ LS|A^{\dagger}\mathcal{V}^0 A|3p\ 3d\ LS\rangle &= \begin{Bmatrix} 1 & 0 & 1 \\ 2 & 1 & 2 \end{Bmatrix} \langle 1\|\mathbf{C}^{(2)}\|1\rangle\langle 0\|\mathbf{C}^{(2)}\|2\rangle R^2(3p\ 3s, 3p\ 3d) \\ &\quad + (-1)^S \begin{Bmatrix} 1 & 0 & 1 \\ 1 & 2 & 1 \end{Bmatrix} \langle 1\|\mathbf{C}^{(1)}\|2\rangle\langle 0\|\mathbf{C}^{(1)}\|1\rangle R^1(3p\ 3s, 3d\ 3p) \\ &= R^2 + (-1)^S R^1.\end{aligned}$$

Thus, although one may obtain a useful approximation by starting with a wavefunction that is a pure configuration, one must often include *configuration mixing* to get a wavefunction that describes the atom as accurately as one would like. The mixing of configurations given by the off-diagonal elements (in n and l) of (6.11) is sometimes called *configuration interaction.*

Thus far we have neglected the spin–orbit interaction $\mathcal{V}^1$. Consider now the matrix elements of $\mathcal{V}^1$ between two arbitrary LSJ functions. If we continue to assume orthogonal radial functions we can neglect the effects of antisymmetrization. Then we have the matrix elements

$$\langle n_a l_a n_b l_b LSJM | \sum_i \xi(r_i)\mathbf{L}(i)\cdot\mathbf{S}(i) | n'_a l'_a n'_b l'_b L'S'J'M' \rangle. \tag{6.19}$$

Apart from the radial factor this is a particular case of the matrix element

$$\langle abJM | \mathbf{A}^{(1)} \cdot \mathbf{B}^{(1)} | a'b'J'M' \rangle,$$

given in Chapter 6; thus (6.19) gives

$$\begin{aligned} &\delta_{MM'}\delta_{JJ'}(-1)^{J+L+S}\begin{Bmatrix} J & L & S \\ 1 & S' & L' \end{Bmatrix} \\ &\qquad \times [\zeta(a) \times \langle l_a l_b L \| \mathbf{L}(a) \| l'_a l'_b L' \rangle \times \langle \tfrac{1}{2}\tfrac{1}{2}S \| \mathbf{S}(a) \| \tfrac{1}{2}\tfrac{1}{2}S' \rangle \\ &\qquad + \zeta(b) \times \langle l_a l_b L \| \mathbf{L}(b) \| l'_a l'_b L' \rangle \times \langle \tfrac{1}{2}\tfrac{1}{2}S \| \mathbf{S}(b) \| S' \tfrac{1}{2}\tfrac{1}{2} \rangle], \end{aligned} \tag{6.20}$$

where the quantity

$$\zeta(a) = \int P_a(r)\xi(r)P_a(r)\, dr, \text{ etc.} \tag{6.21}$$

contains all dependence on the radial functions. Next, using the results of Chapter 6 for matrix elements of the type

$$\langle abJ \| \mathbf{A}^{(1)} \| a'b'J' \rangle \quad \text{and} \quad \langle J \| \mathbf{J}^{(1)} \| J' \rangle,$$

we write (6.20) as

$$\begin{aligned} &\delta_{MM'}\delta_{JJ'}\delta_{l_a l_a'}\delta_{l_b l_b'}(-1)^{J+L+1} \\ &\times \sqrt{\tfrac{3}{2}}\sqrt{2L+1}\sqrt{2L'+1}\sqrt{2S+1}\sqrt{2S'+1}\begin{Bmatrix} J & L & S \\ 1 & S' & L' \end{Bmatrix}\begin{Bmatrix} \tfrac{1}{2} & \tfrac{1}{2} & S \\ 1 & S' & \tfrac{1}{2} \end{Bmatrix} \\ &+ \left[\zeta(a)\sqrt{l_a(l_a+1)(2l_a+1)}\,(-1)^{l_a+l_b+L'}\begin{Bmatrix} l_b & l_a & L \\ 1 & L' & l_a \end{Bmatrix} + (-1)^{S-S'} \right. \\ &\left. \times\, \zeta(b)\sqrt{l_b(l_b+1)(2l_b+1)}\,(-1)^{l_a+l_b+L'}\begin{Bmatrix} l_a & l_b & L \\ 1 & L' & l_b \end{Bmatrix}\right]. \end{aligned} \tag{6.22}$$

If the radial factors $\zeta(a)$ and $\zeta(b)$ are not too large, we may obtain a reasonable estimate of the energy levels from the diagonal elements of (6.22). If either L or S is zero, the diagonal element vanishes. Using the explicit form for the 6-j symbol from Chapter 6, we can write (for $L \neq 0$, $S \neq 0$)

$$\langle n_al_an_bl_bLSJM|\mathcal{V}^1|n_al_an_bl_bLSJM\rangle$$
$$= \tfrac{1}{2}[J(J+1) - L(L+1) - S(S+1)]$$
$$\times\left[\frac{[L(L+1) + l_a(l_a+1) - l_b(l_b+1)]}{4L(L+1)}\zeta(a)\right.$$
$$\left.+\frac{[L(L+1) + l_b(l_b+1) - l_a(l_a+1)]}{4L(L+1)}\zeta(b)\right]$$
$$\equiv \tfrac{1}{2}[J(J+1) - L(L+1) - S(S+1)]\zeta(abSL). \qquad (6.23)$$

[Equation 6.23 defines the quantity $\zeta(abSL)$.] In particular, if one of the electrons is an s electron, then (6.23) gives

$$\langle nlnsLSJM|\mathcal{V}^1|nlnsLSJM\rangle$$
$$= \tfrac{1}{2}[J(J+1) - L(L+1) - 2]\tfrac{1}{2}\zeta(nl) \quad (L = l,\ S \neq 0); \qquad (6.24)$$

If the two electrons have the same l value, (6.23) becomes

$$\langle nln'lLSJM|\mathcal{V}^1|nln'lLSJM\rangle$$
$$= \tfrac{1}{2}[J(J+1) - L(L+1) - 2]\{\tfrac{1}{4}\zeta(nl) + \tfrac{1}{4}\zeta(n'l)\} \quad (L \neq 0,\ S \neq 0.) \qquad (6.25)$$

The spin–orbit interaction removes some of the degeneracy of the energy levels. It separates the *levels* (distinguished by the label J) of a given *term* (labeled by S and L). The diagonal matrix elements are (in atomic units with $e = 1$):

$$\langle n_al_an_bl_bLSJM|\mathcal{A}^\dagger(\mathcal{H}^0 + \mathcal{V}^0 + \mathcal{V}^1)\mathcal{A}|n_al_an_bl_bLSJM\rangle$$
$$= I(a) + I(b) + \sum_k [f_k(l_al_bSL)F^k(a,b) + (-1)^S g_k(l_al_bSL)G^k(a,b)]$$
$$+ \tfrac{1}{2}[J(J+1) - L(L+1) - S(S+1)]\zeta(abSL)$$
$$\equiv E(abSLJ). \qquad (6.26)$$

The splitting between adjacent levels is

$$E(abSLJ) - E(abSLJ-1) = J\zeta(abSL). \qquad (6.27)$$

This is the Landé interval rule (Chapter 2): the level splitting is proportional to J.

The spin–orbit interaction is diagonal in J, but it links functions of different S and L. Since $\mathbf{S}^{(1)}$ and $\mathbf{L}^{(1)}$ are tensors of order 1, there are matrix elements between S and $S' = S \pm 1$ and between L and $L' = L \pm 1$. Thus the interaction mixes singlets and triplets but not singlets and quintets.

The preceding formulas require slight modification for equivalent electrons: i.e., when $n_a l_a = n_b l_b$ or $n'_a l'_a = n'_b l'_b$. Equation 6.12 shows that

$$\Psi(nlnlSLJM|21) = -(-1)^{L+S}\Psi(nlnlSLJM|12). \tag{6.28}$$

Thus the antisymmetrizing operator gives

$$\begin{aligned} \mathcal{A}\Psi(nlnlSLJM|12) &= \tfrac{1}{2}[1 + (-1)^{L+S}]\Psi(nlnlSLJM|12) \\ &= \Psi(nlnlSLJM|12) \quad \text{if} \quad L + S = \text{even}, \\ &= 0 \qquad\qquad\qquad\qquad\quad \text{if} \quad L + S = \text{odd}. \end{aligned} \tag{6.29}$$

Clearly the only *allowed terms* of two electrons, for which the Pauli principle is satisfied, are those with

$$L + S = \text{even integer}. \tag{6.30a}$$

That is, the allowed terms are

$$^1S \quad ^3P \quad ^1D \quad ^3F \quad ^1G \quad ^3H \quad \cdots.$$

The antisymmetrizing operator of (6.29) differs by a numerical factor from the antisymmetrizer for nonequivalent electrons:

$$\begin{aligned} \mathcal{A}\Psi(abSLJM|12) &\equiv \frac{1}{\sqrt{2}}(1 - \mathcal{P}_{12})\Psi(abSLJM|12), \\ \mathcal{A}\Psi(aaSLJM|12) &\equiv \tfrac{1}{2}(1 - \mathcal{P}_{12})\Psi(aaSLJM|12). \end{aligned} \tag{6.30b}$$

These definitions are necessary in order to preserve the normalization of the antisymmetrized function $\tilde{\Psi} \equiv \mathcal{A}\Psi$. It is easy to see then, that for any $\mathfrak{F}$- or $\mathfrak{G}$-type operator $\mathfrak{U}$, the matrix element with no equivalent electrons is (with $\Gamma \equiv SLJM$ and $\Gamma' \equiv S'L'J'M'$ for the moment)

$$\langle ab\Gamma|\mathcal{A}^\dagger\mathfrak{U}\mathcal{A}|a'b'\Gamma'\rangle = \langle ab\Gamma|\mathfrak{U}|a'b'\Gamma'\rangle + (-1)^{l_a+l_b+S+L}\langle ba\Gamma|\mathfrak{U}|a'b'\Gamma'\rangle \tag{6.31}$$

whereas, if a and b are equivalent,

$$\begin{aligned} \langle aa\Gamma|\mathcal{A}^\dagger\mathfrak{U}\mathcal{A}|a'b'\Gamma'\rangle &= \frac{1}{\sqrt{2}}\langle aa\Gamma|\mathfrak{U}|a'b'\Gamma'\rangle + \frac{(-1)^{S+L}}{\sqrt{2}}\langle aa\Gamma|\mathfrak{U}|a'b'\Gamma'\rangle \\ &= \sqrt{2}\,\langle aa\Gamma|\mathfrak{U}|a'b'\Gamma'\rangle \quad \text{if } S + L = \text{even}, \end{aligned} \tag{6.32}$$

and, if both $a = b$ and $a' = b'$, then

$$\langle aa\Gamma|\mathcal{A}^\dagger\mathfrak{U}\mathcal{A}|a'a'\Gamma'\rangle = \langle aa\Gamma|\mathfrak{U}|a'a'\Gamma'\rangle. \tag{6.33}$$

Equation 6.33 shows that to calculate diagonal matrix elements of the Coulomb interaction for equivalent electrons we merely drop the G^k integrals from (6.18) or (6.26). Similarly, we simply set $\zeta(nl) = \zeta(n'l)$ in (6.25) for the spin–orbit interaction. The resulting energy is

$$\langle (nl)^2 LSJM | \mathcal{A}^\dagger(\mathcal{H}^0 + \mathcal{V}^0 + \mathcal{V}^1)\mathcal{A} | (nl)^2 LSJM \rangle$$
$$= 2I(nl) + \sum_k f_k(nlLS)F^k(nl, nl)$$
$$+ \tfrac{1}{2}[J(J+1) - L(L+1) - S(S+1)]\{\tfrac{1}{2}\zeta(nl)\}. \quad (6.34)$$

Despite the existence of off-diagonal matrix elements, (6.26) often provides useful estimates for identifying spectral lines and for predicting energy levels. In the *semiempirical approach*, one leaves the I, F^k, G^k, and ζ integrals as unknown parameters, to be determined from observations. The parameters are not entirely arbitrary, for the F^k and G^k must be *positive* quantities and decreasing functions of k (proven for F^k by Condon and Shortley [1], and for G^k by Racah [2]). Thus (6.34) makes definite predictions about the ordering of energy levels (e.g., Hund's rules) and the relative spacings. Deviations from these predictions can indicate the influence of configuration mixing or spin–orbit interaction. The reader should refer to the article by Edlén [3] for a discussion of the semiempirical method.

If the observed energy levels of an atom fit the pattern predicted by (6.26) or (6.34), then we can expect the LSJ functions to provide reasonable approximations for other atomic properties. With the results of Chapter 6, it is a straightforward task to calculate matrix elements of tensor operators between LSJ functions. As an example, consider the multipole moment operator, $\sum_i r^k(i)\mathbf{C}^{(k)}(i)$. The matrix elements of this $\mathfrak{F}$-type operator will be nonzero only between functions where a single electron orbital changes. Suppose the first orbital remains fixed, $n_a l_a = n_a' l_a'$. Then we obtain

$$\langle n_a l_a n_b l_b LSJM | \mathcal{A}^\dagger (r^k(b) C_q^{(k)}(b)) \mathcal{A} | n_a l_a n_b' l_b' L' S' J' M' \rangle$$
$$= \frac{(J'M', kq | JM)}{\sqrt{2J+1}} \langle l_a l_b LSJ \| r^k(b) \mathbf{C}^{(k)}(b) \| l_a l_b' L' S' J' \rangle$$
$$= \frac{(J'M', kq | JM)}{\sqrt{2J+1}} \sqrt{2J+1}\, \sqrt{2J'+1}\, (-1)^{L+S+J'+k} \begin{Bmatrix} S & L & J \\ k & J' & L' \end{Bmatrix} \delta_{SS'}$$
$$\times \langle l_a l_b L \| r^k(b) \mathbf{C}^{(k)}(b) \| l_a l_b' L' \rangle$$
$$= (J'M', kq | JM) \sqrt{2J'+1}\, (-1)^{L+S+J'+k} \begin{Bmatrix} S & L & J \\ k & J' & L' \end{Bmatrix} \delta_{SS'}$$
$$\times \sqrt{2L+1}\, \sqrt{2L'+1}\, (-1)^{l_b'+l_a+L+k} \begin{Bmatrix} l_a & l_b & L \\ k & L' & l_b' \end{Bmatrix}$$
$$\times \langle l_b \| \mathbf{C}^{(k)} \| l_b' \rangle \langle b | r^k | b' \rangle. \quad (6.35)$$

The entire dependence on the radial functions enters through the radial integral,

$$\langle b|r^k|b'\rangle \equiv \int P_b(r) r^k P_{b'}(r)\, dr. \tag{6.36}$$

The remaining angular factors provide such important selection rules as:

$$\begin{aligned} q &= M' - M, \qquad & |L - k| &\leq L' \leq L + k, \\ S' &= S, & |J - k| &\leq J' \leq J + k, \end{aligned} \tag{6.37}$$

$$l_b + l_b' + k = \text{even integer}.$$

As another example of an $\mathfrak{F}$-type operator, the magnetic dipole has the M, M' dependence

$$\frac{(J'M', 1q|JM)}{\sqrt{2J+1}},$$

with the reduced matrix element

$$\begin{aligned} &\langle l_a l_b LSJ \| \mathbf{L} + 2\mathbf{S} \| l_a l_b L'S'J' \rangle \\ &\quad = \delta_{SS'}[(2J+1)(2J'+1)(2L+1)(2L'+1)]^{1/2}(-1)^{l_a+l_b+S+J'} \begin{Bmatrix} S & L & J \\ 1 & J' & L' \end{Bmatrix} \\ &\qquad \times \left[(-1)^{L'-L} \begin{Bmatrix} l_b & l_a & L \\ 1 & L' & l_a \end{Bmatrix} (l_a \|\mathbf{L}\| l_a) + \begin{Bmatrix} l_a & l_b & L \\ 1 & L & l_b \end{Bmatrix} (l_b \|\mathbf{L}\| l_b) \right] \\ &\quad + \delta_{SS'}[(2J+1)(2J'+1)S(S+1)(2S+1)]^{1/2}(-1)^{1+L+J+S} \begin{Bmatrix} L & S & J \\ 1 & J' & S \end{Bmatrix}. \end{aligned}$$

The diagonal elements are

$$\begin{aligned} &\langle l_a l_b LSJM | L_0 + 2S_0 | l_a l_b LSJM \rangle \\ &\qquad = M \cdot \left[1 + \frac{J(J+1) + S(S+1) - L(L+1)}{2J(J+1)} \right] \\ &\qquad \equiv M \cdot g(SLJ). \end{aligned}$$

REFERENCES

[1] E. U. Condon and G. H. Shortley, *The Theory of Atomic Spectra*, Cambridge University Press, Cambridge, England (1935), p. 177.

[2] G. Racah, *Phys. Rev.* **61,** 186 (1942).

[3] B. Edlén, *Handbuch der Physik* **27,** 80 (1964).

9.7 OTHER TWO-ELECTRON COUPLING SCHEMES: *jj; jK; LK*

Although the *SLJ* functions often provide satisfactory approximate wavefunctions, useful for calculating energies and other atomic properties, they become poorer approximations when the spin–orbit integrals ζ become too large or when configurations mix strongly. When both $\zeta(a)$ and $\zeta(b)$ grow large, as they will for large Z (recall that for hydrogen, ζ is roughly proportional to Z^4/n^3l^3), then it may prove more useful to choose basis functions which are eigenfunctions of parity and the eight operators

$$\mathbf{L}^2(a),\ \mathbf{S}^2(a),\ \mathbf{J}^2(a),\ \mathbf{L}^2(b),\ \mathbf{S}^2(b),\ \mathbf{J}^2(b),\ \mathbf{J}^2,\ J_0, \tag{7.1}$$

where the collective operators are defined by

$$\begin{aligned}\mathbf{J}(a) &= \mathbf{L}(a) + \mathbf{S}(a),\\ \mathbf{J}(b) &= \mathbf{L}(b) + \mathbf{S}(b),\\ \mathbf{J} &= \mathbf{L}(a) + \mathbf{S}(a) + \mathbf{L}(b) + \mathbf{S}(b) \equiv \mathbf{J}(a) + \mathbf{J}(b).\end{aligned}$$

These quantities can be constructed from product functions according to the following coupling prescription:

$$\begin{aligned}\Psi((n_al_aj_a), (n_al_bj_b)JM|12) &\equiv \Psi(j_aj_bJM|12)\\ &\equiv \sum (l_a\overline{m}_a, \tfrac{1}{2}\overline{\mu}_a|j_a\overline{M}_a)(l_b\overline{m}_b, \tfrac{1}{2}\overline{\mu}_b|j_b\overline{M}_b)\\ &\quad\times (j_a\overline{M}_a, j_b\overline{M}_b|JM)\\ &\quad\times \Phi(n_al_a\overline{m}_a\overline{\mu}_a, n_bl_b\overline{m}_b\overline{\mu}_b|12)\end{aligned} \tag{7.2}$$

(sum over barred quantities). Such functions, known as *jj coupling functions*, have been widely studied, particularly in work on nuclear structure (cf. de Shalit and Talmi [1]). As Chapter 6 shows, they can also be expressed as linear combinations of the *LSJ* functions:

$$\begin{aligned}&\Psi((l_aj_a), (l_bj_b)JM|12)\\ &\quad= \sum [(2\overline{S}+1)(2\overline{L}+1)(2j_a+1)(2j_b+1)]^{1/2} \begin{Bmatrix} l_a & \tfrac{1}{2} & j_a\\ l_b & \tfrac{1}{2} & j_b\\ \overline{L} & \overline{S} & J\end{Bmatrix}\\ &\quad\times \Psi(l_al_b\overline{L}\overline{S}JM|12).\end{aligned} \tag{7.3}$$

Both the *jj* function and the *LSJ* function in (7.3) have the same sets of single-particle quantum numbers $n_al_an_bl_b$, and the same total angular momentum numbers JM. They differ only in their intermediate collective quantum numbers j_aj_b or LS.

It is easy to verify that $\mathcal{V}^1$ is a diagonal matrix in this scheme. The diagonal elements are

$$\langle n_a l_a j_a,\, n_b l_b j_b,\, JM|\mathcal{V}^1|n_a l_a j_a,\, n_b l_b j_b JM\rangle$$
$$= \frac{\langle l_a j_a\|\mathbf{L}(a)\cdot\mathbf{S}(a)\|l_a j_a\rangle}{\sqrt{2j_a+1}}\zeta(a) + \frac{\langle l_b j_b\|\mathbf{L}(b)\cdot\mathbf{S}(b)\|l_b j_b}{\sqrt{2j_b+1}}\zeta(b)$$
$$= \tfrac{1}{2}[l_a(l_a+1) + \tfrac{3}{4} - j_a(j_a+1)]\zeta(a) + \tfrac{1}{2}[l_b(l_b+1) + \tfrac{3}{4} - j_a(j_a+1)]\zeta(b)$$
$$\equiv E(aj_a,\, bj_b). \tag{7.4}$$

Thus to the extent that the electrostatic interaction can be neglected, the *jj* coupling functions are degenerate eigenfunctions of $\mathcal{H}$, with energies that do not depend on J or M.

The matrix of $\mathcal{V}^0$ in the *jj* scheme has the direct elements

$$\left\langle n_a l_a j_a,\, n_b l_b j_b JM\left|\frac{e^2}{r_{12}}\right|n'_a l'_a j'_a,\, n'_b l'_b j'_b JM\right\rangle$$
$$= e^2\sum_k (-1)^{J+j_b+j_a'}\begin{Bmatrix} J & j_b & j_a \\ k & j'_a & j'_b \end{Bmatrix}\langle l_a j_a\|\mathbf{C}^{(k)}\|l'_a j'_a\rangle\langle l_b j_b\|\mathbf{C}^{(k)}\|l'_b j'_b\rangle R^k(ab,\, a'b')$$
$$= e^2\sum_k (-1)^{J+j_b-j_b'+1+l_a+l_b}[(2j_a+1)(2j'_a+1)(2j_b+1)(2j'_b+1)]^{1/2}$$
$$\times\begin{Bmatrix} J & j_b & j_a \\ k & j'_a & j'_b \end{Bmatrix}\begin{Bmatrix} \tfrac{1}{2} & j_a & l_a \\ k & l'_a & j'_a \end{Bmatrix}\begin{Bmatrix} \tfrac{1}{2} & j_b & l_b \\ k & l'_b & j'_b \end{Bmatrix}\langle l_a\|\mathbf{C}^{(k)}\|l'_a\rangle\langle l_b\|\mathbf{C}^{(k)}\|l'_b\rangle$$
$$\times R^k(ab,\, a'b'). \tag{7.5}$$

The calculation of the exchange contribution proceeds just as with *LSJ* functions. Recoupling gives

$$\Psi(j_a j_b JM|21) = (-1)^{j_a+j_b-J}\Psi(j_b j_a JM|12), \tag{7.6}$$

which leads to the elements

$$(-1)^{j_a+j_b+J+1}\left\langle n_a l_a j_a,\, n_b l_b j_b JM\left|\frac{e^2}{r_{12}}\right|n'_b l'_b j'_b,\, n'_a l'_a j'_a JM\right\rangle$$
$$= (-1)^{j_a+j_b+J+1}e^2\sum_k (-1)^{J+j_b-j_a'+1}[(2j_a+1)(2j'_a+1)(2j_b+1)(2j'_b+1)]^{1/2}$$
$$\times\begin{Bmatrix} J & j_b & j_a \\ k & j'_b & j'_a \end{Bmatrix}\begin{Bmatrix} \tfrac{1}{2} & j_a & l_a \\ k & l'_b & j'_b \end{Bmatrix}\begin{Bmatrix} \tfrac{1}{2} & j_b & l_b \\ k & l'_a & j'_a \end{Bmatrix}\langle l_a\|\mathbf{C}^{(k)}\|l'_b\rangle\langle l_b\|\mathbf{C}^{(k)}\|l'_a\rangle$$
$$\times R^k(ab,\, b'a'). \tag{7.7}$$

Both the direct and the exchange terms act to mix functions with different l values (configuration mixing) and j values (breakdown of *jj* coupling). However, if the off-diagonal elements are not too large, we may obtain a useful approximation to the energy from the diagonal elements of $\mathcal{H}$. These elements are

$$\langle n_a l_a j_a, n_b l_b j_b JM | A^\dagger(\mathcal{H}^0 + \mathcal{V}^0 + \mathcal{V}^1) A | n_a l_a j_a, n_b l_b j_b JM\rangle$$
$$= I(a) + I(b)$$
$$+ \sum_k \{f_k(l_a j_a l_b j_b J) F^k(a, b) - (-1)^{j_a+j_b+J} g_k(l_a j_a l_b j_b J) G^k(a, b)\}$$
$$+ d(l_a j_a)\zeta(a) + d(l_b j_b)\zeta(b)$$
$$\equiv E(a j_a b j_b J), \tag{7.8}$$

where

$$f_k(l_a j_a l_b j_b J) = (-1)^{J+l_a+l_b+1}(2j_a + 1)(2j_b + 1)$$
$$\times \begin{Bmatrix} J & j_a & j_b \\ k & j_b & j_a \end{Bmatrix} \begin{Bmatrix} \frac{1}{2} & j_a & l_a \\ k & l_a & j_a \end{Bmatrix} \begin{Bmatrix} \frac{1}{2} & j_a & l_b \\ k & l_b & j_b \end{Bmatrix},$$
$$\times \langle l_a \| \mathbf{C}^{(k)} \| l_a \rangle \langle l_b \| \mathbf{C}^{(k)} \| l_b \rangle \tag{7.9}$$

$$g_k(l_a j_a l_b j_b J) = (-1)^{J+j_b-j_a+1+k}(2j_a + 1)(2j_b + 1)$$
$$\times \begin{Bmatrix} J & j_a & j_b \\ k & j_a & j_b \end{Bmatrix} \begin{Bmatrix} \frac{1}{2} & j_a & l_a \\ k & l_b & j_b \end{Bmatrix}^2 \times \langle l_a \| \mathbf{C}^{(k)} \| l_b \rangle^2, \tag{7.10}$$

$$\left.\begin{aligned} d(l, l + \tfrac{1}{2}) &= -\frac{l}{2} \\ d(l, l - \tfrac{1}{2}) &= \frac{l+1}{2} \end{aligned}\right\} \quad (l \neq 0). \tag{7.11}$$
$$d(0, \pm\tfrac{1}{2}) = 0$$

Note, in particular:

$$f_0(l_a j_a l_b j_b J) = 1,$$
$$g_0(l_a j_a l_b j_b J) = 1 \cdot \delta(l_a, l_b)\delta(j_a, j_b),$$

so that the F^0 and G^0 terms are independent of J.

The treatment of equivalent electrons ($n_a l_a = n_b l_b$) in jj coupling follows from considering (7.6). If $j_a \neq j_b$, then calculations proceed as though the electrons were not equivalent, except that the direct and exchange integrals are identical: $F^k(a, a) = G^k(a, a)$. A more appropriate definition of equivalent particles in jj coupling would be $n_a l_a j_a = n_b l_b j_b$. This definition is used in nuclear physics. If $j_a = j_b$, then (7.6) shows that the Pauli principle allows only those states with

$$J = \text{even integer} \quad \text{if} \quad n_a l_a j_a = n_b l_b j_b.$$

Thus the allowed values are

$$\begin{array}{ll} (s_{1/2})^2\ J = 0 & (d_{3/2})^2 J = 0,\ 2 \\ (p_{1/2})^2\ J = 0 & (d_{5/2})^2 J = 0,\ 2,\ 4 \\ (p_{3/2})^2 J = 0,\ 2 & (f_{5/2})^2 J = 0,\ 2,\ 4 \\ & (f_{7/2})^2 J = 0,\ 2,\ 4,\ 6. \end{array} \tag{7.12}$$

Formulas 6.31–6.33 apply to matrix elements in *jj* coupling when $n_a l_a j_a = n_b l_b j_b$. To calculate such matrix elements, drop the exchange term and introduce a factor of either $\sqrt{2}$ or 1, depending on whether one or both sides of the matrix element involve equivalent electrons.

Equation 7.8 provides a useful energy estimate as long as the F^k and G^k integrals are small compared with the two integrals $\zeta(a)$ and $\zeta(b)$. In the limit $F^k = 0$, $G^k = 0$, the energy structure is independent of J, just as in the limit $\zeta(a) = 0$, $\zeta(b) = 0$ the *LSJ*-coupling energies are independent of J. Of course, either *LSJ* or *j–j* coupling functions can serve as *basis functions* even when they are not good approximations to *eigenfunctions* of $\mathcal{H}$ (they then simply provide a reference system for calculating the matrix of $\mathcal{H}$). Early workers in spectroscopy dealt only with *LSJ* or *jj* functions when they used coupled functions. They treated as intermediate cases those atoms that did not satisfy either the *LSJ* or the *jj* approximation. Such cases were referred to as "*intermediate coupling*," and the wavefunctions were obtained by diagonalizing $\mathcal{V}^0 + \mathcal{V}^1$ within a configuration. Because the wavefunctions of this so-called intermediate coupling depend intimately on the values of radial parameters (the ζ and G^k), they are not true coupling schemes as we use the terminology in this book. We will reserve the name *coupling scheme* for functions that can be constructed from product functions by use of angular-momentum theory (or, more generally, group theory) alone.

Although both the *LSJ* scheme and *jj* scheme of functions have received wide application, they do not exhaust the list of possible coupling schemes for two electrons. For example, consider the functions

$$\Psi((l_a j_a) l_b [K] JM \,|\, 12) \equiv \sum (l_a \overline{m}_a, \tfrac{1}{2}\overline{\mu}_a \,|\, j_a \overline{M}_a)(j_a \overline{M}_a, l_b \overline{m}_b \,|\, K\overline{k}) \times (K\overline{k}, \tfrac{1}{2}\overline{\mu}_b \,|\, JM)\Phi(n_a l_a \overline{m}_a \overline{\mu}_a, n_b l_b \overline{m}_b \overline{\mu}_b \,|\, 12). \tag{7.13}$$

These have been referred to as *jl* coupling functions (because j_a and l_b couple to give K; cf. Racah [2]) and, perhaps more appropriately, as *jK*-coupling functions (because j_a and K label the eigenvalues; cf. Cowan and Andrew [3]). These functions can, of course, be expressed in terms of *LSJ* functions:

$$\Psi((l_a j_a) l_b [K] JM \,|\, 12) = \sum [(2K+1)(2j_a+1)(2\overline{L}+1)(2\overline{S}+1)]^{1/2}(-1)^{J+j_a+l_b+J-1/2} \times \begin{Bmatrix} K & l_b & \overline{L} \\ l_a & \tfrac{1}{2} & j_a \end{Bmatrix}\begin{Bmatrix} K & \tfrac{1}{2} & \overline{L} \\ \overline{S} & J & \tfrac{1}{2} \end{Bmatrix} \Psi(l_a l_b \overline{L}\overline{S}JM \,|\, 12), \tag{7.14}$$

or in terms of *jj* functions:

$$\Psi((l_a j_a)l_b[K]JM|12) = \sum [(2K+1)(2\bar{j}_b+1)]^{1/2}(-1)^{J+j_a+1} \times \begin{Bmatrix} j_a & J & \bar{j}_b \\ \frac{1}{2} & \frac{1}{2} & K \end{Bmatrix} \Psi((l_a j_a)(l_b \bar{j}_b)JM|12). \quad (7.15)$$

The summations go over only intermediate collective quantum numbers $\bar{L}\bar{S}$ or $\bar{j}$.

The jK functions are eigenfunctions of parity and of the eight operators

$$\mathbf{L}^2(a),\ \mathbf{L}^2(b),\ \mathbf{S}^2(a),\ \mathbf{S}^2(b),\ \mathbf{J}^2(a),\ \mathbf{K}^2,\ \mathbf{J}^2,\ \mathrm{J}_0, \quad (7.16)$$

where the collective operators are

$$\begin{aligned} \mathbf{J}(a) &= \mathbf{L}(a) + \mathbf{S}(a), \\ \mathbf{K} &= \mathbf{L}(a) + \mathbf{S}(a) + \mathbf{L}(b) \\ \mathbf{J} &= \mathbf{L}(a) + \mathbf{S}(a) + \mathbf{L}(b) + \mathbf{S}(b) = \mathbf{K} + \mathbf{S}(b). \end{aligned} \quad (7.17)$$

It is a simple exercise to find the matrix elements of $\mathcal{V}^1$ in this scheme:

$$\begin{aligned} &\langle (l_a j_a)l_b[K]JM|\mathcal{V}^1|(l'_a j'_a)l'_b[K']JM\rangle \\ &= \delta(K,K')\delta(l_b,l'_b)\delta(j_a,j'_a)\delta(l_a,l'_a)\frac{\zeta(a)}{2}[j_a(j_a+1) - l_a(l_a+1) - \tfrac{3}{4}] \\ &\quad + \delta(l_b,l'_b)\delta(j_a,j'_a)\delta(l'_a,l'_a)\frac{\zeta(b)}{2}[(2K+1)(2K'+1)]^{1/2}(-1)^{J+K'-1/2+l_b+j_a+K} \\ &\quad \times \begin{Bmatrix} J & K & \frac{1}{2} \\ 1 & \frac{1}{2} & K' \end{Bmatrix}\begin{Bmatrix} j_a & l_b & K \\ 1 & K' & l_b \end{Bmatrix}\langle l_b\|\mathbf{L}\|l_b\rangle\sqrt{\tfrac{3}{4}}. \end{aligned} \quad (7.18)$$

Similarly, the direct part of the Coulomb interaction is

$$\begin{aligned} &\langle (l_a j_a)l_b[K]JM|\mathcal{V}^0|(l'_a j'_a)l'_b[K']JM\rangle \\ &= \delta_{KK'}[(2j_a+1)(2j'_a+1)]^{1/2}\sum_k F^k(a,b) \\ &\times(-1)^{K+l_a+l_b-1/2+k}\begin{Bmatrix} K & l_b & j'_a \\ k & j_a & l'_b \end{Bmatrix}\begin{Bmatrix} \frac{1}{2} & l_a & j_a \\ k & j'_a & l'_a \end{Bmatrix}\times\langle l_a\|\mathbf{C}^{(k)}\|l'_a\rangle\langle l_b\|\mathbf{C}^{(k)}\|l'_b\rangle. \end{aligned} \quad (7.19)$$

Calculation of the exchange is more difficult because the interchange of electrons 1 and 2 requires a recoupling of angular momentum. One possible approach is to express the jK functions as jj functions, for which the interchange is quite simple:

$$\Psi((l_a j_a)l_b[K]JM|21)$$
$$= \sum [(2K+1)(2\bar{j}_b+1)]^{1/2}(-1)^{J+j_a+1}$$
$$\times \begin{Bmatrix} j_a & J & j_b \\ \frac{1}{2} & \frac{1}{2} & K \end{Bmatrix} (-1)^{j_a+\bar{j}_b-J}\Psi((l_b\bar{j}_b)(l_a j_a)JM|12)$$
$$= \sum [(2K+1)(2\bar{j}_b+1)(2j_a+1)(2\bar{K}+1)]^{1/2}(-1)^J$$
$$\times \begin{Bmatrix} j_a & J & \bar{j}_b \\ \frac{1}{2} & \frac{1}{2} & K \end{Bmatrix}\begin{Bmatrix} j_a & J & \bar{j}_b \\ \bar{K} & \frac{1}{2} & \frac{1}{2} \end{Bmatrix} \Psi((l_b\bar{j}_b)l_a[\bar{K}]JM|12). \quad (7.20)$$

The exchange contribution now follows from (7.19)

$$\langle (l_a j_a)l_b[K]JM|\mathcal{V}^0\mathcal{P}_{12}|(l'_a j'_a)l'_b[K']JM\rangle$$
$$= \sum [(2K'+1)(2j'_a+1)(2j_b+1)(2\bar{K}+1)]^{1/2}(-1)^J$$
$$\times \begin{Bmatrix} j'_a & J & \bar{j}_b \\ \frac{1}{2} & \frac{1}{2} & K' \end{Bmatrix}\begin{Bmatrix} j'_a & J & \bar{j}_b \\ \bar{K} & \frac{1}{2} & \frac{1}{2} \end{Bmatrix}\langle (l_a j_a)l_b[K]JM|\mathcal{V}^0|(l'_b\bar{j}_b)l'_a(\bar{K})JM\rangle$$
$$= \sum_k g_k G^k(a,b), \quad (7.21)$$

where

$$g_k = \sum [(2j_a+1)(2j'_a+1)(2K+1)(2K'+1)]^{1/2}(2j_b+1)$$
$$\times (-1)^{J+K+l_a+l_a'-1/2+k}$$
$$\times \begin{Bmatrix} j'_a & J & \bar{j}_b \\ \frac{1}{2} & \frac{1}{2} & K' \end{Bmatrix}\begin{Bmatrix} j'_a & J & \bar{j}_b \\ K & \frac{1}{2} & \frac{1}{2} \end{Bmatrix}\begin{Bmatrix} K & l_b & \bar{j}_b \\ k & j_a & l'_a \end{Bmatrix}\begin{Bmatrix} k & j_a & \bar{j}_b \\ \frac{1}{2} & l'_a & l_a \end{Bmatrix}$$
$$\times \langle l_a\|C^{(k)}\|l'_b\rangle\langle l_b\|C^{(k)}\|l'_a\rangle. \quad (7.22)$$

As (7.18)–(7.21) show, the matrix of $\mathcal{H}$ is diagonal in K if $\zeta(b)$ and $G^k(a,b)$ are negligible. More precisely, jK-scheme functions will provide useful approximations as long as both $\zeta(b)$ and $G^k(a,b)$ are much smaller than $\zeta(a)$ and $F^k(a,b)$, and in addition, $F^k(a,b)$ is smaller than $\zeta(a)$. (Of course, configuration mixing must also be negligible.) These conditions often apply to states in which one electron moves in a highly excited orbit ($n_b l_b \gg n_a l_a$) about an ionic core that has a large spin–orbit splitting. In the limit $n_b l_b \to \infty$, the outermost electron is unbound and the energy structure follows from the spin–orbit splitting of the ion as perturbed by the electrostatic interaction with the outlying electron.

It may also happen that, although one electron is highly excited, the remaining electron has only a small spin–orbit splitting. A more appropriate coupling scheme might then be

$$\Psi((l_a l_b)L[K]J|12) = \sum (l_a\bar{m}_a, l_b\bar{m}_b|L\bar{M})(L\bar{M}, \tfrac{1}{2}\bar{\mu}_a|K\bar{k})(K\bar{k}, \tfrac{1}{2}\bar{\mu}_b|JM)$$
$$\Phi(n_a l_a\bar{m}_a\bar{\mu}_a, n_b l_b\bar{m}_b\bar{\mu}_b|12). \quad (7.23)$$

This LK scheme function is an eigenstate of parity and of the operators

$$\mathbf{L}^2(a),\ \mathbf{L}^2(b),\ \mathbf{S}^2(a),\ \mathbf{S}^2(b),\ \mathbf{L}^2,\ \mathbf{K}^2,\ \mathbf{J}^2,\ \mathrm{J}_0,$$

where the collective operators are

$$\begin{aligned}\mathbf{L} &= \mathbf{L}(a) + \mathbf{L}(b),\\ \mathbf{K} &= \mathbf{L}(a) + \mathbf{L}(b) + \mathbf{S}(a) = \mathbf{L} + \mathbf{S}(a),\\ \mathbf{J} &= \mathbf{L}(a) + \mathbf{L}(b) + \mathbf{S}(a) + \mathbf{S}(b) = \mathbf{K} + \mathbf{S}(b).\end{aligned}$$

The direct part of the Coulomb interaction is diagonal in this scheme (apart from the usual configuration mixing):

$$\begin{aligned}\langle (l_a l_b)L[K]JM|\mathcal{V}^0|(l_a l_b)L'[K']JM\rangle &= \delta_{KK'}\delta_{LL'}\sum_k (-1)^{L+l_b+l_a}\begin{Bmatrix} L & l_b & l_a\\ k & l_a & l_b\end{Bmatrix}\\ &\quad\times \langle l_a\|\mathbf{C}^{(k)}\|l_a\rangle\langle l_b\|\mathbf{C}^{(k)}\|l_b\rangle F^k(a,b), \qquad (7.24)\end{aligned}$$

whereas the spin–orbit interaction has the elements

$$\begin{aligned}&\langle (l_a l_b)L[K]JM|\mathcal{V}^1|(l_a l_b)L'[K']JM\rangle\\ &= \delta_{KK'}\zeta(a)[(2L+1)(2L'+1)]^{1/2}(-1)^{K-1/2+L+L'+l_a+l_b}\\ &\quad\times\begin{Bmatrix} K & \frac{1}{2} & L\\ 1 & L' & \frac{1}{2}\end{Bmatrix}\begin{Bmatrix} l_b & l_a & L\\ 1 & L' & l_a\end{Bmatrix}\langle l_a\|\mathbf{L}\|l_a\rangle\sqrt{\tfrac{3}{4}}\\ &\quad+\zeta(b)[(2K+1)(2K'+1)(2L+1)(2L'+1)]^{1/2}(-1)^{l_a+l_b-J}\\ &\quad\times\begin{Bmatrix} J & K' & \frac{1}{2}\\ 1 & \frac{1}{2} & K\end{Bmatrix}\begin{Bmatrix} \frac{1}{2} & L & K\\ 1 & K' & L'\end{Bmatrix}\begin{Bmatrix} l_a & l_b & L\\ 1 & L' & l_b\end{Bmatrix}\langle l_b\|\mathbf{L}\|l_b\rangle\sqrt{\tfrac{3}{4}}. \qquad (7.25)\end{aligned}$$

Again we see that K is a good quantum number for the direct interaction plus $\mathbf{S}(a)\cdot\mathbf{L}(a)$.

Table 9.1 Conditions for Coupling Schemes

Coupling Scheme	Conditions
LSJ	$F^k,\ G^k \gg \zeta(a),\ \zeta(b)$
jj	$\zeta(a),\ \zeta(b) \gg F^k,\ G^k$
j or jK	$\zeta(a) > F^k \gg G^k > \zeta(b)$
L or LK	$F^k > \zeta(a) \gg G^k > \zeta(b)$

The jK- and LK-coupling schemes have been studied extensively by Russian workers [4], and have been reviewed by Cowan and Andrew [3]. Racah [2] gives numerous examples of the occurrence of various coupling schemes.

Table 9.1 (from Cowan and Andrew [3]) summarizes the conditions for each of the four coupling schemes to give good approximations.

REFERENCES

[1] A. de Shalit and I. Talmi, *Nuclear Shell Theory*, Academic, New York, N. Y. (1963).

[2] G. Racah, *Phys. Rev.* **61,** 537 (1942); *J. Opt. Soc. Am.* **50,** 408 (1960).

[3] R. D. Cowan and K. L. Andrew, *J. Opt. Soc. Am.* **55,** 502 (1965).

[4] I. B. Levinson and A. A. Nikitin, *Handbook for Theoretical Computation of Line Intensities in Atomic Spectra*, Davey, New York (1965).

9.8 SEVERAL ELECTRONS: PARENTAGE

Just as the motion of a single isolated electron can be completely described with four quantum numbers (for example $nljm$ or nlm_lm_s), the motion of N electrons generally requires $4N$ quantum numbers for complete specification. (The Pauli principle reduces this number when more than two orbitals are equivalent.) In the preceding section we examined several ways of selecting the eight quantum numbers that prescribe the motion of two electrons. Our choice of quantum numbers was based on the theory of angular momentum. In other words we classified our set of two-particle basis functions according to their rotational symmetry. Such a classification suits a description of central-field motion of electrons in an isolated atom. On the other hand, studies of electron motion in molecules or crystals generally require classification schemes based on other symmetry properties. For example, translational symmetry is connected with linear momentum. For a discussion of such classifications, the reader should refer to texts by Judd [1], Ballhausen [2], and Hamermesh [3].

The angular-momentum classification can be extended to any number of electrons. In principle the extension of the two-electron coupling procedures to three or more electrons is quite straightforward, although in practice the work may be laborious. Essentially, we look for a set of collective quantum numbers to supplement the single-particle quantum numbers $n_1l_1, n_2l_2, \ldots, n_Nl_N$. Some of these collective quantum numbers, such as those for the total angular momentum, J, and its projection, M_J, may be "good quantum numbers"; (i.e., the matrix of our approximate Hamiltonian is diagonal in these labels). Others, such as the total spin, S, provide useful wavefunction labels, even though they are not rigorously good quantum numbers. Still other collective quantum numbers serve merely as computational aids, with no direct physical significance.

The angular-momentum functions that we shall consider are linear combinations of simple product functions, such as

$$\Phi(ab\cdots c|12\cdots N) \equiv \varphi(a|1)\varphi(b|2)\cdots\varphi(c|N). \tag{8.1}$$

(Here we use a single letter a for the four numbers $n_a l_a m_a \mu_a$; the numbers 1, 2, . . . , etc. refer to the coordinates of electrons 1, 2, . . . , etc.) Throughout this section we usually assume the orbitals are nonequivalent; that is, that no two n and l values are the same. Equivalent orbitals are discussed in the following section.

As we have seen, it is a simple procedure to construct coupled wavefunctions from product functions. The linear combination sums over various $\{m\mu\}$ values, and the expansion coefficients are products of CG coefficients. There are many ways of coupling N orbitals, various orderings in which the single-particle quantum numbers can be combined. We have already seen how LS, jj, and jk coupling schemes arise in two-electron atoms. Each different ordering prescribes a different coupling scheme.

Table 9.2 Quantum Numbers for *LSJ* Coupling, Nonequivalent Orbitals

No. of Electrons	Quantum Numbers
1	$n_a l_a\ JM$
2	$n_a l_a\ n_b l_b\ LSJM$
3	$n_a l_a\ n_b l_b\ L_{ab} S_{ab}\ n_c l_c\ LSJM$
4	$n_a l_a\ n_b l_b\ L_{ab} S_{ab}\ n_c l_c\ L_{abc} S_{abc}\ n_d l_d\ LSJM$

For example, in the LSJ coupling scheme, one would use wavefunctions labeled by the quantum numbers given in Table 9.2. In this coupling scheme the successive orbital angular momenta are coupled together in the sequence

$$l_a l_b(L_{ab}),\ l_c(L_{abc}),\ l_d(L_{abcd}),\ \ldots,\ l_N(L),$$

to give a total orbital angular momentum L. The spins are also coupled sequentially,

$$\tfrac{1}{2}\,\tfrac{1}{2}(S_{ab}),\ \tfrac{1}{2}(S_{abc}),\ \tfrac{1}{2}(S_{abcd}),\ \ldots,\ \tfrac{1}{2}(S),$$

to the total spin S. Then L and S are coupled to give a total angular momentum J. If we write the LSJ wavefunction Ψ as the linear combination

$$\Psi(\cdots LSJ|12\cdots N) = \sum C(\cdots LSJ|ab\cdots c)\Phi(ab\cdots c|12\cdots N), \quad (8.2)$$

the expansion coefficient C consists of two CG factors

$$(L_iM_{Li}, l_im_i|L_{i+1}M_{Li+1})(S_iM_{Si}, \tfrac{1}{2}\mu_i|S_{i+1}M_{Si+1}),$$

for each added electron, and a final factor,

$$(LM_L, SM_S|JM).$$

The LSJ function Ψ carries the $2N$ labels $\{n_il_i\}$, the four labels $LSJM$, and $2N-4$ intermediate quantum-number labels $\{L_iS_i\}$. These intermediate quantum numbers are called the *parentage* or *genealogy*. They specify the term of the parent ion after an electron is removed. For example, we might imagine the addition of successive $1s$, $2s$, $2p$, and $3p$ electrons to a beryllium nucleus, $Z = 4$, to obtain the following spectroscopic term of neutral beryllium:

$$1s,\ 2s\ {}^3S,\ 2p\ {}^4P,\ 3p\ {}^3D.$$

This particular ${}^3D$ term results when we couple a $3p$ orbital to the parent term

$$1s,\ 2s\ {}^3S,\ 2p\ {}^4P$$

of Be^+. Other (orthogonal) ${}^3D$ terms are obtained from other parents:

$$1s,\ 2s\ {}^3S,\ 2p\ {}^2P,$$
$$1s,\ 2s\ {}^1S,\ 2p\ {}^2P.$$

The actual ${}^3D$ wavefunctions of the configuration $1s\ 2s\ 2p\ 3p$ will be mixtures of these pure-parentage wavefunctions.

When one deals with equivalent orbitals (i.e., orbitals with the same n and l), it is more convenient first to couple the orbitals within a *subconfiguration* or group of equivalent orbitals, and then couple the groups together. Thus in the configuration $2p^2\ 3d^2$ one would couple the p orbitals to give L_pS_p, couple the d orbitals to give L_dS_d, and then couple L_pS_p and L_dS_p to give $LSJM$:

$$2p^2\ (L_pS_p),\ 3d^2\ (L_dS_d)LSJM.$$

Such a procedure yields such terms as

$$2p^2({}^1S),\ 3d^2({}^3P)\ {}^3P$$
$$2p^2({}^3P),\ 3d^2({}^1S)\ {}^3P$$
$$2p^2({}^3P),\ 3d^2({}^3P)\ {}^3P$$
$$2p^2({}^3P),\ 3d^2({}^1D)\ {}^3P$$
$$2p^2({}^1D),\ 3d^2({}^3P)\ {}^3P$$
$$2p^2({}^1D),\ 3d^2({}^3F)\ {}^3P.$$

Each of these six ^3P terms is orthogonal to the others, although none is an eigenfunction of $\mathcal{H}^0 + \mathcal{V}^1$.

Within a given coupling scheme (i.e., a given ordering of orbitals), wavefunctions with different parentage are orthogonal. This orthogonality follows from the theory of angular momentum: eigenstates of an angular momentum operator $\mathbf{J}^2$ form an orthogonal set. However, functions of one coupling scheme are not, in general, orthogonal to functions in another scheme. For example, the terms

$$2p^2(^3P),\ 3d\ ^2D,\ 3d\ ^3P,$$
$$2p^2(^3P),\ 3d\ ^4D,\ 3d\ ^3P,$$

obtained by sequential coupling of the orbitals $2p^2$, $3d$, $3d$, are orthogonal to each other, but they are not orthogonal to all six ^3P terms of $2p^2\ 3d^2$ above. The two coupling schemes are related by recoupling coefficients, such as

$$\langle 2p^2(^3P), 3d(^2D), 3d^3P | 2p^2(^3P), 3d^2(^1S)^3P\rangle$$
$$= -\sqrt{5}\begin{Bmatrix} 2 & 2 & 0 \\ 1 & 1 & 2 \end{Bmatrix}\sqrt{2}\begin{Bmatrix} \frac{1}{2} & \frac{1}{2} & 0 \\ 1 & 1 & \frac{1}{2} \end{Bmatrix} = \frac{1}{3}. \qquad (8.3)$$

Although we have been stressing the coupling algorithm, whereby one explicitly constructs a coupled wavefunction as a linear combination of product functions with the use of CG coefficients, such an approach is not really necessary. We can equally well define a coupled function by displaying certain operators for which it is an eigenfunction. The function

$$\Psi(2p^2(L_pS_p), 2d^2(L_dS_d)LSJM | 1234), \qquad (8.4)$$

for example, is an eigenfunction of the collective operators

$$\mathbf{L}^2(p), \mathbf{S}^2(p), \mathbf{L}^2(d), \mathbf{S}^2(d), \mathbf{L}^2\ \mathbf{S}^2\ \mathbf{J}^2\ \mathbf{J}_z,$$

with eigenvalues

$$L_p(L_p + 1),\ S_p(S_p + 1),\ L_d(L_d + 1),\ S_d(S_d + 1),\ \text{etc.}$$

These collective operators are defined in terms of single-particle operators by equations like

$$\mathbf{L}(p) = \mathbf{L}(1) + \mathbf{L}(2),$$
$$\mathbf{L}(d) = \mathbf{L}(3) + \mathbf{L}(4),$$
$$\mathbf{L} = \mathbf{L}(1) + \mathbf{L}(2) + \mathbf{L}(3) + \mathbf{L}(4).$$

As we have already seen for the case of two electrons, it is not necessary to use the actual CG expansion when calculating atomic properties. All matrix elements can be calculated directly between coupled wavefunctions by the application of tensor-operator techniques and recoupling procedures. One then calculates matrix elements of the type

$$\langle\Psi(\Gamma JM|12\cdots N)|\mathcal{A}^{\dagger}\mathfrak{U}\mathcal{A}|\Psi(\Gamma'J'M'|12\cdots N)\rangle, \tag{8.5}$$

where $\mathcal{A}$ is the antisymmetrizing operator and $\mathfrak{U}$ is an $\mathfrak{F}$-type or $\mathfrak{G}$-type operator:

$$\mathfrak{F} = \sum_i f(i), \qquad \mathfrak{G} \equiv \sum_i \sum_{j<i} g(ij).$$

To simplify the following discussion, we assume that the same coupling scheme applies to both the *dextral* wavefunction $\Psi(\Gamma'J'M'|12\cdots N)$ and the *sinistral* wavefunction $\Psi(\Gamma JM|12\cdots N)$. This assumption does not imply that one coupling scheme must be used for all the states of a given atom. However, in actual calculations, it is simpler to express all wavefunctions in a common basis. We also assume, for simplicity, that orbitals with different n values are orthogonal. The modification for nonorthogonal orbitals is straightforward but laborious.

Orthogonality permits us to replace the operator $\mathcal{A}^{\dagger}\mathfrak{F}\mathcal{A}$ by the simple operator $\mathfrak{F}$. It restricts the nonzero matrix elements of $\mathfrak{F}$ to those in which the configurations Γ and Γ' are either identical or differ by only one orbital. We require the matrix elements

$$\langle\Gamma JM|f(1) + f(2) + \cdots + f(N)|\Gamma'J'M'\rangle. \tag{8.6}$$

(We implicitly assume that the electrons are in the *standard ordering* 1, 2, 3, . . . , N in both the dextral and the sinistral wavefunctions.) To proceed further, one must express $f(i)$ as a tensor operator times a radial operator. Then the matrix element may be calculated by applying results of Chapter 6.

As an example, consider matrix elements of the one-electron operator $\gamma(r_2)\,T_q^{(k)}(b)$, acting on radial and angular coordinates of electron number 2, between the four-electron wavefunctions:

$$\Psi(n_al_an_bl_b(L_bS_b)n_cl_c(L_cS_c)n_dl_dLSJM|1234).$$

The radial part $\gamma(r)$ factors out as

$$\Gamma(b) \equiv \int P(n_bl_b|r)\gamma(r)P(n_b'l_b'|r) \tag{8.7}$$

to give

$$\Gamma(b)\langle l_al_b(L_bS_b)l_c(L_cS_c)l_dLSJM|\,T_q^{(k)}(b)\,|\,l_al_b'(L_b'S_b')l_c(L_c'S_c')l_dL'S'M'\rangle. \tag{8.8}$$

Then application of the Wigner–Eckart theorem, followed by successive applications of the formula

$$\langle abJ\|\mathbf{T}^{(k)}(a)\|a'bJ'\rangle$$
$$= (-1)^{a+b+J'+k}[(2J+1)(2J'+1)]^{1/2}\begin{Bmatrix} b & a & J \\ k & J' & a \end{Bmatrix}\langle a\|\mathbf{T}^{(k)}\|a'\rangle, \quad (8.9)$$

yields the final result

$$(-1)^{\phi}\times[J, J', L, L', L_c, L_c', L_b, L_b']^{1/2}\,\delta(S_b, S_b')\,\delta(S_c, S_c')\,\delta(S, S')$$
$$\times\begin{pmatrix} J & k & J \\ -M & q & M \end{pmatrix}\begin{Bmatrix} S & L & J \\ k & J' & L' \end{Bmatrix}\begin{Bmatrix} l_d & L_c & L \\ k & L' & L_c' \end{Bmatrix}\begin{Bmatrix} l_c & L_b & L_c \\ k & L_c' & L_b' \end{Bmatrix}$$
$$\times\begin{Bmatrix} l_a & l_b & L_b \\ k & L_b' & l_b' \end{Bmatrix}\langle l_b\|\mathbf{T}^{(k)}\|l_b'\rangle\times\Gamma(b). \quad (8.10)$$

Here the symbol

$$\phi = (J - M) + (S + L + J' + k) + (l_d + L_c + L' + k)$$
$$+ (l_c + L_b + L_c' + k) + (l_a + l_b + L_b' + k)$$

denotes the phase factor, and we have used the notation

$$[J, J', \cdots]^{1/2} \equiv (2J+1)^{1/2}(2J'\times 1)^{1/2}\cdots. \quad (8.11)$$

The calculation for $\mathcal{G}$-type operators requires a bit more labor, since the antisymmetrizers introduce both direct- and exchange-type matrix elements. The work is straightforward though tedious. We must calculate

$$<\Psi(\Gamma|123\cdots N)|\mathcal{A}^{\dagger}\mathcal{G}\mathcal{A}|\Psi(\Gamma'|123\cdots N)> \equiv \langle\Gamma|\mathcal{A}^{\dagger}\mathcal{G}\mathcal{A}|\Gamma'\rangle, \quad (8.12)$$

where Γ denotes the quantum numbers for N coupled orbitals. The antisymmetrizing operators are sums of all possible permutations of 1, 2, . . . , $N - 1$ electrons, taken with appropriate signs. (We continue to assume that no two orbitals have the same n and l value.) Since there are $N!$ such permutations, the antisymmetrizers include a factor $(N!)^{-1/2}$ to preserve normalization. Thus we can write

$$\mathcal{A}\Psi(\Gamma|123\cdots N)$$
$$= \frac{1}{\sqrt{N!}}[\Psi(\Gamma|123\cdots N) - \Psi(\Gamma|132\cdots N) - \cdots + \Psi(\Gamma|321\cdots N) + \cdots]$$
$$\equiv \frac{1}{\sqrt{N!}}\sum_p(-1)^p\mathcal{P}(p)\Psi(\Gamma|123\cdots N). \quad (8.13)$$

To simplify notation we sometimes use a tilde to denote a completely antisymmetrized function:

$$\tilde{\Psi}(\Gamma) \equiv \mathcal{A}\Psi(\Gamma|123\cdots N). \quad (8.14)$$

A function without a tilde has the electrons in some definite ordering (always specified) in the orbitals. Thus in the function

$$\Psi(1s\ 2p\ (^3P)\ 3p\ ^2P_{JM}|\ 123), \tag{8.15}$$

electron 1 occupies a $1s$ orbital, electron 2 occupies a $2p$ orbital, etc. In the antisymmetric function

$$\tilde{\Psi}(1s\ 2p\ (^3P)\ 3p\ ^2P_{JM}), \tag{8.16}$$

a given electron cannot be assigned to any specific orbital.

Using (8.13) to give the action of the sinistral antisymmetrizer $\mathcal{A}^\dagger$, we can see that the matrix element of (8.12) is the sum of elements such as

$$\frac{1}{\sqrt{N!}} \langle\Psi(\Gamma|\,123\cdots N)|\mathcal{G}\mathcal{A}|\Psi(\Gamma'|\,123\cdots N)\rangle. \tag{8.17}$$

Each of the $N!$ distinct sinistral permutations will contribute an identical amount to (8.12); the contributions differ only in their labeling of coordinates. Thus we can simply multiply any one of these contributions, say (8.17), by the number of distinct contributions, $N!$. When we use (8.13) for the dextral antisymmetrizer $\mathcal{A}$, the two factors $(N!)^{-1/2}$ just cancel the number of contributions ($N!$) and we obtain

$$\begin{aligned}\langle\Psi(\Gamma|\,12\cdots N)|\mathcal{A}^\dagger\mathcal{G}\mathcal{A}|\Psi(\Gamma'|\,12\cdots N\rangle \\ = \langle\Psi(\Gamma|\,12\cdots N)|\mathcal{G}\sum(-1)^p\mathcal{P}(p)|\Psi(\Gamma'|\,12\cdots N)\rangle.\end{aligned} \tag{8.18}$$

That is,

$$\begin{aligned}\langle\Gamma|\mathcal{A}^\dagger\mathcal{G}\mathcal{A}|\Gamma'\rangle &= \langle\Psi(\Gamma|\,12\cdots N)|\mathcal{G}|\Psi(\Gamma'|\,12\cdots N)\rangle + \cdots \\ &\quad - \langle\Psi(\Gamma|\,12\cdots N)|\mathcal{G}|\Psi(\Gamma'|\,21\cdots N)\rangle - \cdots.\end{aligned} \tag{8.19}$$

We see here the familiar direct- and exchange-type interactions.

Under our orthogonality assumptions, the *configurations* Γ and Γ' can differ, *at most*, in two places. If precisely *two orbitals* differ, say the first and second orbitals, then we have

$$\begin{aligned}\langle\Gamma|\mathcal{A}^\dagger\mathcal{G}\mathcal{A}|\Gamma'\rangle &= \langle\Psi(\Gamma|\,12\cdots N)|g_{12}|\Psi(\Gamma'|\,12\cdots N)\rangle \\ &\quad - \langle\Psi(\Gamma|\,12\cdots N)|g_{12}|\Psi(\Gamma'|\,21\cdots N)\rangle.\end{aligned} \tag{8.20}$$

If Γ and Γ' differ in only *one orbital*, say the first orbital, then the sum in $\mathcal{G}$ goes over all possible second orbitals:

$$\begin{aligned}\langle\Gamma|\mathcal{A}^\dagger\mathcal{G}\mathcal{A}|\Gamma'\rangle &= \langle\Psi(\Gamma|\,12\cdots N)|\sum_{j=2}^{N} g_{1j}|\Psi(\Gamma'|\,12\cdots N)\rangle \\ &\quad - \langle\Psi(\Gamma|\,12\cdots N)\sum_{j=2}^{N} g_{1j}|\Psi(\Gamma'|\,21\cdots N)\rangle.\end{aligned} \tag{8.21}$$

And if Γ and Γ' have the *same* configurations, we must use (8.19) with

$$\mathcal{G} = \sum_{i=1}^{N-1} \sum_{j=2}^{N} g_{ij}. \tag{8.22}$$

Equations 8.19–8.21 provide the necessary guidelines for the calculation of $\mathcal{G}$-type operators between coupled wavefunctions, but they cannot be used as they stand. In order to apply tensor operator techniques the electrons in both the sinistral and dextral wavefunctions must be in the same ordering, say the *standard ordering* $123\cdots N$. Therefore we must bring the dextral electrons of (8.19)–(8.21) into this ordering by a succession of recouplings. Each angular recoupling introduces a factor such as

$$\begin{aligned}\langle L_0 l_1(L_1), l_2 L | L_0 l_2(\bar{L}_1) l_1 L\rangle &= [L_1, \bar{L}_1]^{1/2} (-1)^{L_1+l_2+l_1+\bar{L}_1} \begin{Bmatrix} L_1 & l_2 & L \\ \bar{L}_1 & l_1 & L_0 \end{Bmatrix} \\ &\equiv [L_1, \bar{L}_1]^{1/2} W(L_1 l_2 l_1 \bar{L}_1; L L_0),\end{aligned} \tag{8.23}$$

and a sum over the variable $\bar{L}_1$. Each spin recoupling introduces a similar sum and factor. Once the dextral electrons have been recoupled, one faces a matrix element of the form

$$\langle l_a l_b(L_{ab}) l_c \cdots | g_{12} | l'_a l'_b(L'_{ab}) l'_c \cdots\rangle. \tag{8.24}$$

After expressing g_{12} as a tensor operator or sum of tensor operators, one can apply the results of Chapter 6 to obtain the matrix elements.

REFERENCES

[1] B. Judd, *Operator Techniques in Atomic Spectroscopy*, McGraw-Hill, New York (1963).
[2] C. J. Ballhausen, *Introduction to Ligand Field Theory*, McGraw-Hill, New York (1962).
[3] M. Hamermesh, *Group Theory*, Addison-Wesley, Reading, Massachusetts (1962).

9.9 EQUIVALENT ORBITALS: FRACTIONAL PARENTAGE

Wavefunctions that involve equivalent orbitals require special consideration. We recall that for two *nonequivalent* electrons, the function

$$\tilde{\Psi}(l_a l_b LSJM) \equiv \frac{1}{\sqrt{2}} [\Psi(l_a l_b LSJM | 12) - \Psi(l_a l_b LSJM | 21)] \tag{9.1}$$

satisfied the interchange equation

$$\mathcal{P}(12)\tilde{\Psi}(l_a l_b LSJM) = -\tilde{\Psi}(l_a l_b LSJM), \tag{9.2}$$

For two *equivalent* electrons, the function

$$\tilde{\Psi}(l^2LSJM) \equiv \Psi(l^2LSJM|12) \tag{9.3}$$

satisfies a similar equation:

$$\mathcal{P}(12)\tilde{\Psi}(l^2LSJM) = -(-1)^{L+S}\tilde{\Psi}(l^2LSJM). \tag{9.4}$$

Suppose we couple a third orbital, *not* equivalent to the first two, to the function $\Psi(l^2LSJM|12)$. When the resulting function is antisymmetrized in all three electrons, we obtain the function

$$\tilde{\Psi}(l^2(L_0S_0)l_aLSJM) \equiv \tilde{\Psi}(\Gamma)$$

$$\equiv \frac{1}{\sqrt{3}}[\Psi(\Gamma|123) - \Psi(\Gamma|132) - \Psi(\Gamma|321)] \tag{9.5}$$

(the factor $3^{-1/2}$ preserves normalization). Since, for example, the function $\Psi(\Gamma|132)$ satisfies (for $L_0 + S_0$ even) the equation

$$\mathcal{P}(13)\Psi(\Gamma|132) = -\Psi(\Gamma|132),$$

it is easy to verify that $\tilde{\Psi}(\Gamma)$ satisfies the equation

$$\mathcal{P}(12)\tilde{\Psi}(\Gamma) = \mathcal{P}(23)\tilde{\Psi}(\Gamma) = \mathcal{P}(13)\tilde{\Psi}(\Gamma) = -\tilde{\Psi}(\Gamma). \tag{9.6}$$

Note that each of the three constituent functions of (9.5) corresponds to a mathematically distinct function: $\Psi(\Gamma|123)$ has electron number 3 in the nonequivalent orbital l_a, whereas $\Psi(\Gamma|132)$ has electron number 2 in this orbital. This distinction still remains after the electrons have been recoupled into the standard ordering. The function of (9.5) can be written, after being recoupled, as

$$\begin{aligned}\tilde{\Psi}(l^2(L_0S_0(l_aLSJM) = \frac{1}{\sqrt{3}}\Big[&\Psi(l^2(L_0S_0)l_aLSJM|123)\\ &-\sum_{\bar{L}\bar{S}}[L_0, S_0, \bar{L}, \bar{S}]^{1/2}W(L_0l_al\bar{L}; Ll)W(S_0\tfrac{1}{2}\tfrac{1}{2}\bar{S}; S\tfrac{1}{2})\\ &\times[1 + (-1)^{L_0+S_0+\bar{L}+\bar{S}}]\Psi(ll_a(\bar{L}\bar{S})lLSJM|123)\Big].\end{aligned} \tag{9.7}$$

Equation 9.7 exhibits the recoupling described in the preceding section on nonequivalent electrons; note that the functions $\Psi(l^2l_a|123)$ and $\Psi(ll_al|123)$ are mathematically distinct.

Suppose now the third orbital is the *same* as the preceding two, so that all three orbitals are equivalent. We can then rewrite (9.7) as (note $L_0 + S_0$ = even and $\bar{L} + \bar{S}$ = even)

$$\tilde{\Psi}(l^2(L_0S_0)lLSJM) = \frac{1}{\sqrt{C}}\{\Psi(l^2(L_0S_0)lLSJM|123) - 2\sum[L_0, S_0, \bar{L}, \bar{S}]^{1/2}W(L_0ll\bar{L}; Ll)W(S_0\tfrac{1}{2}\tfrac{1}{2}\bar{S}; S\tfrac{1}{2}) \times \Psi(l^2(\bar{L}\bar{S})lLSJM|123)\}, \quad (9.8)$$

where C is a normalization constant. Because we cannot distinguish $\Psi(l^2l|123)$ from $\Psi(lll|123)$, we can write (9.8) as

$$\tilde{\Psi}(l^2(L_0S_0)lLSJM) = \sum_{\bar{L}\bar{S}} C_{\bar{L}\bar{S}}\Psi(l^2(\bar{L}\bar{S})lLSJM|123). \quad (9.9)$$

Here we have written $\tilde{\Psi}(l^2(L_0S_0)lLSJM)$, which is antisymmetric in *all three* electrons, as a linear combination of functions that are antisymmetric in the *first two* electrons. The third electron has been singled out and coupled *last*. The summation in (9.9) [or (9.7)] goes over all *allowed* parentage terms, $\bar{L}\bar{S}$, of two electrons. In other words we have expressed a wavefunction of l^3 as a linear combination of functions with different parentage. For this reason the expansion coefficients of (9.9) are called *coefficients of fractional parentage* (CFP). These coefficients were first introduced by Racah [1]. The notion of fractional parentage may be traced further back, to the work of Bacher and Goudsmit [2] and later Menzel and Goldberg [3]. The usual notation for the CFP, following Racah, is

$$(l^2\bar{S}\bar{L}, l|\}l^3\alpha SL).$$

We shall usually abbreviate this to

$$(l^2\bar{S}\bar{L}|\}l^3\alpha SL) \equiv (l^3\alpha SL\{|l^2\bar{S}\bar{L}).$$

That is,

$$\tilde{\Psi}(l^3\alpha SLJM) = \sum_{\bar{L}\bar{S}} (l^3\alpha SL\{|l^2\bar{S}\bar{L})\Psi(l^2(\bar{L}\bar{S})lLSJM|123). \quad (9.10a)$$

The symbol α denotes any quantum numbers other than S and L that are required to completely specify the term of l^3. Such a label is unnecessary for p orbitals, but for d and f orbitals several terms with the same S and L can occur. (For three d electrons there are two ^2D terms; for three f electrons there are two ^2D, ^2F, and ^2G terms.) In (9.9) we have used the *principal parent scheme* (see de Shalit and Talmi [4], p. 274), also called the *godparent scheme* (see Flowers [5]) in which a wavefunction is identified, when necessary, as relating to a particular parent. We should write (9.9) as

$$\tilde{\Psi}(l^2[L_0S_0]lLSJM) = \sum_{\bar{L}\bar{S}} (l^3[L_0S_0]LS\{|l^2\bar{L}\bar{S})\Psi(l^2(\bar{L}\bar{S})lLSJM|123), \quad (9.11)$$

where $[L_0S_0]$ labels the *principal parent* or *godparent*. Equation 9.8 shows that

$$(l^3[L_0S_0]LS\{|l^2\bar{L}\bar{S}) = \frac{1}{\sqrt{C}}\{\delta(L_0, \bar{L})\delta(S_0, \bar{S})$$
$$- 2[L_0, S_0, \bar{L}, \bar{S}]^{1/2} W(L_0 l l \bar{L}; Ll) W(S_0 \tfrac{1}{2}\tfrac{1}{2}\bar{S}; S\tfrac{1}{2})\}, \tag{9.12a}$$

if we restrict the summation to terms with $\bar{L} + \bar{S} =$ even. We could, of course, replace the factor 2 here by

$$2 \rightarrow [1 + (-1)^{\bar{L}+\bar{S}}],$$

and consider (9.11) to be a sum over all terms; the $\bar{L} + \bar{S} = odd$ terms will have zero coefficients.

The preceding remarks apply just as well in *jj* coupling, for which we consider orbitals to be equivalent when they have the same *n*, *l*, and *j*.

The *jj* coupling counterpart of (9.10*a*) is

$$\tilde{\Psi}(j^3\alpha JM) = \sum_{\bar{J}} (j^3\alpha J\{|j^2\bar{J})\Psi(j^2(\bar{J})jJM|123) \tag{9.10b}$$

(sum over allowed or $\bar{J}$ = even states), and the counterpart of (9.12*a*) is

$$(j^3[J_0]J\{|j^2\bar{J}) = \frac{1}{\sqrt{C}}\{\delta(J^0, \bar{J}) - 2[J_0, \bar{J}]^{1/2} W(J_0 jj\bar{J}; Jj)\}. \tag{9.12b}$$

Such *jj* coupling functions find extensive use in theoretical investigations of nuclear structure, where spin–orbit interactions play an important role. They have not yet been applied to atomic-structure calculations.

Once we have obtained properly antisymmetrized three-electron functions for equivalent orbitals, we can repeat the coupling and antisymmetrization process with a fourth electron. If the fourth orbital is not equivalent to the other three, we obtain

$$\tilde{\Psi}(l^3(\alpha_0S_0L_0)l_aSLJM) \equiv \tilde{\Psi}(\Gamma) = \frac{1}{\sqrt{4}}[\Psi(\Gamma|1234) - \Psi(\Gamma|4231)$$
$$- \Psi(\Gamma|1432) - \Psi(\Gamma|1243)]. \tag{9.13}$$

Here, because of our previous antisymmetrization of the first three orbitals, we need antisymmetrize only the fourth orbital, since

$$\Psi(\Gamma|1234) = -\Psi(\Gamma|2134), \qquad \text{etc.}$$

We can again recouple the orbitals of the constituent functions in (9.13) to place the electrons in their standard order. If the fourth orbital is equivalent to the preceding three, this operation leads to an equation of the form

$$\tilde{\Psi}(l^4\alpha SLJM) = \sum_{\bar{\alpha}\bar{S}\bar{L}} (l^4\alpha SL\{|l^3\bar{\alpha}\bar{S}\bar{L})\Psi(l^3(\bar{\alpha}\bar{S}\bar{L})l\alpha SLJM|1234). \tag{9.14}$$

This process of coupling, antisymmetrizing, and recoupling, can evidently be repeated (although not indefinitely—see below). In the general case we obtain the function

$$\tilde{\Psi}(l^N\alpha SLJM) = \sum_{\bar{\alpha}\bar{S}\bar{L}} (l^N\alpha SL\{|l^{N-1}\bar{\alpha}\bar{S}\bar{L})\Psi(l^{N-1}(\bar{\alpha}\bar{S}\bar{L})lSLJM|12\cdots N). \tag{9.15}$$

Equation 9.15 can be thought of as a partial *definition* of the coefficients of fractional parentage. If we express a completely antisymmetrized function of N electrons in terms of functions in which *one* electron [the *last* or Nth in our convention of (9.15) is singled out and coupled last, then the CFP are the expansion coefficients. To complete the definition we must specify a phase convention and the coupling scheme (not only as LS or jj coupling but also any additional specification that may be required, such as principal parent).

However, the process of coupling additional equivalent orbitals and antisymmetrizing must terminate when we reach the *closed l-shell* function that has $N = 2(2l + 1)$ orbitals, because no more than $4l + 2$ equivalent orbitals can occur in a function that satisfies the Pauli principle. The nature of the closed l-shell function is most easily seen from its expansion into simple product functions. Suppose we take the product of $2(2l + 1)$ orbitals, which we abbreviate with the notation

$$\phi(nlm\mu|i) \equiv (m)_i^\mu.$$

Since m and μ can take the values

$$\begin{aligned} m &= l, l-1, \ldots, 0, \ldots, -l+1, -l \qquad &(2l+1 \text{ values})\\ \mu &= +, - &(2 \text{ values}), \end{aligned}$$

clearly the only product functions that do not have repeated m or μ values are those obtained by permutation of the electron coordinates in the function

$$(l)_1^+(l)_2^-(l-1)_3^+(l-1)_4^-\cdots(-l)_{4l+1}^+(-l)_{4l+2}^- \equiv \Phi(l^{4l+2}0|1234\cdots 4l+2). \tag{9.16}$$

This function has $S = L = J = M = 0$, hence our notation $(l^{4l+2}0)$. The antisymmetrized closed l-shell function is a determinantal wavefunction (i.e., an m-scheme function) as well as an LS-scheme function

$$\tilde{\Psi}(l^{4l+2}0) = \mathcal{A}\Phi(l^{4l+2}0|12\cdots 4l+2). \tag{9.17}$$

We have mentioned the fact that equivalent d or f orbitals result in several terms of the same type. One must somehow distinguish these terms. (This problem does not arise with p orbitals. For s orbitals CFP are unnecessary.) In the principal-parent scheme, the label α on the N-electron function $\tilde{\Psi}(l^N \alpha SLJM)$ specifies the principal parent, principal grandparent, etc. This genealogical characterization has not been used as widely as other schemes. The *seniority scheme*, developed by Racah, is based on pairs of orbitals coupled to ^1S. Suppose we couple the two-electron function $\tilde{\Psi}(l^2 0)$ to the antisymmetrized N-electron function $\tilde{\Psi}(l^N \alpha SLJM)$. The result is an $(N + 2)$-electron function with quantum numbers $SLJM$:

$$\Psi(l^N \alpha(SL), l^2(0), SLJM | 12 \cdots N, N + 1, N + 2).$$

(Although this function is not fully antisymmetric, it can readily be antisymmetrized.) As a simple example, such a pair of d orbitals, when coupled to a single d orbital gives the three-electron $d^3\ {}^2D$ function,

$$\Psi(d(^2D), d^2(0), {}^2D_{JM} | 123).$$

Now if another term of the same type is possible (as in another ^2D term for the example d^3), we can construct it to be orthogonal to this first term. By adding further ^1S pairs, we can obtain a sequence of terms of the same type. In our d-orbital example we obtain the sequence of terms

$$d(^2D) \to d^3(^2D) \to d^5(^2D) \to d^7(^2D) \to d^9(^2D).$$

Each of the functions corresponding to these terms differs by a number of ^1S pairs. The structure is readily illustrated with m-scheme wavefunctions. The $d^2(^1S)$ function is

$d^2(^1S)$:

$$\mathcal{A}\frac{1}{\sqrt{5}}[(d_2^+ d_{-2}^-) - (d_2^- d_{-2}^\pm) - (d_1^+ d_{-1}^-) + (d_1^- d_{-1}^\pm) + (d_0^+ d_0^-)]$$

in the notation $\varphi(nlm\mu) = l_m^{\,\mu}$. Then the preceding sequence of ^2D terms, with $M_L = 0$ and $M_S = \frac{1}{2}$, is

$d^1(^2D)$: (d_0^+)

$d^3(^2D)$: $\mathcal{A}\frac{1}{\sqrt{4}}[(d_0^+ d_2^+ d_{-2}^-) - (d_0^+ d_2^- d_{-2}^\pm) - (d_0^+ d_1^+ d_{-1}^-) + (d_0^+ d_1^- d_{-1}^\pm)]$

$d^5(^2D)$: $\mathcal{A}\frac{1}{\sqrt{6}}[(d_0^+ d_2^+ d_{-2}^- d_2^- d_{-2}^\pm) - (d_0^+ d_2^+ d_{-2}^- d_1^- d_{-1}^\pm)$

$+ (d_0^+ d_2^+ d_{-2}^- d_1^+ d_{-1}^-) - (d_0^+ d_2^- d_{-2}^\pm d_1^+ d_{-1}^-)$

$+ (d_0^+ d_2^- d_{-2}^\pm d_1^- d_{-1}^\pm) - (d_0^+ d_1^+ d_{-1}^- d_1^- d_{-1}^\pm)]$

$d^7(^2D)$: $\mathcal{A}\frac{1}{\sqrt{4}}[(d_0^+ d_2^- d_{-2}^\pm d_1^+ d_{-1}^- d_1^- d_{-1}^\pm) - (d_0^+ d_2^+ d_{-2}^- d_1^+ d_{-1}^- d_1^- d_{-1}^\pm)$

$- (d_0^+ d_2^+ d_{-2}^- d_2^- d_{-2}^\pm d_1^- d_{-1}^\pm) + (d_0^+ d_2^+ d_{-2}^- d_2^- d_{-2}^\pm d_1^+ d_{-1}^-)]$

$d^9(^2D)$: $\mathcal{A}(d_0^+ d_2^+ d_{-2}^- d_2^- d_{-2}^\pm d_1^+ d_{-1}^- d_1^- d_{-1}^\pm)$.

The seniority scheme labels each term with a *seniority* or *seniority number*, which can be defined as follows. Start with a function $\Psi(l^N\alpha SLJM|12\cdots N)$, constructed according to the procedure described above. Delete all pairs of ^1S electrons, leaving the function $\Psi(l^v\alpha SLJM12|\cdots v)$. Then v is the *seniority*. In other words, l^v is the configuration in which the term αSL occurs for the first time. The ^2D terms of the above example all have seniority *one*, because they relate to the configuration d^1. An alternative definition of seniority, proposed by Racah, employs a pairing operator $\mathbb{Q}$ whose eigenvalues give the number of ^1S pairs.

Following Racah, one conventionally indicates the seniority by a preceding subscript on the term symbol. For example, the preceding sequence of seniority-one terms is denoted

$$d(^2_1D) \to d^3(^2_1D) \to d^5(^2_1D) \to d^7(^2_1D) \to d^9(^2_1D).$$

In the d-orbital example, a second type of ^2D term appears in d^3. This term will have seniority *three*, and will recur in d^5 but not d^7. By construction, this ^2_3D function is made orthogonal to the ^2_1D function. The d^5 configuration has a third type of ^2D function, with seniority *five:* ^2_5D.

Although the seniority number suffices to distinguish the terms of equivalent d orbitals, additional quantum numbers are required for f orbitals. A systematic treatment of f electrons has been carried out with the aid of the theory of Lie groups. The interested reader should consult the works of Racah [6], Judd [7], or Wybourne [8] for discussion of these important topics.

The preceding discussion of fractional parentage is intended simply to introduce the basic ideas first presented by Racah. Bibliography 8 lists a number of books and articles that discuss CFP in more detail, and the reader should refer to these for questions of phases, normalization, and the calculations of the CFP. A lengthier bibliography has been compiled by Biedenharn and van Dam [9].

For many practical purposes, one needs to know only *how* to introduce CFP [i.e., (9.15)] and *what* the numerical values are. Table 9.3 provides such tables, in Racah's seniority scheme (with Racah's phase convention) for p and d orbitals in LS coupling. Tables for f orbitals may be found in Judd's book [7], and tables for jj coupling may be found in the book by de Shalit and Talmi [4] and in the article by Bayman and Landé [10]. However, a few simple relationships between CFP are often useful. Appendix A provides a few formulas taken from Racah [1]. Further properties were discussed by Layzer [11].

Table 9.2 Coefficients of Fractional Parentage $(l^N\{|l^{N-1})$ Times $\sqrt{N}$

p electrons

p^2 \ p^1	${}^{2}_{1}P$
${}_0{}^1S$	1.41421
${}_2{}^3P$	1.41421
${}_2{}^1D$	1.41421

p^3 \ p^2	${}^{1}_{0}S$	${}^{3}_{2}P$	${}^{1}_{2}D$
${}_3{}^4S$	0.	1.73205	0.
${}_1{}^2P$	0.81650	—1.22474	—0.91287
${}_3{}^2D$	0.	1.22474	—1.22474

p^4 \ p^3	${}^{4}_{3}S$	${}^{2}_{1}P$	${}^{2}_{3}D$
${}_0{}^1S$	0.	2.00000	0.
${}_2{}^3P$	—1.15470	—1.00000	1.29099
${}_2{}^1D$	0.	—1.00000	— 1.73205

p^5 \ p^4	${}^{1}_{0}S$	${}^{3}_{2}P$	${}^{1}_{2}D$
${}_1{}^2P$	0.57735	1.73205	1.29099

d electrons

d^2 \ d^1	${}^{2}_{1}D$
${}_0{}^1S$	1.41421
${}_2{}^3P$	1.41421
${}_2{}^1D$	1.41421
${}_2{}^3F$	1.41421
${}_2{}^1G$	1.41421

d^3 \ d^2	${}^{1}_{0}S$	${}^{3}_{2}P$	${}^{1}_{2}D$	${}^{3}_{2}F$	${}^{1}_{2}G$
${}_3{}^2P$	0.	0.83666	1.22474	—0.89443	0.
${}_3{}^4P$	0.	—1.26491	0.	—1.18322	0.
${}_1{}^2D$	0.89443	—0.67082	—0.50000	—1.02470	—0.67082
${}_3{}^2D$	0.	—1.02470	0.98198	0.67082	—0.73193
${}_3{}^2F$	0.	1.09545	—0.65465	0.54772	—1.03510
${}_3{}^4F$	0.	—0.77460	0.	1.54919	0.
${}_3{}^2G$	0.	0.	—0.84515	1.22474	0.88641
${}_3{}^2H$	0.	0.	0.	—1.22474	1.22474

d^4 \ d^3	${}^{2}_{3}P$	${}^{4}_{3}P$	${}^{2}_{1}D$	${}^{2}_{3}D$	${}^{2}_{3}F$	${}^{4}_{3}F$	${}^{2}_{3}G$	${}^{2}_{3}H$
${}_0{}^1S$	0.	0.	2.00000	0.	0.	0.	0.	0.
${}_4{}^1S$	0.	0.	0.	2.00000	0.	0.	0.	0.
${}_2{}^3P$	—0.39441	—0.84327	1.22474	—0.62361	—0.78881	—0.78881	0.	0.
${}_4{}^3P$	1.05409	—0.78881	0.	0.66667	—1.05409	0.84327	0.	0.
${}_2{}^1D$	—0.77460	0.	1.22474	0.80178	0.63246	0.	—0.92582	0.
${}_4{}^1D$	1.09545	0.	0.	0.75593	1.34164	0.	0.65465	0.
${}_4{}^3D$	0.51640	0.96609	0.	1.06904	—0.63246	—0.63246	0.92582	0.
${}_4{}^5D$	0.	1.09545	0.	0.	0.	1.67332	0.	0.
${}_4{}^1F$	0.92582	0.	0.	1.19523	—0.86603	0.	—0.14639	—0.97101
${}_2{}^3F$	0.27603	—0.51640	1.22474	0.26726	—0.25820	1.03280	0.65465	0.72375
${}_4{}^3F$	—0.69007	—1.03280	0.	0.53452	—0.64550	—0.51640	—0.98198	0.72375
${}_2{}^1G$	0.	0.	1.22474	—0.44544	0.74536	0.	0.72375	—1.10554
${}_4{}^1G$	0.	0.	0.	0.59094	1.23603	0.	—1.41842	—0.33333
${}_4{}^3G$	0.	0.	0.	0.69007	0.86603	—1.15470	0.84092	0.85635
${}_4{}^3H$	0.	0.	0.	0.	0.57735	1.15470	—0.77460	1.31656
${}_4{}^1I$	0.	0.	0.	0.	0.	0.	1.09545	1.67332

Table 9.2 (*continued*)

d^5 \ d^4	${}^1_0S$	${}^1_4S$	${}^3_2P$	${}^3_4P$	${}^1_2D$	${}^1_4D$	${}^3_4D$	${}^5_4D$	${}^1_4F$	${}^3_2F$	${}^3_4F$	${}^1_2G$	${}^1_4G$	${}^3_4G$	${}^3_4H$	${}^1_4I$
${}^2_5S$	0.	0.	0.	0.	0.	−1.41421	1.73205	0.	0.	0.	0.	0.	0.	0.	0.	0.
${}^6_5S$	0.	0.	0.	0.	0.	0.	0.	2.23607	0.	0.	0.	0.	0.	0.	0.	0.
${}^2_3P$	0.	0.	0.68313	0.91287	1.00000	0.70711	0.57735	0.	−0.70711	−0.73030	−0.91287	0.	0.	0.	0.	0.
${}^4_3P$	0.	0.	−1.03280	0.48305	0.	0.	0.76376	−1.11803	0.	−0.96609	0.96609	0.	0.	0.	0.	0.
${}^2_1D$	0.77460	0.	−0.94868	0.	−0.70711	0.	0.	0.	0.	−1.44914	0.	−0.94868	0.	0.	0.	0.
${}^2_3D$	0.	−0.44721	−0.83666	−0.44721	0.80178	−0.37796	0.92582	0.	0.70711	0.54772	−0.54772	−0.59761	−0.39641	0.80178	0.	0.
${}^2_5D$	0.	−0.63246	0.	0.94868	0.	0.80178	0.65465	0.	0.50000	0.	1.16189	0.	0.84092	0.56695	0.	0.
${}^4_5D$	0.	0.	0.	0.94868	0.	0.	−0.98198	−1.11803	0.	0.	−0.77460	0.	0.	1.13389	0.	0.
${}^2_3F$	0.	0.	0.89443	−0.59761	−0.53452	0.56695	0.46291	0.	0.43301	0.44721	−0.55902	−0.84515	0.70076	−0.85042	0.62678	0.
${}^2_5F$	0.	0.	0.	0.80178	0.	−0.42258	1.03510	0.	−0.96825	0.	−0.75000	0.	0.94017	−0.12677	−0.84092	0.
${}^4_3F$	0.	0.	−0.63246	−0.33806	0.	0.	−0.32733	−1.11803	0.	1.26491	0.31623	0.	0.	−0.80178	−0.88641	0.
${}^2_3G$	0.	0.	0.	0.	−0.69007	−0.24398	0.59761	0.	−0.06455	1.00000	0.75000	0.72375	0.70921	0.72826	0.74162	−0.65828
${}^2_5G$	0.	0.	0.	0.	0.	0.62678	0.51177	0.	−0.82916	0.	1.07044	0.	−0.57335	−1.22838	−0.28868	−0.76871
${}^4_5G$	0.	0.	0.	0.	0.	0.	0.54554	−1.11803	0.	0.	−0.91287	0.	0.	−0.88641	1.35401	0.
${}^2_3H$	0.	0.	0.	0.	0.	0.	0.	0.	0.38730	−1.00000	0.50000	1.00000	−0.15076	−0.67082	1.14018	0.90955
${}^2_5I$	0.	0.	0.	0.	0.	0.	0.	0.	0.	0.	0.	0.	−0.63960	0.94868	1.44914	−1.26131

d^6 \ d^5	${}^2_5S$	${}^6_5S$	${}^2_3P$	${}^4_3P$	${}^2_1D$	${}^2_3D$	${}^2_5D$	${}^4_5D$	${}^2_3F$	${}^2_5F$	${}^4_3F$	${}^2_3G$	${}^2_5G$	${}^4_5G$	${}^2_3H$	${}^2_5I$
${}^1_0S$	0.	0.	0.	0.	2.44949	0.	0.	0.	0.	0.	0.	0.	0.	0.	0.	0.
${}^1_4S$	0.	0.	0.	0.	0.	1.41421	−2.00000	0.	0.	0.	0.	0.	0.	0.	0.	0.
${}^3_2P$	0.	0.	0.55777	1.19257	−1.00000	0.88192	0.	0.	1.11555	0.	1.11555	0.	0.	0.	0.	0.
${}^3_4P$	0.	0.	0.74536	−0.55777	0.	0.47140	1.00000	−1.41421	−0.74536	−1.00000	0.59628	0.	0.	0.	0.	0.
${}^1_2D$	0.	0.	1.09545	0.	−1.00000	−1.13389	0.	0.	−0.89443	0.	0.	1.30931	0.	0.	0.	0.
${}^1_4D$	−0.89443	0.	0.77460	0.	0.	0.53452	1.13389	0.	0.94868	0.70711	0.	0.46291	1.18924	0.	0.	0.
${}^3_4D$	0.63246	0.	−0.36515	0.68313	0.	0.75593	−0.53452	−1.13389	−0.44721	1.00000	−0.44721	0.65465	−0.56061	0.84515	0.	0.
${}^5_4D$	0.	1.09545	0.	0.77460	0.	0.	0.	1.00000	0.	0.	1.18322	0.	0.	1.34164	0.	0.
${}^1_4F$	0.	0.	0.65465	0.	0.	0.84515	−0.59761	0.	−0.61237	−1.36931	0.	−0.10351	1.32961	0.	−0.68661	0.
${}^3_2F$	0.	0.	−0.39036	0.73030	−1.00000	−0.37796	0.	0.	0.36515	0.	−1.46059	−0.92582	0.	0.	−1.02353	0.
${}^3_4F$	0.	0.	−0.48795	−0.73030	0.	0.37796	0.80178	0.75593	−0.45644	0.61237	−0.36515	−0.69437	0.99103	1.19523	0.51177	0.
${}^1_4G$	0.	0.	0.	0.	−1.00000	0.62994	0.	0.	−1.05409	0.	0.	−1.02353	0.	0.	1.56347	0.
${}^1_2G$	0.	0.	0.	0.	0.	0.41786	0.88641	0.	0.87401	−1.17260	0.	−1.00297	−0.81084	0.	−0.23570	−1.08711
${}^3_4G$	0.	0.	0.	0.	0.	0.48795	−0.34503	0.97590	0.61237	−0.09129	−0.81650	0.59462	1.00297	−1.02353	0.60553	−0.93095
${}^3_4H$	0.	0.	0.	0.	0.	0.	0.	0.	0.40825	0.54772	0.81650	−0.54772	−0.21320	−1.41421	0.93095	1.28629
${}^1_4I$	0.	0.	0.	0.	0.	0.	0.	0.	0.	0.	0.	0.77460	−0.90453	0.	1.18322	−1.78377

$\mathbf{d^7}$ \ $\mathbf{d^6}$	^1_0S	^1_4S	^3_2P	^3_4P	^1_2D	^1_4D	^3_4D	^5_4D	^1_4F	^3_2F	^3_4F	^1_2G	^1_4G	^3_4G	^3_4H	^1_4I
$_3{}^2P$	0.	0.	0.48305	—1.29099	0.70711	—1.00000	—0.81650	0.	1.00000	—0.51640	1.29099	0.	0.	0.	0.	0.
$_3{}^4P$	0.	0.	—0.73030	—0.68313	0.	0.	—1.08012	1.58114	0.	—0.68313	—1.36626	0.	0.	0.	0.	0.
$_1{}^2D$	0.63246	0.	1.16189	0.	0.86603	0.	0.	0.	0.	1.77482	0.	1.16189	0.	0.	0.	0.
$_3{}^2D$	0.	0.63246	—0.59161	0.63246	0.56695	0.53452	—1.30931	0.	—1.00000	0.38730	0.77460	—0.42258	0.56061	—1.13389	0.	0.
$_3{}^2F$	0.	0.	0.63246	0.84515	—0.37796	—0.80178	—0.65465	0.	—0.61237	0.31623	0.79057	—0.59761	—0.99103	1.20268	—0.88641	0.
$_3{}^4F$	0.	0.	—0.44721	0.47809	0.	0.	0.46291	1.58114	0.	0.89443	—0.44721	0.	0.	1.13389	1.25357	0.
$_3{}^2G$	0.	0.	0.	0.	—0.48795	0.34503	—0.84515	0.	0.09129	0.70711	—1.06066	0.51177	—1.00297	—1.02991	—1.04881	0.93095
$_3{}^2H$	0.	0.	0.	0.	0.	0.	0.	0.	—0.54772	—0.70711	—0.70711	0.70711	0.21320	0.94868	—1.61245	—1.28629

$\mathbf{d^8}$ \ $\mathbf{d^7}$	^2_3P	^4_3P	^2_1D	^2_3D	^2_3F	^4_3F	^2_3G	^2_3H
$_0{}^1S$	0.	0.	2.82843	0.	0.	0.	0.	0.
$_2{}^3P$	—0.68313	—1.46059	—0.70711	—1.08012	—1.36626	—1.36626	0.	0.
$_2{}^1D$	—1.34164	0.	—0.70711	1.38873	1.09545	0.	—1.60357	0.
$_2{}^3F$	0.47809	—0.89443	—0.70711	0.46291	—0.44721	1.78885	1.13389	1.25357
$_2{}^1G$	0.	0.	—0.70711	—0.77152	1.29099	0.	1.25357	—1.91485

$\mathbf{d^9}$ \ $\mathbf{d^8}$	^1_0S	^3_2P	^1_2D	^3_2F	^1_2G
$_1{}^2D$	0.44721	1.34164	1.00000	2.04939	1.34164

Table 9.3 Squares of Coefficients of Fractional Parentage $(l^N\{|l^{N-1})$ Times N

p electrons

p^2 \ p^1	${}^2_1P$
${}_0{}^1S$	2.00000
${}_2{}^3P$	2.00000
${}_2{}^1D$	2.00000

p^3 \ p^2	${}^1_0S$	${}^3_2P$	${}^1_2D$
${}_3{}^4S$	0.	3.00000	0.
${}_1{}^2P$	0.66667	1.50000	0.83333
${}_3{}^2D$	0.	1.50000	1.50000

p^4 \ p^3	${}^4_3S$	${}^2_1P$	${}^2_3D$
${}_0{}^1S$	0.	4.00000	0.
${}_2{}^3P$	1.33333	1.00000	1.66667
${}_2{}^1D$	0.	1.00000	3.00000

p^5 \ p^4	${}^1_0S$	${}^3_2P$	${}^1_2D$
${}_1{}^2P$	0.33333	3.00000	1.66667

d electrons

d^2 \ d^1	${}^2_1D$
${}_0{}^1S$	2.00000
${}_2{}^3P$	2.00000
${}_2{}^1D$	2.00000
${}_2{}^3F$	2.00000
${}_2{}^1G$	2.00000

d^3 \ d^2	${}^1_0S$	${}^3_2P$	${}^1_2D$	${}^3_2F$	${}^1_2G$
${}_3{}^2P$	0.	0.70000	1.50000	0.80000	0.
${}_3{}^4P$	0.	1.60000	0.	1.40000	0.
${}_1{}^2D$	0.80000	0.45000	0.25000	1.05000	0.45000
${}_3{}^2D$	0.	1.05000	0.96429	0.45000	0.53571
${}_3{}^2F$	0.	1.20000	0.42857	0.30000	1.07143
${}_3{}^4F$	0.	0.60000	0.	2.40000	0.
${}_3{}^2G$	0.	0.	0.71429	1.50000	0.78571
${}_3{}^2H$	0.	0.	0.	1.50000	1.50000

d^4 \ d^3	${}^2_3P$	${}^4_3P$	${}^2_1D$	${}^2_3D$	${}^2_3F$	${}^4_3F$	${}^2_3G$	${}^2_3H$
${}_0{}^1S$	0.	0.	4.00000	0.	0.	0.	0.	0.
${}_4{}^1S$	0.	0.	0.	4.00000	0.	0.	0.	0.
${}_2{}^3P$	0.15556	0.71111	1.50000	0.38889	0.62222	0.62222	0.	0.
${}_4{}^3P$	1.11111	0.62222	0.	0.44444	1.11111	0.71111	0.	0.
${}_2{}^1D$	0.60000	0.	1.50000	0.64286	0.40000	0.	0.85714	0.
${}_4{}^1D$	1.20000	0.	0.	0.57143	1.80000	0.	0.42857	0.
${}_4{}^3D$	0.26667	0.93333	0.	1.14286	0.40000	0.40000	0.85714	0.
${}_4{}^5D$	0.	1.20000	0.	0.	0.	2.80000	0.	0.
${}_4{}^1F$	0.85714	0.	0.	1.42857	0.75000	0.	0.02143	0.94286
${}_2{}^3F$	0.07619	0.26667	1.50000	0.07143	0.06667	1.06667	0.42857	0.52381
${}_4{}^3F$	0.47619	1.06667	0.	0.28571	0.41667	0.26667	0.96429	0.52381
${}_2{}^1G$	0.	0.	1.50000	0.19841	0.55556	0.	0.52381	1.22222
${}_4{}^1G$	0.	0.	0.	0.34921	1.52778	0.	2.01190	0.11111
${}_4{}^3G$	0.	0.	0.	0.47619	0.75000	1.33333	0.70714	0.73333
${}_4{}^3H$	0.	0.	0.	0.	0.33333	1.33333	0.60000	1.73333
${}_4{}^1I$	0.	0.	0.	0.	0.	0.	1.20000	2.80000

d⁵ \ d⁴	^1_0S	^1_4S	^3_2P	^3_4P	^1_2D	^1_4D	^3_4D	^5_4D	^1_4F	^3_2F	^3_4F	^1_2G	^1_4G	^3_4G	^3_4H	^1_4I
$_5{}^2S$	0.	0.	0.	0.	0.	2.00000	3.00000	0.	0.	0.	0.	0.	0.	0.	0.	0.
$_5{}^6S$	0.	0.	0.	0.	0.	0.	0.	5.00000	0.	0.	0.	0.	0.	0.	0.	0.
$_3{}^2P$	0.	0.	0.46667	0.83333	1.00000	0.50000	0.33333	0.	0.50000	0.53333	0.83333	0.	0.	0.	0.	0.
$_3{}^4P$	0.	0.	1.06667	0.23333	0.	0.	0.58333	1.25000	0.	0.93333	0.93333	0.	0.	0.	0.	0.
$_1{}^2D$	0.60000	0.	0.90000	0.	0.50000	0.	0.	0.	0.	2.10000	0.	0.90000	0.	0.	0.	0.
$_3{}^2D$	0.	0.20000	0.70000	0.20000	0.64286	0.14286	0.85714	0.	0.50000	0.30000	0.30000	0.35714	0.15714	0.64286	0.	0.
$_5{}^2D$	0.	0.40000	0.	0.90000	0.	0.64286	0.42857	0.	0.25000	0.	1.35000	0.	0.70714	0.32143	0.	0.
$_5{}^4D$	0.	0.	0.	0.90000	0.	0.	0.96429	1.25000	0.	0.	0.60000	0.	0.	1.28571	0.	0.
$_3{}^2F$	0.	0.	0.80000	0.35714	0.28571	0.32143	0.21429	0.	0.18750	0.20000	0.31250	0.71429	0.49107	0.72321	0.39286	0.
$_5{}^2F$	0.	0.	0.	0.64286	0.	0.17857	1.07143	0.	0.93750	0.	0.56250	0.	0.88393	0.01607	0.70714	0.
$_3{}^4F$	0.	0.	0.40000	0.11429	0.	0.	0.10714	1.25000	0.	1.60000	0.10000	0.	0.	0.64286	0.78571	0.
$_3{}^2G$	0.	0.	0.	0.	0.47619	0.05952	0.35714	0.	0.00417	1.00000	0.56250	0.52381	0.50298	0.53036	0.55000	0.43333
$_5{}^2G$	0.	0.	0.	0.	0.	0.39286	0.26190	0.	0.68750	0.	1.14583	0.	0.32873	1.50893	0.08333	0.59091
$_5{}^4G$	0.	0.	0.	0.	0.	0.	0.29762	1.25000	0.	0.	0.83333	0.	0.	0.78571	1.83333	0.
$_3{}^2H$	0.	0.	0.	0.	0.	0.	0.	0.	0.15000	1.00000	0.25000	1.00000	0.02273	0.45000	1.30000	0.82727
$_5{}^2I$	0.	0.	0.	0.	0.	0.	0.	0.	0.	0.	0.	0.	0.40909	0.90000	2.10000	1.59091

d⁶ \ d⁵	^2_5S	^6_5S	^2_3P	^4_3P	^2_1D	^2_3D	^2_5D	^4_5D	^2_3F	^2_5F	^4_3F	^2_3G	^2_5G	^4_5G	^2_3H	^2_5I
$_0{}^1S$	0.	0.	0.	0.	6.00000	0.	0.	0.	0.	0.	0.	0.	0.	0.	0.	0.
$_4{}^1S$	0.	0.	0.	0.	0.	2.00000	4.00000	0.	0.	0.	0.	0.	0.	0.	0.	0.
$_2{}^3P$	0.	0.	0.31111	1.42222	1.00000	0.77778	0.	0.	1.24444	0.	1.24444	0.	0.	0.	0.	0.
$_4{}^3P$	0.	0.	0.55556	0.31111	0.	0.22222	1.00000	2.00000	0.55556	1.00000	0.35556	0.	0.	0.	0.	0.
$_2{}^1D$	0.	0.	1.20000	0.	1.00000	1.28571	0.	0.	0.80000	0.	0.	1.71429	0.	0.	0.	0.
$_4{}^1D$	0.80000	0.	0.60000	0.	0.	0.28571	1.28571	0.	0.90000	0.50000	0.	0.21429	1.41429	0.	0.	0.
$_4{}^3D$	0.40000	0.	0.13333	0.46667	0.	0.57143	0.28571	1.28571	0.20000	1.00000	0.20000	0.42857	0.31429	0.71429	0.	0.
$_4{}^5D$	0.	1.20000	0.	0.60000	0.	0.	0.	1.00000	0.	0.	1.40000	0.	0.	1.80000	0.	0.
$_4{}^1F$	0.	0.	0.42857	0.	0.	0.71429	0.35714	0.	0.37500	1.87500	0.	0.01071	1.76786	0.	0.47143	0.
$_2{}^3F$	0.	0.	0.15238	0.53333	1.00000	0.14286	0.	0.	0.13333	0.	2.13333	0.85714	0.	0.	1.04762	0.
$_4{}^3F$	0.	0.	0.23810	0.53333	0.	0.14286	0.64286	0.57143	0.20833	0.37500	0.13333	0.48214	0.98214	1.42857	0.26190	0.
$_2{}^1G$	0.	0.	0.	0.	1.00000	0.39683	0.	0.	1.11111	0.	0.	1.04762	0.	0.	2.44444	0.
$_4{}^1G$	0.	0.	0.	0.	0.	0.17460	0.78571	0.	0.76389	1.37500	0.	1.00595	0.65747	0.	0.05556	1.18182
$_4{}^3G$	0.	0.	0.	0.	0.	0.23810	0.11905	0.95238	0.37500	0.00833	0.66667	0.35357	1.00595	1.04762	0.36667	0.86667
$_4{}^3H$	0.	0.	0.	0.	0.	0.	0.	0.	0.16667	0.30000	0.66667	0.30000	0.04545	2.00000	0.86667	1.65455
$_4{}^1I$	0.	0.	0.	0.	0.	0.	0.	0.	0.	0.	0.	0.60000	0.81818	0.	1.40000	3.18182

Table 9.3 (*continued*)

d^7 \ d^6	${}^1_0S$	${}^1_4S$	${}^3_2P$	${}^3_4P$	${}^1_2D$	${}^1_4D$	${}^3_4D$	${}^5_4D$	${}^1_4F$	${}^3_2F$	${}^3_4F$	${}^1_2G$	${}^1_4G$	${}^3_4G$	${}^3_4H$	${}^1_4I$
${}_3^2P$	0.	0.	0.23333	1.66667	0.50000	1.00000	0.66667	0.	1.00000	0.26667	1.66667	0.	0.	0.	0.	0.
${}_3^4P$	0.	0.	0.53333	0.46667	0.	0.	1.16667	2.50000	0.	0.46667	1.86667	0.	0.	0.	0.	0.
${}_1^2D$	0.40000	0.	1.35000	0.	0.75000	0.	0.	0.	0.	3.15000	0.	1.35000	0.	0.	0.	0.
${}_3^2D$	0.	0.40000	0.35000	0.40000	0.32143	0.28571	1.71429	0.	1.00000	0.15000	0.60000	0.17857	0.31429	1.28571	0.	0.
${}_3^2F$	0.	0.	0.40000	0.71429	0.14286	0.64286	0.42857	0.	0.37500	0.10000	0.62500	0.35714	0.98214	1.44643	0.78571	0.
${}_3^4F$	0.	0.	0.20000	0.22857	0.	0.	0.21429	2.50000	0.	0.80000	0.20000	0.	0.	1.28571	1.57143	0.
${}_3^2G$	0.	0.	0.	0.	0.23810	0.11905	0.71429	0.	0.00833	0.50000	1.12500	0.26190	1.00595	1.06071	1.10000	0.86667
${}_3^2H$	0.	0.	0.	0.	0.	0.	0.	0.	0.30000	0.50000	0.50000	0.50000	0.04545	0.90000	2.60000	1.65455

d^8 \ d^7	${}^2_3P$	${}^4_3P$	${}^2_1D$	${}^2_3D$	${}^2_3F$	${}^4_3F$	${}^2_3G$	${}^2_3H$
${}_0^1S$	0.	0.	8.00000	0.	0.	0.	0.	0.
${}_2^3P$	0.46667	2.13333	0.50000	1.16667	1.86667	1.86667	0.	0.
${}_2^1D$	1.80000	0.	0.50000	1.92857	1.20000	0.	2.57143	0.
${}_2^3F$	0.22857	0.80000	0.50000	0.21429	0.20000	3.20000	1.28571	1.57143
${}_2^1G$	0.	0.	0.50000	0.59524	1.66667	0.	1.57143	3.66667

d^9 \ d^8	${}^1_0S$	${}^3_2P$	${}^1_2D$	${}^3_2F$	${}^1_2G$
${}_1^2D$	0.200000	1.80000	1.00000	4.20000	1.80000

REFERENCES

[1] G. Racah, *Phys. Rev.* **63,** 367 (1943).
[2] R. F. Bacher and S. Goudsmit, *Phys. Rev.* **46,** 948 (1934).
[3] D. H. Menzel and L. Goldberg, *Ap. J.* **84,** 1 (1935).
[4] A. de Shalit and I. Talmi, *Nuclear Shell Theory*, Academic Press, New York (1963).
[5] B. H. Flowers, *Proc. Roy. Soc.* (London) **A212,** 248 (1952).
[6] G. Racah, *Phys. Rev.* **76,** 1352 (1949).
[7] B. R. Judd, *Operator Techniques in Atomic Spectroscopy*, McGraw-Hill, New York (1963).
[8] B. G. Wybourne, *Spectroscopic Properties of Rare Earths*, Interscience, New York (1965).
[9] L. C. Biedenharn and H. van Dam, *Quantum Theory of Angular Momentum*, Academic, New York (1965).
[10] B. F. Bayman and A. Landé, *Nucl. Phys.* **77,** 1 (1966).
[11] D. Layzer, *Phys. Rev.* **132,** 2125 (1963).

9.10 AVERAGE ENERGIES; CLOSED l SHELLS

In many simple approaches to atomic structure, one wishes to ignore the atomic fine structure (dependence of energy on J) and even the term structure (S and L dependence), and look simply at the average energy of a configuration (dependence on the $\{nl\}$ values). One then calculates the average of the diagonal matrix elements of $\mathcal{H}$:

$$E_{\text{av}} = \frac{\sum \langle \Gamma | \mathcal{A}^{\dagger} \mathcal{H} \mathcal{A} | \Gamma \rangle}{\sum 1} . \tag{10.1a}$$

The sum goes over all (allowed) states of the configuration. This expression can also be written as the trace of the $\mathcal{H}$ matrix, within a configuration, divided by the number of states of the configuration, ϖ (the statistical weight):

$$E_{\text{av}} = \frac{\text{trace } (\mathcal{A}^{\dagger} \mathcal{A} \mathcal{H})}{\varpi} . \tag{10.1b}$$

Because the trace of a matrix remains unchanged when the matrix is subjected to a unitary transformation, one can calculate $\langle \mathcal{H} \rangle_{\text{av}}$ using wavefunctions in any coupling scheme. The result must be the same in the LSJ scheme as in the DWF or m-scheme.

In the calculation of average energies, it suffices to use the nonrelativistic Hamiltonian,

$$\mathcal{H}^1 = \mathcal{H}^0 + \mathcal{V}^0 = \sum_i h + \sum_{i<j} \frac{e^2}{r_{ij}} . \tag{10.2}$$

Then the average energy is the sum of single-particle contributions from the h_i,

$$\langle \mathcal{H}^0 \rangle_{av} = \sum_i I(n_i l_i), \tag{10.3}$$

and a two-particle contribution from $\mathcal{V}^0$:

$$\langle \mathcal{V}^0 \rangle_{av} = \sum \frac{\langle \Gamma | \mathcal{A}^\dagger \mathcal{V}^0 \mathcal{A} | \Gamma \rangle}{\varpi}. \tag{10.4}$$

That is,

$$E_{av} = \langle \mathcal{H}^0 \rangle_{av} + \langle \mathcal{V}^0 \rangle_{av}. \tag{10.5}$$

To obtain $\langle \mathcal{V}^0 \rangle_{av}$, we must add up the contributions from all distinct pairs of electrons. In the m scheme a typical pair contributes:

$$\langle \mathcal{V}^0(ab) \rangle_{av} = \sum \frac{\langle ab | \mathcal{A}^\dagger \mathcal{V}^0 \mathcal{A} | ab \rangle}{\varpi_2}, \tag{10.6}$$

where

$$a \equiv n_a l_a m_a \mu_a, \qquad b \equiv n_b l_b m_b \mu_b,$$

and the summation goes over $m_a m_b \mu_a \mu_b$. The number of two-electron states, ϖ_2, is

$$\varpi_2 = 2(2l_a + 1) \times 2(2l_b + 1), \tag{10.7a}$$

if the orbitals are *not* equivalent. If the orbitals *are* equivalent, the number of allowed states is given by a *binomial coefficient* $\binom{N_0}{n}$, which specifies the number of distinct ways of choosing n objects out of a collection of N_0 objects:

$$\binom{N_0}{n} \equiv \frac{(N_0)!}{(n)!(N_0 - n)!}. \tag{10.8}$$

In the present case we choose a pair of orbitals out of a collection of $2(2l + 1)$ different orbitals, so that the statistical weight is

$$\varpi_2 = \binom{4l+2}{2} = (2l + 1)(4l + 1). \tag{10.7b}$$

The matrix element (10.6) can be expressed in terms of F^k and G^k Slater integrals:

$$\begin{aligned}\langle ab | \mathcal{A}^\dagger \mathcal{V}^0 \mathcal{A} | ab \rangle &\times \sum_k [F^k \langle ab | \mathbf{C}^{(k)} \cdot \mathbf{C}^{(k)} | ab \rangle - G^k \langle ab | \mathbf{C}^{(k)} \cdot \mathbf{C}^{(k)} | ba \rangle] \\ &\equiv \sum_k [F^k f_k - G^k g_k].\end{aligned} \tag{10.9}$$

For nonequivalent orbitals the direct-interaction coefficient is

$$f_k = \langle ab|\mathbf{C}^{(k)}\cdot\mathbf{C}^{(k)}|ab\rangle = \sum_q (-1)^q \langle ab|C_q^{(k)}C_{-q}^{(k)}|ab\rangle$$

$$= \langle l_a\|\mathbf{C}^{(k)}\|l_a\rangle\langle l_b\|\mathbf{C}^{(k)}\|l_b\rangle \sum_{qm_am_b} (-1)^q \frac{(l_am_a, kq|l_am_a)}{\sqrt{2l_a+1}} \frac{(l_bm_b, k-q|l_bm_b)}{\sqrt{2l_b+1}}$$

$$\times \sum_{\mu_a\mu_b} 1. \tag{10.10}$$

The summation over $\mu_a\mu_b$ gives 4. Only $q = 0$ contributes to the q sum, and we can evaluate the m_am_b sums by using the formula

$$\sum_m (lm, kq|lm) = (2l+1)\delta_{k0}\delta_{q0}. \tag{10.11}$$

We finally obtain

$$f_k = \delta_{k0}\, 4(2l_a+1)(2l_b+1). \tag{10.12}$$

Similarly, the exchange-interaction coefficient is:

$$g^k = \langle ab|\mathbf{C}^{(k)}\cdot\mathbf{C}^{(k)}|ba\rangle = \sum_q (-1)^q \langle ab|C_q^{(k)}C_{-q}^{(k)}|ba\rangle$$

$$= \langle l_a\|\mathbf{C}^{(k)}\|l_b\rangle\langle l_b\|\mathbf{C}^{(k)}\|l_a\rangle \sum_{qm_am_b} (-1)^q \frac{(l_bm_b, kq|l_am_a)}{\sqrt{2l_a+1}} \frac{(l_am_a, k-q|l_bm_b)}{\sqrt{2l_b+1}}$$

$$\times \sum_{\mu_a\mu_b} \delta(\mu_a, \mu_b). \tag{10.13}$$

The summation over $\mu_a\mu_b$ now gives 2. We can carry out the m_1m_2q summation after rearranging the arguments of the CG coefficients, using

$$\sum_{mm'q} (lm, kq|l'm')^2 = (2l'+1). \tag{10.14}$$

The result is

$$g_k = 2\langle l_a\|\mathbf{C}^{(k)}\|l_b\rangle^2. \tag{10.15}$$

Thus (10.6) gives, for nonequivalent orbitals,

$$\langle \mathcal{V}^0(l_al_b)\rangle_{\text{av}} = \frac{2}{N_2}\left[2(2l_a+1)(2l_b+1)F^0 - \sum_k \langle l_a\|\mathbf{C}^{(k)}\|l_b\rangle^2 G^k\right]. \tag{10.16}$$

For equivalent orbitals the G^k integrals are indistinguishable from F^k integrals, and the summations in (10.10) and (10.13) must be divided by two in order to count distinct orbitals only once. The result again has the form of (10.16) but without the factor of 2 on the right-hand side. Inserting the appropriate values for N_2, we obtain the average energy of nonequivalent orbitals,

$$E_{\text{av}}(a, b) = I(a) + I(b) + \langle \mathcal{V}^0(a, b)\rangle_{\text{av}}, \tag{10.17a}$$

where

$$\langle \mathcal{V}^0(a, b)\rangle_{av} = F^0(a, b) - \sum_k \frac{\langle l_a \| \mathbf{C}^{(k)} \| l_b \rangle^2}{2(2l_a + 1)(2l_b + 1)} G^k(a, b);$$

and the average energy of equivalent orbitals,

$$E_{av}(l^2) = 2I(l) + \langle \mathcal{V}^0(l^2)\rangle_{av}, \tag{10.17b}$$

where

$$\langle \mathcal{V}^0(l^2)\rangle_{av} = F^0(l, l) - \sum_{k>0} \frac{\langle l \| \mathbf{C}^{(k)} \| l \rangle^2}{(2l + 1)(4l + 1)} F^k(l, l).$$

These results can, of course, be obtained from *LSJ*-scheme functions. In this scheme the f_k and g_k coefficients of (10.9) are

$$f_k = \langle l_a \| \mathbf{C}^{(k)} \| l_a \rangle \langle l_b \| \mathbf{C}^{(k)} \| l_b \rangle \sum_L (2L + 1)(-1)^{L+l_b+l_a} \begin{Bmatrix} L & l_b & l_a \\ k & l_a & l_b \end{Bmatrix} \tag{10.18a}$$

$$\times \sum_S (2S + 1),$$

$$g_k = \langle l_a \| \mathbf{C}^{(k)} \| l_b \rangle^2 \sum_L (2L + 1) \begin{Bmatrix} L & l_b & l_a \\ k & l_b & l_a \end{Bmatrix} \sum_S (-1)^S (2S + 1). \tag{10.18b}$$

(These equations also apply to equivalent orbitals if a factor of $\frac{1}{2}$ is inserted on the right-hand side; the sums still go over all S and L separately.) We can carry out the summations in (10.18) by using formulas from Chapter 6. The results are again (10.17).

Given the average energy of an electron pair, (10.17), we obtain the average energy of any configuration simply by adding the contributions of each pair of electrons. For example, the configuration l^N has N equivalent orbitals. The number of distinct ways to select a pair of electrons out of a population of N is

$$\binom{N}{2} = \frac{N(N-1)}{2}.$$

Thus the average energy of the l^N configuration is the sum of N single-particle energies and $N(N - 1)/2$ pair energies:

$$E_{av}(l^N) = NI(l) + \langle \mathcal{V}^0(l^N)\rangle_{av}, \tag{10.19a}$$

where

$$\langle \mathcal{V}^0(l^N)\rangle_{av} = \frac{N(N-1)}{2}\left[F^0(l, l) - \sum_{k>0} \frac{\langle l \| \mathbf{C}^{(k)} \| l \rangle^2}{(2l + 1)(4l + 1)} F^k(l, l)\right]. \tag{10.19b}$$

In particular, the average energy of a closed shell is

$$E_{av}(l^{4l+2}) = (4l + 2)I(l) + \langle \mathcal{V}^0(l^{4l+2})\rangle_{av}, \tag{10.20a}$$

with

$$\langle \mathcal{V}^0(l^{4l+2})\rangle_{\text{av}} = (2l+1)(4l+1)F^0(l,l) - \sum_{k>0} \langle l\|\mathbf{C}^{(k)}\|l\rangle^2 F^k(l,l). \quad (10.20b)$$

When more than one group of equivalent orbitals occurs in the configuration, the average energy is the sum of the energies of each group plus the average interaction between the groups. If the configuration is $l_a^p l_b^q$ then there are $p \times q$ ways of choosing the pair $l_a l_b$:

$$E_{\text{av}}(l_a^p l_b^q) = E_{\text{av}}(l_a^q) + E_{\text{av}}(l_b^p) + pq\langle \mathcal{V}^0(a,b)\rangle_{\text{av}}. \quad (10.21)$$

Thus the average energy of any configuration can be obtained quite easily from tables of the average pair interactions $\langle \mathcal{V}^0(a,b)\rangle_{\text{av}}$. The results are collected in Table 9.4.

Table 9.4 Values of Average Pair Energy

These are the coefficients in

$$\langle \mathcal{V}(a,b)\rangle_{\text{av}} = \sum_k (f_k F^k + g_k G^k)$$

Equivalent orbitals

(a, b)	f_0	f_2	f_4	f_6
s, s	1	0	0	0
p, p	1	$-\frac{2}{25}$	0	0
d, d	1	$-\frac{2}{63}$	$-\frac{2}{63}$	0
f, f	1	$-\frac{4}{195}$	$-\frac{2}{143}$	$-\frac{100}{5577}$

Nonequivalent orbitals

(a, b)	f_0	g_0	g_1	g_2	g_3	g_4	g_5	g_6
s, s'	1	$-\frac{1}{2}$						
s, p	1	0	$-\frac{1}{6}$					
s, d	1	0	0	$-\frac{1}{10}$				
s, f	1	0	0	0	$-\frac{1}{14}$			
p, p'	1	$-\frac{1}{6}$	0	$-\frac{1}{15}$				
p, d	1	0	$-\frac{1}{15}$	0	$-\frac{3}{70}$			
p, f	1	0	0	$-\frac{3}{70}$	0	$-\frac{2}{63}$		
d, d'	1	$-\frac{1}{10}$	0	$-\frac{1}{35}$	0	$-\frac{1}{35}$		
d, f	1	0	$-\frac{3}{70}$	0	$-\frac{2}{105}$	0	$-\frac{5}{231}$	
f, f'	1	0	0	$-\frac{2}{105}$	0	$-\frac{1}{77}$	0	$-\frac{50}{3003}$

For configurations consisting entirely of closed l-shells, only one term, ^1S occurs. (In fact only a single *state* occurs.) In this case the average energy of the configuration is also the term energy. Similarly, a configuration of closed l shells plus a single additional orbital (or hole) has only one term, a doublet l. Again, the average energy is also the term energy. The energy of this configuration is independent of the quantum numbers m, μ of the added orbital. By extension, we see that the interaction energy between a closed l shell and several additional equivalent orbitals is independent of the $\{m\mu\}$ quantum numbers of the added orbitals. It is therefore independent of the $SLJM$ value for the group of added electrons. If $l_0^{N_0}$ is a closed l shell, then we can write

$$\langle l_0^{N_0} l^N \alpha SLJM | \mathcal{A}^\dagger \mathcal{V}^0 \mathcal{A} | l_0^{N_0} l^N \alpha SLJM \rangle$$
$$= \frac{N_0(N_0 - 1)}{2} \langle \mathcal{V}^0(l_0, l_0) \rangle_{\text{av}} + N_0 N \langle \mathcal{V}^0(l_0, l) \rangle_{\text{av}}$$
$$+ \langle l^N \alpha SLJM | \mathcal{A}^\dagger \mathcal{V}^0 \mathcal{A} | l^N \alpha SLJM \rangle. \tag{10.22}$$

The presence of closed l shells introduces additional terms into the energy expression, as we see. But these terms are independent of $\alpha SLJM$; they occur for each state. Thus if we are concerned with only *relative* spacings of energy levels or differences in *term energies* within a configuration, we can ignore the presence of closed l-shell orbitals. Thus we can treat sodium or calcium, for example, as one- and two-electron atoms: When we consider the diagonal elements of the Hamiltonian, closed shells can be ignored.

9.11 TERM ENERGIES

When the importance of the Coulomb interaction $\mathcal{V}^0$ outweighs the importance of the spin-orbit interaction $\mathcal{V}^1$, as it does in many atoms, LS-coupling functions provide useful approximations to the actual wavefunctions. Using LS-coupling functions, we obtain approximate values for energy levels from the expectation values of the Hamiltonian

$$\mathcal{H} = \mathcal{H}^0 + \mathcal{V}^0 + \mathcal{V}^1. \tag{11.1}$$

The energies can be expressed as

$$E(SLJ) \equiv \langle \mathcal{H} \rangle = E^0 + \Delta E^0(SL) + \Delta E^1(J), \tag{11.2}$$

where $E^0 \equiv \langle \mathcal{H}^0 \rangle$ gives the configuration energy, $\Delta E^0(SL) \equiv \langle \mathcal{V}^0 \rangle$ accounts for the relative spacing of spectroscopic terms, and $\Delta E^1(J) \equiv \langle \mathcal{V}^1 \rangle$ is the fine structure splitting. (Spectroscopic terms, characterized by quantum numbers SL, are now often called *multiplets* and $\Delta E^0(SL)$ is then called *multiplet splitting*. In the present book we reserve the name multiplet for the collection of spectral lines between two spectroscopic terms.) In Section 9.6 we expressed these energies in the form

$$E^0 = \sum I(nl), \tag{11.3}$$

$$\Delta E^0(SL) = \sum (f_k F^k + g_k G^k), \tag{11.4a}$$

$$\Delta E^1(J) = \tfrac{1}{2}[J(J+1) - L(L+1) + S(S+1)]\zeta, \tag{11.5}$$

where I is a single-particle integral, F^k and G^k are Slater integrals, f_k and g_k are angular-momentum dependent quantities, and ζ is a spin-orbit parameter; for example [1], the d^2 configuration yields the following expressions [with $F^k \equiv F^k(d, d)$]:

$$\begin{aligned}
\Delta E^0(^1S) &= F^0 + \tfrac{2}{7}F^2 + \tfrac{2}{7}F^4, & \zeta(^1S) &= 0,\\
\Delta E^0(^3P) &= F^0 + \tfrac{1}{7}F^2 - \tfrac{84}{441}F^4, & \zeta(^3P) &= \tfrac{1}{2}\zeta(d),\\
\Delta E^0(^1D) &= F^0 - \tfrac{3}{49}F^2 + \tfrac{4}{49}F^4, & \zeta(^1D) &= 0,\\
\Delta E^0(^3F) &= F^0 - \tfrac{8}{49}F^2 - \tfrac{1}{49}F^4, & \zeta(^3F) &= \tfrac{1}{2}\zeta(d),\\
\Delta E^0(^1G) &= F^0 + \tfrac{4}{49}F^2 + \tfrac{1}{441}F^4, & \zeta(^1G) &= 0.
\end{aligned}$$

Slater [2] uses a slightly different expression:

$$E(SLJ) = E_{\text{av}} + \overline{\Delta E}^0(SL) + \Delta E^1(J).$$

(Here we use an unconventional bar to designate Slater's term splittings.) In the d^2 example Slater's average energy is

$$E_{\text{av}} = E^0 + F^0 - \tfrac{14}{441}F^2 - \tfrac{14}{441}F^4$$

and the term splittings are [2]

$$\begin{aligned}
\overline{\Delta E}^0(^1S) &= \tfrac{140}{441}F^2 + \tfrac{140}{441}F^4,\\
\overline{\Delta E}^0(^3P) &= \tfrac{77}{441}F^2 - \tfrac{70}{441}F^4,\\
\overline{\Delta E}^0(^1D) &= -\tfrac{13}{441}F^2 + \tfrac{50}{441}F^4,\\
\overline{\Delta E}^0(^3F) &= -\tfrac{58}{441}F^2 + \tfrac{5}{441}F^4,\\
\overline{\Delta E}^0(^1G) &= \tfrac{50}{441}F^2 + \tfrac{15}{441}F^4.
\end{aligned}$$

In applying semiempirical methods, we take the Slater integrals as adjustable parameters, chosen to fit the observed term-splitting best. If the observed energy levels are $E_{\text{obs}}(SLJ)$, the *center of gravity* of the term SL is

$$E_{\text{obs}}(SL) = \frac{\sum_J (2J+1)E_{\text{obs}}(SLJ)}{\sum_J (2J+1)} .$$

We equate these observed quantities with the theoretical expressions

$$E(SL) \equiv \frac{\sum_J (2J+1)E(SLJ)}{\sum_J (2J+1)}$$

$$= E^0 + \Delta E^0(SL) = E_{\text{av}} + \overline{\Delta E}^0(SL)$$

and solve for the F^k and G^k integrals. To simplify (11.4*a*) Condon and Shortley suggested the use of integer coefficients f^k and g^k by introducing parameters F_k and G_k,

$$F_k = \frac{F^k}{D_k}, \qquad G_k = \frac{G^k}{D_k},$$

$$f^k = f_k D_k, \qquad g^k = g_k D_k,$$

and then writing (11.4*a*) as

$$\Delta E^0(SL) = \sum (f^k F_k + g^k G_k); \tag{11.4b}$$

for example, the expressions for the d^2 terms become

$$\Delta E^0(^1S) = F_0 + 14F_2 + 126F_4,$$
$$\Delta E^0(^3P) = F_0 + 7F_2 - 84F_4,$$
$$\Delta E^0(^1D) = F_0 - 3F_2 + 36F_4,$$
$$\Delta E^0(^3F) = F_0 - 8F_2 - 9F_4,$$
$$\Delta E^0(^1G) = F_0 + 4F_2 + F_4,$$

where

$$F_0 = F^0(d,d), \qquad F_2 = \frac{F^2(d,d)}{49}, \qquad F_4 = \frac{F^4(d,d)}{441} .$$

Table 9.5 Denominators D_k for Slater Integrals

$D_1(s,p) = 3$	$D_2(p,p) = 25$	$D_2(d,d) = 49$	$D^2(f,f) = 225$
$D_2(s,d) = 5$	$D_1(p,d) = 15$	$D_4(d,d) = 441$	$D_4(f,f) = 1089$
$D_3(s,f) = 7$	$D_3(p,d) = 245$	$D_1(d,f) = 35$	$D_6(f,f) = 7361.64$
	$D_2(p,f) = 175$	$D_3(d,f) = 315$	
	$D_4(p,f) = 189$	$D_5(d,f) = 1524.6$	

Table 9.6 Racah Parameters A, B, C, D

For d^N	For f^N
$A = F_0 - 49F_4$	$A = F_0 - 21F_4 - 468F_6$
$B = F_2 - 5F_4$	$B = F_2 + \frac{6}{5}F_4 - \frac{91}{5}F_6$
$C = 35F_4$	$C = \frac{7}{5}F_4 - \frac{6}{5}F_6$
	$D = 462F_6$

Table 9.5 gives values of the denominators D_k. Note that

$$D_0(l, l) = 1 \quad \text{and} \quad D_k(l, l') = D_k(l', l).$$

Racah pointed out [3] that simplified energy expressions obtain for equivalent orbitals with the use of particular linear combinations of Slater integrals. Using these *Racah parameters*, given in Table 9.6, we can write the d^2 term splittings as

$$\Delta E^0(^1S) = A + 14B + 7C,$$

$$\Delta E^0(^3P) = A + 7B,$$

$$\Delta E^0(^1D) = A - 3B + 2C,$$

$$\Delta E^0(^3F) = A - 8B,$$

$$\Delta E^0(^1G) = A + 4B + 2C.$$

Racah later proposed [4] parameters E^i for use with f orbitals. By the use of these Racah parameters, given in Table 9.7, term splittings of configuration f^N take the form

$$\Delta E^0(SL) = \sum_i e_i E^i. \tag{11.4c}$$

Although we have discussed only two-electron configurations, (11.3)–

Table 9.7 Racah Parameters E^i

$E^0 = F_0 - 10F_2 - 33F_4 - 286F_6$
$E^1 = \frac{70}{9}F_2 + \frac{231}{9}F_4 + \frac{2002}{9}F_6$
$E^2 = \frac{1}{9}F_2 - \frac{3}{9}F_4 + \frac{7}{9}F_6$
$E^3 = \frac{5}{3}F_2 + \frac{6}{3}F_4 - \frac{91}{3}F_6$

(11.5) apply as well to more complex atoms. Several standard references tabulate values for the angular coefficients f^k and g^k (or f_k and g_k), most notably Condon and Shortley [1], Slater [2], Racah [3, 4], Edlén [5], Nielson and Koster [6], and Stevenson [7]. The reader should consult these references for further discussion.

Because the preceding treatment (sometimes referred to as the *Slater method* [8]) neglects configuration mixing and takes diagonal matrix elements of the Hamiltonian of (11.1) as energy estimates, the resulting expression (11.2) is not always able to account for observed term structure. An example occurs for the configuration p^2. Equation 11.4 predicts the energy structure [1]

$$\Delta E^0(^1S) = F_0 + 10F_2,$$
$$\Delta E^0(^3P) = F_0 - 5F_2,$$
$$\Delta E^0(^1D) = F_0 + F_2$$

and therefore predicts the ratio

$$\frac{E(^1S) - E(^1D)}{E(^1D) - E(^3P)} = \frac{3}{2}$$

(assuming the Slater integrals are independent of S and L). The observed ratios differ systematically and significantly from the value 1.5 predicted by the Slater theory.

To account for such observed deviations from (11.2), Trees suggested [9] the addition of a phenomenological correction proportional to $L(L + 1)$:

$$E(SLJ) = E^0 + \Delta E^0(SL) + \Delta E^1(J) + \alpha L(L + 1). \qquad (11.6)$$

Racah suggested [8] an additional parameter β for configurations d^N:

$$E(SLJ) = E^0 + \Delta E^0(SL) + \Delta E^1(J) + \alpha[L(L + 1) - 6N] + \beta\langle Q\rangle. \qquad (11.7)$$

Here Q, Racah's seniority operator, has the expectation value

$$\langle Q\rangle = \tfrac{1}{4}(N - v)(4l + 4 - N - v) \qquad (11.8)$$

for a term of l^N with seniority v. Such modifications, equivalent to the introduction of an effective Hamiltonian [11], have significantly improved the theoretical predictions for the iron group elements [12]. This L-dependent correction is a manifestation of mixing configurations that have the same principal quantum numbers, as Layzer [13], Trees and Jørgensen [14], and Godfredsen [15] have shown; for example, the previously mentioned discrepancy with p^2 terms traces to the mixing of $1s^22s^22p^2$ and $1s^22p^4$. More recently Rajnak and Wybourne [15] have shown that the use of suitable interaction-operators in an effective Hamiltonian can duplicate the major effects of configuration mixing. The Rajnak-Wybourne operators derive from second-order perturbation theory and reproduce, in part, the $L(L + 1)$ and Q corrections of (11.7). The use of an effective Hamiltonian that would reproduce the energies of (11.7) is sometimes called the "linear theory," in distinction to the simpler "Slater theory" of (11.2) or more refined "nonlinear" diagonalization of matrices.

REFERENCES

[1] E. U. Condon and G. H. Shortley, *The Theory of Atomic Spectra*, Cambridge University Press, Cambridge (1935), Chapter VII, The Russell-Saunders Case: Energy Levels.

[2] J. C. Slater, *Quantum Theory of Atomic Structure*, McGraw-Hill, New York (1960) vol. II, Appendix 21, Tabulation of Energies of Multiplets.

[3] G. Racah, *Phys. Rev.* **62,** 438 (1942).

[4] G. Racah, *Phys. Rev.* **76,** 187 (1949).

[5] B. Edlén, *Handbuch der Physik* **27,** 80 (1964).

[6] C. W. Nielson, and G. F. Koster, *Spectroscopic Coefficients for p^n, d^n, and f^n Configurations*, M.I.T. Press, Cambridge, Mass. (1963).

[7] R. Stevenson, *Multiplet Structure of Atoms and Molecules*, Saunders, Philadelphia (1965), Chapter 3, The Calculation of Multiplet Energies.

[8] J. C. Slater, *Phys. Rev.* **34,** 1293 (1929).

[9] R. E. Trees, *Phys. Rev.* **83,** 756 (1951); *ibid* **84,** 1089 (1951); *ibid* **85,** 382 (1952); *ibid* **129,** 1220 (1962).

[10] G. Racah, *Phys. Rev.* **85,** 381 (1952).

[11] G. Racah, Rydberg Centennial Conference, *Lunds Univ. Arsskrift* **50,** 31 (1955); *J. Quantitative Spectroscopy and Radiative Transfer* **4,** 617 (1964).

[12] G. Racah and Y. Shadmi, *Bulletin Research Council Israel* **8F,** 15 (1959); *Phys. Rev.* **119,** 156 (1960).
Y. Shadmi, *Bulletin Research Council Israel*, **9F,** 141 (1961); *ibid* **10F,** 104 (1962); *J. Research, Natl. Bur. Stds.* **70A,** 435 (1966).

[13] D. Layzer, *Ann. Phys.* **8,** 271 (1959).

[14] R. E. Trees and C. K. Jørgensen, *Phys. Rev.* **123,** 1278 (1961).

[15] E. Godfredsen, *Astrophys. J.* **145,** 308 (1966).

[16] K. Rajnak and B. G. Wybourne, *Phys. Rev.* **132,** 280 (1963); *ibid* **134,** A596 (1964); *J. Chem. Phys.* **41,** 565 (1965).
B. G. Wybourne, *J. Math. Phys.* **4,** 354 (1963); *Phys. Rev.* **137,** A364 (1965).

APPENDIX A: PROPERTIES OF COEFFICIENTS OF FRACTIONAL PARENTAGE

The CFP are defined [1] so that

$$\tilde{\Psi}(l^N\alpha SLJM) = \sum \Psi(l^{N-1}(\bar{\alpha}\bar{S}\bar{L})l(\alpha SLJM|12\cdots N)(l^{N-1}\bar{\alpha}\bar{S}\bar{L}|\}l^N\alpha SL), \tag{A.1}$$

and therefore also

$$\tilde{\Psi}(l^N \alpha SLJM) = \sum \Psi(l^{N-2}(\bar{\bar{\alpha}}\bar{\bar{S}}\bar{\bar{L}})l(\alpha \bar{S}\bar{L})l\alpha SLJM|12\cdots N)$$
$$\times (l^{N-2}\bar{\bar{\alpha}}\bar{\bar{S}}\bar{\bar{L}}|\}l^{N-1}\bar{\alpha}\bar{S}\bar{L}) \times (l^{N-1}\bar{\alpha}\bar{S}\bar{L}|\}l\alpha^N SL), \quad (A.2)$$

where the sums go over all barred quantum numbers ($\bar{\alpha}$, $\bar{\bar{\alpha}}$, etc.). The CFP may be written in either of two ways:

$$(l^N \alpha SL\{|l^{N-1}\alpha' S' L') = (l^{N-1}\alpha' S' L'|\}l^N \alpha SL). \quad (A.3)$$

The CFP satisfy an orthogonality relation when summed over *parent* terms,

$$\sum (l^N \alpha SL\{|l^{N-1}\bar{\alpha}\bar{S}\bar{L})(l^{N-1}\bar{\alpha}\bar{S}\bar{L}|\}l^N \alpha' SL) = \delta_{\alpha\alpha'}; \quad (A.4)$$

and for summation over *daughter terms*, they satisfy

$$\sum [\bar{S}, \bar{L}](l^{N-1}\alpha SL|\}l^N \bar{\alpha}\bar{S}\bar{L})(l^N \bar{\alpha}\bar{S}\bar{L}\{|l^{N-1}\alpha' SL)$$
$$= \delta_{\alpha\alpha'}\left(\frac{4l+2-N}{N}\right)(2S+1)(2L+1). \quad (A.5)$$

In the seniority scheme the CFP for p and d orbitals satisfy the *parent* summation equations

$$\sum (l^N vSL\{|l^{N-1}v'\bar{S}\bar{L})(l^{N-1}v'\bar{S}\bar{L}|\}l^N vSL)$$
$$= \frac{(4l+4-N-v)}{2N(2l+2-v)} \quad \text{for} \quad v' = v-1$$
$$= \frac{(4l+4-v)(N-v)}{2N(2l+2-v)} \quad \text{for} \quad v' = v+1, \quad (A.6)$$

and the *daughter* summation equations

$$\sum [\bar{S}, \bar{L}](l^{N-1}v'SL|\}lv^N \bar{S}\bar{L})(l^N v\bar{S}\bar{L}\{|l^{N-1}v'SL)$$
$$= (2S+1)(2L+1)\frac{(N-v)(v+1)}{2N(2l+1-v)} \quad \text{for} \quad v' = v+1$$
$$= (2S+1)(2L+1)\frac{(4l+4-N-v)(4l+5-N)}{2N(2l+3-v)} \quad \text{for} \quad v' = v-1.$$
$$(A.7)$$

Layzer [2] gives several additional summation properties. The CFP for two orbitals is

$$(l|\}l^2 SL) = \tfrac{1}{2}[1 + (-1)^{S+L}]$$
$$= 1 \quad \text{if} \quad S + L = \text{even}$$
$$= 0 \quad \text{if} \quad S + L = \text{odd}. \quad (A.8)$$

For a closed l-shell the CFP is unity:

$$(l^{4l+1}\,|\}\,l^{4l+2}0) = 1 \tag{A.9}$$

(the only allowed term of l^{4l+1} is $L = l$, $S = \frac{1}{2}$). For an almost-closed shell the CFP is

$$(l^{4l}\alpha SL\,|\}\,l^{4l+1}) = \left[\frac{(2S + 1)(2L + 1)}{(2l + 1)(4l + 1)}\right]^{1/2}. \tag{A.10}$$

REFERENCES

[1] G. Racah, *Phys. Rev.* **63,** 367 (1943).
[2] D. Layzer, *Phys. Rev.* **132,** 2152 (1963).

10. The Electromagnetic Field

10.1 MAXWELL'S EQUATIONS

Our knowledge of atomic structure comes to us primarily from studies of how atoms absorb and emit electromagnetic radiation: visible light, radio waves, and x-rays. Whether our interest centers on calculating energy levels or on interpreting the spectrum of a star, we need a modest knowledge of the properties of radiation. In the following sections, we summarize the essential properties of radiation and interaction with matter. For more details, consult the standard texts listed in the references.

The theory of electromagnetic radiation dates back to the monumental work of James Clark Maxwell [1] (1891). Maxwell's equations are discussed in such standard references as Stratton [2], Joos [3], or Jackson [4]. Maxwell began with the experimental laws governing the behavior of *charges* and *currents* discovered by Faraday, Ampère, and others, and recast these as equations for *electric* and *magnetic fields.* Although in many problems with charges and currents we can view these fields as merely convenient mathematical crutches, when we study radiation it becomes more convenient to think of these fields as physically observable entities, independent of their original source in charges and currents. This view becomes especially appropriate when we interpret experiments which detect individual photons, the quanta of the electromagnetic field.

Maxwell's equations relate the electric field $\mathbf{E}(r, t)$ and magnetic field $\mathbf{H}(r, t)$ [or the magnetic induction $\mathbf{B}(r, t)$] to various sources: electric current density $\mathbf{j}$, magnetization $\mathbf{M}$, and polarization density $\mathbf{P}$. In the Gaussian units traditional to quantum mechanics, the two fundamental Maxwell equations provide a differential-equation statement of *Faraday's Law* of inductance,

$$\nabla \times \mathbf{E} \equiv \mathbf{curl}\,\mathbf{E} = -\frac{1}{c}\frac{\partial}{\partial t}(\mathbf{H} + 4\pi\mathbf{M}), \tag{1.1}$$

and *Ampère's Circuital Law*,

$$\nabla \times \mathbf{H} \equiv \mathbf{curl}\,\mathbf{H} = \frac{4\pi}{c}\mathbf{j} + \frac{1}{c}\frac{\partial}{\partial t}(\mathbf{E} + 4\pi\mathbf{P}), \tag{1.2}$$

where c has the units of a velocity; we shall see that it gives the velocity of propagation of electromagnetic waves in free space, that is, the speed of light (cf. Joos [3], Chapter XVII; these equations appear in integral form in Stratton [2]). These differential equations for the fields must be supplemented by the *conservation equation*,

$$\operatorname{div} \mathbf{j} = \frac{\partial}{\partial t}\rho, \tag{1.3}$$

where $\rho(r, t)$ is the charge density.

We shall be primarily concerned with fields in "free space," i.e., beyond any charges, currents, magnetization, etc.:

$$\mathbf{M} = 0, \qquad \mathbf{P} = 0, \qquad \mathbf{j} = 0, \qquad \rho = 0.$$

We can readily obtain separate unlinked equations for **E** and **H** in free space from (1.1) and (1.2). These are the *vector wave equation:*

$$\mathbf{curl}\,\mathbf{curl}\,\mathbf{E} + \frac{1}{c^2}\frac{\partial^2}{\partial t^2}\mathbf{E} = 0 \tag{1.4a}$$

$$\mathbf{curl}\,\mathbf{curl}\,\mathbf{H} + \frac{1}{c^2}\frac{\partial^2}{\partial t^2}\mathbf{H} = 0. \tag{1.4b}$$

It is convenient to introduce auxiliary fields, the *vector potential* **A**, and the *electrostatic potential* φ, through the definition

$$\mathbf{H} = \mathbf{curl}\,\mathbf{A} \tag{1.5a}$$

$$\mathbf{E} = -\frac{1}{c}\frac{\partial}{\partial t}\mathbf{A} - \mathbf{grad}\,\varphi. \tag{1.5b}$$

At the moment this is merely a convenient mathematical artifice, for (1.5*a*) insures that div **H** = 0. The vector potential also satisfies the vector wave equation,

$$\mathbf{curl}\,\mathbf{curl}\,\mathbf{A} + \frac{1}{c^2}\frac{\partial^2}{\partial t^2}\mathbf{A} = 0. \tag{1.4c}$$

We have a certain amount of leeway in choosing **A**, since only **H** and **E** actually produce observable forces. In particular, we shall use the so-called

Coulomb gauge and let div $\mathbf{A} = 0$. The electrostatic potential does not then contribute to the radiation field.

We shall find it convenient to introduce a set of *vector* basis fields

$$\mathbf{U}^{\gamma} \exp(-i\omega_{\gamma} t)$$

whose spatial part satisfies the *vector Helmholtz equation:*

$$\textbf{curl curl } \mathbf{U}^{\gamma}(\mathbf{r}) = k_{\gamma}{}^{2}\mathbf{U}^{\gamma}(\mathbf{r}),$$
$$\omega_{\gamma} = ck_{\gamma}. \tag{1.6}$$

With this choice of exponential time dependence, these fields correspond to *running waves.* (The minus sign in the exponential has become conventional in quantum mechanics.) Both the basis fields and the spatial part $\mathbf{U}^{\gamma}(\mathbf{r})$ are complex quantities; we must ultimately take the real part of any expression involving such fields.

Note that a vector wave $\mathbf{U}$ involves two directions: the propagation direction $\mathbf{k}$, and the direction of the $\mathbf{U}$ field. By definition, the *polarization direction* of an electromagnetic wave is the direction of the *electric vector.* According to (1.5*b*), the $\mathbf{U}$ vector also is in the direction of the vector potential $\mathbf{A}$ (we neglect static electric fields here). Thus a wave linearly polarized in the x direction has an electric vector proportional to $\mathbf{e}_x$. A circularly polarized wave has an electric vector that rotates with time, as viewed by a stationary observer.

The single index γ on $\mathbf{U}^{\gamma}$ is actually an abbreviation for a collection of indices specifying all the attributes of a given wave (such as propagation direction, frequency and polarization).

The basis fields should be constructed to form a complete set of vector fields, so that any arbitrary vector field can be expressed in terms of them. We shall find it convenient to assume that the basis fields are orthogonal and normalized to

$$\int \mathbf{U}^{\gamma'}\cdot(\mathbf{U}^{\gamma})^{*}\, dv = \delta_{\gamma\gamma'}, \tag{1.7}$$

The symbol $\delta_{\gamma\gamma'}$ here is just the Kronecker δ for discrete indices. More generally, it is defined by

$$\underset{\gamma}{\mathsf{S}}\, \mathbf{U}^{\gamma}\delta_{\gamma\gamma'} = \mathbf{U}^{\gamma'}; \qquad \underset{\gamma}{\mathsf{S}}\, \delta_{\gamma\gamma'} = 1. \tag{1.8}$$

The symbol S_{γ} stands for summation over any *discrete* indices (such as polarization) and integration over all continuous indices (such as frequency):

$$\underset{\gamma}{\mathsf{S}} \rightarrow \sum_{m} \quad \text{or} \quad \int d\omega.$$

One can construct a great variety of such vector waves by combining scalar functions with unit vectors. For example, in rectangular coordinates these are *plane waves*. A plane wave of angular frequency ω and time dependence $\exp(-i\omega t)$ propagating along the positive z direction has a spatial dependence proportional to $\exp(ikz)$, where $k = \omega/c$. In a more general case, we describe the propagation direction by the *propagation vector* $\mathbf{k}$: this vector points in the direction of propagation,

$$\mathbf{k} = k_x\mathbf{e}_x + k_y\mathbf{e}_y + k_z\mathbf{e}_z, \tag{1.9}$$

with magnitude $k = \omega/c$. The direction cosines are k_x/k, k_y/k, and k_z/k. The amplitude of this wave is

$$\exp(i\mathbf{k}\cdot\mathbf{r}) \equiv \exp(ik_xx + ik_yy + ik_zz). \tag{1.10}$$

It is a straightforward matter to construct orthogonal plane waves with amplitude $\exp(i\mathbf{k}\cdot\mathbf{r})$ over a cubical box of side L. We require the amplitudes to vanish along the box faces at some instant. (Alternatively, the "box" and waves travel together with velocity c.) This condition in turn requires k_x, k_y, and k_z to be integral multiples of $2\pi/L$. This boundary condition then produces our desired orthogonal waves: waves having different k_x, k_y, or k_z are orthogonal. If we pass to the limit of normalizing over all space, then k_x, k_y, and k_z take continuous values, but different wave vectors still produce orthogonal waves.

We can express any given vector potential $\mathbf{A}(\mathbf{r}, t)$ as a linear combination of these basis fields or *wave modes* $\mathbf{U}^\gamma(\mathbf{r})$:

$$\mathbf{A}(\mathbf{r}, t) = \mathop{\mathsf{S}}_{\gamma} \left(\frac{2\pi\hbar c}{k_\gamma}\right)^{1/2} [a_\gamma(t)\mathbf{U}^\gamma(\mathbf{r}) + a_\gamma(t)^*\mathbf{U}^\gamma(\mathbf{r})^*]. \tag{1.11a}$$

(The convenience of inserting the numerical factor $\sqrt{2\pi\hbar c/k}$ will appear below.) We shall refer to the *dimensionless* expansion coefficients,

$$a_\gamma(t) = \alpha_\gamma \exp(-i\omega_\gamma t), \tag{1.12}$$

as *wave amplitudes:* they tell how much radiation of the γth type (or γth *mode*) the given $\mathbf{A}(\mathbf{r}, t)$ field contains. With this choice of vector potential, the electric and magnetic fields are

$$\mathbf{E}(\mathbf{r}, t) = -i \mathop{\mathsf{S}}_{\gamma} \sqrt{2\pi\hbar c k_\gamma}\,(a_\gamma\mathbf{U}^\gamma - a_\gamma^*\mathbf{U}^{\gamma *}) \tag{1.11b}$$

$$\mathbf{H}(\mathbf{r}, t) = \mathop{\mathsf{S}}_{\gamma} \left(\frac{2\pi\hbar c}{k^\gamma}\right)^{1/2} (a_\gamma\,\mathbf{curl}\,\mathbf{U}^\gamma + a_\gamma^*\,\mathbf{curl}\,\mathbf{U}^{\gamma *}). \tag{1.11c}$$

As a specific example, a plane wave propagating along the z axis and polarized in the x direction is

$$\mathbf{U}^{\gamma}(\mathbf{r}) = \mathbf{e}_x \frac{\exp(ikz)}{(2\pi)^{3/2}}. \tag{1.13}$$

The index m here stands for polarization direction $\mathbf{e}_x$ and propagation vector $\mathbf{k} = k\mathbf{e}_z$. The expansion of $\mathbf{A}(\mathbf{r}, t)$ into plane-wave modes reads

$$\mathbf{A}(\mathbf{r}, t) = \int dk_x \int dk_y \int dk_z \sum_n \frac{1}{2\pi} \left(\frac{\hbar c}{k}\right)^{1/2} \times [a_{n\mathbf{k}} \mathbf{e}_n \exp(i\mathbf{k}\cdot\mathbf{r}) + a_{n\mathbf{k}}^* \mathbf{e}_n \exp(-i\mathbf{k}\cdot\mathbf{r})] \tag{1.14}$$

In order to satisfy div $\mathbf{A} = 0$, we must have $\mathbf{k}\cdot\mathbf{e}_n = 0$, so the waves must be transverse.

Although plane waves provide particularly simple vector waves, they are not always the most useful basis waves. In Section 10.3 we shall discuss running-wave solutions to (1.6) in spherical coordinates; these are *multipole fields*. For the remainder of this chapter we leave the construction of the $\mathbf{U}^{\gamma}$ fields arbitrary.

In passing note that the field **curl** $\mathbf{U}^{\gamma}$ also satisfies the vector Helmholtz equation. If the field $\mathbf{U}^{\gamma}$ has parity π_{γ}, then the field **curl** $\mathbf{U}^{\gamma}$ has the opposite parity $-\pi_{\gamma}$. (Recall that the parity π is the eigenvalue of the inversion operator: "even" parity is $\pi = 1$, "odd" parity is $\pi = -1$).

With our choice of time dependence, (1.12), each independent amplitude $a_{\gamma}(t)$ satisfies the *harmonic-oscillator* equation:

$$\frac{\partial^2}{\partial t^2} a_{\gamma} + \omega_{\gamma}{}^2 a_{\gamma} = 0, \qquad \frac{\partial^2}{\partial t^2} a_{\gamma}^* + \omega_{\gamma}{}^2 a_{\gamma}^* = 0. \tag{1.15}$$

We might imagine (with cultivated imagination) the radiation field as a collection of oscillators. The amplitude a_{γ} of the γth oscillator denotes the amount of radiation in the γth mode, having the spatial distribution and polarization given by $\mathbf{U}^{\gamma}(\mathbf{r})$.

We shall be particularly interested in a quantum-mechanical theory of the radiation field. One way of introducing quantum theory is to find an appropriate Hamiltonian (a function of generalized coordinates $\mathcal{Q}_i$ and momenta $\mathcal{P}_i$) and then postulate commutation relations between coordinates and the conjugate momenta. Aiming toward this goal, we shall now show that the (classical) radiation field has the Hamiltonian

$$\mathcal{H}_{\text{field}} = \tfrac{1}{2} \mathop{\mathrm{S}}_{\gamma} \hbar\omega_{\gamma}(a_{\gamma}^* a_{\gamma} + a_{\gamma} a_{\gamma}^*). \tag{1.16}$$

That is, Maxwell's equations are the equations of motion derived from this Hamiltonian, and the energy contained in the field has the value $\mathcal{H}_{\text{field}}$. This can be shown in two ways.

The first "proof" follows a completely classical argument. As standard texts show (cf. Stratton [2], Chapter 2; Jackson [4], p. 189; or Panofsky and Phillips [5], p. 160), the energy W in an electromagnetic radiation field is

$$W = \frac{1}{8\pi}\int (|\mathbf{H}|^2 + |\mathbf{E}|^2)\, dv. \tag{1.17}$$

We use (1.5) to write this in terms of the vector potential as

$$W = \frac{1}{8\pi c^2}\int (|\dot{\mathbf{A}}|^2 + c^2|\mathbf{curl\ A}|^2)\, dv. \tag{1.18}$$

We then use an identity from vector analysis (cf. Stratton [2] or Morse and Feshbach [6]),

$$\int \mathbf{curl\ V}\cdot\mathbf{curl\ V}\, dv = \int d\mathbf{S}\cdot(\mathbf{V} \times \mathbf{curl\ V}) + \int dv\mathbf{V}\cdot\mathbf{curl\ curl\ V}, \tag{1.19}$$

to transform the second term of (1.18) into a surface integral plus a volume integral. The time derivative of this surface integral is just the integrated momentum flux across the surface $d\mathbf{S}$, given by the *Poynting vector:*

$$\mathbf{P} = \frac{1}{8\pi c}\int (\mathbf{E} \times \mathbf{H})\cdot d\mathbf{S}.$$

We can either express the vector potential $\mathbf{A}$ in terms of standing waves which vanish over this surface, or we can imagine a surface so far away that any traveling waves have not yet reached it after the fields have been "turned on." With such a choice of basis fields $\mathbf{U}^\gamma$, the surface integral vanishes. The substitution of (1.11) for $\dot{\mathbf{A}}$ and **curl curl A** then gives

$$W = \frac{1}{4\pi c^2}\int \left| \mathop{\mathsf{S}}_{\gamma} dv\, \sqrt{2\pi\hbar c^2\omega_\gamma}\,(a_\gamma \mathbf{U}^\gamma - a_\gamma^* \mathbf{U}^{\gamma *})\right|^2. \tag{1.20}$$

Because of the orthogonality of the $\mathbf{U}^\gamma$ fields, we are left with the desired result,

$$W = \mathcal{H}_{\text{field}} = \tfrac{1}{2} \mathop{\mathsf{S}}_{\gamma} \hbar\omega_\gamma(a_\gamma^* a_\gamma + a_\gamma a_{\gamma}^*).$$

The second proof starts from the harmonic-oscillator equation (1.15) If we introduce the (real) variables $\mathcal{Q}_\gamma$ and $\mathcal{P}_\gamma$ corresponding to the real and imaginary parts of a_γ according to

$$\mathcal{Q}_\gamma = \left(\frac{\hbar}{2\omega_\gamma}\right)^{1/2}(a_\gamma + a_\gamma^*) \tag{1.21a}$$

$$\mathcal{P}_\gamma = -i\omega_\gamma\left(\frac{\hbar}{2\omega_\gamma}\right)^{1/2}(a_\gamma - a_\gamma^*) \tag{1.21b}$$

then $\mathcal{P}_\gamma = (\partial/\partial t)\mathcal{Q}_\gamma$. With these new variables, the harmonic-oscillator equation becomes:

$$\frac{\partial \mathcal{P}_\gamma}{\partial t} + \omega_\gamma{}^2 \mathcal{Q}_\gamma = 0. \tag{1.22}$$

But this formula is just the equation of motion for $\mathcal{P}_\gamma$ and $\mathcal{Q}_\gamma$ derived from the following Hamiltonian:

$$\mathcal{H}_{\text{field}} = \tfrac{1}{2} \underset{\gamma}{\mathsf{S}} (\mathcal{P}_\gamma{}^2 + \omega_\gamma{}^2 \mathcal{Q}_\gamma{}^2). \tag{1.23}$$

That is, Hamilton's equations for the $\{\mathcal{P}_\gamma\}$ and $\{\mathcal{Q}_\gamma\}$ are

$$\frac{\partial \mathcal{H}_{\text{field}}}{\partial \mathcal{P}_\gamma} = \frac{\partial}{\partial t} \mathcal{Q}_\gamma \quad \text{or} \quad \mathcal{P}_\gamma = \frac{\partial}{\partial t} \mathcal{Q}_\gamma \tag{1.24a}$$

$$-\frac{\partial \mathcal{H}_{\text{field}}}{\partial \mathcal{Q}_\gamma} = \frac{\partial}{\partial t} \mathcal{P}_\gamma \quad \text{or} \quad -\omega_\gamma{}^2 \mathcal{Q}_\gamma = \frac{\partial}{\partial t} \mathcal{P}_\gamma. \tag{1.24b}$$

Substituting the definitions (1.21) into (1.23), we obtain again (1.16). As the notation suggests, we can interpret $\mathcal{Q}_\gamma$ and $\mathcal{P}_\gamma$ as a generalized coordinate (for the γth radiation mode) and the canonically conjugate momentum. Mathematically they meet the essential requirements of a coordinate and a momentum; we must see in the next section what they correspond to physically.

REFERENCES

[1] J. C. Maxwell, *Electricity and Magnetism*, 3rd ed. (1891), reprinted by Dover, New York (1954).

[2] J. A. Stratton, *Electromagnetic Theory*, McGraw-Hill, New York (1941), Chap. 1.

[3] G. Joos, *Theoretical Physics*, Hafner, New York (1950), 2nd ed., Part 3.

[4] J. D. Jackson, *Classical Electrodynamics*, Wiley, New York (1962).

[5] W. K. H. Panofsky and M. Phillips, *Classical Electricity and Magnetism*, Addison-Wesley, Reading, Massachusetts (1962), 2nd ed.

[6] P. M. Morse and H. Feshbach, *Methods of Theoretical Physics*, McGraw-Hill, New York (1953) vol. 1, Sec. 1.4.

10.2 MULTIPOLE FIELDS

When we discuss electromagnetic radiation it is sometimes convenient to express the electromagnetic field, which is a *vector* field, in terms of some set of basic solutions to the vector Helmholtz equation,

$$\textbf{curl curl U} - k^2\mathbf{U} = 0. \tag{2.1}$$

A convenient way to construct such vector solutions $\mathbf{U}(\mathbf{r})$ (see for example

Stratton [1], de Shalit and Talmi [2], Blatt and Weisskopf [3]), begins from solutions to the scalar Helmholtz equation,

$$\nabla^2 Z_m^{(l)} + k^2 Z_m^{(l)} = 0 \tag{2.2}$$

having the form

$$Z_m^{(l)} = i^l k \left(\frac{2}{\pi}\right)^{1/2} g_l(kr) Y_{lm}(\theta, \phi), \tag{2.3}$$

where $g_l(kr)$ is some suitable radial solution, say a spherical Bessel function $j_l(kr)$, a spherical Neumann function $n_l(kr)$, or a spherical Hankel function $h_l(kr)$. (See Appendix B to Chapter 3 or Morse and Feshbach [4], p. 1576.) We want to use the spherical Bessel functions, since they are finite at the origin:

$$j_0(kr) = \frac{\sin(kr)}{kr} \xrightarrow{kr\to 0} 1$$

$$j_1(kr) = -\frac{\cos(kr)}{kr} - \frac{\sin(kr)}{(kr)^2} \longrightarrow \frac{kr}{3}$$

$$j_2(kr) = -\frac{\sin(kr)}{kr} + \frac{3\cos(kr)}{(kr)^2} + \frac{3\sin(kr)}{(kr)^3} \longrightarrow \frac{(kr)^2}{15}.$$

However, the general formulation does not require this condition at the origin, and we shall leave g_l unspecified for the moment.

The function $Z_m^{(l)}$ provides a scalar field, since a *single* value defines the field of every point in space. To construct a vector field, we must combine these quantities with three independent unit vectors in the form

$$\mathbf{U} = \sum_{i=1}^{3} U_i \mathbf{e}_i.$$

The complex spherical unit vectors $\mathbf{e}_{+1}$, $\mathbf{e}_0$, and $\mathbf{e}_{-1}$ best serve our purpose here. These vectors are eigenstates of spin angular momentum $\mathbf{S}^2$ for $S = 1$ (*spin-one* eigenstates for short). When we observe further that the $Z_m^{(l)}$ are eigenfunctions of orbital angular momentum $\mathbf{L}^2$, we can use the techniques of angular-momentum coupling to construct the desired vector fields. That is, we can use vector fields which are simultaneous eigenstates of orbital angular momentum [$\mathbf{L}^2$ having eigenvalue $l(l+1)$], spin one, and total angular momentum $\mathbf{J} = \mathbf{L} + \mathbf{S}$. [$\mathbf{J}^2$ has eigenvalue $j(j+1)$.] We shall use the notation of Fano and Racah [5]:

$$[\mathbf{Z}^{(l)} \times \mathbf{e}^{(1)}]_m^{(j)} \equiv i^l k \left(\frac{2}{\pi}\right)^{1/2} g_l(kr)[\mathbf{Y}^{(l)} \times \mathbf{e}^{(1)}]_m^{(j)}$$

$$\equiv i^l k \left(\frac{2}{\pi}\right)^{1/2} g_l(kr) \sum_{pq} (lp, 1q|jm) Y_{lq}(\theta, \phi)\mathbf{e}_p \tag{2.4}$$

for such a *multipole field* of order j. To describe an arbitrary vector field in three dimensions, we need three independent (orthogonal) sets of basis fields. For example, in rectangular coordinates these might be the sets $X_n\mathbf{e}_x$, $Y_n\mathbf{e}_y$, and $Z_n\mathbf{e}_z$. Let us see how to construct such a set of three independent solutions in spherical coordinates; that is, multipole fields.

The simplest set of multipole fields has $l = j$. Denoting this basic field by $\mathbf{II}_m^{(l)}$ we have

$$\begin{aligned}\mathbf{II}_m^{(l)} &\equiv [\mathbf{Z}^{(l)} \times \mathbf{e}^{(1)}]_m^{(l)} \\ &= \frac{i^l k g_l(kr)}{\sqrt{2\pi}\sqrt{l(l+1)}}\Big[\sqrt{2}\sqrt{l(l+1) - m(m+1)}\, Y_{lm+1}\mathbf{e}_{-1} \\ &\quad + 2mY_{lm}\mathbf{e}_0 - \sqrt{2}\sqrt{l(l+1) - m(m-1)}\, Y_{lm-1}\mathbf{e}_{+1}\Big].\end{aligned} \tag{2.5}$$

By noting the action of the orbital angular-momentum operator,

$$\mathbf{L} = -L_{+1}\mathbf{e}_{-1} + L_0\mathbf{e}_0 - L_{-1}\mathbf{e}_{+1},$$

we can write

$$\begin{aligned}\mathbf{II}_m^{(l)} &= \frac{1}{\sqrt{l(l+1)}}\,\mathbf{L}Z_m^{(l)} \\ &= -\frac{i}{\sqrt{l(l+1)}}\,\mathbf{r} \times \nabla Z_m^{(l)}.\end{aligned} \tag{2.6}$$

From this expression it follows that $\mathbf{II}_m^{(l)}$ is transverse,

$$\mathbf{II}_m^{(l)} \cdot \mathbf{r} = 0, \tag{2.7}$$

and *solenoidal* (that is divergenceless,

$$\operatorname{div} \mathbf{II}_m^{(l)} = 0. \tag{2.8}$$

Since the components of an arbitrary vector $\mathbf{a}$ are determined from

$$\mathbf{e}_p . \mathbf{a} = a_p,$$

we can write the scalar product of $\mathbf{a}$ and $\mathbf{II}_m^{(l)}$ as

$$\begin{aligned}\mathbf{II}_m^{(l)} \cdot \mathbf{a} &= \sum_{pq} (lp, 1q|lm) Z_q^{(l)} \mathbf{e}_p \cdot \mathbf{a} \\ &= [\mathbf{Z}^{(l)} \times \mathbf{a}^{(l)}]_m^{(l)}.\end{aligned} \tag{2.9}$$

Now, using an identity from vector analysis, we can write (2.9) in the alternative form

$$\begin{aligned}\mathbf{II}_m^{(l)} \cdot \mathbf{a} &= -\frac{i}{\sqrt{l(l+1)}}\,[\mathbf{r} \times \nabla Z_m^{(l)}] \cdot \mathbf{a} \\ &= -\frac{i}{\sqrt{l(l+1)}}\,[\mathbf{grad}\ Z_m^{(l)}] \cdot (\mathbf{r} \times \mathbf{a}).\end{aligned} \tag{2.10}$$

We can obtain a second independent set of multipole fields from the curl of $\mathbf{II}_m^{(l)}$:

$$\boldsymbol{\Sigma}_m^{(l)} \equiv \frac{\mathbf{curl}}{k} \mathbf{II}_m^{(l)}$$

$$= -\left(\frac{l+1}{2l+1}\right)^{1/2} [\mathbf{Z}^{(l-1)} \times \mathbf{e}^{(1)}]_m^{(l)} - \left(\frac{l}{2l+1}\right)^{1/2} [\mathbf{Z}^{(l+1)} \times \mathbf{e}^{(1)}]_m^{(l)} \quad (2.11)$$

(This follows from formulas given by Edmonds [6] or Hill [7].) Although $\boldsymbol{\Sigma}_m^{(l)}$ is a solenoidal field,

$$\operatorname{div} \boldsymbol{\Sigma}_m^{(l)} = 0, \quad (2.12)$$

it is not quite transverse, since

$$\boldsymbol{\Sigma}_m^{(l)} \cdot \mathbf{r} = \frac{\mathbf{curl}}{k} \mathbf{II}_m^{(l)} \cdot \mathbf{r} = \mathbf{r} \cdot \boldsymbol{\nabla} \times \mathbf{L} \frac{Z_m^{(l)}}{k\sqrt{l(l+1)}} = \frac{i}{k} \frac{\mathbf{L}^2}{\sqrt{l(l+1)}} Z_m^{(l)}$$

$$= \frac{i}{k} \sqrt{l(l+1)}\, Z_m^{(l)} . \quad (2.13)$$

However, since the radial (or longitudinal) component falls off as r^{-1} compared with the transverse part, at large distances both $\mathbf{II}_m^{(l)}$ and $\boldsymbol{\Sigma}_m^{(l)}$ become essentially transverse vectors. Such a sufficiently great distance defines the *wave zone*. The scalar product of $\boldsymbol{\Sigma}_m^{(l)}$ with an arbitrary vector $\mathbf{a}$ can be written as

$$\mathbf{curl}\, \mathbf{II}^{(l)} \cdot \mathbf{a} = -\left(\frac{l+1}{2l+1}\right)^{1/2} [\mathbf{Z}^{(l-1)} \times \mathbf{a}^{(1)}]_m^{(l)}$$

$$- \left(\frac{l}{2l+1}\right)^{1/2} [\mathbf{Z}^{(l+1)} \times \mathbf{a}^{(1)}]_m^{(l)} . \quad (2.14)$$

These two vector fields satisfy

$$\mathbf{curl}\, \boldsymbol{\Sigma}_m^{(l)} = -k\mathbf{II}_m^{(l)} \quad (2.15a)$$

$$\mathbf{curl}\, \mathbf{II}_m^{(l)} = k\boldsymbol{\Sigma}_m^{(l)} \quad (2.15b)$$

as well as the vector Helmholtz equation. We note in passing that the field $\mathbf{II}_m^{(l)}$ has the parity

$$\text{parity of } \mathbf{II}_m^{(l)} = (-1)^{l+1}$$

[an "intrinsic parity" of -1 from $\mathbf{e}_p$ and an "orbital parity" of $(-1)^l$ from Y_{lm}], so that the field **curl** $\mathbf{II}_m^{(l)}$ has parity

$$\text{parity of } \mathbf{curl}\, \mathbf{II}_m^{(l)} = (-1)^l.$$

For the third and final set of multipole fields we can take the *lamellar* field (that is, a field with zero curl)

Table 10.1 Properties of Multipole Fields [a]

U		r·U	div U	curl U	parity
$\mathbf{II}_m^{(l)}$	$\dfrac{\mathbf{L}Z_m^{(l)}}{\sqrt{l(l+1)}} = [\mathbf{Z}^{(l)} \times \mathbf{e}]_m^{(l)}$	0	0	$k\boldsymbol{\Sigma}_m^{(l)}$	$(-1)^{l+1}$
$\boldsymbol{\Sigma}_m^{(l)}$	$\dfrac{\mathbf{curl}\ \mathbf{II}_m^{(l)}}{k} = -\left(\dfrac{l+1}{2l+1}\right)^{1/2}[\mathbf{Z}^{(l-1)} \times \mathbf{e}]_m^{(l)} - \left(\dfrac{l}{2l+1}\right)^{1/2}[\mathbf{Z}^{(l+1)} \times \mathbf{e}]_m^{(l)}$	$\dfrac{i\sqrt{l(l+1)}\,Z_m^{(l)}}{k}$	0	$-k\mathbf{II}_m^{(l)}$	$(-1)^l$
$\boldsymbol{\Lambda}_m^{(l)}$	$\dfrac{\mathbf{grad}\ Z_m^{(l)}}{k} = i\left(\dfrac{l}{2l+1}\right)^{1/2}[\mathbf{Z}^{(l-1)} \times \mathbf{e}]_m^{(l)} - i\left(\dfrac{l+1}{2l+1}\right)^{1/2}[\mathbf{Z}^{(l+1)} \times \mathbf{e}]_m^{(l)}$	$-r\dfrac{d}{dr}Z_m^{(l)}$	$k^2Z_m^{(l)}$	0	$(-1)^l$

[a] $Z_m^{(l)} \equiv i^l k\sqrt{2/\pi}\,j_l(kr)\,Y_{lm}(\theta,\phi)$.

Table 10.2 Spherical Components of Multipole Fields

	r	θ	ϕ
Magnetic: $\mathbf{\Pi}_m^{(l)}$	0	$-i^l \frac{k}{2\pi} (j_l) \left[\frac{8\pi}{l(l+1)}\right]^{1/2} \frac{mY_{lm}}{\sin\theta}$	$-i^{l+1} \frac{k}{2\pi} (j_l) \left[\frac{8\pi}{l(l+1)}\right]^{1/2} \frac{\partial}{\partial\theta} Y_{lm}$
Electric: $\mathbf{\Sigma}_m^{(l)}$	$i^{l+1} \frac{k}{2\pi} \left(\frac{j_l}{kr}\right) \sqrt{8\pi l(l+1)}\, Y_{lm}$	$i^{l+1} \frac{k}{2\pi} \left(\frac{1}{kr}\frac{d}{dr} r j_l\right) \left[\frac{8\pi}{l(l+1)}\right]^{1/2} \frac{\partial}{\partial\theta} Y_{lm}$	$-i^l \frac{k}{2\pi} \left(\frac{1}{kr}\frac{d}{dr} r j_l\right) \left[\frac{8\pi}{l(l+1)}\right]^{1/2} \frac{mY_{lm}}{\sin\theta}$
Longitudinal: $\mathbf{\Lambda}_m^{(l)}$	$i^l \frac{k}{2\pi} \left(\frac{1}{k}\frac{d}{dr} j_l\right) \sqrt{8\pi}\, Y_{lm}$	$i^l \frac{k}{2\pi} \left(\frac{j_l}{kr}\right) \sqrt{8\pi} \frac{\partial}{\partial\theta} Y_{lm}$	$i^l \frac{k}{2\pi} \left(\frac{j_l}{kr}\right) \sqrt{8\pi} \frac{mY_{lm}}{\sin\theta}$

		Near Zone ($kr \ll 1$)		Wave Zone ($kr \gg 1$)
(j_l)	$\rightarrow$	$\frac{(kr)^l}{(2l+1)!!}$	$\rightarrow$	$\frac{\sin(kr - l\pi/2)}{kr}$
$\left(\frac{1}{kr}\frac{d}{dr} r j_l\right)$	$\rightarrow$	$\frac{(l+1)(kr)^{l-1}}{(2l+1)!!}$	$\rightarrow$	$\frac{\cos(kr - l\pi/2)}{kr}$
$\left(\frac{1}{k}\frac{d}{dr} j_l\right)$	$\rightarrow$	$\frac{l(kr)^{l-1}}{(2l+1)!!}$	$\rightarrow$	$\frac{\cos(kr - l\pi/2)}{kr}$
$\left(\frac{j_l}{k}\right)$	$\rightarrow$	$\frac{(kr)^{l-1}}{(2l+1)!!}$	$\rightarrow$	$\frac{\sin(kr - l\pi/2)}{(kr)^2}$

Table 10.3 Components of Multipole Fields in Wave Zone

$m = 0$	θ component	ϕ component	Intensity
$\mathcal{E}1 = \mathbf{\Sigma}_0^{(1)}$	$\sqrt{3}\sin\theta\left(\frac{kj_1}{2\pi}\right)$	0	$\frac{3}{8\pi}(1-\cos^2\theta)\left(\frac{2}{\pi}k^2 j_1{}^2\right)$
$\mathcal{M}1 = \mathbf{\Pi}_0^{(1)}$	0	$\sqrt{3}\sin\theta\left(\frac{kj_1}{2\pi}\right)$	
$\mathcal{E}2 = \mathbf{\Sigma}_0^{(2)}$	$i\sqrt{15}\sin\theta\cos\theta\left(\frac{kj_2}{2\pi}\right)$	0	$\frac{15}{8\pi}\sin^2\theta\cos^2\theta\left(\frac{2}{\pi}k^2 j_2{}^2\right)$
$\mathcal{M}2 = \mathbf{\Pi}_0^{(2)}$	0	$-i\sqrt{15}\sin\theta\cos\theta\left(\frac{kj_2}{2\pi}\right)$	
$\mathcal{E}3 = \mathbf{\Sigma}_0^{(3)}$	$-\sqrt{\frac{21}{8}}\sin^3\theta\left(\frac{kj_3}{2\pi}\right)$	0	$\frac{21}{64\pi}\sin^3\theta\left(\frac{2}{\pi}k^2 j_3{}^2\right)$
$m = \pm 1$			
$\mathcal{E}1 = \mathbf{\Sigma}_{\pm 1}^{(1)}$	$\pm\sqrt{\frac{3}{2}}\cos\theta e^{\pm i\phi}\left(\frac{kj_1}{2\pi}\right)$	$i\sqrt{\frac{3}{2}}e^{\pm i\phi}\left(\frac{kj_1}{2\pi}\right)$	$\frac{3}{16\pi}(1+\cos^2\theta)\left(\frac{2}{\pi}k^2 j_1{}^2\right)$
$\mathcal{M}1 = \mathbf{\Pi}_{\pm 1}^{(1)}$	$i\sqrt{\frac{3}{2}}e^{\pm i\phi}\left(\frac{kj_1}{2\pi}\right)$	$\mp\sqrt{\frac{3}{2}}\cos\theta\, e^{\pm i\phi}\left(\frac{kj_1}{2\pi}\right)$	

$\mathcal{E}2 = \mathbf{\Sigma}^{(2)}_{\pm 1}$	$\pm i\sqrt{\frac{5}{2}}\,(2\cos^2\theta - 1)\, e^{\pm i\phi}\left(\frac{kj_2}{2\pi}\right)$	$-\sqrt{\frac{5}{2}}\cos\theta\, e^{\pm i\phi}\left(\frac{kj_2}{2\pi}\right)$	$\frac{5}{16\pi}(1 - 3\cos^2\theta + 4\cos^4\theta)\left(\frac{2}{\pi}k^2{j_2}^2\right)$
$\mathfrak{M}2 = \mathbf{II}^{(2)}_{\pm 1}$	$-\sqrt{\frac{5}{2}}\cos\theta\, e^{\pm i\phi}\left(\frac{kj_2}{2\pi}\right)$	$\mp i\sqrt{\frac{5}{2}}\,(2\cos^2\theta - 1)\, e^{\pm i\phi}\left(\frac{kj_2}{2\pi}\right)$	
$\mathcal{E}3 = \mathbf{\Sigma}^{(3)}_{\pm 1}$	$\mp\sqrt{\frac{7}{32}}\cos\theta\,(11 - 15\cos^2\theta)e^{\pm i\phi}\left(\frac{kj_3}{2\pi}\right)$	$-i\sqrt{\frac{7}{32}}\,(5\cos^2\theta - 1)e^{\pm i\phi}\left(\frac{kj_3}{2\pi}\right)$	$\frac{7}{256\pi}(1 + 111\cos^2\theta - 305\cos^4\theta + 225\cos^6\theta)\left(\frac{2}{\pi}k^2{j_3}^2\right)$
$m = \pm 2$			
$\mathcal{E}2 = \mathbf{\Sigma}^{(2)}_{\pm 2}$	$-i\sqrt{\frac{5}{2}}\sin\theta\cos\theta\, e^{\pm 2i\phi}\left(\frac{kj_2}{2\pi}\right)$	$\pm\sqrt{\frac{5}{2}}\sin\theta\, e^{\pm 2i\phi}\left(\frac{kj_2}{2\pi}\right)$	$\frac{5}{16\pi}(1 - \cos^4\theta)\left(\frac{2}{\pi}k^2{j_2}^2\right)$
$\mathfrak{M}2 = \mathbf{II}^{(2)}_{\pm 2}$	$\pm\sqrt{\frac{5}{2}}\sin\theta\, e^{\pm 2i\phi}\left(\frac{kj_2}{2\pi}\right)$	$i\sqrt{\frac{5}{2}}\sin\theta\cos\theta\, e^{\pm 2i\phi}\left(\frac{kj_2}{2\pi}\right)$	
$\mathcal{E}3 = \mathbf{\Sigma}^{(3)}_{\pm 2}$	$-\sqrt{\frac{35}{16}}\sin\theta(1 - 3\cos^2\theta)e^{\pm 2i\phi}\left(\frac{kj_3}{2\pi}\right)$	$\pm i\sqrt{\frac{35}{16}}\,2\sin\theta\cos\theta\, e^{\pm 2i\phi}\left(\frac{kj_3}{2\pi}\right)$	$\frac{35}{128\pi}\sin^2\theta(1 - 2\cos^2\theta + 9\cos^4\theta)\times\left(\frac{2}{\pi}k^2{j_3}^2\right)$

$$\mathbf{\Lambda}_m^{(l)} \equiv \frac{\mathbf{grad}}{k} Z_m^{(l)}$$

$$= i\left(\frac{l}{2l+1}\right)^{1/2}[\mathbf{Z}^{(l-1)} \times \mathbf{e}^{(1)}]_m^{(l)} + i\left(\frac{l+1}{2l+1}\right)^{1/2}[\mathbf{Z}^{(l-1)} \times \mathbf{e}^{(1)}]_m^{(l)}. \quad (2.16)$$

(This relation follows from formulas given by Edmonds [6] or Hill [7].) These fields satisfy

$$\operatorname{div} \mathbf{\Lambda}_m^{(l)} = kZ_m^{(l)} \quad (2.17)$$

$$\mathbf{curl}\, \mathbf{\Lambda}_m^{(l)} = 0 \quad (2.18)$$

$$\mathbf{\Lambda}_m^{(l)} \cdot \mathbf{r} = r\frac{\partial}{\partial r} Z_m^{(l)} = i^l\left(\frac{2}{\pi}\right)^{1/2} Y_{lm} r \frac{\partial}{\partial r} g_l \quad (2.19)$$

and for an arbitrary vector **a**,

$$\mathbf{\Lambda}_m^{(l)} \cdot \mathbf{a} = \left(\frac{\mathbf{grad}}{k} Z_m^{(l)}\right) \cdot \mathbf{a} = i\left(\frac{l}{2l+1}\right)^{1/2}[\mathbf{Z}^{(l-1)} \times \mathbf{a}^{(1)}]_m^{(l)}$$

$$+ i\left(\frac{l+1}{2l+1}\right)^{1/2}[\mathbf{Z}^{(l+1)} \times \mathbf{a}^{(1)}]_m^{(l)}. \quad (2.20)$$

At any point in space, the field $\mathbf{\Pi}_m^{(l)}$ is perpendicular to $\mathbf{\Sigma}_m^{(l)}$ and $\mathbf{\Lambda}_m^{(l)}$:

$$\mathbf{\Pi}_m^{(l)} \cdot \mathbf{\Sigma}_m^{(l)} = \mathbf{\Pi}_m^{(l)} \cdot \mathbf{\Lambda}_m^{(l)} = 0. \quad (2.21)$$

In the wave zone ($kr \gg 1$) both $\mathbf{\Pi}_m^{(l)}$ and $\mathbf{\Sigma}_m^{(l)}$ are transverse fields, whereas $\mathbf{\Lambda}_m^{(l)}$ becomes a longitudinal field. This means that $\mathbf{\Lambda}_m^{(l)}$ does not contribute to a pure radiation field; that is, a field without static electric charges. (In treating the radiation field it is convenient to use the subsidiary condition $\operatorname{div} \mathbf{A} = 0$. This procedure then rules out the longitudinal field, since $\operatorname{div} \mathbf{\Lambda}_m^{(l)} \neq 0$.) Table 10.1 summarizes the properties of these multipole fields. Table 10.2 provides expressions for the spherical components. Table 10.3 gives specific examples of the transverse fields in the wave zone.

We now want to connect these multipole fields with the $\mathbf{U}^{\gamma}$ fields in the expansion of the radiation-field vector potential. In order to obtain the normalization assumed in Section 9.1 we need the integral (cf. Morse and Feshbach [4], p. 765) for Bessel functions

$$\int_0^\infty x\, dx\, J_m(kx) J_m(k'x) = \frac{\delta(k-k')}{k}. \quad (2.22)$$

Here $\delta(k - k')$ is the Dirac delta function, defined by

$$\int_0^\infty f(k)\, \delta(k-k_0)\, dk = f(k_0). \quad (2.23)$$

For spherical Bessel functions $[j_l(z) = (\pi/2z)^{1/2} J_{l+1/2}(z)]$ (2.22) becomes

$$\int_0^\infty r^2\, dr\, j_l(kr) j_l(k'r) = \frac{\pi}{2k^2}\, \delta(k - k'). \tag{2.24}$$

Thus the multipole field $\mathbf{II}_m^{(l)}$ satisfies

$$\int dv\, \mathbf{II}_m^{(l)}(k\mathbf{r})^* \cdot \mathbf{II}_{m'}^{(l')}(k'\mathbf{r}) = \delta(k - k')\, \delta_{ll'}\, \delta_{mm'}. \tag{2.25}$$

Identical integrals hold for $\mathbf{\Sigma}_m^{(l)}$ and $\mathbf{\Lambda}_m^{(l)}$. Fields of different type satisfy the relations

$$0 = \int dv\, \mathbf{II}_m^{(l)*} \cdot \mathbf{\Sigma}_{m'}^{(l')} = \int dv\, \mathbf{II}_m^{(l)*} \cdot \mathbf{\Lambda}_{m'}^{(l')}$$

$$= \int dv\, \mathbf{\Sigma}_m^{(l)*} \cdot \mathbf{\Lambda}_{m'}^{(l')}. \tag{2.26}$$

Thus the multipole fields $\mathbf{II}_m^{(l)}$, $\mathbf{\Sigma}_m^{(l)}$, and $\mathbf{\Lambda}_m^{(l)}$ are particular examples of the $\mathbf{U}^\gamma$ fields discussed in Section 9.1. For convenience, we introduce the notation

$$\mathbf{U}^{k\mathfrak{M}lm}(\mathbf{r}) \equiv \mathbf{II}_m^{(l)}(k\mathbf{r}), \qquad \mathbf{U}^{k\mathcal{E}lm}(\mathbf{r}) \equiv \mathbf{\Sigma}_m^{(l)}(k\mathbf{r}). \tag{2.27}$$

The reason for the labels $\mathfrak{M}$ (for *magnetic multipole*) and $\mathcal{E}$ (for *electric multipole*) will become apparent in Section 9.5. There we shall see that moments of electric charge distribution give rise to the electric multipole radiation, and magnetic moments give rise to the magnetic multipole radiation. (In subsequent sections we will use λ in place of l to denote multipole order.) The expansion of $\mathbf{A}$ into multipoles (1.11*a*) is

$$\mathbf{A}(r, t) = \sum_{lm} \int dk \{ a_{k\mathfrak{M}lm} \mathbf{U}^{k\mathfrak{M}lm} + a_{k\mathcal{E}lm} \mathbf{U}^{k\mathcal{E}lm}$$

$$+ \text{complex conjugate}\}$$

$$= \sum_{lm} \int dk \sqrt{4\hbar c k}\, [a_{k\mathfrak{M}lm} \mathbf{II}_m^{(l)} + a_{k\mathcal{E}lm}\, \mathbf{curl}\, \mathbf{II}_m^{(l)}$$

$$+ \text{complex conjugate}]. \tag{2.28}$$

The radiation-field energy is

$$W = \sum_{lm} \int dk\, \hbar c k (a_{k\mathfrak{M}lm}^* a_{k\mathfrak{M}lm} + a_{k\mathcal{E}lm}^* a_{k\mathcal{E}lm})$$

$$= \sum_{lm} \int \frac{dE_{klm}}{\hbar c}\, E_{klm} (a_{kl\mathfrak{M}m}^* a_{k\mathfrak{M}lm} + a_{k\mathcal{E}lm}^* a_{k\mathcal{E}lm}). \tag{2.29}$$

Interestingly, the separation of the electromagnetic field into a part due to magnetic sources [our field $\mathbf{II}_m^{(l)}$] and a field due to electric sources [our field $\Sigma_m^{(l)}$] was first carried out by Hertz [8] in 1888. This approach is treated by Stratton [1].

The expansion of a scalar plane wave into angular-momentum *partial waves* is given by the Rayleigh formula

$$e^{i\mathbf{k}\cdot\mathbf{r}} = \sum_{l=0}^{\infty} i^l(2l+1)j_l(kr)P_l(\cos \mathbf{k}, \mathbf{r})$$
$$= \sum_{l=0}^{\infty} i^l\sqrt{4\pi}\,\sqrt{2l+1}\,j_l(kr)Y_{l0}(\Omega_{kr}). \tag{2.30}$$

The vector counterpart of this equation gives the expansion of a transverse plane wave into multipole waves:

$$\mathbf{e}_m e^{i\mathbf{k}\cdot\mathbf{r}} = -\sum_{L=1}^{\infty} \frac{\pi}{k}\sqrt{2L+1}\,[\mathbf{II}_m^{(L)} + m\Sigma_m^{(L)}]. \tag{2.31}$$

Here the vector $\mathbf{e}_m$ is one of the two spherical vectors $\mathbf{e}_{+1}, \mathbf{e}_{-1}$ that are transverse to the propagation direction $\mathbf{e}_0$. The proof of this expansion (cf. Rose [9]), starting from the Rayleigh expansion, is straightforward, when one uses the formula

$$\mathbf{e}_m Y_{l0} = \sum_L (l0, 1m|\,Lm)[\mathbf{Y}^{(l)} \times \mathbf{e}]_m^{(L)}$$
$$= -\frac{m}{\sqrt{2}}\left(\frac{l+2}{2l+1}\right)^{1/2}[\mathbf{Y}^{(l)} \times \mathbf{e}]_m^{(L+1)} + \frac{1}{\sqrt{2}}[\mathbf{Y}^{(l)} \times \mathbf{e}]_m^{(L)}$$
$$-\frac{m}{\sqrt{2}}\left(\frac{l-1}{2l+1}\right)^{1/2}[\mathbf{Y}^{(l)} \times \mathbf{e}]_m^{(L-1)} \tag{2.32}$$

and the definitions of $\mathbf{II}_m^{(L)}$ and $\Sigma_m^{(L)}$ [(2.5) and (2.16)].

Since these multipole waves represent running waves, it is of interest to calculate the intensity of the radiation passing outward through an element of solid angle. For the $\mathbf{II}_m^{(l)}$ multipole field we find

$$|\mathbf{II}_M^{(l)}|^2 = \sum_{mp} (lm, 1p\,|\,lM)Y_{lm}^* \sum_{m'p'} (lm', 1p'\,|\,lM)Y_{lm'}(\mathbf{e}_{p'}^*\cdot\mathbf{e}_p)$$
$$= \frac{2}{\pi}k^2(j_l)^2 \sum_{mp} (lm, 1p\,|\,lM)^2|\,Y_{lm}|^2$$
$$\equiv \frac{2}{\pi}k^2(j_l)^2 I_{lm}(\theta). \tag{2.33}$$

This equation defines the angular distribution of the radiation intensity,

$$I_{lm}(\theta) = \sum_{mp} (lm, 1p\,|\,lM)^2|\,Y_{lm}|^2. \tag{2.34}$$

In the wave zone $\Sigma_m^{(l)}$ has this same angular distribution:

$$|\Sigma_m^{(l)}|^2 \xrightarrow{kr \gg 1} \frac{2}{\pi} k^2 (j_{l-1})^2 I_{lm}(\theta).$$

Written out explicitly, this angular distribution is

$$I_{lm}(\theta) = \frac{l(l+1) - m(m-1)}{2l(l+1)} |Y_{l,m-1}|^2 + \frac{m^2}{l(l+1)} |Y_{lm}|^2 + \frac{l(l+1) - m(m+1)}{2l(l+1)} |Y_{l,m+1}|^2. \qquad (2.35)$$

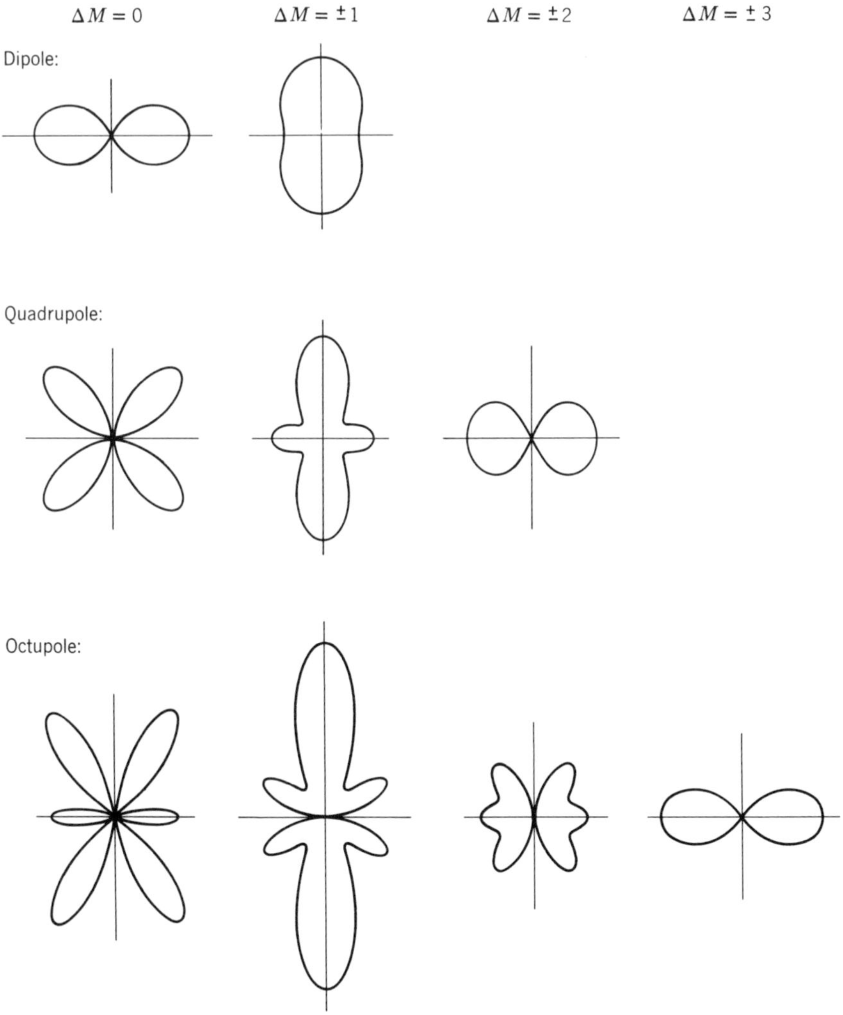

Fig. 10.1 Angular distribution of multipole radiation, $I_{\lambda M}(\theta)$, drawn to scale.

Since $|Y_{lm}|^2$ is independent of the angle ϕ, the angular distribution $I_{lm}(\theta)$ only depends on θ. Note particularly that along the z axis ($\theta = 0$) the intensity $I_{lm}(0)$ is zero unless $m = +1$ or -1. (Y_{lm} is zero at $\theta = 0$ except for $m = 0$.) Note also that $I_{lm}(\theta) = I_{l,-m}(\theta)$. The angular distributions for dipole ($l = 1$), quadrupole ($l = 2$) and octupole ($l = 3$) fields may be found in Table 10.2. Figure 10.1 illustrates these intensity distributions. Because the spherical harmonics are normalized to unity, and the double summation over a squared CG coefficient gives unity, the angular distribution integrated over a sphere is unity:

$$\int I_{lm}(\theta)\, d\Omega = 1. \tag{2.36}$$

Furthermore, the sum of the $2l + 1$ components is a quantity independent of angle:

$$\sum_m I_{lm}(\theta) = \frac{2l+1}{4\pi}. \tag{2.37}$$

Thus if one does not distinguish the separate m components, the radiation appears isotropic. The angular distribution may also be written in terms of Legendre polynomials of even order:

$$I_{lm}(\theta) = (-1)^{m+1} \frac{(2l+1)^2}{4\pi} \sum_n (l0, l0|2n0) \quad (lm, l-m|2n0) \times \begin{Bmatrix} l & l & 2n \\ l & l & 1 \end{Bmatrix} P_{2n}(\cos\theta). \tag{2.38}$$

Table 10.4 Notation for Vector Spherical Harmonics

		a	b	c	d
$[\mathbf{Y}^{(l)} \times \mathbf{e}^{(1)}]^{(j)}_m$	=	$\mathbf{Y}^m_{jl1}$	$\mathbf{Y}^{j(l1)}_m$	$\mathbf{Y}_{jlm}$	$\mathbf{V}_{lm}$ and $\mathbf{W}_{lm}$
$[\mathbf{Y}^{(l)} \times \mathbf{e}^{(1)}]^{(l)}_m$	=	$\mathbf{X}_{lm}$	$\mathbf{Y}^{l(l1)}_m$	$\mathbf{Y}_{llm}$	$\mathbf{X}_{lm}$

a. J. Blatt and V. F. Weisskopf, *Theoretical Nuclear Physics*, Wiley, New York (1952).
b. A. de Shalit and I. Talmi, *Nuclear Shell Theory*, Academic, New York (1963).
c. A. Edmonds, *Angular Momentum in Quantum Mechanics*, Princeton Univ. Press, Princeton, N.J. (1957).
d. E. L. Hill, *Am. J. Phys.* **22**, 211 (1954).

Multipole fields were first used by Mie [10]. An elegant approach was given by Corben and Schwinger [11]. Customarily, the angular part

$[\mathbf{Y}^{(l)} \times \mathbf{e}^{(1)}]_m^{(j)}$ of our fields $\mathbf{II}_m^{(l)}$, $\Sigma_m^{(l)}$, and $\Lambda_m^{(l)}$ is known as a *vector spherical harmonic*. Table 10.4 shows some of the common notations for these fields. The Bibliography lists a number of varied references to multipole fields.

REFERENCES

[1] J. A. Stratton, *Electromagnetic Theory*, McGraw-Hill, New York (1941), Chap. 1.
[2] A. de Shalit and I. Talmi, *Nuclear Shell Theory*, Academic, New York (1963) Chap. 16.
[3] J. M. Blatt and V. F. Weisskopf, *Theoretical Nuclear Physics*, Wiley, New York (1952), Appendix B.
[4] P. M. Morse and H. Feshbach, *Methods of Theoretical Physics*, McGraw-Hill, New York (1953).
[5] U. Fano and G. Racah, *Irreducible Tensorial Sets*, Academic, New York (1959).
[6] A. R. Edmonds, *Angular Momentum in Quantum Mechanics*, Princeton University Press, Princeton, New Jersey (1957).
[7] E. L. Hill, *Am. J. Phys.* **22,** 211 (1954).
[8] H. Hertz, *Ann. d. Physik* **36,** 1 (1888).
[9] M. E. Rose, *Elementary Theory of Angular Momentum*, Wiley, New York (1957).
[10] A. Mie, *Ann. d. Physik* **25,** 377 (1908).
[11] H. C. Corben and J. Schwinger, *Phys. Rev.* **58,** *953* (1940).

10.3 QUANTIZED FIELDS

So far our results are purely "classical." We now introduce quantization (following closely the treatment in Heitler [1]) by analogy with the quantum mechanics of particles: we require that the field "coordinate" $\mathcal{Q}_\gamma$ and the conjugate momentum $\mathcal{P}_\gamma$ satisfy the commutation relation

$$[\mathcal{Q}_\gamma, \mathcal{P}_{\gamma'}] = i\hbar\delta_{\gamma\gamma'}. \tag{3.1}$$

This postulate requires that the amplitudes satisfy

$$[a_\gamma, a^*_{\gamma'}] = \delta_{\gamma\gamma'}. \tag{3.2}$$

The postulate that these $\mathcal{P}$'s and $\mathcal{Q}$'s should be taken as noncommuting *operators* is known as *second quantization*. (The postulate on $\mathcal{P}$ and $\mathcal{Q}$ for a *particle* is the "first" quantization.)

We note that the field Hamiltonian (1.16) can be written

$$\mathop{\mathsf{S}}_{\gamma} \hbar\omega_\gamma(a^*_\gamma a_\gamma + \tfrac{1}{2}).$$

Since the summation goes over an infinite set of modes (in order that the vectors $\mathbf{U}^\gamma$ form a complete set) the last factor contributes

$$\tfrac{1}{2} \mathop{\mathsf{S}}_{\gamma} \hbar\omega_\gamma,$$

an infinite quantity! This infinite energy causes no observable effects, however, and it is permissible and customary to subtract this (infinite) constant amount from the Hamiltonian, which is then redefined as

$$\mathcal{H}_{\text{field}} = \mathop{\mathsf{S}}_{\gamma} \hbar\omega_\gamma a_\gamma^* a_\gamma. \tag{3.3}$$

If we are to view the $\mathcal{P}_\gamma$ and $\mathcal{Q}_\gamma$ (or the a_γ^* and a_γ) as operators, they must operate *on* something—a state in some abstract space. Just as with previous collections of eigenstates, we can deduce all the important physical and mathematical properties of these states from commutation relations.

It is useful now to introduce the *number operator*,

$$\mathfrak{N}_\gamma \equiv a_\gamma^* a_\gamma, \tag{3.4}$$

(the reason for this name will appear as we progress) and write the radiation field Hamiltonian as

$$\mathcal{H}_{\text{field}} = \mathop{\mathsf{S}}_{\gamma} \hbar\omega_\gamma \mathfrak{N}_\gamma. \tag{3.5}$$

We now want to introduce radiation field eigenstates as eigenstates of $\mathcal{H}_{\text{field}}$ and each of the $\mathfrak{N}_\gamma$ operators. We shall denote the eigenvalue of $\mathcal{H}_{\text{field}}$ by W and the eigenvalue of $\mathfrak{N}_\gamma$ by N_γ. A field eigenstate Ψ then satisfies the equations

$$\mathcal{H}_{\text{field}}\Psi = W\Psi \tag{3.6}$$

and

$$\mathfrak{N}_\gamma \Psi = N_\gamma \Psi \tag{3.7}$$

for *each operator* $\mathfrak{N}_\gamma$.

The use of (3.5) in (3.6) gives

$$W\Psi = \left(\mathop{\mathsf{S}}_{\gamma} \hbar\omega_\gamma N_\gamma\right)\Psi.$$

Thus W, the energy of the field, is the sum of energies in all the various modes of the field (the energies in all of our basic $\mathbf{U}^\gamma$ fields). It is a simple exercise to show, from the commutation relations of a_γ^* and a_γ, that the eigenvalues $\mathfrak{N}_\gamma$ take only integral values: if Ψ satisfies the equation

$$\mathfrak{N}\Psi \equiv a^* a\Psi = N\Psi,$$

then $a\Psi$ satisfies the equation

$$\mathfrak{N}a\Psi = a^* a(a\Psi) = aa^* a\Psi - a\Psi = (N-1)a\Psi.$$

Similarly, we can show that $a^*\Psi$ satisfies

$$\mathfrak{N}a^*\Psi = (N+1)a^*\Psi.$$

Therefore the permissible eigenvalues of $\mathfrak{N}$ differ by integers. The a and a^* operators are evidently ladder operators; if we write their action as

$$a^*\Psi(N) = C_{N+1}\Psi(N+1)$$
$$a\Psi(N) = C_N\Psi(N-1),$$

then the constant C_N is readily obtained from

$$\mathfrak{N}\Psi(N) = a^*a\Psi(N) = C_N a^*\Psi(N-1) = C_N{}^2\Psi(N)$$

and the convention that C_N be real and positive. The result is

$$a^*\Psi(N) = \sqrt{N+1}\,\Psi(N+1) \tag{3.8a}$$
$$a\Psi(N) = \sqrt{N}\,\Psi(N-1). \tag{3.8b}$$

We see from this that the energy of an electromagnetic field is *quantized:* the energy of a wave of angular frequency ω comes in integral multiples of $\hbar\omega$. These quantized units of the electromagnetic field are *photons*. That is, a *single photon is a field of energy* $\hbar\omega$, *with the spatial distribution* $\mathbf{U}(\mathbf{r})e^{-i\omega t}$. The field $\mathbf{U}(\mathbf{r})$ prescribes the propagation direction and polarization of the photon. To be more precise, the quantities

$$\frac{1}{8\pi}\,|\,\mathbf{curl}\,\mathbf{U}(\mathbf{r})\,|^2 \quad \text{and} \quad \frac{1}{8\pi}\left|\frac{\omega}{c}\,\mathbf{U}(\mathbf{r})\right|^2$$

give, respectively, the energy density of the magnetic and electric fields at point r and time t. For monochromatic radiation of angular frequency ω, we then divide the total energy density by $\hbar\omega$ to find the number of photons per unit volume. Since the radiation energy propagates with velocity c, the *flux* of photons (the number of photons passing through unit area at $\mathbf{r}$ in unit time) is just c times the photon density. We can also think of a photon as a single unit of excitation of a mode of the radiation field.

A general radiation field eigenstate Ψ may consist of many photons of assorted frequencies and propagation characteristics. Such a state can be described completely by the list N_1, N , . . . , of eigenvalues of the number operators $\mathfrak{N}_1$, $\mathfrak{N}_2$, ... These numbers are commonly called *occupation numbers*, because they specify the number of photons of each type composing the field, and the state $\Psi(N_1, N_2, \ldots)$ labeled by these values is a state in the *occupation-number* (or second-quantization) representation. It is natural to refer to a^* as a *creation* operator, since it adds a photon from the state Ψ. Similarly the *annihilation* operator a removes a photon.

If our interpretation of N_γ as an occupation number is to be meaningful, there must exist a state with *no* photons present. This *vacuum state*, $\Psi(\text{vac})$, for which all the occupation numbers are zero, can also be defined by the equivalent requirement

$$a_\gamma \Psi(\text{vac}) = 0 \qquad \text{for all } \gamma. \tag{3.9}$$

Thus the expectation value for the field energy of the vacuum state is zero:

$$\langle \Psi(\text{vac}) | \mathcal{H}_{\text{field}} | \Psi(\text{vac}) \rangle = 0. \tag{3.10}$$

Of course, we have already subtracted an infinite constant from $\mathcal{H}_{\text{field}}$. We see that this subtraction corresponds physically to choosing this vacuum state as our zero point of field energy.

REFERENCE

[1] W. Heitler, *The Quantum Theory of Radiation*, Oxford University Press, New York (1953), 3rd ed.

10.4 MATTER AND RADIATION

The motion of a charged point particle in electric and magnetic fields follows the *Lorentz equation*,

$$\frac{d}{dt} m\mathbf{v} = e\left(\mathbf{E} + \frac{1}{c}\mathbf{v} \times \mathbf{H}\right), \tag{4.1}$$

where $\mathbf{v} \equiv dr/dt$. If we introduce scalar and vector potential functions φ and $\mathbf{A}$ by the conditions

$$\mathbf{E} = -\frac{1}{c}\frac{\partial}{\partial t}\mathbf{A} - \mathbf{grad}\,\phi \tag{4.2}$$

$$\mathbf{H} = \mathbf{curl}\,\mathbf{A}, \tag{4.3}$$

then we can write the *Lorentz force* on the right-hand side of (4.1) as

$$-\frac{e}{c}\frac{\partial}{\partial t}\mathbf{A} + \frac{e}{c}\mathbf{V} \times \mathbf{curl}\,\mathbf{A} - e\,\mathbf{grad}\,\phi. \tag{4.4}$$

With the aid of the vector identities

$$\frac{d}{dt}\mathbf{A} = \frac{\partial}{\partial t}\mathbf{A} + (\mathbf{v}\cdot\mathbf{grad})\mathbf{A} \tag{4.5}$$

$$\begin{aligned}\mathbf{grad}\,(\mathbf{v}\cdot\mathbf{A}) &= (\mathbf{v}\cdot\mathbf{grad})\mathbf{A} + (\mathbf{A}\cdot\mathbf{grad})\mathbf{A} + \mathbf{A} \times \mathbf{curl}\,\mathbf{v} + \mathbf{v} \times \mathbf{curl}\,\mathbf{A} \\ &= (\mathbf{v}\cdot\mathbf{grad})\mathbf{A} + \mathbf{v} \times \mathbf{curl}\,\mathbf{A}\end{aligned} \tag{4.6}$$

(note that $\partial v_j/\partial x_i \equiv 0$), the equation of motion can be written

$$\frac{d}{dt}\left(m\mathbf{v} + \frac{e}{c}\mathbf{A}\right) = -\,\mathbf{grad}\left(e\phi - \frac{e}{c}\mathbf{v}\cdot\mathbf{A}\right). \tag{4.7}$$

If we compare this expression with the Lagrangian equation of motion,

$$\frac{d}{dt}\left(\frac{\partial \mathcal{L}}{\partial \mathbf{v}}\right) = \mathbf{grad}\ \mathcal{L}, \tag{4.8}$$

we see that the Lagrangian is

$$\mathcal{L} = \frac{mv^2}{2} - e\phi + \frac{e}{c}\,\mathbf{v}\cdot\mathbf{A}. \tag{4.9}$$

The generalized momentum **p** for a charged particle in the presence of an electromagnetic field is no longer simply the "mechanical" momentum $m\mathbf{v}$. Instead, it includes a contribution from the vector potential:

$$\mathbf{p} \equiv \frac{\partial \mathcal{L}}{\partial \mathbf{v}} = m\mathbf{v} + \frac{e}{c}\,\mathbf{A}. \tag{4.10}$$

The Hamiltonian $\mathcal{H}(\mathbf{p}, \mathbf{r}, t)$ must be written in terms of this momentum rather than the mechanical momentum $m\mathbf{v}$. Thus the nonrelativistic Hamiltonian function for a (point) charged particle in an electromagnetic field becomes

$$\mathcal{H} = \frac{1}{2m}\left(\mathbf{p} - \frac{e}{c}\,\mathbf{A}\right)^2 + e\phi. \tag{4.11}$$

That is, from this Hamiltonian, the equation of motion given by Hamilton's equation,

$$\frac{d}{dt}\,\mathbf{p} = -\ \mathbf{grad}\ \mathcal{H}, \tag{4.12}$$

is just the Lorentz equation.

According to (4.7), it is the generalized momentum **p**, rather than the mechanical momentum $m\mathbf{v}$ alone, which is conserved in a field derivable solely from a uniform vector potential **A** (i.e., $\phi = 0$). Since the operators for the components of **p** and **r** still satisfy the commutation relations discussed earlier, **p** can still be represented by the operator $-i\hbar\nabla$. These points are discussed more fully by Messiah [1], and by Landau and Lifshitz [2].

The Hamiltonian for a charged particle with spin (and therefore with a magnetic moment $\boldsymbol{\mu}$) includes an interaction between $\boldsymbol{\mu}$ and the magnetic field, $\mathbf{H} = \mathbf{curl}\ \mathbf{A}$, as well as a spin–orbit interaction:

$$\mathcal{H} = \frac{1}{2m}\left(\mathbf{p} - \frac{e}{c}\,\mathbf{A}\right)^2 + e\phi - \boldsymbol{\mu}\cdot\mathbf{H} + \xi\mathbf{s}\cdot\mathbf{l}. \tag{4.13}$$

We shall here consider radiation fields or static magnetic fields. Then $\operatorname{div}\mathbf{A} = 0$ and we can write

$$\mathcal{H} = \left[\frac{p^2}{2m} + e\phi + \xi\mathbf{s}.\mathbf{l}\right] - \left[\frac{e}{mc}\,\mathbf{A}\cdot\mathbf{p} + \boldsymbol{\mu}\cdot\mathbf{curl}\ \mathbf{A}\right] + \frac{e^2}{2mc^2}\,\mathbf{A}^2. \tag{4.14}$$

The first bracketed term in (4.14) is the Hamiltonian for a spinning particle free of the radiation field or external magnetic field. We can immediately generalize this equation to give the Hamiltonian for a collection of particles, say the electrons constituting an atom:

$$\mathcal{H}_{\text{atom}} = \sum_i \left[\frac{p^2(i)}{2m} + e\phi(i) + \xi(i)\mathbf{s}(i)\cdot\mathbf{l}(i) \right]. \tag{4.15}$$

Here $\phi(i)$ is the electrostatic potential at the ith particle due to all other particles.

The next bracketed term in (4.14) represents the interaction between the particle and the field. This, too, generalizes:

$$\mathcal{H}_{\text{int}} = -\sum_i \left(\frac{e}{2m_i c}\right) [2\mathbf{A}(i)\cdot\mathbf{p}(i) + g_i\hbar\mathbf{s}(i)\cdot\mathbf{curl}\,\mathbf{A}(i)]. \tag{4.16}$$

Here $\mathbf{A}(i)$ is the electromagnetic vector potential evaluated at the position of the ith particle. Generally $\mathbf{A}$ consists of two parts: the vector potential of a static or slowly varying external magnetic field, and the vector potential of the radiation field:

$$\mathbf{A} = \mathbf{A}_{\text{ext}} + \mathbf{A}_{\text{rad}}.$$

We shall treat the external field part as a classical field, and the radiation field as a quantized field. This means we shall allow the atom to influence the radiation field but not the external field. (Both fields will, of course, influence the atom.)

For the simple case of a constant, uniform field $\mathbf{H}(\mathbf{r}, t) = \mathbf{H}$, we have

$$\begin{aligned} \mathbf{H} &= \mathbf{curl}\,\mathbf{A} \\ \mathbf{A} &= \tfrac{1}{2}(\mathbf{H} \times \mathbf{r}). \end{aligned} \tag{4.17}$$

Thus the terms of (4.16) give

$$\begin{aligned} 2\mathbf{A}\cdot\mathbf{p} &= (\mathbf{H} \times \mathbf{r})\cdot\mathbf{p} = \mathbf{H}\cdot\mathbf{r} \times \mathbf{p} = \hbar\mathbf{H}\cdot\mathbf{l} \\ g\hbar\mathbf{s}\cdot\mathbf{curl}\,\mathbf{A} &= g\hbar\mathbf{s}\cdot\mathbf{H}, \end{aligned}$$

and we obtain the interaction of the atom with this static field as

$$\mathcal{H}_{\text{int}} = -\sum_i \mu_i\mathbf{H}\cdot[\mathbf{l}(i) + g_i\mathbf{s}(i)]. \tag{4.18}$$

This interaction is responsible for the Zeeman effect, discussed in the next chapter.

Consider now the interaction with the radiation field. If we insert the expansion of $\mathbf{A}_{\text{rad}}$ into wave modes, (1.11a),

$$\mathbf{A}_{\text{rad}} = \mathop{\mathsf{S}}_{\gamma} \left(\frac{2\pi\hbar c}{k_\gamma}\right)^{1/2} (a_\gamma\mathbf{U}^\gamma + a_\gamma^*\mathbf{U}^{\gamma*}), \tag{4.19}$$

into (4.16), the interaction becomes

$$\mathcal{H}_{\text{int}} = -\mathop{\mathsf{S}}_{\gamma}\left(\frac{2\pi\hbar c}{k_\gamma}\right)^{1/2}\sum_i\left(\frac{e}{2m_ic}\right)(2a_\gamma\mathbf{U}^\gamma\cdot\mathbf{p}(i) + g_i\hbar a_n\mathbf{s}(i)\cdot\mathbf{curl}\;\mathbf{U}^\gamma$$
$$+ \text{complex conjugate}). \tag{4.20}$$

For convenience, we introduce the operators

$$\mathfrak{F}_\gamma(i) \equiv -\frac{2\pi}{\sqrt{k_\gamma}}\frac{e}{2m_ic}(2\mathbf{U}^\gamma\cdot\mathbf{p}(i) + \hbar g_i\mathbf{s}(i)\cdot\mathbf{curl}\;\mathbf{U}^\gamma) \tag{4.21}$$

and write the interaction as

$$\mathcal{H}_{\text{int}} = \mathop{\mathsf{S}}_{\gamma}\left(\frac{\hbar c}{2\pi}\right)^{1/2}\left[a_\gamma\sum_i\mathfrak{F}_\gamma(i) + a_\gamma^*\sum_i\mathfrak{F}_\gamma^*(i)\right]. \tag{4.22}$$

In particular, for the expansion into multipole fields $\mathbf{\Pi}_m^{(l)}$ and $\mathbf{\Sigma}_m^{(l)}$ [we omit the longitudinal field $\mathbf{\Lambda}_m^{(l)}$], the interaction is

$$\mathcal{H}_{\text{int}} = -\sum_{lm}\int dk\left(\frac{\hbar c}{2\pi}\right)^{1/2}\Bigg[[a_{k\mathfrak{M}lm}\sum_i\mathfrak{F}_{k\mathfrak{M}lm}(i)$$
$$+ a_{k\mathcal{E}lm}\sum_i\mathfrak{F}_{k\mathcal{E}lm}(i) + \text{complex conjugate}\Bigg]. \tag{4.23}$$

where the operators

$$\mathfrak{F}_{k\mathfrak{M}lm}(i) \equiv -\frac{2\pi}{\sqrt{k}}\left(\frac{e}{2m_ic}\right)[2\mathbf{\Pi}_m^{(l)}\cdot\mathbf{p}(i) + g_i\hbar\mathbf{s}(i)\cdot\mathbf{curl}\;\mathbf{\Pi}_m^{(l)}] \tag{4.24a}$$

$$\mathfrak{F}_{k\mathcal{E}lm}(i) \equiv -\frac{2\pi}{\sqrt{k}}\left(\frac{e}{2m_ic}\right)[2\mathbf{\Sigma}_m^{(l)}\cdot\mathbf{p}(i) + g_i\hbar\mathbf{s}(i)\cdot\mathbf{curl}\;\mathbf{\Sigma}_m^{(l)}] \tag{4.24b}$$

act upon atomic states and the a_{klm} operators act on field states. In the next section we shall see that $\mathfrak{F}_{k\mathfrak{M}lm}$ is a magnetic moment of order l, and $\mathfrak{F}_{k\mathcal{E}lm}$ is an electric moment of order l. With second quantization, a_{klm} and a_{klm}^* become photon annihilation and creation operators.

The final term in (4.14) has important significance for the part of the vector potential which corresponds to radiation fields. Using the expansion into wave modes, we find

$$\frac{e^2}{2mc^2}A^2 = \frac{e^2}{2mc^2}\mathop{\mathsf{S}}_{\gamma}\left(\frac{2\pi\hbar c}{k_\gamma}\right)^{1/2}(a_\gamma\mathbf{U}^\gamma + a_\gamma\mathbf{U}^{\gamma *})\mathop{\mathsf{S}}_{\gamma'}\left(\frac{2\pi\hbar c}{k_\gamma}\right)^{1/2}(a_{\gamma'}\mathbf{U}^{\gamma'} + a_{\gamma'}^*\mathbf{U}^{\gamma' *})$$
$$= \frac{e^2}{2mc^2}\mathop{\mathsf{S}}_{\gamma\gamma'}\frac{2\pi\hbar c}{\sqrt{k_\gamma k_{\gamma'}}}(a_\gamma a_{\gamma'}\mathbf{U}^\gamma\cdot\mathbf{U}^{\gamma'} + a_\gamma a_{\gamma'}^*\mathbf{U}^\gamma\cdot\mathbf{U}^{\gamma' *}$$
$$+ a_\gamma^* a_{\gamma'}\mathbf{U}^{\gamma *}\cdot\mathbf{U}^{\gamma'} + a_\gamma^* a_{\gamma'}^*\mathbf{U}^{\gamma *}\cdot\mathbf{U}^{\gamma' *}). \tag{4.25}$$

These terms correspond to various two-photon processes: absorption of two photons; absorption and re-emission; emission followed by absorption; and emission of two photons. These processes are important in studying the scattering of photons, but we neglect them here.

To complete our description of matter in the presence of radiation fields, we need to include the Hamiltonian for the radiation field alone,

$$\mathcal{H}_{\text{field}} = \underset{\gamma}{\mathsf{S}}\, \hbar\omega_\gamma a_\gamma^* a_\gamma. \tag{4.26}$$

In particular, for the multipole fields [neglecting the longitudinal fields $\Lambda_m^{(l)}$ this is

$$\mathcal{H}_{\text{field}} = \sum_{lm} \int dk\, \hbar ck(a_{k\mathfrak{M}lm}^* a_{k\mathfrak{M}lm} + a_{k\mathcal{E}lm}^* a_{k\mathcal{E}lm}). \tag{4.27}$$

The total Hamiltonian is then

$$\mathcal{H} = \mathcal{H}_{\text{atom}} + \mathcal{H}_{\text{field}} + \mathcal{H}_{\text{int}}. \tag{4.28}$$

The point to note here is that (at least in principle) we can obtain eigenstates of $\mathcal{H}_{\text{atom}}$ and $\mathcal{H}_{\text{field}}$ and that, for our purposes, $\mathcal{H}_{\text{int}}$ is small. Therefore we can apply perturbation theory to the problem.

REFERENCES

[1] A. Messiah, *Quantum Mechanics*, Wiley, New York (1962), pp. 54, 883, 1013, 1025.
[2] L. D. Landau and E. M. Lifshitz, *The Classical Theory of Fields*, Addison-Wesley, Reading, Massachusetts (1962), p. 42.

10.5 RADIATIVE TRANSITIONS

We have previously seen that the eigenstates of $\mathcal{H}_{\text{field}}$ are states in which definite numbers of photons are present. A particular state is labeled by the occupation numbers prescribing the number of photons of each wave mode (that is, the number of photons having particular wavenumbers, traveling in particular directions, with particular polarization).

In principle, we can also obtain the eigenstates of $\mathcal{H}_{\text{atom}}$, although our solutions may in fact be quite crude approximations to the actual eigenstates. The eigenvalues of $\mathcal{H}_{\text{atom}}$ are very nearly the observed atomic energy levels. The interaction with the field shifts the eigenstates of $\mathcal{H}$ slightly from the values for $\mathcal{H}_{\text{atom}}$, but we do not consider these small effects here. (Interaction with an external classical field produces the Zeeman splitting of the energy levels. Interaction with the radiation field produces very small—but important—corrections such as the Lamb shift.)

Without the interaction term, the Hamiltonian

$$\mathcal{H}^0 \equiv \mathcal{H}_{\text{atom}} + \mathcal{H}_{\text{field}} \tag{5.1}$$

has, as eigenstates, products of atomic eigenstates $|\psi_m\rangle$ and field eigenstates $|\varphi_m\rangle$. We denote such a product as $|m\rangle$:

$$|m\rangle \equiv |\psi_m\rangle|\varphi_m\rangle \equiv |\psi_m, \varphi_m\rangle.$$

Here ψ_m denotes the mth list of atomic quantum numbers and φ_m denotes the mth list of photon occupation numbers. An eigenstate $|E\rangle$ of the total Hamiltonian $\mathcal{H} = \mathcal{H}^0 + \mathcal{H}_{\text{int}}$ can then be expanded as

$$|E\rangle \equiv \mathop{\mathsf{S}}_{m} c_m(t)|\psi_m\rangle|\varphi_m\rangle.$$

If we view $\mathcal{H}_{\text{int}}$ as a small perturbation turned on at time $t = 0$ (or alternatively think of preparing the atom in a particular state at $t = 0$), then we can apply the time-dependent perturbation theory. Suppose the atom is initially in state $|\psi_i\rangle$ and the field is in state $|\varphi_i\rangle$. For example, the atom may be in an excited state, the field may be the vacuum state, or perhaps the atom is in the ground state and the field contains one photon in a particular mode. If the combined system is in a particular state, then only the single coefficient c_i is nonzero initially. The presence of the small interaction term produces transitions between these unperturbed states. As time passes, various other c_m's grow larger. At some later time there will be a finite probability $|c_m|^2$ of finding the atom in the state $|\psi_m\rangle$. Concomitantly, the field must then be in the state $|\varphi_m\rangle$. According to the time-dependent perturbation theory, the combined final state $|f\rangle$ can grow by direct transitions,

$$|i\rangle \rightarrow |f\rangle,$$

by indirect transitions,

$$|i\rangle \rightarrow |m\rangle \rightarrow |f\rangle,$$

or by higher-order transitions. We consider here only the direct transitions. These occur between states having the same unperturbed energy. That is, the total energy, atom + field, remains constant. If the atom passes to a state of lower atom energy, the field must increase in energy. The probability per unit time of observing a direct transition to a state having the same total energy E is

$$w(i \rightarrow f) = \frac{2\pi}{\hbar}\rho(E)|\langle\psi_f, \varphi_f|\mathcal{H}_{\text{int}}|\psi_i, \varphi_i\rangle|^2. \tag{5.2}$$

where $\rho(E)$ is the number of states having the energy E. Inserting the expansion of the radiation-field vector potential $\mathbf{A}$ in terms of the radiation modes $\mathbf{U}^\gamma$, we obtain [cf. (4.22)]

$$w(i \to f) = c\rho(E) \left| \mathop{\mathsf{S}}_{\gamma} \langle \varphi_f | a_\gamma | \varphi_i \rangle \left\langle \psi_f \middle| \sum_j \mathfrak{F}^\gamma(j) \middle| \psi_i \right\rangle + \mathop{\mathsf{S}}_{\gamma} \langle \varphi_f | a_\gamma^* | \varphi_i \rangle \left\langle \psi_f \middle| \sum_j \mathfrak{F}_\gamma^*(j) \middle| \psi_i \right\rangle \right|^2, \tag{5.3}$$

where the summation index j in

$$\mathfrak{F}_\gamma(j) = -\frac{2\pi}{\sqrt{k_\gamma}} \left(\frac{e_j}{2m_j c}\right) (2\mathbf{U}^\gamma \cdot \mathbf{p}(j) + g_j \hbar \mathbf{s}(j) \cdot \mathbf{curl}\, \mathbf{U}^\gamma) \tag{5.4}$$

runs over all the particles composing the atom, including the protons and neutrons. We shall be interested only in electron transitions, and will neglect the interactions between atomic nuclei and fields. Thus we let j run over electrons only. To simplify the following formulas, we frequently drop the label j of the jth electron.

Now, according to Section 10.3, the field operator a_n annihilates a photon (in the nth mode), and a_n^* creates a photon:

$$\langle \varphi_f | a_\gamma | \varphi_i \rangle \begin{cases} = \sqrt{N_\gamma} \text{ if } |\varphi_f\rangle \text{ has } \textit{one more } \gamma\text{th-mode photon than } |\varphi_i\rangle \\ = 0 \text{ otherwise.} \end{cases}$$

$$\langle \varphi_f | a_\gamma^* | \varphi_i \rangle \begin{cases} = \sqrt{N_\gamma + 1} \text{ if } |\varphi_f\rangle \text{ has } \textit{one less } \gamma\text{th-mode photon than } |\varphi_i\rangle \\ = 0 \text{ otherwise.} \end{cases}$$

N_γ is the number of γth-mode photons initially present. Thus $\langle \psi_f | \mathfrak{F}_\gamma | \psi_i \rangle$ describes a transition where one photon is *absorbed*, and $\langle \psi_f | \mathfrak{F}_\gamma^* | \psi_i \rangle$ describes a transition *emitting* a photon. Note particularly that although the probability for absorption is proportional to the initial number of photons N_γ, the emission probability is proportional to $N_\gamma + 1$. Emission can therefore be *induced* by the presence of a field, or can take place *spontaneously*. Absorption only occurs if photons are present initially. The absorption rate is

$$w_{\text{abs}}(i \to f) = c\rho(E) \left| \mathop{\mathsf{S}}_{\gamma} \sqrt{N_\gamma} \left\langle \psi_f \middle| \sum_j \mathfrak{F}_\gamma(j) \middle| \psi_i \right\rangle \right|^2 \tag{5.6}$$

and the emission rate is

$$w_{\text{emiss}}(i \to f) = c\rho(E) \left| \mathop{\mathsf{S}}_{\gamma} \sqrt{N_\gamma + 1} \left\langle \psi_f \middle| \sum_j \mathfrak{F}_\gamma^*(j) \middle| \psi_i \right\rangle \right|^2. \tag{5.7}$$

At this point it becomes useful to deal with the multipole fields $\mathbf{\Pi}_m^{(l)}$ and $\Sigma_m^{(l)}$ as the basic $\mathbf{U}^\gamma$ fields [neglecting the longitudinal field $\Lambda_m^{(l)}$]. According to (2.29), the density of energy states $\rho(E)\, dE$ is $dE/\hbar c$ so $\rho(E) = 1/\hbar c$. In terms of the $\mathfrak{F}_{k\mathcal{E}lm}$ and $\mathfrak{F}_{k\mathfrak{M}lm}$ operators of Section 10.4 we obtain the absorption rate

$$w_{\text{abs}}(i \rightarrow f) = \frac{1}{\hbar}$$

$$\times \left| \sum_{lm} \left\langle \psi_f \right| \sqrt{N_{k\mathfrak{M}lm}} \sum_j \mathfrak{F}_{k\mathfrak{M}lm}(j) + \sqrt{N_{k\mathcal{E}lm}} \sum_j \mathfrak{F}_{k\mathcal{E}lm}(j) \left| \psi_i \right\rangle \right|^2 \tag{5.8}$$

and the emission rate

$$w_{\text{emiss}}(i \rightarrow f) = \frac{1}{\hbar}$$

$$\times \left| \sum_{lm} \left\langle \psi_f \right| \sqrt{N_{k\mathfrak{M}lm} + 1} \sum_j \mathfrak{F}^*_{k\mathfrak{M}lm}(j) + \sqrt{N_{k\mathcal{E}lm} + 1} \sum_j \mathfrak{F}^*_{k\mathcal{E}lm}(j) \left| \psi_i \right\rangle \right|^2 \tag{5.9}$$

It might appear from these equations that a calculation of a transition probability would require calculation of matrix elements of both $\mathfrak{F}_{k\mathfrak{M}lm}$ and $\mathfrak{F}_{k\mathcal{E}lm}$ for an infinite number of values of l and m. However, we shall see that usually only a single matrix element contributes appreciably to the transition probability.

The first limitation comes from considering reflection symmetry. The parity π_{atom} of an atomic wavefunction is a well-defined quantity given by

$$\pi_{\text{atom}} = (-1)^{l_1 + l_2 + \cdots + l_N} \tag{5.10}$$

(since each of the N electrons has an angular dependence given by Y_{lm}). A multipole field also has well-defined parity. According to Section 10.3 the parity of $\mathbf{II}_m^{(l)}$, the magnetic multipole radiation, is

$$\pi_{\mathfrak{M}l} = (-1)^{l+1}, \tag{5.11}$$

Table 10.5 Atomic Parity Change in Multipole Radiation

	Magnetic Multipole	Electric Multipole
$l = 1$ (dipole)	no	yes
$l = 2$ (quadrupole)	yes	no
$l = 3$ (octopole)	no	yes

The parity of **curl** $\mathbf{II}_m^{(l)}$, the electric multipole radiation, is

$$\pi_{\mathcal{E}l} = (-1)^l. \tag{5.12}$$

Since these parities remain well defined, they must satisfy

$$(\pi_{\text{atom}})_{\text{initial}} = (\pi_{\text{atom}} \times \pi_{\text{field}})_{\text{final}}. \tag{5.13}$$

Therefore if the parity of the atom *changes* during the transition, the radiation must be either *even-order magnetic* multipole or *odd-order electric* multipole. If the parity does *not* change the radiation must be *odd-order magnetic* multipole or *even-order electric* multipole. These selection rules are displayed in Table 10.5.

10.6 MAGNETIC-MULTIPOLE RADIATION

Let us consider first magnetic-multipole radiation. The operator responsible for this radiation was given in (4.24*a*),

$$\mathfrak{F}_{k\mathfrak{M}\lambda m} = \frac{2}{\hbar}\beta[\mathbf{II}_m^{(\lambda)}\cdot\mathbf{p} + \hbar\mathbf{s}\cdot\mathbf{curl}\ \mathbf{II}_m^{(\lambda)}], \tag{6.1}$$

where the Bohr magneton is $\beta = e\hbar/2mc$ and the electron g factor is 2.0. (To avoid confusion with l, the electron angular momentum, we designate the multipole order by λ.) Using the relationships of Section 10.2, we can write the first part of the operator as

$$\begin{aligned}\mathbf{II}_m^{(\lambda)}\cdot\mathbf{p} &= -\frac{i}{\sqrt{\lambda(\lambda+1)}}[\mathbf{r}\times\mathbf{grad}\ Z_m^{(\lambda)}]\cdot\mathbf{p}\\ &= \frac{i\hbar}{\sqrt{\lambda(\lambda+1)}}[\mathbf{grad}\ Z_m^{(\lambda)}]\cdot\mathbf{l}\\ &= \frac{-k\hbar}{\sqrt{2\lambda+1}\sqrt{\lambda(\lambda+1)}}\{\sqrt{\lambda+1}\,[\mathbf{Z}^{(\lambda+1)}\times\mathbf{l}^{(1)}]_m^{(\lambda)}\\ &\quad+\sqrt{\lambda}\,[\mathbf{Z}^{(\lambda-1)}\times\mathbf{l}^{(1)}]_m^{(\lambda)}\}.\end{aligned} \tag{6.2}$$

The second part becomes

$$\begin{aligned}&\hbar\ \mathbf{curl}\ \mathbf{II}_m^{(\lambda)}\cdot\mathbf{s}\\ &= \frac{-k\hbar}{\sqrt{2\lambda+1}}\{\sqrt{\lambda}\,[\mathbf{Z}^{(\lambda+1)}\times\mathbf{s}^{(1)}]_m^{(\lambda)} + \sqrt{\lambda+1}\,[\mathbf{Z}^{(\lambda-1)}\times\mathbf{s}^{(1)}]_m^{(\lambda)}\}\\ &= i\hbar\left(\frac{\lambda+1}{\lambda}\right)^{1/2}\mathbf{grad}\ (Z_m^{\lambda})\cdot\mathbf{s} - \hbar k\left(\frac{2\lambda+1}{\lambda}\right)^{1/2}[\mathbf{Z}^{(\lambda+1)}\times\mathbf{s}]_m^{(\lambda)}.\end{aligned} \tag{6.3}$$

The interaction operator of order λ becomes

$$\mathfrak{F}_{k\mathfrak{M}\lambda m} = -2\beta\sqrt{k}\left\{\left(\frac{\lambda+1}{2\lambda+1}\right)^{1/2}\left[\mathbf{Z}^{(\lambda-1)} \times \left(\frac{2\mathbf{l}}{\lambda+1} - 2\mathbf{s}\right)\right]_m^{(\lambda)} - \left(\frac{\lambda}{2\lambda+1}\right)^{1/2}\left[\mathbf{Z}^{(\lambda+1)} \times \left(\frac{2\mathbf{l}}{\lambda} - 2\mathbf{s}\right)\right]_m^{(\lambda)}\right\}$$

$$= -2\pi i\beta\sqrt{k}\,\frac{\mathbf{grad}\,(Z_m^\lambda)}{k}\cdot\left(\frac{2}{\lambda+1}\mathbf{l} + 2\mathbf{s}\right) + 4\pi\beta\sqrt{k}\left(\frac{2\lambda+1}{\lambda}\right)^{1/2}[\mathbf{Z}^{(\lambda+1)} \times \mathbf{s}]_m^{(\lambda)}. \tag{6.4}$$

To proceed further, it becomes useful to introduce the *long-wavelength approximation:* we assume the wavelength of the radiation (typically longer than 2000Å) is much longer than atomic dimensions (typically a few angstroms), so that $kr \ll 1$ throughout the volume of integration for the matrix element $\langle\psi_f|\mathfrak{F}|\psi_i\rangle$. In this approximation the multipole fields which are finite at the origin have a radial dependence given by the spherical Bessel function

$$Z_m^{(\lambda)} \equiv i^\lambda k\left(\frac{2}{\pi}\right)^{1/2} j_\lambda(kr)Y_{\lambda m}$$

$$\simeq i^\lambda k\left(\frac{2}{\pi}\right)^{1/2} Y_{\lambda m}\frac{(kr)^\lambda}{1\cdot3\cdot5\cdots(2\lambda+1)}\left[1 - \frac{(kr)^2}{2(2\lambda+3)} + \cdots\right]. \tag{6.5}$$

In the long-wavelength approximation we take only the first term of the expansion in powers of (kr), because the second term is roughly 10^{-5}. Using the Racah tensor $C_m^{(\lambda)}$ we obtain

$$Z_m^{(\lambda)} \to \frac{i^\lambda}{2\pi}k^{\lambda+1}\frac{1}{(2\lambda-1)!!}\left(\frac{2}{2\lambda+1}\right)^{1/2} r^\lambda C_m^{(\lambda)}, \tag{6.6}$$

where $(2\lambda - 1)!! \equiv 1 \times 3 \times 5 \times \cdots \times (2\lambda - 1)$. We thereby obtain the operator responsible for the λth-order magnetic-multipole radiation:

$$\mathfrak{F}_{k\mathfrak{M}\lambda m} = \beta i^{\lambda+1}\frac{\sqrt{k^{2\lambda+1}}}{(2\lambda-1)!!}\left(\frac{2(\lambda+1)}{\lambda(2\lambda+1)}\right)^{1/2}\left\{\mathrm{grad}\,[r^\lambda C_m^{(\lambda)}]\cdot\left(\frac{2}{\lambda+1}\mathbf{l} + 2\mathbf{s}\right) + \frac{k^2 r^{\lambda+1}}{\sqrt{\lambda(\lambda+1)(2\lambda+3)}}[\mathbf{C}^{(\lambda+1)} \times \mathbf{s}]_m^{(\lambda)}\right\}. \tag{6.7}$$

The second part of this operator may be neglected in the region of long wavelengths. We now define the magnetic moment of order λ either by

$$M_m^{(\lambda)} = \sum_j \beta\,\mathbf{grad}\,[r^\lambda(j)C_m^{(\lambda)}(j)]\cdot\left(\frac{2}{\lambda+1}\mathbf{l}(j) + 2\mathbf{s}(j)\right) \tag{6.8a}$$

or else by

$$M_m^{(\lambda)} = \sum_j \beta\sqrt{\lambda(2\lambda-1)}\, r^{\lambda}(j)\left[\mathbf{C}^{(\lambda-1)}(j) \times \left\{\frac{2}{\lambda+1}\mathbf{l}(j) + 2\mathbf{s}(j)\right\}\right]_m^{(\lambda)} \tag{6.8b}$$

(These definitions differ by a negligible quantity when $kr \ll 1$.) Specifically, these multipole operators are

$$\mathbf{M}^{(1)} = \sum_j \beta\,[\mathbf{l}(j) + 2\mathbf{s}(j)]^{(1)}, \tag{6.9a}$$

$$\mathbf{M}^{(2)} = \sqrt{\tfrac{8}{3}}\sum_j \beta r(j)[\mathbf{C}^{(1)}(j) \times \{\mathbf{l}(j) + 3\mathbf{s}(j)\}]^{(2)}, \tag{6.9b}$$

$$\mathbf{M}^{(3)} = \sqrt{\tfrac{15}{3}}\sum_j \beta r^2(j)[\mathbf{C}^{(2)}(j) \times \{\mathbf{l}(j) + 4\mathbf{s}(j)\}]^{(3)}. \tag{6.9c}$$

The magnetic contribution to the interaction Hamiltonian then reads

$$\begin{aligned}\sum_{\lambda m} a_{k\mathfrak{M}\lambda m}\sum_j \mathfrak{F}_{k\mathfrak{M}\lambda m}(j) &= \sum_{\lambda m} a_{k\mathfrak{M}\lambda m} i^{\lambda+1}\frac{\sqrt{k^{2\lambda+1}}}{(2\lambda-1)!!}\left[\frac{2(\lambda+1)}{\lambda(2\lambda+1)}\right]^{1/2}\mathbf{M}_m^{(\lambda)}\\ &= -a_{k\mathfrak{M}1m}\sqrt{k^3}\sqrt{\tfrac{4}{3}}\,M_m^{(1)}\\ &\quad - i a_{k\mathfrak{M}1m}\sqrt{k^5}\sqrt{\tfrac{1}{15}}\,M_m^{(2)}\\ &\quad + a_{k\mathfrak{M}3m}\sqrt{k^7}\sqrt{\tfrac{8}{4725}}\,M_m^{(3)}\\ &\quad + \cdots.\end{aligned} \tag{6.10}$$

The expansion of the interaction Hamiltonian into this series of multipole operators does not depend on the long-wavelength approximation. The multipole expansion is essentially an angular relationship. The long-wavelength approximation enters only in the replacement of $j_l(kr)$ by the first term in the power-series expansion.

The numerical factors in this series drop off rapidly for atomic transitions, where $kr < 10^{-4}$, and we need retain only the first nonzero term. The first term in the series is proportional to the magnetic dipole moment $\beta(\mathbf{l} + 2\mathbf{s})$, and gives, according to (5.9), the spontaneous emission rate for magnetic-dipole radiation (sometimes abbreviated as $\mathfrak{M}1$ radiation):

$$w_{\text{spont }\mathfrak{M}1}(i \to f) = \frac{4}{3}\frac{k^3}{\hbar}\,|\langle\psi_f|\,M_m^{(1)*}\,|\psi_i\rangle|^2. \tag{6.11}$$

The next term produces magnetic-quadrupole radiation (or $\mathfrak{M}2$ radiation)

$$w_{\text{spont }\mathfrak{M}2}(i \to f) = \frac{1}{15}\frac{k^5}{\hbar}\,|\langle\psi_f|\,M_m^{(2)*}\,|\psi_i\rangle|^2. \tag{6.12}$$

It is most convenient to work with matrix elements measured in atomic units. We then measure angular momentum in units of $\hbar$; lengths in units of $a_0 = \hbar^2/me^2$, the Bohr radius; and magnetic moments in units of $2\beta = e\hbar/mc$, twice the Bohr magneton. (Note that $\beta = ea_0\alpha/2$, where $\alpha = e^2/\hbar c$ is Sommerfeld's fine-structure constant.) Using the wavenumber $\tilde{\nu}$ or wavelength λ,

$$\tilde{\nu} = \frac{1}{\lambda} = \frac{k}{2\pi},$$

and the Rydberg unit

$$R_\infty = \frac{\alpha}{4\pi a_0} = 109737.3 \text{ cm}^{-1},$$

we obtain the numerical factors

$$\mathfrak{M}1: \quad \frac{4}{3}\frac{\beta^2 k^3}{\hbar} = \frac{8\pi^3 e^2\hbar(\tilde{\nu})^3}{3m^2c^2} = \frac{\pi}{6}\frac{\alpha^5 c}{R_\infty{}^2}(\tilde{\nu})^3 = 2.6971 \times 10^{-11}(\tilde{\nu}\text{ cm}^{-1})^3$$

$$\mathfrak{M}2: \quad \frac{1}{15}\frac{\beta^2 k^3}{\hbar}(a_0 k)^2 = \frac{\pi}{480}\frac{\alpha^7 c}{R_\infty{}^4}(\tilde{\nu})^5 = 1.491 \times 10^{-27}(\tilde{\nu}\text{ cm}^{-1})^5$$

For an optical transition with a wavelength of 5000 Å (or $\tilde{\nu} = 20{,}000$ cm^{-1}), the rates are

$$w_{\text{spont}\,\mathfrak{M}1}(i \to f) = 2.1577 \times 10^2 |\langle f| M_m^{(1)*} |i\rangle|^2 \text{ sec}^{-1},$$
$$w_{\text{spont}\,\mathfrak{M}2}(i \to f) = 4.7704 \times 10^{-6} |\langle f| M_m^{(2)*} |i\rangle|^2 \text{ sec}^{-1}.$$

10.7 ELECTRIC-MULTIPOLE RADIATION

Let us look now at the electric-multipole radiation. Using the vector Helmholtz equation, we can write the operator of (4.24*b*) as

$$\mathfrak{F}_{k\varepsilon\lambda m} = \frac{2\pi}{\sqrt{k}}\left[\frac{e}{mc}\,\boldsymbol{\Sigma}_m^{(\lambda)}\cdot\mathbf{p} + 2k^2\beta\mathbf{s}\cdot\mathbf{\Pi}_m^{(\lambda)}\right]. \tag{7.1}$$

In the long-wavelength approximation we can write

$$\boldsymbol{\Sigma}_m^{(\lambda)} \simeq ik\left(\frac{\lambda+1}{\lambda}\right)^{1/2} \textbf{grad } Z_m^{(\lambda)} \tag{7.2}$$

by neglecting the terms involving $Z^{(\lambda+1)}$ in (2.12) and (2.17). Then we can employ the identity

$$\frac{i\hbar}{m}(\textbf{grad } X)\cdot\mathbf{p}Y = -\frac{\mathbf{p}^2}{2m}(XY) + X\frac{\mathbf{p}^2}{2m}Y + Y\frac{\mathbf{p}^2}{2m}X, \tag{7.3}$$

(which holds for any functions X and Y) and the fact that, in the long-wavelength approximation,

$$\nabla^2 Z_m^{(\lambda)} \simeq i^\lambda k \left(\frac{2}{\pi}\right)^{1/2} \nabla^2 \left[\frac{(kr^\lambda)}{(2\lambda+1)!!} Y_{\lambda m}\right] = 0, \tag{7.4}$$

in order to write

$$\frac{e}{mc} \Sigma_m^{(\lambda)} \cdot \mathbf{p} \simeq -k \frac{e}{\hbar c} \left(\frac{\lambda+1}{\lambda}\right)^{1/2} \left[Z_m^{(\lambda)} \frac{\mathbf{p}^2}{2m} - \frac{\mathbf{p}^2}{2m} Z_m^{(\lambda)}\right]. \tag{7.5}$$

If we introduce the Hamiltonian of the isolated atom

$$\mathcal{H}_{\text{atom}} = \sum_i \frac{\mathbf{p}^2(i)}{2m} + \sum_i \frac{Ze^2}{r_i} - \sum_{i<j} \frac{e^2}{r_{ij}} \tag{7.6}$$

(we neglect here the smaller spin–orbit interactions), then we can write

$$\begin{aligned} &\langle \psi_f | \Sigma_m^{(\lambda)} \cdot \mathbf{p} | \psi_i \rangle \\ &= i \frac{e}{\hbar c} \left(\frac{\lambda+1}{\lambda}\right)^{1/2} \langle \psi_f | Z_m^{(\lambda)} \mathcal{H}_{\text{atom}} - \mathcal{H}_{\text{atom}} Z_m^{(\lambda)} | \psi_i \rangle \\ &= \frac{i^{\lambda+1}}{\pi \hbar c k} \left[\frac{(\lambda+1)(2\lambda+1)}{2\lambda}\right]^{1/2} \frac{(E_i - E_f) k^{\lambda+1}}{(2\lambda+1)!!} \langle \psi_f | e r^\lambda C_m^{(\lambda)} | \psi_i \rangle. \end{aligned} \tag{7.7}$$

The matrix element

$$\langle \psi_f | \sum_j e r^\lambda(j) C_m^{(\lambda)}(j) | \psi_i \rangle$$

is the moment of order λ of the electric charge distribution; hence our label "electric-multipole radiation." When we identify the energy difference between atomic states with the energy carried away by radiation,

$$E_i - E_f = \hbar c k, \tag{7.8}$$

we can write the first part of the operator $\mathfrak{F}_{k\varepsilon l \mathfrak{M}}$ as

$$\mathfrak{F}_{k\varepsilon lm} = i^\lambda \frac{\sqrt{k^{2\lambda+1}}}{(2\lambda-1)!!} \left[\frac{2(\lambda+1)}{\lambda(2\lambda+1)}\right]^{1/2} e r^\lambda C_m^{(\lambda)}. \tag{7.9}$$

The second part of the $\mathfrak{F}_{k\varepsilon\lambda m}$ operator is, in the long-wavelength approximation,

$$\begin{aligned} 2k^2 \beta \mathbf{s} \cdot \mathbf{II}_m^{(\lambda)} &= 2\beta k^3 \left(\frac{2}{\pi}\right)^{1/2} [\mathbf{Z}^{(\lambda)} \times \mathbf{s}^{(1)}]_m^{(\lambda)} \\ &= \frac{\beta k^3}{2\pi} \frac{(kr)^\lambda \sqrt{2\lambda+1}\sqrt{8}}{(2\lambda+1)!!} [\mathbf{C}^{(\lambda)} \times \mathbf{s}^{(1)}]_m^{(\lambda)}. \end{aligned} \tag{7.10}$$

These spin-dependent terms are smaller than the electric-moment terms of the same order (unless the electric moment vanishes), since $k\beta = e(a_0 k)\alpha/2 \leq 10^{-5}$ and we therefore neglect them. By introducing the electric multipole-moment operators,

$$Q_m^{(\lambda)} = \sum_j e r^\lambda(j) C_m^{(\lambda)}(j) \tag{7.11}$$

we obtain the contribution to the interaction Hamiltonian of electric-multipole radiation:

$$\begin{aligned}
\sum_{\lambda m} a_{k\varepsilon\gamma m} \sum \mathfrak{F}_{k\varepsilon m\lambda} &= \sum_{\lambda m} a_{k\varepsilon\lambda m}\, i^\lambda \frac{\sqrt{k^{2\lambda+1}}}{(2\lambda-1)!!}\left[\frac{2(\lambda+1)}{\lambda(2\lambda+1)}\right]^{1/2} Q_m^{(\lambda)} \\
&= i a_{k\varepsilon 1m}\sqrt{k^3}\sqrt{\tfrac{4}{3}}\, Q_m^{(1)} \\
&- a_{k\varepsilon 2m}\sqrt{k^5}\sqrt{\tfrac{1}{15}}\, Q_m^{(2)} \\
&- i a_{k\varepsilon 3m}\sqrt{k^7}\sqrt{\tfrac{8}{4725}}\, Q_m^{(3)} \\
&+ \cdots.
\end{aligned} \tag{7.12}$$

From the first term in this series we obtain the spontaneous emission rate for electric dipole radiation (sometimes abbreviated $\mathcal{E}1$ radiation):

$$w_{\text{spont }\mathcal{E}1}(i \to f) = \frac{4}{3}\frac{k^3}{\hbar}\,|\langle\psi_f|\, Q_m^{(1)*}\,|\psi_i\rangle|^2, \tag{7.13}$$

The next terms produce electric-quadrupole radiation (abbreviated $\mathcal{E}2$),

$$w_{\text{spont }\mathcal{E}2}(i \to f) = \frac{1}{15}\frac{k^5}{\hbar}\,|\langle\psi_f|\, Q_m^{(2)*}\,|\psi_i\rangle|^2 \tag{7.14}$$

and electric octupole (or $\mathcal{E}3$) radiation:

$$w_{\text{spont }\mathcal{E}3}(i \to f) = \frac{8}{525}\frac{k^7}{\hbar}\,|\langle\psi_f|\, Q_m^{(3)*}\,|\psi_i\rangle|^2. \tag{7.15}$$

The numerical factors are

$$\begin{aligned}
\mathcal{E}1:&\quad \frac{4}{3}\frac{k^3}{\hbar}e^2(a_0)^2 = \frac{2\pi}{3}\frac{c}{R_\infty{}^2}\alpha^3(\tilde{\nu})^3 = 2.0260 \times 10^{-6}\,(\tilde{\nu}\text{ cm}^{-1})^3,\\
\mathcal{E}2:&\quad \frac{1}{15}\frac{k^5}{\hbar}e^2(a_0)^4 = \frac{\pi}{120}\frac{c}{R_\infty{}^4}\alpha^5(\tilde{\nu})^5 = 1.120 \times 10^{-22}\,(\tilde{\nu}\text{ cm}^{-1})^5,\\
\mathcal{E}3:&\quad \frac{8}{4725}\frac{k^7}{\hbar}e^2(a_0)^6 = \frac{\pi}{18900}\frac{c}{R_\infty{}^6}\alpha^7(\tilde{\nu})^7 = 3.144 \times 10^{-39}\,(\tilde{\nu}\text{ cm}^{-1})^7.
\end{aligned}$$

For an optical transition with a wavelength of 5000 Å ($\tilde{\nu} = 20{,}000\text{ cm}^{-1}$) these emission rates are

$$\begin{aligned}
w_{\text{spont}\,\mathcal{E}1}(i \to f) &= 1.6208 \times 10^7\,|\langle f|\, Q_m^{(1)*}\,|i\rangle|^2\text{ sec}^{-1},\\
w_{\text{spont}\,\mathcal{E}2}(i \to f) &= 0.3583\,|\langle f|\, Q_m^{(2)*}\,|i\rangle|^2\text{ sec}^{-1},\\
w_{\text{spont}\,\mathcal{E}3}(i \to f) &= 4.024 \times 10^{-9}\,|\langle f|\, Q_m^{(3)*}\,|i\rangle|^2\text{ sec}^{-1}.
\end{aligned}$$

Table 10.6 Spontaneous Emission Probabilities (Einstein's A)[a]

Parity Change	No Parity Change
($\mathcal{E}1$) $\bar{\nu}^3 \cdot \lvert\langle f \rvert \mathbf{Q}^{(1)} \lvert i\rangle\rvert^2 \cdot \frac{8}{3}\pi c\alpha\left(\frac{\alpha}{2R_\infty}\right)^2$ $(2.0260 \times 10^{-6}\ \mathrm{cm}^3\ \mathrm{sec}^{-1})$	($\mathcal{M}1$) $\bar{\nu}^3 \cdot \lvert\langle f \rvert \mathbf{M}^{(2)} \lvert i\rangle\rvert^2 \cdot \frac{2}{3}\pi c\alpha^3\left(\frac{\alpha}{2R_\infty}\right)^2$ $(2.6971 \times 10^{-11}\ \mathrm{cm}^3\ \mathrm{sec}^{-1})$
($\mathcal{M}2$) $\bar{\nu}^5 \cdot \lvert\langle f \rvert \mathbf{M}^{(2)} \lvert i\rangle\rvert^2 \cdot \frac{1}{30}\pi c\alpha^3\left(\frac{\alpha}{2R_\infty}\right)^4$ $(1.4908 \times 10^{-27}\ \mathrm{cm}\ \mathrm{sec}^{-1})$	($\mathcal{E}2$) $\bar{\nu}^5 \cdot \lvert\langle f \rvert \mathbf{Q}^{(2)} \lvert i\rangle\rvert^2 \cdot \frac{2}{15}\pi c\alpha\left(\frac{\alpha}{2R_\infty}\right)^4$ $(1.1198 \times 10^{-22}\ \mathrm{cm}^5\ \mathrm{sec}^{-1})$
($\mathcal{E}3$) $\bar{\nu}^7 \cdot \lvert\langle f \rvert \mathbf{Q}^{(3)} \lvert i\rangle\rvert^2 \cdot \frac{16}{4725}\pi c\alpha\left(\frac{\alpha}{2R_\infty}\right)^6$ $(3.1440 \times 10^{-39}\ \mathrm{cm}^7\ \mathrm{sec}^{-1})$	
Electric Operators[a]	Magnetic Operators[a]
$Q_m^{(1)} \equiv \sum rC_m^{(1)} \equiv r_m^{(1)}$	$M_m^{(1)} = \frac{1}{2}\sum [l_m^{(1)} + 2s_m^{(1)}] = \frac{1}{2}\sum [j_m^{(1)} + s_m^{(1)}]$
$Q_m^{(2)} = \sum rC_m^{(2)}$	$M_m^{(2)} = \sqrt{\frac{2}{3}}\sum r[\mathbf{C}^{(1)} \times [\mathbf{l}^{(1)} + 3\mathbf{s}^{(1)}]]_m^{(2)}$
$Q_m^{(3)} = \sum r^3C_m^{(3)}$	

[a] r in units of a_0; $\mathbf{l}$ and $\mathbf{s}$ in units of $\hbar$; $\bar{\nu}$ in reciprocal centimeters.

Comparing the results of this chapter and the previous chapter on magnetic radiation, we can get a rough estimate of the relative likelihood of various multipole transitions. Tables 10.6 and 10.7 collect these results.

Table 10.7 Einstein Transition Probabilities, $\lambda = 5000$ Å

Parity Change		No Parity Change	
($\mathcal{E}1$)	$1.6208 \times 10^{7} \, |\langle f| \mathbf{Q}^{(1)} | i\rangle|^2$	($\mathfrak{M}1$)	$2.1577 \times 10^{2} \, |\langle f| \mathbf{M}^{(1)} | i\rangle|^2$
($\mathfrak{M}2$)	$4.770 \times 10^{-6} \, |\langle f| \mathbf{M}^{(2)} | i\rangle|^2$	($\mathcal{E}2$)	$3.583 \times 10^{-1} \, |\langle f| \mathbf{Q}^{(2)} | i\rangle|^2$
($\mathcal{E}3$)	$4.024 \times 10^{-9} \, |\langle f| \mathbf{Q}^{(3)} | i\rangle|^2$		

Electric dipole transitions account for the overwhelming majority of spectral lines, and so the calculation of electric-dipole transitions has held the center of attention in atomic spectroscopy. For many purposes, one can neglect other transitions entirely. However, magnetic-dipole and electric-quadrupole transitions do give rise to important spectral lines, the so-called "forbidden" lines [1, 2].

The spontaneous transition rates calculated above are often referred to as Einstein transition probabilities and are denoted by the letter A:

$$w_{\text{spont}}(i \rightarrow f) = A(i,f)$$

REFERENCES

[1] I. S. Bowen, *Rev. Mod. Phys.* **8,** 55 (1936).
[2] R. H. Garstang, in *Atomic and Molecular Processes*, edited by D. R. Bates, Academic, New York (1962), p. 1.

10.8 LINE STRENGTHS

The preceding formulas provide the probability per unit time, $w_{\text{spont}}(i \rightarrow f)$ or $A(i,f)$, that an atom, excited to state ψ_i, will spontaneously emit a photon and change to state ψ_f. If we have a collection of $N(i)$ excited atoms per unit volume, the rate of spontaneous emission per unit volume will be

$$\begin{aligned} \text{spontaneous rate} &= N(i) w_{\text{spont}}(i \rightarrow f) \\ &= N(i) A(i,f) \text{ cm}^{-3} \text{ sec}^{-1}. \end{aligned} \tag{8.1}$$

The power radiated (in all directions) by these transitions is the product of this emission rate for individual photons times $\hbar\omega_{if}$, the energy carried by each photon:

$$\text{spontaneous power} = \hbar\omega_{if}N(i)A(i,f)\ \text{erg cm}^{-3}\ \text{sec}^{-1}. \tag{8.2}$$

As the photon from one atom encounters other atoms, during its passage out of the light source, it may be absorbed or it may stimulate emission of additional identical photons. When such processes are important, the calculation of the emergent radiation field can become quite complicated. However, one may often neglect these effects within a small element of the light source. The rate of photon emission from this element is then given by (8.1).

Consider the processes of spontaneous emission. Let the initial state be specified by angular-momentum quantum numbers J' and M' and additional quantum numbers α':

$$i = \alpha' J' M'.$$

Similarly, let the final state be specified by

$$f = \alpha JM.$$

The rate of transitions $i \to f$ is

$$\text{spontaneous rate} = N(\alpha' J' M')A(\alpha' J' M', \alpha JM). \tag{8.3}$$

For electric-dipole transitions, this rate is

$$\mathcal{E}1\ \text{spontaneous rate} = N(\alpha' J' M')\frac{4}{3}\frac{k^3}{\hbar}\,|\langle \alpha JM|\,Q_m^{(1)}\,|\,\alpha' J' M'\rangle|^2,$$

$$Q_m^{(1)} = e\sum_j r(j)C_m^{(1)}(j) \tag{8.4}$$

Similar expressions apply for other multipole transition rates.

With the aid of the Wigner–Eckart theorem, we can factor the dipole matrix element:

$$\begin{aligned}\langle \alpha JM|\,Q_m^{(1)}\,|\,\alpha' J' M'\rangle &= \frac{(J'M', 1m|JM'}{\sqrt{2J+1}}\langle \alpha J\|\mathbf{Q}^{(1)}\|\alpha' J'\rangle \\ &= (-1)^{J-M}\begin{pmatrix} J & 1 & J' \\ -M & m & M' \end{pmatrix}\langle \alpha J\|\mathbf{Q}^{(1)}\|\alpha' J'\rangle.\end{aligned} \tag{8.5}$$

Thus the spontaneous emission rate is

$$\mathcal{E}1\ \text{spontaneous rate} = N(\alpha' J' M')\frac{4}{3}\frac{k^3}{\hbar}\frac{(J'M', 1m|JM)^2}{(2J+1)}\,|\langle \alpha J\|\mathbf{Q}^{(1)}\|\alpha' J'\rangle|^2. \tag{8.6}$$

This step separates the part of the matrix element that depends on M and

M' (the "geometrical part") from the reduced matrix element (the "physical part"). The CG coefficient selects the component of the dipole operator responsible for the radiation:

$$m = M - M'.$$

The intensity of the electric field in any direction (measured from the axis that defines the quantum numbers M' and M) is proportional to the product of the emission rate for individual photons (8.3) and the appropriate multipole angular distribution $I_{lm}(\theta)$ of Section 10.2. For $\mathcal{E}1$ radiation, this intensity is

$$N(\alpha'J'M')\,\frac{ck^4}{2}\,|\langle\alpha J\|\mathbf{Q}^{(1)}\|\alpha'J'\rangle|^2 \times \frac{(J'M',\,1m|JM)^2}{(2J+1)} \times \begin{cases}\frac{1}{2}(1+\cos^2\theta) & m = \pm 1,\\ \sin^2\theta & m = 0.\end{cases} \quad (8.7)$$

This formula gives the intensity distribution of the *Zeeman components* of a line—transitions between the *sublevels* M' and M comprising the *levels* $\alpha'J'$ and αJ—for $\mathcal{E}1$ radiation. Similar results apply for other multipoles. We shall discuss the angular distribution further in the next chapter.

The CG coefficient also contains a selection rule on $\Delta J \equiv J' - J$. For dipole radiation this rule is

$$\mathcal{E}1 \text{ or } \mathcal{M}1 \text{ radiation:} \quad \Delta J = -1, 0, +1$$

(but not $J = 0$ to $J' = 0$). For quadrupole radiation, it is

$$\mathcal{E}2 \text{ or } \mathcal{M}2 \text{ radiation:} \quad \Delta J = -2, -1, 0, +1, +2$$

(but not $J = 0$ to $J' = 0$, nor $J = \frac{1}{2}$ to $J' = \frac{1}{2}$, nor $J = 1$ to $J' = 0$). These conditions are simply examples of the triangle rule: J, J', and λ (the multipole order) form a triangle of integral perimeter.

Unless the light source is imbedded in a strong magnetic field, one does not resolve the individual Zeeman components. Rather, one observes the sum of all components comprising a given line:

$$\text{observed rate} = \sum_{M}\sum_{M'} N(\alpha'J'M')A(\alpha'J'M', \alpha JM). \quad (8.8)$$

If conditions in the light source are nearly isotropic, so that selective excitation of one particular sublevel does not occur, all sublevels of a given level will be equally populated. The population $N(\alpha'J')$ of the level $\alpha'J'$ will be the number of sublevels [given by the statistical weight $\varpi(J') = (2J'+1)$] times the population in any one sublevel:

$$\begin{aligned} N(\alpha'J') &= (2J'+1)N(\alpha'J'M') \\ &\equiv \varpi(J')N(\alpha'J'M'). \end{aligned} \quad (8.9)$$

We can then define an Einstein coefficient for the line (as opposed to a coefficient for individual *line components*) by the relation

$$N(\alpha'J')A(\alpha'J', \alpha J) = \sum_{MM'} N(\alpha'J'M')A(\alpha'J'M', \alpha JM). \tag{8.10}$$

That is, $A(\alpha'J', \alpha J)$ is an average over initial sublevels M' and a sum over final sublevels M:

$$A(\alpha'J', \alpha J) = \frac{1}{\varpi(J')} \sum_{MM'} A(\alpha'J'M', \alpha JM). \tag{8.11}$$

Equation 8.8 thereby becomes

$$\text{observed rate} = \varpi(J')A(\alpha'J', \alpha J). \tag{8.12}$$

We can readily perform the summation over M and M', with the use of the summation properties of CG coefficients. For any tensor operator, we have

$$\begin{aligned}\sum_{M}\sum_{M'} |\langle\alpha JM|T_m^{(\lambda)}|\alpha'J'M'\rangle|^2 &= |\langle\alpha J\|\mathbf{T}^{(\lambda)}\|\alpha'J'\rangle|^2 \sum_{MM'} \frac{(J'M, \lambda m|JM)^2}{(2J+1)} \\ &= |\langle\alpha J\|\mathbf{T}^{(\lambda)}\|\alpha'J'\rangle|^2.\end{aligned} \tag{8.13}$$

Equation 8.13 permits us to write the multipole transition probabilities as

$$\begin{aligned}\varpi(J')A_{\mathcal{E}1}(\text{n}'J', \text{n}J) &= \frac{4}{3}\frac{k^3}{\hbar}\mathbf{S}_d(\alpha'J', \alpha J) \\ \varpi(J')A_{\mathcal{M}1}(\alpha'J', \alpha J) &= \frac{4}{3}\frac{k^3}{\hbar}\mathbf{S}M(\alpha'J', \alpha J) \\ \varpi(J')A_{\mathcal{E}2}(\alpha'J', \alpha J) &= \frac{1}{10}\frac{k^5}{\hbar}\mathbf{S}_Q(\alpha'J', \alpha J)\end{aligned} \tag{8.14}$$

where, in the notation of Condon and Shortley [1], the *line strengths* **S** are:

$$\begin{aligned}\mathbf{S}_d(\alpha'J', \alpha J) &= |\langle\alpha J\|\mathbf{Q}^{(1)}\|\alpha'J'\rangle|^2 \\ \mathbf{S}_M(\alpha'J', \alpha J) &= |\langle\alpha J\|\mathbf{M}^{(1)}\|\alpha'J'\rangle|^2 \\ \mathbf{S}_Q(\alpha'J', \alpha J) &= \tfrac{2}{3}|\langle\alpha J\|\mathbf{Q}^{(2)}\|\alpha'J'\rangle|^2.\end{aligned} \tag{8.15}$$

(The factor $\frac{2}{3}$ appears because of the connection between the quadrupole dyadic and the spherical tensor of order 2; see (10.38) in Chapter 3.) The line strengths, like the quantities ϖA, are symmetrical:

$$\begin{aligned}\mathbf{S}(\alpha'J', \alpha J) &= \mathbf{S}(\alpha J, \alpha'J') \\ \varpi(J')A(J', J) &= \varpi(J)A(J, J').\end{aligned}$$

With line strengths expressed in atomic units and wavelengths λ expressed in angstroms, we have

$$\varpi(J')A_{\mathcal{E}1}(\alpha'J', \alpha J) = \frac{2.026 \times 10^{18}}{\lambda^3} \mathbf{S}_d$$

$$\varpi(J')A_{\mathfrak{M}1}(\alpha'J', \alpha J) = \frac{2.697 \times 10^{13}}{\lambda^3} \mathbf{S}M$$

$$\varpi(J')A_{\mathcal{E}2}(\alpha'J', \alpha J) = \frac{1.680 \times 10^{18}}{\lambda^5} \mathbf{S}_Q.$$

The description of radiation absorption, in the atomic transition $\alpha J \rightarrow \alpha'J'$, often uses the following quantities:

$B(\alpha J, \alpha'J')$: The Einstein coefficient for absorption
$\kappa_\omega = 2\pi\kappa_\nu$: The absorption coefficient per unit mass per unit frequency interval (often denoted by k_ν)
α_ν: The absorption coefficient per atom per unit frequency interval
$f(\alpha J, \alpha'J')$: The *oscillator strength*—the effective number of electrons per atom (often denoted $f_{JJ'}$).

These quantities are related as follows:

$$\int \kappa_\omega \, d\omega = \int \kappa_\nu \, d\nu = N(\alpha J) \int \alpha_\nu \, d\nu = N(\alpha J)\hbar k B(\alpha J, \alpha'J')$$

$$= \frac{\pi e^2}{mc} N(\alpha J) f(\alpha J, \alpha'J'). \quad (8.16)$$

The statistical weight $\varpi(J) = 2J + 1$ is often denoted $g(J)$ or simply g, so that ϖA becomes gA.

From considerations of equilibrium, Einstein obtained the relation

$$gB \equiv \varpi(J)B(\alpha J, \beta'J') = \varpi(J')A(\alpha'J', \alpha J) \frac{\pi}{2\hbar k^3}$$

$$= \varpi(J')A(\alpha'J', \alpha J) \frac{c^3}{8\pi h \nu^3} . \quad (8.17)$$

Therefore the weighted oscillator strength (or *gf value*) of an absorption transition is

$$gf \equiv \varpi(J)f(\alpha J, \alpha'J') = \varpi(J')A(\alpha'J', \alpha J) \frac{mc\lambda^2}{8\pi e^2}$$

$$= 1.4993 \times 10^{-16} \lambda^2 gA$$

$$= \frac{4}{3} \frac{\pi mc}{\hbar e^2} \frac{\mathbf{S}(\alpha'J', \alpha J)}{\lambda} . \quad (8.18)$$

(Recall that αJ is the lower level, $\alpha' J'$ is the upper level.) By definition, the oscillator strength is positive for absorption. This condition may be written

$$\varpi(J) f(\alpha J, \alpha' J') = \frac{2}{3} \frac{m}{\hbar^2 e^2} (E_{J'} - E_J) \mathbf{S}(\alpha' J', \alpha J). \tag{8.19}$$

Induced emission (negative absorption) is then described by a negative oscillator strength:

$$\varpi(J) f(\alpha J, a' J') = -\varpi(J') f(\alpha' J', \alpha J). \tag{8.20}$$

For electric-dipole transitions, the gf value takes the numerical value

$$gf = \frac{303.7}{\lambda} \mathbf{S}$$

where λ is expressed in angstrom units.

Monochromatic radiation, traversing a short distance x through matter of density ρ, diminishes in intensity according to the law

$$\frac{d}{dx} I(x) = -\kappa \rho I(x) \tag{8.21a}$$

or

$$I(x) = I(0)\, e^{-\kappa \rho x}. \tag{8.21b}$$

The absorption coefficient κ_ω shows a large variation with frequency near the frequency ω_0 of a spectral line. Typically this variation assumes the form of a Lorentz profile,

$$\kappa_\omega \rho = \frac{e^2}{mc} N(\alpha J) f(\alpha J, \alpha' J') \cdot \frac{(\gamma/2)}{(\omega - \omega_0)^2 + (\gamma/2)^2} \cdot \tag{8.22}$$

Whether we characterize a process by an Einstein coefficient or by an oscillator strength, all explicit reference to atomic structure occurs in the line strength **S**, the square of a multipole-moment matrix element:

$$\mathbf{S}(\alpha J, \alpha' J') = |\langle \alpha J \| \mathbf{T}^{(k)} \| \alpha' J' \rangle|^2. \tag{8.23}$$

In practice, calculation of **S** proceeds in two steps. First one calculates the appropriate matrix elements of a multipole operator using some simple convenient coupling scheme (usually LS coupling). Then one transforms this matrix into the energy scheme, using the unitary transformation $\langle \alpha J | \Gamma J \rangle$ between the LS coupling states $\Psi(\Gamma J M)$ and the energy eigenstates $\Phi(\alpha J M)$. The result is

$$\mathbf{S}(\alpha J, \alpha' J') = \Big| \sum_{\Gamma \Gamma'} \langle \alpha J | \Gamma J \rangle \langle \Gamma J \| \mathbf{T}^{(k)} \| \Gamma' J' \rangle \langle \Gamma' J' | \alpha J' \rangle \Big|^2. \tag{8.24}$$

Equation 8.24 shows the necessity for calculating the phases (signs $\pm$) of the elements $\langle \Gamma J \| \mathbf{T}^{(k)} \| \Gamma' J' \rangle$. These elements are added before being squared.

REFERENCE

[1] E. U. Condon and G. H. Shortley, *The Theory of Atomic Spectra*, Cambridge University Press, Cambridge, England (1935).

10.9 THE LINE FACTOR

Electric-dipole transitions play a dominant role in atomic spectra. As a consequence, the calculation of electric-dipole matrix elements has received much attention. Most calculations have been based on LS coupling, where the matrix-elements have the form

$$\langle \alpha SLJ \| \mathbf{Q}^{(1)} \| \alpha' S' L' J' \rangle, \tag{9.1}$$

although other coupling schemes (as well as higher multipoles) have also been examined. The use of LS-coupling states is not a serious limitation, because one can, in principle, transform to other coupling schemes or to other basis states.

Equation 5.13 of Chapter 6 provides the key formula for line strengths:

$$\begin{aligned}\langle abJ \| \mathbf{T}^{(k)}(a) \| a'b'J' \rangle \\ &= \delta_{aa'} \sqrt{2J+1}\,\sqrt{2J'+1}\; W(aJb'k;\, bJ') \langle b \| \mathbf{T}^{(k)} \| b' \rangle \\ &= \delta_{aa'} \sqrt{2J+1}\,\sqrt{2J'+1}\,(-1)^{a+J+b'+k} \begin{Bmatrix} a & J & b \\ k & b' & J' \end{Bmatrix} \langle b \| \mathbf{T}^{(k)} \| b' \rangle. \end{aligned} \tag{9.2}$$

The 6-j symbols provide a more useful way of writing (9.2) when we are concerned with algebraic manipulation. On the other hand, when we write matrix elements in terms of Racah coefficients, we can usually eliminate an explicit phase factor, and thereby simplify formulas such as (9.2).

Applied to expression (9.1), (9.2) gives

$$\begin{aligned}\langle \alpha SLJ \| \mathbf{Q}^{(1)} \| \alpha' S' L' J' \rangle \\ &= \sqrt{2J+1}\,\sqrt{2J'+1}\; W(SJL'1;\, LJ') \langle \alpha L \| \mathbf{Q}^{(1)} \| \alpha' L' \rangle \delta_{SS'}. \end{aligned} \tag{9.3}$$

Thus, if we define a *line factor* $\mathcal{R}_{\text{line}}$ by

$$\begin{aligned}\mathcal{R}_{\text{line}}(SLJ,\, SL'J') \\ &\equiv \sqrt{2J+1}\,\sqrt{2J'+1}\; W(SJL'1;\, LJ') \\ &= \sqrt{2J+1}\,\sqrt{2J'+1}\,(-1)^{S+J+L'+1} \begin{Bmatrix} S & J & L \\ 1 & L' & J' \end{Bmatrix}, \end{aligned} \tag{9.4}$$

we can place into this factor all the explicit dependence of the matrix element on J, J', and spin:

$$\langle \alpha SLJ \| \mathbf{Q}^{(1)} \| \alpha' S'L'J' \rangle = \mathcal{R}_{\text{line}}(SLJ, SL'J') \langle \alpha L \| \mathbf{Q}^{(1)} \| \alpha' L' \rangle \delta_{SS'}. \tag{9.5}$$

The line strength then becomes

$$\mathbf{S}(\alpha SLJ, \alpha' S'L'J') = [\mathcal{R}_{\text{line}}(SLJ, SL'J')]^2 \times |\langle \alpha L \| \mathbf{Q}^{(1)} \| \alpha' L' \rangle|^2. \tag{9.6}$$

That is, $(\mathcal{R}_{\text{line}})^2$ gives the relative strengths of the *lines* within a *multiplet.* The Kronecker delta, $\delta_{SS'}$ occurs because the electric-dipole operator does not depend on spin. We thereby obtain the selection rule

$$\Delta S = 0$$

for $\mathcal{E}1$ transitions between LS-coupling states. In other words, the matrix of $\mathbf{Q}^{(1)}$ is diagonal in S. The properties of the Racah coefficient include the further selection rule

$$\Delta L = +1, 0, -1$$

with the proviso

$$L = 0 \text{ to } L' = 0 \text{ forbidden.}$$

The line factor for the inverse transition,

$$\langle \alpha' S'L'J' \| \mathbf{Q}^{(1)} \| \alpha SLJ \rangle,$$

has the same value apart from a possible sign change:

$$\mathcal{R}_{\text{line}}(SLJ, S'L'J') = (-1)^{L-L'+J-J'} \mathcal{R}_{\text{line}}(S'L'J', SLJ). \tag{9.7}$$

Table 10.8 gives values of this line factor, along with values of the square of $\mathcal{R}_{\text{line}}$. Elements whose sign changes for the inverse transition are marked by an [a]. Thus we find

$$\mathcal{R}_{\text{line}}(^3P_1 - {}^3D_1) = -0.5,$$
$$\mathcal{R}_{\text{line}}(^3D_1 - {}^3P_1) = +0.5.$$

Table 10.8 shows that within a multiplet the strongest line originates with the level having the largest J value, $J = L + S$. Note that for the multiplet $L \rightarrow L + 1$ the lines $J \rightarrow J + 1$ are strongest, the lines $J \rightarrow J$ are weaker, and the lines $J \rightarrow J - 1$ are quite weak. When $L \rightarrow L$, the lines $J \rightarrow J$ are stronger than the lines $J \rightarrow J \pm 1$.

In a similar way a line factor may be defined for electric-quadupole transitions:

$$\langle \alpha SLJ \| \mathbf{Q}^{(2)} \| \alpha' S'L'J' \rangle = \mathcal{R}^Q_{\text{line}}(SLJ, SL'J') \langle \alpha L \| \mathbf{Q}^{(2)} \| \alpha' L' \rangle \delta_{SS'} \tag{9.8}$$

$$\mathcal{R}^Q_{\text{line}}(SLJ, SL'J') = \sqrt{2J+1}\,\sqrt{2J'+1}\; W(SJL'2; LJ'). \tag{9.9}$$

Table 10.8.

Line Factor for Singlet Terms

L_1	L_2	J_1	J_2	Factor	Square	L_1	L_2	J_1	J_2	Factor	Square
S	*P*	0	1	1.00000	1.00000	*G*	*H*	4	5	1.00000	1.00000
P	*P*	1	1	1.00000	1.00000	*H*	*H*	5	5	1.00000	1.00000
P	*D*	1	2	1.00000	1.00000	*H*	*I*	5	6	1.00000	1.00000
D	*D*	2	2	1.00000	1.00000	*I*	*I*	6	6	1.00000	1.00000
D	*F*	2	3	1.00000	1.00000	*I*	*K*	6	7	1.00000	1.00000
F	*F*	3	3	1.00000	1.00000	*K*	*K*	7	7	1.00000	1.00000
F	*G*	3	4	1.00000	1.00000	*K*	*L*	7	8	1.00000	1.00000
G	*G*	4	4	1.00000	1.00000						

Line Factor for Doublet Terms

L_1	L_2	J_1	J_2	Factor	Square	L_1	L_2	J_1	J_2	Factor	Square
S	*S*	0.5	0.5	0.	0.			4.5	3.5	−0.15713[a]	0.02469
S	*P*	0.5	0.5	−0.81650[a]	0.66667			4.5	4.5	1.04231	1.08642
		0.5	1.5	1.15470	1.33333	*G*	*H*	3.5	4.5	0.94281	0.88889
P	*P*	0.5	0.5	0.66667	0.44444			4.5	4.5	−0.14213[a]	0.02020
		0.5	1.5	0.47140[a]	0.22222			4.5	5.5	1.04447	1.09091
		1.5	0.5	−0.47140[a]	0.22222	*H*	*H*	4.5	4.5	0.94475	0.89256
		1.5	1.5	1.05409	1.11111			4.5	5.5	0.12856[a]	0.01653
P	*D*	0.5	1.5	0.81650	0.66667			5.5	4.5	−0.12856[a]	0.01653
		1.5	1.5	−0.36515[a]	0.13333			5.5	5.5	1.03652	1.07438
		1.5	2.5	1.09545	1.20000	*H*	*I*	4.5	5.5	0.95346	0.90909
D	*D*	1.5	1.5	0.84853	0.72000			5.5	5.5	−0.11826[a]	0.01399
		1.5	2.5	0.28284[a]	0.08000			5.5	6.5	1.03775	1.07692
		2.5	1.5	−0.28284[a]	0.08000	*I*	*I*	5.5	5.5	0.95459	0.91124
		2.5	2.5	1.05830	1.12000			5.5	6.5	0.10879[a]	0.01183
D	*F*	1.5	2.5	0.89443	0.80000			6.5	5.5	−0.10879[a]	0.01183
		2.5	2.5	−0.23905[a]	0.05714			6.5	6.5	1.03203	1.06509
		2.5	3.5	1.06904	1.14286	*I*	*K*	5.5	6.5	0.96077	0.92308
F	*F*	2.5	2.5	0.90351	0.81633			6.5	6.5	−0.10127[a]	0.01026
		2.5	3.5	0.20203[a]	0.04082			6.5	7.5	1.03280	1.06667
		3.5	2.5	−0.20203[a]	0.04082	*K*	*K*	6.5	6.5	0.96148	0.92445
		3.5	3.5	1.04978	1.10204			6.5	7.5	0.09428[a]	0.00889
F	*G*	2.5	3.5	0.92582	0.85714			7.5	6.5	−0.09428[a]	0.00889
		3.5	3.5	−0.17817[a]	0.03175			7.5	7.5	1.02848	1.05778
		3.5	4.5	1.05409	1.11111	*K*	*L*	6.5	7.5	0.96609	0.93333
G	*G*	3.5	3.5	0.92962	0.86420			7.5	7.5	−0.08856[a]	0.00784
		3.5	4.5	0.15713[a]	0.02469			7.5	8.5	1.02899	1.05882

[a] Inverse factor has opposite sign.

Table 10.8 (*continued*)

Line Factor for Triplet Terms

L_1 L_2	J_1	J_2	Factor	Square
S S	1	1	0.	0.
S P	1	0	0.57735	0.33333
	1	1	−1.00000[a]	1.00000
	1	2	1.29099	1.66667
P P	0	1	0.57735[a]	0.33333
	1	0	−0.57735[a]	0.33333
	1	1	0.50000	0.25000
	1	2	0.64550[a]	0.41667
	2	1	−0.64550[a]	0.41667
	2	2	1.11803	1.25000
P D	0	1	0.57735	0.33333
	1	1	−0.50000[a]	0.25000
	1	2	0.86603	0.75000
	2	1	0.12910	0.01667
	2	2	−0.50000[a]	0.25000
	2	3	1.18322	1.40000
D D	1	1	0.67082	0.45000
	1	2	0.38730[a]	0.15000
	2	1	−0.38730[a]	0.15000
	2	2	0.83333	0.69444
	2	3	0.39441[a]	0.15556
	3	2	−0.39441[a]	0.15556
	3	3	1.11555	1.24444
D F	1	2	0.77460	0.60000
	2	2	−0.33333[a]	0.11111
	2	3	0.94281	0.88889
	3	2	0.05634	0.00317
	3	3	−0.33333[a]	0.11111
	3	4	1.13389	1.28571
F F	2	2	0.79682	0.63492
	2	3	0.28172[a]	0.07937
	3	2	−0.28172[a]	0.07937
	3	3	0.91667	0.84028
	3	4	0.28347[a]	0.08036
	4	3	−0.28347[a]	0.08036
	4	4	1.09789	1.20536
F G	2	3	0.84515	0.71429
	3	3	−0.25000[a]	0.06250
	3	4	0.96825	0.93750
	4	3	0.03150	0.00099

L_1 L_2	J_1	J_2	Factor	Square
	4	4	−0.25000[a]	0.06250
	4	5	1.10554	1.22222
G G	3	3	0.85391	0.72917
	3	4	0.22048[a]	0.04861
	4	3	−0.22048[a]	0.04861
	4	4	0.95000	0.90250
	4	5	0.22111[a]	0.04889
	5	4	−0.22111[a]	0.04889
	5	5	1.08320	1.17333
G H	3	4	0.88192	0.77778
	4	4	−0.20000[a]	0.04000
	4	5	0.97980	0.96000
	5	4	0.02010	0.00040
	5	5	−0.20000[a]	0.04000
	5	6	1.08711	1.18182
H H	4	4	0.88626	0.78545
	4	5	0.18091[a]	0.03273
	5	4	−0.18091[a]	0.03273
	5	5	0.96667	0.93444
	5	6	0.18119[a]	0.03283
	6	5	−0.18119[a]	0.03283
	6	6	1.07191	1.14899
H I	4	5	0.90453	0.81818
	5	5	−0.16667[a]	0.02778
	5	6	0.98601	0.97222
	6	5	0.01394	0.00019
	6	6	−0.16667[a]	0.02778
	6	7	1.07417	1.15384
I I	5	5	0.90700	0.82265
	5	6	0.15331[a]	0.02350
	6	5	−0.15331[a]	0.02350
	6	6	0.97619	0.95295
	6	7	0.15345[a]	0.02355
	7	6	−0.15345[a]	0.02355
	7	7	1.06315	1.13030
I K	5	6	0.91987	0.84615
	6	6	−0.14286[a]	0.02041
	6	7	0.98974	0.97959
	7	6	0.01023	0.00010
	7	7	−0.14286[a]	0.02041
	7	8	1.06458	1.13333

[a] Inverse factor has opposite sign.

Line Factor for Triplet Terms (*continued*)

L_1 L_2	J_1	J_2	Factor	Square	L_1 L_2	J_1	J_2	Factor	Square
						8	8	1.05623	1.11563
K K	6	6	0.92140	0.84898	*K L*	6	7	0.93095	0.86667
	6	7	0.13299[a]	0.01769		7	7	−0.12500[a]	0.01562
	7	6	−0.13299[a]	0.01769		7	8	0.99216	0.98438
	7	7	0.98214	0.96460		8	7	0.00783	0.00006
	7	8	0.13307[a]	0.01771		8	8	−0.12500[a]	0.01563
	8	7	−0.13307[a]	0.01771		8	9	1.05719	1.11765

Line Factor for Quartet Terms

L_1 L_2	J_1	J_2	Factor	Square	L_1 L_2	J_1	J_2	Factor	Square
S S	1.5	1.5	0.	0.		3.5	2.5	−0.47809[a]	0.22857
P P	1.5	0.5	0.81650	0.66667		3.5	3.5	1.17108	1.37143
	1.5	1.5	−1.15470[a]	1.33333	*D F*	0.5	1.5	0.63246	0.40000
	1.5	2.5	1.41421	2.00000		1.5	1.5	−0.40000[a]	0.16000
P P	0.5	0.5	−0.33333	0.11111		1.5	2.5	0.80000	0.64000
	0.5	1.5	0.74536[a]	0.55556		2.5	1.5	0.10690	0.01143
	1.5	0.5	−0.74536[a]	0.55556		2.5	2.5	−0.45714[a]	0.20898
	1.5	1.5	0.42164	0.17778		2.5	3.5	0.98974	0.97959
	1.5	2.5	0.77460[a]	0.60000		3.5	2.5	0.09035	0.00816
	2.5	1.5	−0.77460[a]	0.60000		3.5	3.5	−0.40406[a]	0.16327
	2.5	2.5	1.18322	1.40000		3.5	4.5	1.19523	1.42857
P D	0.5	0.5	−0.57735[a]	0.33333	*F F*	1.5	1.5	0.67612	0.45714
	0.5	1.5	0.57735	0.33333		1.5	2.5	0.33806[a]	0.11429
	1.5	0.5	0.25820	0.06667		2.5	1.5	−0.33806[a]	0.11429
	1.5	1.5	−0.65320[a]	0.42667		2.5	2.5	0.76798	0.58980
	1.5	2.5	0.91652	0.84000		2.5	3.5	0.39123[a]	0.15306
	2.5	1.5	0.20000	0.04000		3.5	2.5	−0.39123[a]	0.15306
	2.5	2.5	−0.60000[a]	0.36000		3.5	3.5	0.93314	0.87075
	2.5	3.5	1.26491	1.60000		3.5	4.5	0.34503[a]	0.11905
D D	0.5	0.5	0.44721	0.20000		4.5	3.5	−0.34503[a]	0.11905
	0.5	1.5	0.44721[a]	0.20000		4.5	4.5	1.14434	1.30952
	1.5	0.5	−0.44721[a]	0.20000	*F G*	1.5	2.5	0.75593	0.57143
	1.5	1.5	0.56569	0.32000		2.5	2.5	−0.30305[a]	0.09184
	1.5	2.5	0.52915[a]	0.28000		2.5	3.5	0.87482	0.76531
	2.5	1.5	−0.52915[a]	0.28000		3.5	2.5	0.05832	0.00340
	2.5	2.5	0.83152	0.69143		3.5	3.5	−0.34776[a]	0.12094
	2.5	3.5	0.47809[a]	0.22857		3.5	4.5	1.00922	1.01852

[a] Inverse factor has opposite sign.

Line Factor for Quartet Terms (*continued*)

L_1	L_2	J_1	J_2	Factor	Square
F	*G*	4.5	3.5	0.05143	0.00265
		4.5	4.5	−0.30429[a]	0.09259
		4.5	5.5	1.15470	1.33333
G	*G*	2.5	2.5	0.77152	0.59524
		2.5	3.5	0.26726[a]	0.07143
		3.5	2.5	−0.26726[a]	0.07143
		3.5	3.5	0.84994	0.72240
		3.5	4.5	0.30832[a]	0.09506
		4.5	3.5	−0.30832[a]	0.09506
		4.5	4.5	0.97125	0.94332
		4.5	5.5	0.26968[a]	0.07273
		5.5	4.5	−0.26968[a]	0.07273
		5.5	5.5	1.12277	1.26061
G	*H*	2.5	3.5	0.81650	0.66667
		3.5	3.5	−0.24343[a]	0.05926
		3.5	4.5	0.91084	0.82963
		4.5	3.5	0.03670	0.00135
		4.5	4.5	−0.27993[a]	0.07836
		4.5	5.5	1.01558	1.03140
		5.5	4.5	0.03320	0.00110
		5.5	5.5	−0.24393[a]	0.05950
		5.5	6.5	1.12815	1.27273
H	*H*	3.5	3.5	0.82389	0.67879
		3.5	4.5	0.22019[a]	0.04848
		4.5	3.5	−0.22019[a]	0.04848
		4.5	4.5	0.89227	0.79614
		4.5	5.5	0.25390[a]	0.06446
		5.5	4.5	−0.25390[a]	0.06446
		5.5	5.5	0.98868	0.97749
		5.5	6.5	0.22125[a]	0.04895
		6.5	5.5	−0.22125[a]	0.04895
		6.5	6.5	1.10624	1.22378
H	*I*	3.5	4.5	0.85280	0.72727
		4.5	4.5	−0.20328[a]	0.04132
		4.5	5.5	0.93154	0.86777
		5.5	4.5	0.02521	0.00064
		5.5	5.5	−0.23403[a]	0.05477
		5.5	6.5	1.01760	1.03550
		6.5	5.5	0.02319	0.00054
		6.5	6.5	−0.20352[a]	0.04142
		6.5	7.5	1.10940	1.23077
I	*I*	4.5	4.5	0.85689	0.73426
		4.5	5.5	0.18699[a]	0.03497
		5.5	4.5	−0.18699[a]	0.03497
		5.5	5.5	0.91740	0.84162
		5.5	6.5	0.21562[a]	0.04649
		6.5	5.5	−0.21562[a]	0.04649
		6.5	6.5	0.99763	0.99527
		6.5	7.5	0.18752[a]	0.03516
		7.5	6.5	−0.18752[a]	0.03516
		7.5	7.5	1.09344	1.19560
I	*K*	4.5	5.5	0.87706	0.76923
		5.5	5.5	−0.17445[a]	0.03043
		5.5	6.5	0.94480	0.89265
		6.5	5.5	0.01839	0.00034
		6.5	6.5	−0.20098[a]	0.04039
		6.5	7.5	1.01793	1.03619
		7.5	6.5	0.01712	0.00029
		7.5	7.5	−0.17457[a]	0.03048
		7.5	8.5	1.09545	1.20000
K	*K*	5.5	5.5	0.87956	0.77363
		5.5	6.5	0.16240[a]	0.02637
		6.5	5.5	−0.16240[a]	0.02637
		6.5	6.5	0.93374	0.87188
		6.5	7.5	0.18729[a]	0.03508
		7.5	6.5	−0.18729[a]	0.03508
		7.5	7.5	1.00256	1.00512
		7.5	8.5	0.16270[a]	0.02647
		8.5	7.5	−0.16270[a]	0.02647
		8.5	8.5	1.08330	1.17353
K	*L*	5.5	6.5	0.89443	0.80000
		6.5	6.5	−0.15275[a]	0.02333
		6.5	7.5	0.95394	0.91000
		7.5	6.5	0.01400	0.00020
		7.5	7.5	−0.17608[a]	0.03100
		7.5	8.5	1.01758	1.03547
		8.5	7.5	0.01315	0.00017
		8.5	8.5	−0.15283[a]	0.02336
		8.5	9.5	1.08465	1.17647

[a] Inverse factor has opposite sign.

Line Factor for Quintet Terms

L_1	L_2	J_1	J_2	Factor	Square
S	*S*	2	2	0.	0.
S	*P*	2	1	1.00000	1.00000
		2	2	−1.29099[a]	1.66667
		2	3	1.52753	2.33333
P	*P*	1	1	−0.50000	0.25000
		1	2	0.86603[a]	0.75000
		2	1	−0.86603[a]	0.75000
		2	2	0.37268	0.13889
		2	3	0.88192[a]	0.77778
		3	2	−0.88192[a]	0.77778
		3	3	1.24722	1.55556
P	*D*	1	0	0.44721	0.20000
		1	1	−0.67082[a]	0.45000
		1	2	0.59161	0.35000
		2	1	0.38730	0.15000
		2	2	−0.76376[a]	0.58333
		2	3	0.96609	0.93333
		3	2	0.25820	0.06667
		3	3	−0.68313[a]	0.46667
		3	4	1.34164	1.80000
D	*D*	0	1	0.44721[a]	0.20000
		1	0	−0.44721[a]	0.20000
		1	1	0.22361	0.05000
		1	2	0.59161[a]	0.35000
		2	1	−0.59161[a]	0.35000
		2	2	0.50000	0.25000
		2	3	0.63246[a]	0.40000
		3	2	−0.63246[a]	0.40000
		3	3	0.83666	0.70000
		3	4	0.54772[a]	0.30000
		4	3	−0.54772[a]	0.30000
		4	4	1.22475	1.50000
D	*F*	0	1	0.44721	0.20000
		1	1	−0.44721[a]	0.20000
		1	2	0.63246	0.40000
		2	1	0.16903	0.02857
		2	2	−0.53452[a]	0.28571
		2	3	0.82808	0.68571
		3	2	0.16903	0.02857
		3	3	−0.54772[a]	0.30000
		3	4	1.03510	1.07143
		4	3	0.11952	0.01429
		4	4	−0.46291[a]	0.21429
		4	5	1.25357	1.57143
F	*F*	1	1	0.53452	0.28571
		1	2	0.37796[a]	0.14286
		2	1	−0.37796[a]	0.14286
		2	2	0.59761	0.35714
		2	3	0.46291[a]	0.21429
		3	2	−0.46291[a]	0.21429
		3	3	0.75000	0.56250
		3	4	0.47246[a]	0.22321
		4	3	−0.47246[a]	0.22321
		4	4	0.95150	0.90536
		4	5	0.39641[a]	0.15714
		5	4	−0.39641[a]	0.15714
		5	5	1.18924	1.41428
F	*G*	1	2	0.65465	0.42857
		2	2	−0.34503[a]	0.11905
		2	3	0.77152	0.59524
		3	2	0.08909	0.00794
		3	3	−0.41667[a]	0.17361
		3	4	0.90468	0.81845
		4	3	0.09449	0.00893
		4	4	−0.42046[a]	0.17679
		4	5	1.04881	1.10000
		5	4	0.06901	0.00476
		5	5	−0.34960[a]	0.12222
		5	6	1.20185	1.44445
G	*G*	2	2	0.68041	0.46296
		2	3	0.30429[a]	0.09259
		3	2	−0.30429[a]	0.09259
		3	3	0.74006	0.54768
		3	4	0.37081[a]	0.13750
		4	3	−0.37081[a]	0.13750
		4	4	0.85000	0.72250
		4	5	0.37417[a]	0.14000
		5	4	−0.37417[a]	0.14000
		5	5	0.99294	0.98593
		5	6	0.31032[a]	0.09630

[a] Inverse factor has opposite sign.

Line Factor for Quintet Terms (*continued*)

L_1 L_2	J_1	J_2	Factor	Square
G G	6	5	−0.31032[a]	0.09630
	6	6	1.16110	1.34815
G H	2	3	0.74536	0.55556
	3	3	−0.27889[a]	0.07778
	3	4	0.83666	0.70000
	4	3	0.05505	0.00303
	4	4	−0.33845[a]	0.11455
	4	5	0.93937	0.88242
	5	4	0.06030	0.00364
	5	5	−0.33993[a]	0.11556
	5	6	1.05025	1.10303
	6	5	0.04495	0.00202
	6	6	−0.28069[a]	0.07879
	6	7	1.16775	1.36364
H H	3	3	0.75679	0.57273
	3	4	0.25226[a]	0.06364
	4	3	−0.25226[a]	0.06364
	4	4	0.81240	0.66000
	4	5	0.30748[a]	0.09455
	5	4	−0.30748[a]	0.09455
	5	5	0.90000	0.81000
	5	6	0.30896[a]	0.09545
	6	5	−0.30896[a]	0.09545
	6	6	1.01066	1.02143
	6	7	0.25482[a]	0.06494
	7	6	−0.25482[a]	0.06494
	7	7	1.13961	1.29871
H I	3	4	0.79772	0.63636
	4	4	−0.23355[a]	0.05455
	4	5	0.87386	0.76364
	5	4	0.03740	0.00140
	5	5	−0.28420[a]	0.08077
	5	6	0.95804	0.91783
	6	5	0.04181	0.00175
	6	6	−0.28490[a]	0.08117
	6	7	1.04829	1.09890
	7	6	0.03161	0.00100
	7	7	−0.23440[a]	0.05495
	7	8	1.14354	1.30769
I I	4	4	0.80384	0.64615
	4	5	0.21483[a]	0.04615
	5	4	−0.21483[a]	0.04615
	5	5	0.85517	0.73132
	5	6	0.26207[a]	0.06868
	6	5	−0.26207[a]	0.06868
	6	6	0.92857	0.86225
	6	7	0.26282[a]	0.06907
	7	6	−0.26282[a]	0.06907
	7	7	1.01886	1.03807
	7	8	0.21611[a]	0.04670
	8	7	−0.21611[a]	0.04670
	8	8	1.12294	1.26099
I K	4	5	0.83205	0.69231
	5	5	−0.20073[a]	0.04029
	5	6	0.89770	0.80586
	6	5	0.02707	0.00073
	6	6	−0.24467[a]	0.05986
	6	7	0.96923	0.93940
	7	6	0.03069	0.00094
	7	7	−0.24504[a]	0.06005
	7	8	1.04540	1.09286
	8	7	0.02344	0.00055
	8	8	−0.20119[a]	0.04048
	8	9	1.12546	1.26667
K K	5	5	0.83571	0.69841
	5	6	0.18687[a]	0.03492
	6	5	−0.18687[a]	0.03492
	6	6	0.88301	0.77970
	6	7	0.22812[a]	0.05204
	7	6	−0.22812[a]	0.05204
	7	7	0.94643	0.89573
	7	8	0.22854[a]	0.05223
	8	7	−0.22854[a]	0.05223
	8	8	1.02270	1.04592
	8	9	0.18758[a]	0.03519
	9	8	−0.18758[a]	0.03519
	9	9	1.10972	1.23148
K L	5	6	0.85635	0.73333
	6	6	−0.17593[a]	0.03095
	6	7	0.91417	0.83571

[a] Inverse factor has opposite sign.

Line Factor for Quintet Terms (*continued*)

L_1 L_2	J_1	J_2	Factor	Square	L_1 L_2	J_1	J_2	Factor	Square
K L	7	6	0.02050	0.00042		8	9	1.04240	1.08660
	7	7	−0.21468[a]	0.04609		9	8	0.01808	0.00033
	7	8	0.97647	0.95349		9	9	−0.17620[a]	0.03105
	8	7	0.02348	0.00055		9	10	1.11144	1.23529
	8	8	−0.21490[a]	0.04618					

Line Factor for Sextet Terms

L_1 L_2	J_1	J_2	Factor	Square	L_1 L_2	J_1	J_2	Factor	Square
S S	2.5	2.5	0.	0.		3.5	4.5	0.60858[a]	0.37037
S P	2.5	1.5	1.15470	1.33333		4.5	3.5	−0.60858[a]	0.37037
	2.5	2.5	−1.41421[a]	2.00000		4.5	4.5	1.27657	1.62963
	2.5	3.5	1.63299	2.66667	*D F*	0.5	0.5	−0.47140[a]	0.22222
P P	1.5	1.5	−0.63246	0.40000		0.5	1.5	0.42164	0.17778
	1.5	2.5	0.96609[a]	0.93333		1.5	0.5	0.25198	0.06349
	2.5	1.5	−0.96609[a]	0.93333		1.5	1.5	−0.57016[a]	0.32508
	2.5	2.5	0.33806	0.11429		1.5	2.5	0.64143	0.41143
	2.5	3.5	0.97590[a]	0.95238		2.5	1.5	0.26186	0.06857
	3.5	2.5	−0.97590[a]	0.95238		2.5	2.5	−0.62987[a]	0.39673
	3.5	3.5	1.30931	1.71428		2.5	3.5	0.85714	0.73469
P D	1.5	0.5	0.63246	0.40000		3.5	2.5	0.22131	0.04898
	1.5	1.5	−0.74833[a]	0.56000		3.5	3.5	−0.62209[a]	0.38700
	1.5	2.5	0.61101	0.37333		3.5	4.5	1.07890	1.16402
	2.5	1.5	0.48990	0.24000		4.5	3.5	0.14548	0.02116
	2.5	2.5	−0.85524[a]	0.73143		4.5	4.5	−0.51434[a]	0.26455
	2.5	3.5	1.01418	1.02857		4.5	5.5	1.30931	1.71428
	3.5	2.5	0.30861	0.09524	*F F*	0.5	0.5	0.35635	0.12698
	3.5	3.5	−0.75593[a]	0.57143		0.5	1.5	0.39841[a]	0.15873
	3.5	4.5	1.41421	2.00000		1.5	0.5	−0.39841[a]	0.15873
D D	0.5	0.5	−0.29814	0.08889		1.5	1.5	0.39441	0.15556
	0.5	1.5	0.55777[a]	0.31111		1.5	2.5	0.50709[a]	0.25714
	1.5	0.5	−0.55777[a]	0.31111		2.5	1.5	−0.50709[a]	0.25714
	1.5	1.5	0.09428	0.00889		2.5	2.5	0.54211	0.29388
	1.5	2.5	0.69282[a]	0.48000		2.5	3.5	0.55328[a]	0.30612
	2.5	1.5	−0.69282[a]	0.48000		3.5	2.5	−0.55328[a]	0.30612
	2.5	2.5	0.45356	0.20571		3.5	3.5	0.73873	0.54573
	2.5	3.5	0.71714[a]	0.51429		3.5	4.5	0.53945[a]	0.29101
	3.5	2.5	−0.71714[a]	0.51429		4.5	3.5	−0.53945[a]	0.29101
	3.5	3.5	0.84578	0.71535		4.5	4.5	0.97096	0.94276

[a] Inverse factor has opposite sign.

Line Factor for Sextet Terms (*continued*)

L_1 L_2	J_1	J_2	Factor	Square	L_1 L_2	J_1	J_2	Factor	Square
F F	4.5	5.5	0.44137[a]	0.19481		4.5	3.5	0.08989	0.00808
	5.5	4.5	−0.44137[a]	0.19481		4.5	4.5	−0.40881[a]	0.16713
	5.5	5.5	1.23267	1.51948		4.5	5.5	0.96742	0.93591
F G	0.5	1.5	0.53452	0.28571		5.5	4.5	0.08131	0.00661
	1.5	1.5	−0.37796[a]	0.14286		5.5	5.5	−0.38974[a]	0.15190
	1.5	2.5	0.65465	0.42857		5.5	6.5	1.08389	1.17482
	2.5	1.5	0.12599	0.01587		6.5	5.5	0.05575	0.00311
	2.5	2.5	−0.46657[a]	0.21769		6.5	6.5	−0.31289[a]	0.09790
	2.5	3.5	0.78967	0.62358		6.5	7.5	1.20605	1.45455
	3.5	2.5	0.14286	0.02041	*H H*	2.5	2.5	0.68376	0.46753
	3.5	3.5	−0.49943[a]	0.24943		2.5	3.5	0.27915[a]	0.07792
	3.5	4.5	0.93435	0.87302		3.5	2.5	−0.27915[a]	0.07792
	4.5	3.5	0.12599	0.01587		3.5	3.5	0.72580	0.52679
	4.5	4.5	−0.48050[a]	0.23088		3.5	4.5	0.35008[a]	0.12256
	4.5	5.5	1.08712	1.18182		4.5	3.5	−0.35008[a]	0.12256
	5.5	4.5	0.08494	0.00722		4.5	4.5	0.80479	0.64769
	5.5	5.5	−0.38925[a]	0.15152		4.5	5.5	0.37262[a]	0.13884
	5.5	6.5	1.24722	1.55556		5.5	4.5	−0.37262[a]	0.13884
G G	1.5	1.5	0.57735	0.33333		5.5	5.5	0.90895	0.82619
	1.5	2.5	0.33333[a]	0.11111		5.5	6.5	0.35479[a]	0.12587
	2.5	1.5	−0.33333[a]	0.11111		6.5	5.5	−0.35479[a]	0.12587
	2.5	2.5	0.61721	0.38095		6.5	6.5	1.03249	1.06604
	2.5	3.5	0.41786[a]	0.17460		6.5	7.5	0.28427[a]	0.08081
	3.5	2.5	−0.41786[a]	0.17460		7.5	6.5	−0.28427[a]	0.08081
	3.5	3.5	0.71714	0.51429		7.5	7.5	1.17207	1.37374
	3.5	4.5	0.44721[a]	0.20000	*H I*	2.5	3.5	0.73855	0.54545
	4.5	3.5	−0.44721[a]	0.20000		3.5	3.5	−0.25950[a]	0.06734
	4.5	4.5	0.85280	0.72727		3.5	4.5	0.81236	0.65993
	4.5	5.5	0.42876[a]	0.18384		4.5	3.5	0.05089	0.00259
	5.5	4.5	−0.42876[a]	0.18384		4.5	4.5	−0.32478[a]	0.10548
	5.5	5.5	1.01481	1.02984		4.5	5.5	0.89500	0.80102
	5.5	6.5	0.34592[a]	0.11966		5.5	4.5	0.06176	0.00381
	6.5	5.5	−0.34592[a]	0.11966		5.5	5.5	−0.34472[a]	0.11883
	6.5	6.5	1.19829	1.43590		5.5	6.5	0.98400	0.96826
G H	1.5	2.5	0.66667	0.44444		6.5	5.5	0.05681	0.00323
	2.5	2.5	−0.30861[a]	0.09524		6.5	6.5	−0.32727[a]	0.10711
	2.5	3.5	0.75593	0.57143		6.5	7.5	1.07814	1.16239
	3.5	2.5	0.07597	0.00577		7.5	6.5	0.03942	0.00155
	3.5	3.5	−0.38440[a]	0.14776		7.5	7.5	−0.26149[a]	0.06838
	3.5	4.5	0.85753	0.73535		7.5	8.5	1.17670	1.38461

[a] Inverse factor has opposite sign.

Line Factor for Sextet Terms (*continued*)

L_1 L_2	J_1	J_2	Factor	Square	L_1 L_2	J_1	J_2	Factor	Square
I I	3.5	3.5	0.74726	0.55840	*K K*	4.5	4.5	0.78954	0.62338
	3.5	4.5	0.23870[a]	0.05698		4.5	5.5	0.20806[a]	0.04329
	4.5	3.5	−0.23870[a]	0.05698		5.5	4.5	−0.20806[a]	0.04329
	4.5	4.5	0.78889	0.62234		5.5	5.5	0.82959	0.68821
	4.5	5.5	0.29985[a]	0.08991		5.5	6.5	0.26172[a]	0.06850
	5.5	4.5	−0.29985[a]	0.08991		6.5	5.5	−0.26172[a]	0.06850
	5.5	5.5	0.85541	0.73173		6.5	6.5	0.88752	0.78769
	5.5	6.5	0.31849[a]	0.10144		6.5	7.5	0.27775[a]	0.07714
	6.5	5.5	−0.31849[a]	0.10144		7.5	6.5	−0.27775[a]	0.07714
	6.5	6.5	0.94030	0.88416		7.5	7.5	0.95934	0.92034
	6.5	7.5	0.30221[a]	0.09133		7.5	8.5	0.26304[a]	0.06919
	7.5	6.5	−0.30221[a]	0.09133		8.5	7.5	−0.26304[a]	0.06919
	7.5	7.5	1.03984	1.08126		8.5	8.5	1.04257	1.08695
	7.5	8.5	0.24120[a]	0.05818		8.5	9.5	0.20943[a]	0.04386
	8.5	7.5	−0.24120[a]	0.05818		9.5	8.5	−0.20943[a]	0.04386
	8.5	8.5	1.15171	1.32644		9.5	9.5	1.13555	1.28947
J K	3.5	4.5	0.78446	0.61538	*K L*	4.5	5.5	0.81650	0.66667
	4.5	4.5	−0.22349[a]	0.04995		5.5	5.5	−0.19612[a]	0.03846
	4.5	5.5	0.84810	0.71928		5.5	6.5	0.87266	0.76154
	5.5	4.5	0.03650	0.00133		6.5	5.5	0.02746	0.00075
	5.5	5.5	−0.28052[a]	0.07869		6.5	6.5	−0.24661[a]	0.06081
	5.5	6.5	0.91818	0.84306		6.5	7.5	0.93368	0.87177
	6.5	5.5	0.04504	0.00203		7.5	6.5	0.03430	0.00118
	6.5	6.5	−0.29752[a]	0.08852		7.5	7.5	−0.26148[a]	0.06837
	6.5	7.5	0.99316	0.98637		7.5	8.5	0.99856	0.99712
	7.5	6.5	0.04193	0.00176		8.5	7.5	0.03222	0.00104
	7.5	7.5	−0.28184[a]	0.07943		8.5	8.5	−0.24737[a]	0.06119
	7.5	8.5	1.07218	1.14958		8.5	9.5	1.06666	1.13777
	8.5	7.5	0.02936	0.00086		9.5	8.5	0.02272	0.00052
	8.5	8.5	−0.22454[a]	0.05042		9.5	9.5	−0.19672[a]	0.03870
	8.5	9.5	1.15470	1.33333		9.5	10.5	1.13759	1.29412

Line Factor for Septet Terms

L_1 L_2	J_1	J_2	Factor	Square	L_1 L_2	J_1	J_2	Factor	Square
S S	3	3	0.	0.	*P P*	2	2	−0.74536	0.55556
S P	3	2	1.29099	1.66667		2	3	1.05409[a]	1.11111
	3	3	−1.52753[a]	2.33333		3	2	−1.05409[a]	1.11111
	3	4	1.73205	3.00000		3	3	0.31180	0.09722

[a] Inverse factor has opposite sign.

Line Factor for Septet Terms (*continued*)

L_1 L_2	J_1	J_2	Factor	Square	L_1 L_2	J_1	J_2	Factor	Square
P P	3	4	1.06066[a]	1.12500	*F F*	0	1	0.37796[a]	0.14286
	4	3	−1.06066[a]	1.12500		1	0	−0.37796[a]	0.14286
	4	4	1.36931	1.87500		1	1	0.13363	0.01786
P D	2	1	0.77460	0.60000		1	2	0.51755[a]	0.26786
	2	2	−0.81650[a]	0.66667		2	1	−0.51755[a]	0.26786
	2	3	0.63246	0.40000		2	2	0.29881	0.08929
	3	2	0.57735	0.33333		2	3	0.59761[a]	0.35714
	3	3	−0.93541[a]	0.87500		3	2	−0.59761[a]	0.35714
	3	4	1.06066	1.12500		3	3	0.50000	0.25000
	4	3	0.35355	0.12500		3	4	0.62678[a]	0.39286
	4	4	−0.82158[a]	0.67500		4	3	−0.62678[a]	0.39286
	4	5	1.48324	2.20000		4	4	0.73192	0.53571
D D	1	1	−0.44721	0.20000		4	5	0.59761[a]	0.35714
	1	2	0.63246[a]	0.40000		5	4	−0.59761[a]	0.35714
	2	1	−0.63246[a]	0.40000		5	5	0.99103	0.98214
	2	2	0.	0.		5	6	0.48181[a]	0.23214
	2	3	0.77460[a]	0.60000		6	5	−0.48181[a]	0.23214
	3	2	−0.77460[a]	0.60000		6	6	1.27475	1.62500
	3	3	0.41833	0.17500	*F G*	0	1	0.37796	0.14286
	3	4	0.79057[a]	0.62500		1	1	−0.40089[a]	0.16071
	4	3	−0.79057[a]	0.62500		1	2	0.51755	0.26786
	4	4	0.85732	0.73500		2	1	0.17252	0.02976
	4	5	0.66332[a]	0.44000		2	2	−0.49801[a]	0.24802
	5	4	−0.66332[a]	0.44000		2	3	0.66069	0.43651
	5	5	1.32665	1.76000		3	2	0.19920	0.03968
D F	1	0	0.37796	0.14286		3	3	−0.55277[a]	0.30556
	1	1	−0.53452[a]	0.28571		3	4	0.80917	0.65476
	1	2	0.41404	0.17143		4	3	0.18898	0.03571
	2	1	0.37796	0.14286		4	4	−0.56695[a]	0.32143
	2	2	−0.65465[a]	0.42857		4	5	0.96362	0.92857
	2	3	0.65465	0.42857		5	4	0.15430	0.02381
	3	2	0.33806	0.11429		5	5	−0.53266[a]	0.28373
	3	3	−0.70711[a]	0.50000		5	6	1.12423	1.26389
	3	4	0.88641	0.78572		6	5	0.09960	0.00992
	4	3	0.26726	0.07143		6	6	−0.42492[a]	0.18056
	4	4	−0.68661[a]	0.47143		6	7	1.29099	1.66667
	4	5	1.12122	1.25714	*G G*	1	1	0.45644	0.20833
	5	4	0.16903	0.02857		1	2	0.35355[a]	0.12500
	5	5	−0.56061[a]	0.31429		2	1	−0.35355[a]	0.12500
	5	6	1.36277	1.85714		2	2	0.47629	0.22685

[a] Inverse factor has opposite sign.

Line Factor for Septet Terms (*continued*)

L_1 L_2	J_1	J_2	Factor	Square	L_1 L_2	J_1	J_2	Factor	Square
G G	2	3	0.45134[a]	0.20370		4	5	0.42212[a]	0.17818
	3	2	−0.45134[a]	0.20370		5	4	−0.42212[a]	0.17818
	3	3	0.56927	0.32407		5	5	0.80000	0.64000
	3	4	0.50000[a]	0.25000		5	6	0.42640[a]	0.18182
	4	3	−0.50000[a]	0.25000		6	5	−0.42640[a]	0.18182
	4	4	0.70000	0.49000		6	6	0.91878	0.84416
	4	5	0.50990[a]	0.26000		6	7	0.39477[a]	0.15584
	5	4	−0.50990[a]	0.26000		7	6	−0.39477[a]	0.15584
	5	5	0.85754	0.73537		7	7	1.05413	1.11120
	5	6	0.47629[a]	0.22685		7	8	0.31079[a]	0.09659
	6	5	−0.47629[a]	0.22685		8	7	−0.31079[a]	0.09659
	6	6	1.03669	1.07473		8	8	1.20369	1.44887
	6	7	0.37796[a]	0.14286	*H I*	2	3	0.67420	0.45455
	7	6	−0.37796[a]	0.14286		3	3	−0.28024[a]	0.07955
	7	7	1.23443	1.52381		3	4	0.74620	0.55682
G H	1	2	0.57735	0.33333		4	3	0.06611	0.00437
	2	2	−0.33333[a]	0.11111		4	4	−0.34846[a]	0.12850
	2	3	0.66667	0.44444		4	5	0.82784	0.68531
	3	2	0.10050	0.01010		5	4	0.08362	0.00699
	3	3	−0.42044[a]	0.17677		5	5	−0.39223[a]	0.15385
	3	4	0.76871	0.59091		5	6	0.91606	0.83916
	4	3	0.12309	0.01515		6	5	0.08362	0.00699
	4	4	−0.46122[a]	0.21273		6	6	−0.39477[a]	0.15584
	4	5	0.87870	0.77212		6	7	1.00945	1.01898
	5	4	0.12060	0.01455		7	6	0.07068	0.00500
	5	5	−0.46667[a]	0.21778		7	7	−0.36425[a]	0.13268
	5	6	0.99494	0.98990		7	8	1.10723	1.22596
	6	5	0.10050	0.01010		8	7	0.04675	0.00219
	6	6	−0.43312[a]	0.18759		8	8	−0.28589[a]	0.08173
	6	7	1.11658	1.24675		8	9	1.20894	1.46154
	7	6	0.06580	0.00433	*I I*	3	3	0.68641	0.47115
	7	7	−0.34188[a]	0.11688		3	4	0.25944[a]	0.06731
	7	8	1.24316	1.54546		4	3	−0.25944[a]	0.06731
H H	2	2	0.60302	0.36364		4	4	0.71771	0.51511
	2	3	0.30151[a]	0.09091		4	5	0.33150[a]	0.10989
	3	2	−0.30151[a]	0.09091		5	4	−0.33150[a]	0.10989
	3	3	0.63066	0.39773		5	5	0.77743	0.60440
	3	4	0.38435[a]	0.14773		5	6	0.36314[a]	0.13187
	4	3	−0.38435[a]	0.14773		6	5	−0.36314[a]	0.13187
	4	4	0.70162	0.49227		6	6	0.85714	0.73469

[a] Inverse factor has opposite sign.

Line Factor for Septet Terms (*continued*)

L_1 L_2	J_1	J_2	Factor	Square	L_1 L_2	J_1	J_2	Factor	Square
I I	6	7	0.36529[a]	0.13344		6	5	−0.29039[a]	0.08433
	7	6	−0.36529[a]	0.13344		6	6	0.82542	0.68132
	7	7	0.95241	0.90709		6	7	0.31784[a]	0.10102
	7	8	0.33664[a]	0.11332		7	6	−0.31784[a]	0.10102
	8	7	−0.33664[a]	0.11332		7	7	0.89286	0.79719
	8	8	1.06055	1.12477		7	8	0.31904[a]	0.10179
	8	9	0.26381[a]	0.06960		8	7	−0.31904[a]	0.10179
	9	8	−0.26381[a]	0.06960		8	8	0.97240	0.94557
	9	9	1.17980	1.39194		8	9	0.29322[a]	0.08598
I K	3	4	0.73380	0.53846		9	8	−0.29322[a]	0.08598
	4	4	−0.24360[a]	0.05934		9	9	1.06216	1.12819
	4	5	0.79559	0.63297		9	10	0.22913[a]	0.05250
	5	4	0.04688	0.00220		10	9	−0.22913[a]	0.05250
	5	5	−0.31097[a]	0.09670		10	10	1.16082	1.34750
	5	6	0.86444	0.74725	*K L*	4	5	0.77460	0.60000
	6	5	0.06052	0.00366		5	5	−0.21409[a]	0.04583
	6	6	−0.34007[a]	0.11565		5	6	0.82916	0.68750
	6	7	0.93845	0.88069		6	5	0.03501	0.00123
	7	6	0.06138	0.00377		6	6	−0.27405[a]	0.07511
	7	7	−0.34141[a]	0.11656		6	7	0.88901	0.79034
	7	8	1.01662	1.03352		7	6	0.04583	0.00210
	8	7	0.05241	0.00275		7	7	−0.29968[a]	0.08981
	8	8	−0.31400[a]	0.09860		7	8	0.95294	0.90809
	8	9	1.09834	1.20635		8	7	0.04697	0.00221
	9	8	0.03494	0.00122		8	8	−0.30046[a]	0.09028
	9	9	−0.24560[a]	0.06032		8	9	1.02022	1.04085
	9	10	1.18322	1.40000		9	8	0.04042	0.00163
K K	4	4	0.74066	0.54857		9	9	−0.27579[a]	0.07606
	4	5	0.22678[a]	0.05143		9	10	1.09040	1.18897
	5	4	−0.22678[a]	0.05143		10	9	0.02712	0.00074
	5	5	0.77303	0.59758		10	10	−0.21523[a]	0.04632
	5	6	0.29039[a]	0.08433		10	11	1.16316	1.35294

Line Factor for Octet Terms

L_1 L_2	J_1	J_2	Factor	Square	L_1 L_2	J_1	J_2	Factor	Square
S S	3.5	3.5	0.	0.		3.5	4.5	1.82574	3.33333
S P	3.5	2.5	1.41421	2.00000	*P P*	2.5	2.5	−0.84515	0.71429
	3.5	3.5	−1.63299[a]	2.66667		2.5	3.5	1.13389[a]	1.28571

[a] Inverse factor has opposite sign.

Line Factor for Octet Terms *(continued)*

L_1 L_2	J_1	J_2	Factor	Square
P P	3.5	2.5	−1.13389[a]	1.28571
	3.5	3.5	0.29096	0.08466
	3.5	4.5	1.13855[a]	1.29630
	4.5	3.5	−1.13855[a]	1.29630
	4.5	4.5	1.42725	2.03704
P D	2.5	1.5	0.89443	0.80000
	2.5	2.5	−0.87831[a]	0.77143
	2.5	3.5	0.65465	0.42857
	3.5	2.5	0.65465	0.42857
	3.5	3.5	−1.00791[a]	1.01587
	3.5	4.5	1.10554	1.22222
	4.5	3.5	0.39441	0.15556
	4.5	4.5	−0.88192[a]	0.77778
	4.5	5.5	1.54919	2.40000
D D	1.5	1.5	−0.56569	0.32000
	1.5	2.5	0.69282[a]	0.48000
	2.5	1.5	−0.69282[a]	0.48000
	2.5	2.5	−0.07559	0.00571
	2.5	3.5	0.84515[a]	0.71429
	3.5	2.5	−0.84515[a]	0.71429
	3.5	3.5	0.39036	0.15238
	3.5	4.5	0.85635[a]	0.73333
	4.5	3.5	−0.85635[a]	0.73333
	4.5	4.5	0.87039	0.75757
	4.5	5.5	0.71351[a]	0.50909
	5.5	4.5	−0.71351[a]	0.50909
	5.5	5.5	1.37510	1.89091
D F	1.5	0.5	0.53452	0.28571
	1.5	1.5	−0.58554[a]	0.34286
	1.5	2.5	0.41404	0.17143
	2.5	1.5	0.47809	0.22857
	2.5	2.5	−0.72281[a]	0.52245
	2.5	3.5	0.67006	0.44898
	3.5	2.5	0.40406	0.16327
	3.5	3.5	−0.77372[a]	0.59864
	3.5	4.5	0.91547	0.83809
	4.5	3.5	0.30861	0.09524
	4.5	4.5	−0.74439[a]	0.55411
	4.5	5.5	1.16217	1.35065
	5.5	4.5	0.19069	0.03636
	5.5	5.5	−0.60302[a]	0.36364
	5.5	6.5	1.41421	2.00000
F F	0.5	0.5	−0.26726	0.07143
	0.5	1.5	0.46291[a]	0.21429
	1.5	0.5	−0.46291[a]	0.21429
	1.5	1.5	0.	0.
	1.5	2.5	0.59761[a]	0.35714
	2.5	1.5	−0.59761[a]	0.35714
	2.5	2.5	0.22588	0.05102
	2.5	3.5	0.67006[a]	0.44898
	3.5	2.5	−0.67006[a]	0.44898
	3.5	3.5	0.46657	0.21769
	3.5	4.5	0.69007[a]	0.47619
	4.5	3.5	−0.69007[a]	0.47619
	4.5	4.5	0.72822	0.53030
	4.5	5.5	0.64968[a]	0.42208
	5.5	4.5	−0.64968[a]	0.42208
	5.5	5.5	1.01142	1.02298
	5.5	6.5	0.51887[a]	0.26923
	6.5	5.5	−0.51887[a]	0.26923
	6.5	6.5	1.31559	1.73077
F G	0.5	0.5	−0.40825[a]	0.16667
	0.5	1.5	0.34503	0.11905
	1.5	0.5	0.23570	0.05556
	1.5	1.5	−0.50395[a]	0.25397
	1.5	2.5	0.51177	0.26191
	2.5	1.5	0.26726	0.07143
	2.5	2.5	−0.58029[a]	0.33673
	2.5	3.5	0.67006	0.44898
	3.5	2.5	0.26082	0.06803
	3.5	3.5	−0.62209[a]	0.38700
	3.5	4.5	0.82936	0.68783
	4.5	3.5	0.23002	0.05291
	4.5	4.5	−0.62515[a]	0.39081
	4.5	5.5	0.99240	0.98485
	5.5	4.5	0.18019	0.03247
	5.5	5.5	−0.57937[a]	0.33566
	5.5	6.5	1.16024	1.34615
	6.5	5.5	0.11323	0.01282
	6.5	6.5	−0.45760[a]	0.20940
	6.5	7.5	1.33333	1.77778

[a] Inverse factor has opposite sign.

Line Factor for Octet Terms (*continued*)

L_1 L_2	J_1	J_2	Factor	Square	L_1 L_2	J_1	J_2	Factor	Square
						6.5	7.5	1.14838	1.31879
G G	0.5	0.5	0.30429	0.09259		7.5	6.5	0.07521	0.00566
	0.5	1.5	0.36004[a]	0.12963		7.5	7.5	−0.36845[a]	0.13576
	1.5	0.5	−0.36004[a]	0.12963		7.5	8.5	1.27920	1.63636
	1.5	1.5	0.30792	0.09481	*H H*	1.5	1.5	0.51168	0.26182
	1.5	2.5	0.46904[a]	0.22000		1.5	2.5	0.31909[a]	0.10182
	2.5	1.5	−0.46904[a]	0.22000		2.5	1.5	−0.31909[a]	0.10182
	2.5	2.5	0.40119	0.16095		2.5	2.5	0.52422	0.27481
	2.5	3.5	0.53452[a]	0.28571		2.5	3.5	0.41089[a]	0.16883
	3.5	2.5	−0.53452[a]	0.28571		3.5	2.5	−0.41089[a]	0.16883
	3.5	3.5	0.53121	0.28219		3.5	3.5	0.58849	0.34632
	3.5	4.5	0.56656[a]	0.32099		3.5	4.5	0.46057[a]	0.21212
	4.5	3.5	−0.56656[a]	0.32099		4.5	3.5	−0.46057[a]	0.21212
	4.5	4.5	0.68698	0.47194		4.5	4.5	0.68232	0.46556
	4.5	5.5	0.56408[a]	0.31818		4.5	5.5	0.48105[a]	0.23140
	5.5	4.5	−0.56408[a]	0.31818		5.5	4.5	−0.48105[a]	0.23140
	5.5	5.5	0.86367	0.74592		5.5	5.5	0.79733	0.63573
	5.5	6.5	0.51887[a]	0.26923		5.5	6.5	0.47305[a]	0.22378
	6.5	5.5	−0.51887[a]	0.26923		6.5	5.5	−0.47305[a]	0.22378
	6.5	6.5	1.05849	1.12040		6.5	6.5	0.92924	0.86349
	6.5	7.5	0.40734[a]	0.16593		6.5	7.5	0.43064[a]	0.18545
	7.5	6.5	−0.40734[a]	0.16593		7.5	6.5	−0.43064[a]	0.18545
	7.5	7.5	1.26959	1.61185		7.5	7.5	1.07554	1.15679
G H	0.5	1.5	0.47140	0.22222		7.5	8.5	0.33511[a]	0.11230
	1.5	1.5	−0.35277[a]	0.12444		8.5	7.5	−0.33511[a]	0.11230
	1.5	2.5	0.56569	0.32000		8.5	8.5	1.23453	1.52407
	2.5	1.5	0.13027	0.01697	*H I*	1.5	2.5	0.60302	0.36364
	2.5	2.5	−0.44663[a]	0.19948		2.5	2.5	−0.30151[a]	0.09091
	2.5	3.5	0.67098	0.45022		2.5	3.5	0.67420	0.45455
	3.5	2.5	0.16116	0.02597		3.5	2.5	0.08362	0.00699
	3.5	3.5	−0.50012[a]	0.25012		3.5	3.5	−0.38624[a]	0.14918
	3.5	4.5	0.78281	0.61279		3.5	4.5	0.75571	0.57110
	4.5	3.5	0.16412	0.02694		4.5	3.5	0.10796	0.01166
	4.5	4.5	−0.52370[a]	0.27426		4.5	4.5	−0.43060[a]	0.18542
	4.5	5.5	0.89995	0.80992		4.5	5.5	0.84381	0.71202
	5.5	4.5	0.14845	0.02204		5.5	4.5	0.11276	0.01271
	5.5	5.5	−0.51673[a]	0.26701		5.5	5.5	−0.44755[a]	0.20030
	5.5	6.5	1.02190	1.04429		5.5	6.5	0.93696	0.87789
	6.5	5.5	0.11826	0.01399		6.5	5.5	0.10372	0.01076
	6.5	6.5	−0.47200[a]	0.22278		6.5	6.5	−0.43822[a]	0.19204

[a] Inverse factor has opposite sign.

Line Factor for Octet Terms (*continued*)

L_1 L_2	J_1	J_2	Factor	Square
H I	6.5	7.5	1.03437	1.06993
	7.5	6.5	0.08362	0.00699
	7.5	7.5	−0.39744[a]	0.15796
	7.5	8.5	1.13560	1.28959
	8.5	7.5	0.05366	0.00288
	8.5	8.5	−0.30826[a]	0.09502
	8.5	9.5	1.24035	1.53846
I I	2.5	2.5	0.62017	0.38462
	2.5	3.5	0.27735[a]	0.07692
	3.5	2.5	−0.27735[a]	0.07692
	3.5	3.5	0.64051	0.41026
	3.5	4.5	0.35806[a]	0.12821
	4.5	3.5	−0.35806[a]	0.12821
	4.5	4.5	0.69368	0.48119
	4.5	5.5	0.39980[a]	0.15984
	5.5	4.5	−0.39980[a]	0.15984
	5.5	5.5	0.76863	0.59079
	5.5	6.5	0.41526[a]	0.17244
	6.5	5.5	−0.41526[a]	0.17244
	6.5	6.5	0.86003	0.73964
	6.5	7.5	0.40600[a]	0.16484
	7.5	6.5	−0.40600[a]	0.16484
	7.5	7.5	0.96480	0.93084
	7.5	8.5	0.36756[a]	0.13510
	8.5	7.5	−0.36756[a]	0.13510
	8.5	8.5	1.08099	1.16854
	8.5	9.5	0.28456[a]	0.08097
	9.5	8.5	−0.28456[a]	0.08097
	9.5	9.5	1.20727	1.45749
I K	2.5	3.5	0.67937	0.46154
	3.5	3.5	−0.26149[a]	0.06838
	3.5	4.5	0.73960	0.54701
	4.5	3.5	0.05847	0.00342
	4.5	4.5	−0.33714[a]	0.11366
	4.5	5.5	0.80756	0.65215
	5.5	4.5	0.07742	0.00599
	5.5	5.5	−0.37562[a]	0.14109
	5.5	6.5	0.88090	0.77599
	6.5	5.5	0.08223	0.00676
	6.5	6.5	−0.38920[a]	0.15148
	6.5	7.5	0.95848	0.91868
	7.5	6.5	0.07656	0.00586
	7.5	7.5	−0.37961[a]	0.14411
	7.5	8.5	1.03962	1.08080
	8.5	7.5	0.06228	0.00388
	8.5	8.5	−0.34290[a]	0.11758
	8.5	9.5	1.12390	1.26316
	9.5	8.5	0.04024	0.00162
	9.5	9.5	−0.26491[a]	0.07018
	9.5	10.5	1.21106	1.46667
K K	3.5	3.5	0.68853	0.47407
	3.5	4.5	0.24343[a]	0.05926
	4.5	3.5	−0.24343[a]	0.05926
	4.5	4.5	0.71278	0.50806
	4.5	5.5	0.31520[a]	0.09935
	5.5	4.5	−0.31520[a]	0.09935
	5.5	5.5	0.75962	0.57702
	5.5	6.5	0.35161[a]	0.12363
	6.5	5.5	−0.35161[a]	0.12363
	6.5	6.5	0.82281	0.67701
	6.5	7.5	0.36428[a]	0.13270
	7.5	6.5	−0.36428[a]	0.13270
	7.5	7.5	0.89884	0.80792
	7.5	8.5	0.35504[a]	0.12605
	8.5	7.5	−0.35504[a]	0.12605
	8.5	8.5	0.98556	0.97132
	8.5	9.5	0.32036[a]	0.10263
	9.5	8.5	−0.32036[a]	0.10263
	9.5	9.5	1.08148	1.16959
	9.5	10.5	0.24721[a]	0.06111
	10.5	9.5	−0.24721[a]	0.06111
	10.5	10.5	1.18556	1.40555
K L	3.5	4.5	0.73030	0.53333
	4.5	4.5	−0.23028[a]	0.05303
	4.5	5.5	0.78335	0.61364
	5.5	4.5	0.04326	0.00187
	5.5	5.5	−0.29808[a]	0.08885
	5.5	6.5	0.84219	0.70928
	6.5	5.5	0.05826	0.00339
	6.5	6.5	−0.33216[a]	0.11033

[a] Inverse factor has opposite sign.

Line Factor for Octet Terms *(continued)*

L_1 L_2	J_1	J_2	Factor	Square	L_1 L_2	J_1	J_2	Factor	Square
K L	6.5	7.5	0.90532	0.81961		9.5	8.5	0.04819	0.00232
	7.5	6.5	0.06262	0.00392		9.5	9.5	−0.30136[a]	0.09082
	7.5	7.5	−0.34367[a]	0.11811		9.5	10.5	1.11364	1.24020
	7.5	8.5	0.97192	0.94464		10.5	9.5	0.03131	0.00098
	8.5	7.5	0.05882	0.00346		10.5	10.5	−0.23221[a]	0.05392
	8.5	8.5	−0.33446[a]	0.11187		10.5	11.5	1.18818	1.41176
	8.5	9.5	1.04148	1.08468					

[a] Inverse factor has opposite sign.

Just as with $\mathcal{E}1$ transitions, the relevant operator is independent of spin, and hence spin does not change during the transition. The following selection rules apply to $\mathcal{E}2$ transitions between *LS*-coupling states:

$$\Delta S = 0$$

$$\Delta L = +2, +1, 0, -1, -2$$

(but not $L = 0$ to $L = 0$, nor $L = 1$ to $L = 0$). Shortley [1] and Garstang [2] discuss $\mathcal{E}2$ line strengths and provide formulas and numerical values.

Magnetic-dipole radiation is governed by the matrix elements of the operator $\mathbf{M}^{(1)} = \beta(\mathbf{L} + 2\mathbf{S})$, for which (9.2) gives

$$\langle \alpha LSJ \| \mathbf{L} + 2\mathbf{S} \| \alpha' L' S' J' \rangle = \sqrt{2J+1}\,\sqrt{2J'+1}\,[\delta_{SS'} W(L1SJ'; L'J)\langle \alpha L \| \mathbf{L} \| \alpha' L' \rangle + \delta_{LL'} 2W(S'1LJ; SJ')\langle \alpha S \| \mathbf{S} \| \alpha' S' \rangle]. \quad (9.10)$$

The reduced matrix elements here are both examples of the general case

$$\langle \alpha J \| \mathbf{J} \| \alpha' J' \rangle = \delta_{\alpha\alpha'} \delta_{JJ'} \sqrt{J(J+1)(2J+1)}. \quad (9.11)$$

We therefore see that magnetic-dipole transitions require

$$\Delta L = 0, \qquad \Delta S = 0, \qquad \Delta\alpha = 0.$$

That is, $\mathfrak{M}1$ transitions occur only within a term. The transition amplitude for magnetic-dipole radiation between *LS*-coupling states is

$$\langle \alpha LSJ \| \mathbf{M}^{(1)} \| \alpha' L' S' J \rangle' = \delta_{\alpha\alpha'} \delta_{LL'} \delta_{SS'} \sqrt{2J+1}\,\sqrt{2J'+1} \times [W(L1SJ', LJ)\sqrt{L(L+1)(2L+1)} + 2W(S1LJ; SJ')\sqrt{S(S+1)(2S+1)}]. \quad (9.12)$$

Because $\mathbf{J} = \mathbf{L} + \mathbf{S}$, this amplitude may also be written

$$\langle \alpha LSJ \| \mathbf{M}^{(1)} \| \alpha' L' S' J' \rangle = \delta_{\alpha\alpha'} \delta_{LL'} \delta_{SS'} \sqrt{2J+1} \times [\delta_{JJ'} \sqrt{J(J+1)} + W(S1LJ; SJ') \sqrt{S(S+1)(2S+1)}]. \quad (9.12b)$$

Magnetic dipole transitions have been discussed by Shortley [1]. The combined effect of $\mathfrak{M}1$ and $\mathcal{E}2$ radiation and departures from LS coupling were treated in reference [3]. Mizushima [4] and Garstang [5] have discussed magnetic quadrupole transitions.

REFERENCES

[1] G. H. Shortley, *Phys. Rev.* **57**, 225 (1940).
[2] R. H. Garstang, *Monthly Notices, Roy. Astron. Soc.* **111,** 115 (1940); *ibid.*, **120,** 201 (1960); *Astrophys. J.* **115,** 506 (1952).
[3] G. H. Shortley, L. H. Aller, J. G. Baker, and D. H. Menzel, *Astrophys. J.* **93,** 178 (1941).
[4] M. Mizushima, *Phys. Rev.* **134,** *A638* (1964).
[5] R. H. Garstang, *Astrophys. J.*, **148,** 579 (1967).

10.10 THE MULTIPLET FACTOR

The summation properties of Racah coefficients provide two useful *sum rules.* The sum of the transitions, within a multiplet, that begin or end with the level $SL'J'$ is

$$\sum_J \mathbf{S}(SL'J', SLJ) = |\langle \alpha L \| \mathbf{Q}^{(1)} \| \alpha' L' \rangle|^2 \sum_J (2J'+1)(2J+1) \begin{Bmatrix} S & L & J \\ 1 & J' & L' \end{Bmatrix}^2 = \frac{(2J'+1)}{(2L'+1)} |\langle \alpha L \| \mathbf{Q}^{(1)} \| \alpha L' \rangle|^2. \quad (10.1)$$

In turn, the sum of the line strengths for all transitions in a multiplet is

$$\sum_{JJ,} \mathbf{S}(SL'J', SLJ) = (2S+1) |\langle \alpha L \| \mathbf{Q}^{(1)} \| \alpha' L' \rangle|^2, \quad (10.2)$$

Thus the reduced matrix element $\langle \alpha L \| \mathbf{Q}^{(1)} \| \alpha' L' \rangle$ provides the relative strengths of different multiplets. Through repeated application of the formulas in Chapter 6, we can ultimately write this reduced matrix element as the product of a single-electron reduced matrix element $\langle nl \| \mathbf{r} \| n'l' \rangle$, which depends on only the quantum numbers of the jumping electron (say, the jth electron) and a factor that we shall call the *multiplet factor*, $\mathcal{R}_{\text{mult}}$:

$$\langle \alpha L \| \mathbf{Q}^{(1)} \| \alpha' L' \rangle = \mathcal{R}_{\text{mult}}(\alpha L, \alpha' L') \times \langle nl \| \mathbf{r} \| n'l' \rangle \quad (10.3)$$

We shall denote the latter factor by $\mathcal{g}(nl, n'l')$:

$$
\begin{aligned}
\mathcal{g}(nl, n'l') &= \langle nl \| \mathbf{r} \| n'l' \rangle \\
&\equiv \langle l \| \mathbf{C}^{(1)} \| l' \rangle \int P_{nl}(r) P_{n'l'}(r) r \, dr \\
&= \begin{cases} (-1)^{l-l_>} \sqrt{l_>} \int P_{nl}(r) P_{n'l'}(r) r \, dr & (\text{if } l' = l \pm 1) \\ 0 & (\text{if } l' \neq l \pm 1), \end{cases}
\end{aligned}
\tag{10.4}
$$

where $l_>$ indicates the larger of the two orbital quantum numbers l and l'. The reduced matrix element $\langle l \| \mathbf{C}^{(1)} \| l' \rangle$ subsumes the selection rule (for $\mathcal{E}1$ transitions)

$$\Delta l = +1, -1,$$

and with this, Laporte's rule that parity changes in allowed transitions. Many authors use a quantity σ^2 in place of our $\mathcal{g}^2$:

$$\sigma^2 = \frac{\mathcal{g}^2}{l_>(4l_>{}^2 - 1)} \, . \tag{10.5}$$

Both σ and $\mathcal{g}$ contain a phase factor,

$$
\begin{aligned}
\sigma(l, l') &= -\sigma(l', l') \\
\mathcal{g}(l, l') &= -\mathcal{g}(l', l).
\end{aligned}
$$

For transitions between LS coupling states, $\mathcal{g}$ contains the only reference to the radial structure of the central field in which the electrons move. In another coupling scheme the transformation matrix of (8.24) also depends on the radial structure. It is often convenient to use the *transition integral*

$$
\begin{aligned}
I(nl, n'l') &= \int P_{nl}(r) P_{n'l'}(r) r \, dr \\
&= I(n'l', nl),
\end{aligned}
\tag{10.6}
$$

and write

$$\langle \alpha L \| \mathbf{Q}^{(1)} \| \alpha' L' \rangle = \mathcal{R}_{\text{mult}}(\alpha L, \alpha' L') \times (-1)^{l-l_>} \sqrt{l_>} \, I(nl, n'l'). \tag{10.7}$$

With these definitions, the line strength is

$$
\begin{aligned}
&(\mathbf{S}\alpha SLJ, \alpha' S'L'J') \\
&\quad = \delta_{SS'} |\mathcal{R}_{\text{line}}(SLJ, SL'J') \times \mathcal{R}_{\text{mult}}(\alpha L, \alpha' L') \times \mathcal{g}(nl, n'l'|^2 \\
&\quad = \delta_{SS'} |\mathcal{R}_{\text{line}}(SLJ, SL'J') \times \mathcal{R}_{\text{mult}}(\alpha L, \alpha' L') \\
&\qquad \times (-1)^{l-l_>} \sqrt{l_>} \times I(nl, n'l')|^2.
\end{aligned}
\tag{10.8}
$$

In turn the total strength of a multiplet, (10.1), may be written

$$\sum \mathbf{S}(SL'J', SLJ) = (2S+1)[\mathcal{R}_{\text{mult}}(\alpha L, \alpha L')]^2 \times [\mathcal{I}(nl, n'l')]^2$$
$$= (2S+1)[\mathcal{R}_{\text{mult}}(\alpha L, \alpha' L')]^2 \times l_> \times [I(nl, n'l')]^2$$
$$= (2S+1)[\mathcal{R}_{\text{mult}}(\alpha L, \alpha' L')]^2 \times l_>(4l_<^2 - 1)\sigma^2. \qquad (10.9)$$

A similar factoring applies for $\mathcal{E}2$ transitions. By analogy with (10.3) we write

$$\langle \alpha L \| \mathbf{Q}^{(2)} \| \alpha' L' \rangle = \mathcal{R}^{Q}_{\text{mult}}(\alpha L, \alpha' L') \times \mathcal{I}^{Q}(nl, n'l'), \qquad (10.10)$$

where

$$\mathcal{I}^{Q}(nl, n'l') \equiv \langle l \| \mathbf{C}^{(2)} \| l' \rangle \int P_{nl}(r) P_{n'l'} r^2 \, dr. \qquad (10.11)$$

Equation 10.11 yields the selection rule for $\mathcal{E}2$ transitions,

$$\Delta l = +2, 0, -2.$$

Thus $\mathcal{E}2$ transitions are possible within a configuration.

The multiplet factor $\mathcal{R}_{\text{mult}}$ depends upon the two particular configurations involved in the transition. Multiplet factors may be calculated by straightforward application of the results of Chapters 6 and 9. We require the formula

$$\langle L_c l L \| \mathbf{Q}^{(1)} \| L_c' l' L' \rangle = \delta_{cc'} \sqrt{2L+1} \sqrt{2L'+1}\, W(L_c L l' 1, l L') \times \langle nl \| \mathbf{r} \| n'l' \rangle \qquad (10.12)$$

which, with the introduction of the notation

$$\mathcal{W}_{ll'}(L_c, LL') \equiv \sqrt{2L+1} \sqrt{2L'+1}\, W(L_c L l' 1; l L'), \qquad (10.13)$$

may be written as

$$\langle L_c l L \| \mathbf{Q}^{(1)} \| L_c' l' L' \rangle = \delta_{cc'} \mathcal{W}_{ll'}(L_c, LL') \mathcal{I}(nl, n'l'). \qquad (10.14)$$

We also need formula (9.15) of Chapter 9 for expressing an antisymmetric state of n equivalent orbitals as a linear combination of states in which the nth orbital is singled out and coupled last:

$$\tilde{\Psi}(l^n \Gamma) = \sum_{\bar{\Gamma}} \psi(l^{n-1}\bar{\Gamma}, l\Gamma | 1, 2 \cdots n)(l^n \Gamma \{| l^{n-1} \bar{\Gamma}). \qquad (10.15)$$

[The state $\tilde{\Psi}$ is antisymmetric in coordinates of all n electrons; the state ψ is antisymmetric in the coordinates of the first $(n-1)$ electrons. The expansion coefficients or coefficients of fractional parentage, CFP, were discussed in Section 9.9.] We further require the recoupling formulas, (3.10) of Chapter 6:

$$\langle ab(D), cJ | ac(E), bJ \rangle = \sqrt{2D+1} \sqrt{2E+1}\, W(EbcD; aJ) \qquad (10.16a)$$

$$\langle ab(D), cJ | a, bc(F), J \rangle = \sqrt{2D+1} \sqrt{2F+1}\, W(abJc; DF). \qquad (10.16b)$$

Table 10.9 Formulas for the Multiplet Factor[a]

Transition[b]		αSL–	$\alpha' SL'$	$\mathcal{R}_{\mathrm{mult}}$	$\mathcal{G}$
ls	$-lp$	$(S_cL_c)sSL_s$	$-(S_cL_c)pSL_p$	$\mathcal{W}_{sp}(L_cL_cL_p)$	$\mathcal{G}(s,p)$
ld	$-lp$	$(S_cL_c)dSL_d$	$-(S_cL_c)pSL_p$	$\mathcal{W}_{dp}(L_cL_dL_p)$	$\mathcal{G}(d,p)$
ld	$-lf$	$(S_cL_e)sSL_d$	$-(S_cL_c)fSL_f$	$\mathcal{W}_{df}(L_cL_dL_f)$	$\mathcal{G}(d,f)$
ls^2	$-lsp$	(SL_c)	$-(SL_c)s(\bar{S})pSL_p$	$\mathcal{W}_{sp}(L_cL_cL_p)\left(\frac{2\bar{S}+1}{2S+1}\right)^{1/2}(-1)^{S+1/2-\bar{S}}$	$\mathcal{G}(s,p)$
s^2p	$-p^2s$	(^2P)	$-p^2(S_pL_p)s\ ^2L_p$	$\mathcal{W}_{sp}(PPL_p)(2S_p+1)^{1/2}(-1)^{1-S_p}$	$\mathcal{G}(s,p)$
$p^{n-1}s^2$	$-p^ns$	(SL_c)	$-(S_pL_p)sSL_p$	$\mathcal{W}_{sp}(L_cL_cL_p)\sqrt{n}\,(p^nS_pL_p\{\vert SL_c)\left(\frac{2S_p+1}{2S+1}\right)^{1/2}(-1)^{S+1/2-S_p}$	$\mathcal{G}(s,p)$
$p^{n-1}ss'$	$-p^ns$	$(S_cL_c)s(\bar{S})s'SL_c$	$-(S_pL_p)sSL_s$	$\mathcal{W}_{sp}(L_cL_cL_p)\sqrt{n}\,(p^nS_pL_p\{\vert S_cL_c)\,\mathcal{S}_s(S_c\bar{S}S_p)$	$\mathcal{G}(s',p)$
$p^{n-1}s's$	$-p^ns$	$(S_cL_c)s'(S_p)sSL_c$	$-(S_pL_p)sSL_s$	$\mathcal{W}_{sp}(L_cL_cL_p)\sqrt{n}\,(p^nS_pL_p\{\vert S_cL_c)$	$\mathcal{G}(s',p)$
$p^{n-1}s$	$-p^n$	$(S_cL_c)sSL_c$	$-(SL_p)$	$\mathcal{W}_{sp}(L_cL_cL_p)\sqrt{n}\,(p^nSL_p\{\vert S_cL_c)$	$\mathcal{G}(s,p)$
$p^{n-1}d$	$-p^n$	$(S_cL_c)dS_pL_d$	$-S_pL_p$	$\mathcal{W}_{dp}(L_cL_dL_p)\sqrt{n}\,(p^nS_pL_p\{\vert S_cL_c)$	$\mathcal{G}(d,p)$
$p^{n-1}ds$	$-p^ns$	$(S_cL_c)d(S_pL_d)sSL_d$	$-(S_pL_p)sSL_p$	$\mathcal{W}_{dp}(L_cL_dL_p)\sqrt{n}\,(p^nS_pL_p\{\vert S_cL_c)$	$\mathcal{G}(d,p)$
$p^{n-1}sd$	$-p^ns$	$(S_cL_c)s(\bar{S}L_c)dSL_d$	$-(S_pL_p)sSL_p$	$\mathcal{W}_{dp}(L_cL_dL_p)\sqrt{n}\,(p^nS_pL_p\{\vert S_cL_c)\,\mathcal{S}_s(S_c\bar{S}S_p)$	$\mathcal{G}(d,p)$
d^n	$-d^{n-1}p$	(vSL_d)	$-(v_cS_cL_c)pSL_p$	$\mathcal{W}_{dp}(L_cL_dL_p)\sqrt{n}\,(d^nvSL_d\{\vert v_cS_cL_c)$	$\mathcal{G}(d,p)$
d^ns	$-d^{n-1}ps$	$(vS_dL_d)sSL_d$	$-(v_cS_cL_c)pS_dL_psSL_p$	$\mathcal{W}_{dp}(L_cL_dL_p)\sqrt{n}\,(d^nvS_dL_d\{\vert v_cS_cL_c)$	$\mathcal{G}(d,p)$
d^ns	$-d^{n-1}sp$	$(vS_dL_d)sSL_d$	$-(v_cS_cL)s_c(\bar{S})pSL_p$	$\mathcal{W}_{dp}(L_cL_dL_p)\sqrt{n}\,(d^nvS_dL_d\{\vert v_cS_cL_c)\,\mathcal{S}_s(S_c\bar{S}S_d)$	$\mathcal{G}(d,p)$
$p^{n-1}s^2$	$-d^{n-1}sp$	(S_cL_c)	$-(S_cL_c)s(\bar{S})pSL_p$	$\mathcal{W}_{sp}(L_cL_cL_p)\left(\frac{2\bar{S}+1}{2S+1}\right)^{1/2}(-1)^{S+1/2-\bar{S}}$	$\mathcal{G}(s,p)$
d^n	$-d^{n-1}f$	(vSL_d)	$-(v_cS_cL_c)fSL_f$	$\mathcal{W}_{df}(L_cL_dL_f)\sqrt{n}\,(d^nvSL_d\{\vert v_cS_cL_c)$	$\mathcal{G}(d,f)$
d^ns	$-d^{n-1}fs$	$(vS_dL_d)sSL_d$	$-(v_cS_cL_c)fS_dL_fsSL_f$	$\mathcal{W}_{df}(L_cL_dL_f)\sqrt{n}\,(d^nvS_dL_d\{\vert vS_cL_c)$	$\mathcal{G}(d,f)$
d^ns	$-d^{n-1}sf$	$(vS_dL_d)sSL_d$	$-(v_cS_cL_c)s(\bar{S})fSL_f$	$\mathcal{W}_{df}(L_cL_dL_f)\sqrt{n}\,(d^nvS_dL_d\{\vert v_cS_cL_c)\,\mathcal{S}_s(S_c\bar{S}S_f)$	$\mathcal{G}(d,f)$

[a] For all transitions, $\mathbf{S}^{1/2} = \langle \alpha SLJ \Vert \mathbf{Q}^{(1)} \Vert \alpha' SL'J' \rangle = \mathcal{R}_{\mathrm{line}} \times \mathcal{R}_{\mathrm{mult}} \times \mathcal{G}$.

[b] To obtain the *inverse* transition: take the tabulated value of $\mathcal{W}$ for the *direct* transition, with the opposite sign *if marked by* [a], and take the tabulated $\mathcal{G}$ for the *direct* transition *always with the opposite sign.*

Table 10.10

$\mathcal{W}_{sp}(L_cL_sL_p)$ Factor for s–p Multiplet Factor

Core	L_s	L_p	Factor	Square	Core	L_s	L_p	Factor	Square
S	*S*	*P*	1.00000	1.00000			*G*	1.73205[a]	3.00000
P	*P*	*S*	0.57735	0.33333			*H*	1.91485	3.66667
		P	1.00000[a]	1.00000	*H*	*H*	*G*	1.73205	3.00000
		D	1.29099	1.66667			*H*	1.91485[a]	3.66667
D	*D*	*P*	1.00000	1.00000			*I*	2.08167	4.33333
		D	1.29099[a]	1.66667	*I*	*I*	*H*	1.91485	3.66667
		F	1.52753	2.33333			*I*	2.08167[a]	4.33333
F	*F*	*D*	1.29099	1.66667			*K*	2.23607	5.00000
		F	1.52753[a]	2.33333	*K*	*K*	*I*	2.08167	4.33333
		G	1.73205	3.00000			*K*	2.23607[a]	5.00000
G	*G*	*F*	1.52753	2.33333			*L*	2.38048	5.66667

$\mathcal{W}_{dp}(L_cL_dL_p)$ Factor for d–p Multiplet Factor

Core	L_d	L_p	Factor	Square	Core	L_d	L_p	Factor	Square
S	*D*	*P*	1.00000	1.00000	*G*	*D*	*F*	1.00000	1.00000
P	*P*	*S*	0.57735	0.33333		*F*	*F*	0.93541[a]	0.87500
		P	0.50000[a]	0.25000			*G*	0.72457	0.52500
		D	0.12910	0.01667		*G*	*F*	0.67700	0.45833
	D	*P*	0.86603	0.75000			*G*	1.07471[a]	1.15500
		D	0.50000[a]	0.25000			*H*	0.43205	0.18667
	F	*D*	1.18322	1.40000		*H*	*G*	1.14891	1.32000
D	*S*	*P*	0.44721	0.20000			*H*	0.93808[a]	0.88000
	P	*P*	0.67082[a]	0.45000		*I*	*H*	1.61245	2.60000
		D	0.38730	0.15000	*H*	*F*	*G*	1.18322	1.40000
	D	*P*	0.59161	0.35000		*G*	*G*	1.03923[a]	1.08000
		D	0.76376[a]	0.58333			*H*	0.84853	0.72000
		F	0.25820	0.06667		*H*	*G*	0.72111	0.52000
	F	*D*	0.96609	0.93333			*H*	1.19583[a]	1.43000
		F	0.68313[a]	0.46667			*I*	0.50000	0.25000
	G	*F*	1.34164	1.80000		*I*	*H*	1.23153	1.51667
F	*P*	*D*	0.77460	0.60000			*I*	1.04083[a]	1.08333
	D	*D*	0.81650[a]	0.66667		*K*	*I*	1.73205	3.00000
		F	0.57735	0.33333	*I*	*G*	*H*	1.34164	1.80000
	F	*D*	0.63246	0.40000		*H*	*H*	1.13284[a]	1.28333
		F	0.93541[a]	0.87500			*I*	0.95743	0.91667
		G	0.35355	0.12500		*I*	*H*	0.76376	0.58333
	G	*F*	1.06066	1.12500			*I*	1.30475[a]	1.70238
		G	0.82158[a]	0.67500			*K*	0.56061	0.31429
	H	*G*	1.48324	2.20000					

[a] Inverse factor has opposite sign.

$\mathcal{W}_{dp}$ $(L_c L_d L_p)$ Factor for *d–p* Multiplet Factor (*continued*)

Core	L_d	L_p	Factor	Square	Core	L_d	L_f	Factor	Square
I	*K*	*I*	1.30931	1.71429		*K*	*I*	0.80475	0.64762
		K	1.13389[a]	1.28571			*K*	1.40471[a]	1.97321
	L	*K*	1.84391	3.40000			*L*	0.61577	0.37917
K	*H*	*I*	1.48324	2.20000		*L*	*K*	1.38293	1.91250
	I	*I*	1.21890[a]	1.48571			*L*	1.21963[a]	1.48750
		K	1.05560	1.11429		*M*	*L*	1.94936	3.80000

$\mathcal{W}_{df}$ $(L_c L_d L_f)$ Factor for *d–f* Multiplet Factor

Core	L_d	L_f	Factor	Square	Core	L_d	L_f	Factor	Square
S	*D*	*F*	1.00000	1.00000			*G*	−0.68661[a]	0.47143
P	*P*	*D*	0.77460	0.60000			*H*	1.12122	1.25174
	D	*D*	−0.33333[a]	0.11111		*H*	*G*	0.16903	0.02857
		F	0.94281	0.88889			*H*	−0.56061[a]	0.31429
	F	*D*	0.05634	0.00317			*I*	1.36277	1.85714
		F	−0.33333[a]	0.11111	*G*	*D*	*P*	0.65465	0.42857
		G	1.13389	1.28571			*D*	−0.62994[a]	0.39683
D	*S*	*P*	0.44721	0.20000			*F*	0.41786	0.17460
	P	*P*	−0.44721[a]	0.20000		*F*	*D*	0.56344	0.31746
		D	0.63246	0.40000			*F*	−0.78174[a]	0.61111
	D	*P*	0.16903	0.02857			*G*	0.68661	0.47143
		D	−0.53452[a]	0.28571		*G*	*F*	0.46291	0.21429
		F	0.82808	0.68571			*G*	−0.83324[a]	0.69429
	F	*D*	0.16903	0.02857			*H*	0.94415	0.89143
		F	−0.54772[a]	0.30000		*H*	*G*	0.34641	0.12000
		G	1.03510	1.07143			*H*	−0.79722[a]	0.63556
	G	*F*	0.11952	0.01429			*I*	1.20185	1.44445
		G	−0.46291[a]	0.21429		*I*	*H*	0.21082	0.04444
		H	1.25357	1.57143			*I*	−0.64242[a]	0.41270
F	*P*	*S*	0.37796	0.14286			*K*	1.46385	2.14286
		P	−0.53452[a]	0.28571	*H*	*F*	*D*	0.84515	0.71429
		D	0.41404	0.17143			*F*	−0.70711[a]	0.50000
	D	*P*	0.37796	0.14286			*G*	0.43095	0.18571
		D	−0.65465[a]	0.42857		*G*	*F*	0.70711	0.50000
		F	0.65465	0.42857			*G*	−0.88318[a]	0.78000
	F	*D*	0.33806	0.11429			*H*	0.72111	0.52000
		F	−0.70711[a]	0.50000		*H*	*G*	0.56569	0.32000
		G	0.88641	0.78572			*H*	−0.93808[a]	0.88000
	G	*F*	0.26726	0.07143			*I*	1.00000	1.00000

[a] Inverse factor has opposite sign.

$\mathcal{W}_{df}(L_cL_dL_f)$ **Factor for** d–f **Multiplet Factor** *(continued)*

Core	L_d	L_f	Factor	Square	Core	L_d	L_f	Factor	Square
H	I	H	0.41404	0.17143		L	K	0.28031	0.07857
		I	−0.89214[a]	0.79592			L	−0.77919[a]	0.60714
		K	1.27775	1.63265			M	1.64751	2.71429
	K	I	0.24744	0.06122	K	H	G	1.13389	1.28571
		K	−0.71429[a]	0.51020			H	−0.83571[a]	0.69841
		L	1.55839	2.42857			I	0.46462	0.21587
I	G	F	1.00000	1.00000		I	H	0.93435	0.87302
		G	−0.77460[a]	0.60000			I	−1.05000[a]	1.10249
		H	0.44721	0.20000			K	0.79025	0.62449
	H	G	0.82808	0.68571		K	I	0.73401	0.53877
		H	−0.97101[a]	0.94286			K	−1.11346[a]	1.23980
		I	0.75593	0.57143			L	1.10518	1.22143
	I	H	0.65465	0.42857		L	K	0.52780	0.27857
		I	−1.03016[a]	1.06123			L	−1.05397[a]	1.11085
		K	1.05366	1.11020			M	1.41795	2.01058
	K	I	0.47380	0.22449		M	L	0.31032	0.09630
		K	−0.97677[a]	0.95408			M	−0.83887[a]	0.70370
		L	1.34960	1.82143			N	1.73205	3.00000

[a] Inverse factor has opposite sign.

Applied to electron spins, this transformation function can be denoted as a spin-recoupling factor $\mathcal{S}$:

$$\langle S_c \tfrac{1}{2}(S'), \tfrac{1}{2}\, S | S_c \tfrac{1}{2}(S''), \tfrac{1}{2}\, S\rangle = \sqrt{2S'+1}\ \sqrt{2S''+1}\ W(S'\tfrac{1}{2}\tfrac{1}{2}S''; SS_c)$$
$$\equiv \mathcal{S}_S(S_c, S'S''). \qquad (10.17)$$

Most common multiplet factors can be expressed as products of CFP and the $\mathcal{W}$ and $\mathcal{S}$ factors defined above. Table 10.9 gives a number of such expressions. Details of these calculations will be found in the article by Shore and Menzel [1], from which Table 10.10 (the $\mathcal{W}$ factor) and Table 10.11 (the $\mathcal{S}$ factor) have been taken. Table 10.10 gives values of the $\mathcal{W}$ factors for s–p, d–p, and d–f transitions. The inverse transition is given by

$$\mathcal{W}_{l'l}(L_cL'L) = (-1)^{L-L'+1}\mathcal{W}_{ll'}(L_c, LL'). \qquad (10.18)$$

A superscript [a] in the tables denotes a value where the inverse transition has the opposite sign. Note that because of the phase relations in $\mathcal{R}_{\text{line}}$, $\mathcal{R}_{\text{mult}}$, and $\mathcal{J}$, the following general result holds:

$$\langle \alpha SLJ \| \mathbf{Q}^{(1)} \| \alpha' S'L'J'\rangle = (-1)^{J-J'}\langle \alpha' S'L'J' \| \mathbf{Q}^{(1)} \| \alpha SLJ\rangle. \qquad (10.19)$$

Table 10.11 Spin Recoupling Factor

from (Core 1 + s + l) to (Core 2 + s) for Given Total Spin

Singlet Terms

Core 1	+Added s	Core 2	Factor	Square
Singlet	Doublet	Doublet	−1.00000	1.00000
Triplet	Doublet	Doublet	1.00000	1.00000

Doublet Terms

Core 1	+Added s	Core 2	Factor	Square
Doublet	Singlet	Singlet	0.50000	0.25000
		Triplet	0.86603	0.75000
	Triplet	Singlet	0.86603	0.75000
		Triplet	−0.50000	0.25000
Quartet	Triplet	Triplet	1.00000	1.00000

Triplet Terms

Core 1	+Added s	Core 2	Factor	Square
Singlet	Doublet	Doublet	1.00000	1.00000
Triplet	Doublet	Doublet	0.33333	0.11111
		Quartet	0.94281	0.88889
	Quartet	Doublet	0.94281	0.88889
		Quartet	−0.33333	0.11111
Quintet	Quartet	Quartet	1.00000	1.00000

Quartet Terms

Core 1	+Added s	Core 2	Factor	Square
Doublet	Triplet	Triplet	1.00000	1.00000
Quartet	Triplet	Triplet	0.25000	0.06250
		Quintet	0.96825	0.93750
	Quintet	Triplet	0.96825	0.93750
		Quintet	−0.25000	0.06250
Sextet	Quintet	Quintet	1.00000	1.00000

Quintet Terms

Core 1	+Added s	Core 2	Factor	Square
Triplet	Quartet	Quartet	1.00000	1.00000
Quintet	Quartet	Quartet	0.20000	0.04000
		Sextet	0.97980	0.96000
	Sextet	Quartet	0.97980	0.96000
		Sextet	−0.20000	0.04000
Septet	Sextet	Sextet	1.00000	1.00000

Sextet Terms

Core 1	+Added s	Core 2	Factor	Square
Quartet	Quintet	Quintet	1.00000	1.00000
Sextet	Quintet	Quintet	0.16667	0.02778
		Septet	0.98601	0.97222
	Septet	Quintet	0.98601	0.97222
		Septet	−0.16667	0.02778
Octet	Septet	Septet	1.00000	1.00000

REFERENCE

[1] B. W. Shore and D. H. Menzel, *Astrophys. J. Suppl.* **12,** 187 (1965).

10.11 SUM RULES

The preceding formulas for the line strength

$$\mathbf{S} \equiv \mathbf{S}(\alpha SLJ, \alpha' S' L' J')$$

permit us to carry out useful summations over quantum numbers, by using the summation properties of 6-j symbols. For example, the total strength of those lines in a multiplet which begin (or end) on the level LJ is obtained by summing $(\mathcal{R}_{\text{line}})^2$ over J'. The result is

$$\sum_{J'} \mathbf{S} = \frac{(2J+1)}{(2L+1)} (\mathcal{R}_{\text{mult}})^2 \mathcal{g}^2. \tag{11.1}$$

Alternatively, the symmetry between J and J' permits us to write

$$\sum_{J} \mathbf{S} = \frac{(2J'+1)}{(2L'+1)} (\mathcal{R}_{\text{mult}})^2 \mathcal{g}^2. \tag{11.2}$$

The total strength of all lines in a multiplet is therefore

$$\sum_{JJ'} \mathbf{S} = (2S + 1)(\mathcal{R}_{\text{mult}})^2 \mathcal{G}^2. \tag{11.3}$$

Next, consider the lines of a transition array that originate (or end) in a *level SLJ*. The summation of $(\mathcal{R}_{\text{mult}})^2$ then gives the following strengths:

for $Il - Il'$: $$\sum_{L'J'} \mathbf{S} = \frac{(2J+1)}{(2l'+1)} \mathcal{G}^2$$

for $l^N - l^{N-1}l'$: $$\sum_{L'J'} \mathbf{S} = \frac{(2J+1)}{(2l'+1)} N(l^N\{|l^{N-1})^2 \mathcal{G}^2$$

for $l^N s - l^{N-1}sl'$: $$\sum_{L'J'} \mathbf{S} = \frac{(2J+1)}{(2l'+1)} N(l^N\{|l^{N-1})^2 \mathcal{S}^2 \mathcal{G}^2$$

for $Is^2 - Isp$: $$\sum_{L'J'} \mathbf{S} = \frac{(2J+1)(2S_s+1)}{(2S+1)} 2\mathcal{G}^2$$

where I denotes a fixed core. In turn these strengths can be summed over additional quantum numbers. For example

for $Il - Il'$:

$$\mathbf{S} \equiv \mathbf{S}(S_c L_c l SLJ, S_c L_c l' SL'J')$$

$$\sum_{L} \sum_{JJ'} \mathbf{S} = \frac{(2S+1)(2L'+1)}{(2l'+1)} \mathcal{G}^2$$

$$\sum_{LL'} \sum_{JJ'} \mathbf{S} = (2S+1)(2L_c+1)\mathcal{G}^2$$

$$\sum_{S} \sum_{LL'} \sum_{JJ'} \mathbf{S} = 2(2S_c+1)(2L_c+1)\mathcal{G}^2$$

for $l^N - l^{N-1}l'$:

$$\mathbf{S} \equiv (\mathbf{S} l^N v SL, l^{N-1} v' S_c L_c l' SL'J')$$

$$\sum_{L'} \sum_{JJ'} \mathbf{S} = \frac{(2S+1)(2L+1)}{(2l'+1)} \cdot N \cdot (l^N\{|l^{N-1})^2 \mathcal{G}^2$$

$$\sum_{vS} \sum_{LL} \sum_{JJ'} \mathbf{S} = \frac{(2S_c+1)(2L_c+1)}{2(2l'+1)} \cdot (4l + 3 - N)\mathcal{G}^2$$

These and other sum rules were derived by Ornstein and Burger [1], Burger and Dorgelo [2], Shortley [3], Menzel and Goldberg [4], Menzel [5], and Rohrlich [6].

The oscillator strength also satisfies several useful sum rules. With the use of atomic units ($e = m = \hbar = 1$, energy expressed in units of 27.196 eV) the definition (8.18) reads

$$\begin{aligned} f_{nn'} &= \tfrac{2}{3}E_{n'n}\frac{\mathbf{S}(n,n')}{\varpi_n} \\ &= \tfrac{2}{3}E_{n'n}\frac{|\langle n\|\mathbf{Q}^{(1)}\|n'\rangle|^2}{\varpi_n} \\ &= \tfrac{2}{3}E_{n'n}\sum_{M'q}|\langle nM|Q_q^{(1)}|n'M'\rangle|^2 \end{aligned} \tag{11.4}$$

where n denotes the label of the lower level, n' denotes the upper level, $E_{n'n} = E_{n'} - E_n$, ϖ_n is the statistical weight of lower level ($\varpi_n = 2J_n + 1$), and M, M' are magnetic quantum numbers. Then summation over a complete set of levels yields the following expressions:

$$\sum_{n'}\frac{f_{nn'}}{(E_{n'n})^2} = \frac{2}{3\varpi_n}\sum_{n'}\frac{|\langle n\|\mathbf{R}\|n'\rangle|^2}{E_{n'} - E_n} \tag{11.5}$$

$$\sum_{n'}\frac{f_{nn'}}{E_{n'n}} = \frac{2}{3}\frac{\langle n\|(\mathbf{R})^2\|n\rangle}{\varpi_n} \tag{11.6}$$

$$\sum_{n'} f_{nn'} = N \tag{11.7}$$

$$\begin{aligned} \sum_{n'} E_{nn'}f_{nn'} &= \frac{2}{3}\frac{\langle n\|(\mathbf{P})^2\|n\rangle}{\varpi_n} \\ &= \frac{4}{3}\left[E_n + \frac{1}{2\varpi_n}\sum_i\sum_{j\neq i}\langle n\|\mathbf{p}(i)\cdot\mathbf{p}(j)\|n\rangle\right] \end{aligned} \tag{11.8}$$

where

$$\mathbf{R} = \sum_{i=1}^{N}\mathbf{r}_i \qquad \mathbf{P} = \sum_{i=1}^{N}\mathbf{p}(i).$$

Expression (11.7), known as the Reiche-Thomas-Kuhn [7] f-sum rule, states that the sum of all oscillator strengths from a given level n is equal to the number of electrons, N. The sums in (11.5)–(11.8) go over a complete set of states n', including levels below n, above n, and continuum states. These and similar other sum rules are discussed by Vinti [8], Dalgarno and his collaborators [9], and Rebane and Sil'd [10]. Special sum rules for hydrogenic atoms are discussed by Bethe and Salpeter [11]. Jackiw [12] has discussed sum rules for more general matrix elements. It should be noted that many authors, when discussing sum rules, use the definition

$$\begin{aligned} f_{MM'} \equiv f_{nM,n'M'} &= 2E_{n'n}|\langle nM|Q_0^{(1)}|n'M'\rangle|^2 \\ &= 2E_{n'n}|\langle nM|\sum_i z_i|n'M'\rangle|^2. \end{aligned}$$

The oscillator strength of (11.4) is then

$$f_{nn'} \equiv \frac{1}{\varpi_n} \sum_{MM'} f_{nM,n'M'}.$$

REFERENCES

[1] L. S. Ornstein and H. C. Burger, *Zeits. f. Phys.* **24,** 41 (1924).
[2] H. C. Burger and H. B. Dorgelo, *Zeits. f. Phys.* **23,** 258 (1924).
[3] G. H. Shortley, *Phys. Rev.* **47,** 295 (1935); *ibid.*, p. 419 (1935).
[4] D. H. Menzel and L. Goldberg, *Astrophys. J.* **84,** 1 (1936).
[5] D. H. Menzel, *Astrophys. J.* **105,** 126 (1947).
[6] F. Rohrlich, *Astrophys. J.* **129,** 449 (1959).
[7] F. Reiche and W. Thomas, *Naturwiss.* **13,** 627 (1925); W. Kuhn, *Zeits. f. Phys.* **33,** 408 (1925).
[8] J. P. Vinti, *Phys. Rev.* **41,** 432 (1932).
[9] A. Dalgarno and J. Lewis, *Proc. Roy. Soc.* (Lond.) **A233,** 70 (1955); A. Dalgarno and N. Lynn, *Proc. Phys. Soc.* **A70,** 802 (1957); A. Dalgarno, *Rev. Mod. Phys.* **35,** 522 (1963); *Proc. Phys. Soc.* **76,** 422 (1966).
[10] K. K. Rebane and O. I. Sil'd, *Optics and Spectroscopy* **13,** 259 (1962).
[11] H. Bethe and E. Salpeter, *The Quantum Mechanics of One- and Two-Electron Atoms,* Academic, New York (1957), Sections 59–62 and p. 358.
[12] R. Jackiw, *Phys. Rev.* **157,** 1220 (1967).

10.12 THE TRANSITION INTEGRAL

The radial part P_{nl} of the wavefunctions contains implicitly the structure of the central field. Methods for finding these functions vary widely; Slater [2] provides an introduction to the customary approaches. For transitions in hydrogen, one may refer to the formulas in Bethe and Salpeter [3] or to the tables of Green, Rush, and Chandler [4] which provide values of

$$I(nl, n'l') = \int P_{nl}P_{n'l'}r\,dr = (-1)^{l_>-l}\frac{\mathcal{G}(l, l')}{\sqrt{l_>}}.$$

Bates and Damgaard [5] gave tables from which one can calculate

$$\sigma = \frac{1}{\sqrt{4l_>^2 - 1}}\int P_{nl}P_{n'l'}r\,dr = (-1)^{l_>-l}\frac{\mathcal{G}(l, l')}{\sqrt{l_>(4l_>^2 - 1)}}.$$

Their wavefunctions were based on a Coulomb approximation to the central field, and their tables have been widely used. (The recent book by Griem [6], contains tables of these integrals.) Varsavsky [7] applied a

Table 10.12 Hydrogenic Radial Factor $\mathcal{J}$ for s-p Transitions[a]

Radial Factor

	2p	3p	4p	5p	6p	7p	8p	9p
1s	−1.2903(00)	−5.1669(−01)	−3.0458(−01)	−2.0870(−01)	−1.5514(−01)	−1.2142(−01)	−9.8498(−02)	−8.2045(−02)
2s	5.1962(00)	−3.0648(00)	−1.2823(00)	−7.7395(−01)	−5.4037(−01)	−4.0801(−01)	−3.2359(−01)	−2.6548(−01)
3s	−9.3840(−01)	1.2728(01)	−5.4693(00)	−2.2596(00)	−1.3602(00)	−9.5143(−01)	−7.2107(−01)	−5.7442(−01)
4s	−3.8230(−01)	−2.4435(00)	2.3238(01)	−8.5178(00)	−3.4545(00)	−2.0619(00)	−1.4371(00)	−1.0882(00)
5s	−2.2803(−01)	−9.6961(−01)	−4.6003(00)	3.6742(01)	−1.2214(01)	−4.8699(00)	−2.8795(00)	−1.9966(00)
6s	−1.5820(−01)	−5.7227(−01)	−1.7883(00)	−7.4086(00)	5.3245(01)	−1.6559(01)	−6.5071(00)	−3.8137(00)
7s	−1.1900(−01)	−3.9579(−01)	−1.0437(00)	−2.8348(00)	−1.0868(01)	7.2746(01)	−2.1553(01)	−8.3669(00)
8s	−9.4151(−02)	−2.9785(−01)	−7.1765(−01)	−1.6381(00)	−4.1077(00)	−1.4978(01)	9.5247(01)	−2.7197(01)
9s	−7.7114(−02)	−2.3614(−01)	−5.3861(−01)	−1.1195(00)	−2.3535(00)	−5.6059(00)	−1.9739(01)	1.2075(02)

Square of Radial Factor ($3\sigma^2$)

	2p	3p	4p	5p	6p	7p	8p	9p
1s	1.6648(00)	2.6697(−01)	9.2771(−02)	4.3557(−02)	2.4067(−02)	1.4743(−02)	9.7019(−03)	6.7314(−03)
2s	2.7000(01)	9.3931(00)	1.6442(00)	5.9900(−01)	2.9200(−01)	1.6647(−01)	1.0471(−01)	7.0477(−02)
3s	8.8060(−01)	1.6200(02)	2.9914(01)	5.1057(00)	1.8502(00)	9.0421(−01)	5.1995(−01)	3.2996(−01)
4s	1.4615(−01)	5.9709(00)	5.4000(02)	7.2553(01)	1.1934(01)	4.2513(00)	2.0653(00)	1.1842(00)
5s	5.1997(−02)	9.4014(−01)	2.1163(01)	1.3500(03)	1.4918(02)	2.3716(01)	8.2915(00)	3.9865(00)
6s	2.5028(−02)	3.2749(−01)	3.1978(00)	5.4887(01)	2.8350(03)	2.7419(02)	4.2342(01)	1.4545(01)
7s	1.4162(−02)	1.5665(−01)	1.0893(00)	8.0363(00)	1.1811(02)	5.2920(03)	4.6453(02)	7.0005(01)
8s	8.8644(−03)	8.8712(−02)	5.1503(−01)	2.6834(00)	1.6873(01)	2.2435(02)	9.0720(03)	7.3968(02)
9s	5.9465(−03)	5.5764(−02)	2.9011(−01)	1.2533(00)	5.5390(00)	3.1426(01)	3.8964(02)	1.4580(04)

[a] Inverse transition always has opposite sign. Bracketed numbers are powers of 10.

Table 10.12 (*continued*)

Hydrogenic Radial Factor $\mathcal{G}$ for d - p Transitions[a]

Radial Factor

	2p	3p	4p	5p	6p	7p	8p	9p
3d	6.7147(00)	−1.4230(01)	1.8417(00)	6.8278(−01)	3.8932(−01)	2.6391(−01)	1.9609(−01)	1.5413(−01)
4d	2.4179(00)	1.0699(01)	−2.9394(01)	4.3067(00)	1.5880(00)	9.0020(−01)	6.0796(−01)	4.5087(−01)
5d	1.3790(00)	4.1978(00)	1.5611(01)	−4.8606(01)	7.6749(00)	2.8128(00)	1.5850(00)	1.0658(00)
6d	9.3594(−01)	2.4623(00)	6.2034(00)	2.1447(01)	−7.2000(01)	1.1957(01)	4.3577(00)	2.4423(00)
7d	6.9526(−01)	1.6966(00)	3.6570(00)	8.4919(00)	2.8205(01)	−9.9612(01)	1.7156(01)	6.2221(00)
8d	5.4575(−01)	1.2736(00)	2.5286(00)	4.9943(00)	1.1081(01)	3.5883(01)	−1.3145(02)	2.3273(01)
9d	4.4464(−01)	1.0081(00)	1.9042(00)	3.4494(00)	6.4853(00)	1.3977(01)	4.4482(01)	−1.6753(02)

Square of Radial Factor ($30\sigma^2$)

	2p	3p	4p	5p	6p	7p	8p	9p
3d	4.5087(01)	2.0250(02)	3.3917(00)	4.6619(−01)	1.5157(−01)	6.9650(−02)	3.8451(−02)	2.3757(−02)
4d	5.8462(00)	1.1447(02)	8.6400(02)	1.8548(01)	2.5218(00)	8.1037(−01)	3.6962(−01)	2.0328(−01)
5d	1.9016(00)	1.7622(01)	2.4372(02)	2.3625(03)	5.8904(01)	7.9118(00)	2.5123(00)	1.1360(00)
6d	8.7599(−01)	6.0627(00)	3.8482(01)	4.5998(02)	5.1840(03)	1.4297(02)	1.8990(01)	5.9649(00)
7d	4.8339(−01)	2.8784(00)	1.3374(01)	7.2112(01)	7.9551(02)	9.9225(03)	2.9432(02)	3.8715(01)
8d	2.9784(−01)	1.6221(00)	6.3937(00)	2.4943(01)	1.2278(02)	1.2876(03)	1.7280(04)	5.4161(02)
9d	1.9770(−01)	1.0163(00)	3.6261(00)	1.1898(01)	4.2059(01)	1.9535(02)	1.9787(03)	2.8066(04)

Hydrogenic Radial Factor $\mathcal{G}$ for d-f Transitions[a]

Radial Factor

	4f	5f	6f	7f	8f	9f
3d	−1.7719(01)	−5.7481(00)	−3.1145(00)	−2.0570(00)	−1.5050(00)	−1.1713(00)
4d	2.7495(01)	−2.4362(01)	−8.9676(00)	−5.0740(00)	−3.4219(00)	−2.5351(00)
5d	−2.8775(00)	5.1962(01)	−3.2190(01)	−1.2274(01)	−7.0523(00)	−4.7960(00)
6d	−9.7845(−01)	−6.3239(00)	8.1000(01)	−4.1175(01)	−1.5859(01)	−9.1552(00)
7d	−5.3065(−01)	−2.1796(00)	−1.0854(01)	1.1502(02)	−5.1303(01)	−1.9779(01)
8d	−3.4879(−01)	−1.1850(00)	−3.7653(00)	−1.6493(01)	1.5414(02)	−6.2568(01)
9d	−2.5407(−01)	−7.7868(−01)	−2.0478(00)	−5.7402(00)	−2.3247(01)	1.9841(02)

Square of Radial Factor ($105\sigma^2$)

	4f	5f	6f	7f	8f	9f
3d	3.1398(02)	3.3041(01)	9.7003(00)	4.2312(00)	2.2651(00)	1.3720(00)
4d	7.5600(02)	5.9350(02)	8.0418(01)	2.5745(01)	1.1710(01)	6.4265(00)
5d	8.2798(00)	2.7000(03)	1.0362(03)	1.5065(02)	4.9736(01)	2.3002(01)
6d	9.5736(−01)	3.9992(01)	6.5610(03)	1.6954(03)	2.5151(02)	8.3817(01)
7d	2.8159(−01)	4.7505(00)	1.1782(02)	1.3230(04)	2.6320(03)	3.9122(02)
8d	1.2166(−01)	1.4042(00)	1.4178(01)	2.7201(02)	2.3760(04)	3.9147(03)
9d	6.4552(−02)	6.0634(−01)	4.1933(00)	3.2950(01)	5.4042(02)	3.9366(04)

[a] Inverse transition always has opposite sign. Bracketed numbers are powers of 10.

screening theory to obtain an extensive set of values of σ^2. Kelley [8] used Hartree–Fock–Slater wavefunctions to obtain extensive tables of σ^2 for oxygen and nitrogen transitions. Additional references may be found in the National Bureau of Standards Bibliographies [9] or the National Standard Reference Data Series monographs on Atomic Transition probabilities [10].

For reference, Table 10.12 gives values of $\mathcal{g}(nl, n'l')$ computed for hydrogen [1].

REFERENCES

[1] This section is reprinted from B. W. Shore and D. H. Menzel, *Astrophys. J. Suppl.* **12,** 187 (1965).

[2] J. C. Slater, *Quantum Theory of Atomic Structure*, McGraw-Hill, New York (1960), Vol. 1.

[3] H. Bethe and E. E. Salpeter, *Quantum Mechanics of One- and Two-Electron Atoms*, Academic, New York (1957).

[4] L. C. Green, P. P. Rush, and C. D. Chandler, *Astrophys. J. Suppl.* **3,** 37 (1957).

[5] D. R. Bates and A. Damgaard, *Phil. Trans. Roy. Soc.* (London) **A242,** 101 (1949).

[6] H. Griem, *Plasma Spectroscopy*, McGraw-Hill, New York (1964).

[7] C. M. Varsavsky, *Astrophys. J. Suppl.* **7,** 75 (1961); *Planet. Space Sci.* **11,** 1001 (1963).

[8] P. S. Kelley, *J. Quant. Spectry. & Radiative Transfer* **4,** 117 (1964).

[9] B. M. Glennon and W. L. Wiese, *Bibliography on Atomic Transition Probabilities*, National Bureau of Standards Misc. Publ. 278 (1966). [This supersedes National Bureau of Standards Monograph 50 (1962)].

[10] W. L. Wiese, M. W. Smith, and B. M. Glennon, *Atomic Transition Probabilities*, Vol. 1, National Standard Reference Data Series–National Bureau of Standards **4** (1966).

APPENDIX A: NOTATION CONVENTIONS [1]

Many workers (cf. Rohrlich [2], or Nicholls and Stewart [3]) factor the line strength $\mathbf{S}(\Gamma J, \Gamma' J')$ rather than the reduced matrix element

$$\langle \Gamma J \| \mathbf{Q}^{(1)} \| \Gamma' J' \rangle$$

into a relative line strength $\mathfrak{S}(\mathcal{L})$, a relative multiplet strength $\mathfrak{S}(\mathcal{M})$, and a radial part $\mathbf{s}^2$ or σ^2:

$$\mathbf{S}(\Gamma J, \Gamma' J') = \mathfrak{S}(\mathcal{L})\mathfrak{S}(\mathcal{M})\sigma^2. \tag{A.1}$$

The symbol $\mathcal{S}$ sometimes appears in place of $\mathfrak{S}$. In the preceding sections we use the factorization:

$$\mathbf{S}(\Gamma J, \Gamma' J') = (\mathcal{R}_{\text{line}})^2(\mathcal{R}_{\text{mult}})^2\mathcal{g}^2. \tag{A.2}$$

The strengths as defined by Rohrlich and Nicholls and Stewart relate to the quantities $\mathcal{R}_{\text{line}}$ and $\mathcal{R}_{\text{mult}}$ by

$$\mathfrak{S}(\mathcal{L}) = \frac{(\mathcal{R}_{\text{line}})^2}{2S+1} \tag{A.3}$$

$$\mathfrak{S}(\mathfrak{M}) = (2S+1)(4l_>^2 - 1)(\mathcal{R}_{\text{mult}})^2. \tag{A.4}$$

The "radial quantum integral" of Condon and Shortley [4] is

$$\sigma^2 = \frac{\mathcal{g}^2}{(4l_>^2 - 1)l_>} . \tag{A.5}$$

$$= \frac{I^2}{(4l_>^2 - 1)} .$$

Russell [5] and White and Eliason [6, 4] tabulated values for $\mathfrak{S}'(\mathcal{L})$ normalized so that the strongest line of a multiplet had intensity 100. Allen [7] tabulates $\mathfrak{S}''(\mathcal{L})$

$$\mathfrak{S}(\mathcal{L}) = \frac{\mathfrak{S}''(\mathcal{L})}{(2S+1)(2L+1)(2L'+1)} = \frac{(\mathcal{R}_{\text{line}})^2}{(2S+1)} . \tag{A.6}$$

Horie [8] tabulated $\mathcal{R}_{\text{line}}$ with a different phase. Goldberg [9] tabulated values of $\mathfrak{S}'(\mathfrak{M})$, to be multiplied by a normalizing factor [10] that depends on the particular transition array. (This factor is incorporated into the tables of Allen [7].)

REFERENCES

[1] This appendix is reprinted from B. W. Shore and D. H. Menzel, *Astrophys. J. Suppl.* **12,** 187 (1965).

[2] F. Rohrlich, *Astrophys. J.* **129,** 441 (1959).

[3] R. W. Nicholls and A. L. Stewart, in *Atomic and Molecular Processes,* D. R. Bates (ed.), Academic, New York, (1962) Chap. 2.

[4] E. U. Condon and G. H. Shortley, *The Theory of Atomic Spectra,* Cambridge University Press, Cambridge, England (1935).

[5] H. N. Russell, *Proc. Natl. Acad. Sci.* **2,** 314 (1925).

[6] H. E. White and A. Y. Eliason, *Phys. Rev.* **44,** 753 (1933).

[7] C. W. Allen, *Astrophysical Quantities,* Athlone, London (1963), 2nd ed.

[8] H. Horie, *J. Phys. Soc. Japan* **7,** 58 (1952).

[9] L. Goldberg, *Astrophys. J.* **82,** 1 (1935).

[10] L. Goldberg, *Astrophys. J.* **84,** 11 (1936).

11. Static Fields

11.1 INTRODUCTION

In the last several sections we have idealized atoms as isolated systems, free from external forces except those of the radiation field. Real atoms are, of course, not truly isolated, and they interact variously with their surroundings. For the atoms bound into molecules or solids, these interactions significantly alter the structure of the valence orbitals. In a gas, atoms continually encounter other atoms, ions, or electrons with consequent alteration of atomic structure. Historically, the study of atoms in magnetic fields—the Zeeman effect and Stern–Gerlach experiment—provided important guides to the development of quantum theory. Such studies continue to play an important part in the analysis of spectra and the investigation of laboratory and astronomical magnetic fields. In this chapter we shall consider the effect of weak, static, electric, and magnetic fields on the structure of atoms.

Suppose that the free atom (in the absence of external fields) is governed by the Hamiltonian $\mathcal{H}^1$, whose eigenstates are ψ_n. The static field introduces an additional term $\mathcal{V}_{\text{stat}}$ into the Hamiltonian $\mathcal{H}$ of the disturbed atom:

$$\mathcal{H} = \mathcal{H}^1 + \mathcal{V}_{\text{stat}}. \tag{1.1}$$

Knowing the interaction $\mathcal{V}_{\text{stat}}$, we seek the properties of eigenstates Ψ_n of $\mathcal{H}$.

Ideally we should construct these eigenstates as linear combinations either of undisturbed states ψ_n or of some other convenient basis states φ_n, such that the matrix of $\mathcal{H}$ is diagonal. In practice we content ourselves with approximations to this goal. If we use the undisturbed states as our basis (assuming these to be known exactly), the matrix of $\mathcal{H}^1$ is diagonal, while the matrix of $\mathcal{V}_{\text{stat}}$ in this basis has off-diagonal elements. The diago-

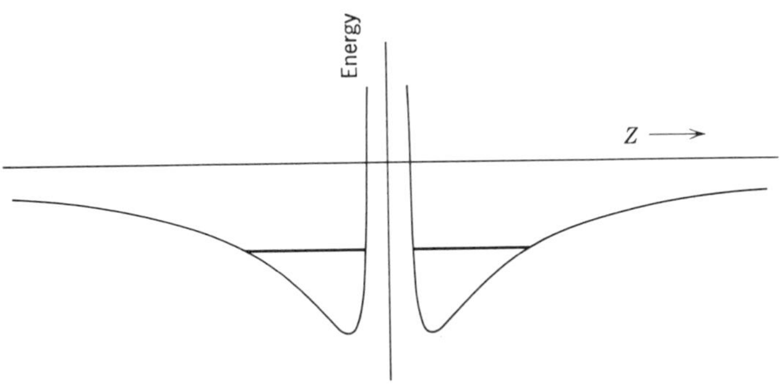

Fig. 11.1 An effective potential for Coulomb field. Heavy horizontal line shows region of classically allowed motion for a particular negative energy.

nalization of the $\mathcal{H}$ matrix introduces mixtures of undisturbed states as the disturbed eigenstates. When $\mathcal{V}_{\text{stat}}$ has no matrix elements between degenerate states, perturbation theory gives the eigenstates as

$$\Psi_n = \psi_n + \mathop{\mathsf{S}}_m \psi_m \frac{\langle\psi_m|\mathcal{V}_{\text{stat}}|\psi_n\rangle}{E_m^{(1)} - E_n^{(1)}} + \cdots \tag{1.2}$$

and the eigenvalues as

$$E_n = E_n^{(1)} + \langle\psi_n|\mathcal{V}_{\text{stat}}|\psi_n\rangle + \mathop{\mathsf{S}}_m \frac{|\langle\psi_m|\mathcal{V}_{\text{stat}}|\psi_n\rangle|^2}{E_m^{(1)} - E_n^{(1)}} + \cdots, \tag{1.3}$$

where $E_n^{(1)}$ denotes an eigenvalue of $\mathcal{H}^1$. We see that the interaction $\mathcal{V}_{\text{stat}}$ produces two obvious effects.

First, it alters the positions of energy levels, and thereby shifts the positions of spectral lines. When the undisturbed states ψ_n are degenerate, different degenerate levels may shift by different amounts so that the field may remove or partially remove the degeneracy. We then observe a splitting of spectral lines into components.

Second, the interaction alters the properties of the wavefunctions through mixing. As a result, new spectral lines may appear, while other lines may weaken. For example, a slight admixture of the hydrogen $2s$ and $2p$ states will permit the $2s \rightarrow 1s$ radiative transition previously forbidden by the l selection rule.

A third and more subtle change occurs in a uniform electric field. Suppose that, in the absence of any field, an electron moves in the effective potential $V(z)$ shown in Fig. 11.1. The dark horizontal line shows the region of classically allowed motion for an electron having negative energy E. As we have seen, where E is less than V, the wavefunction must diminish

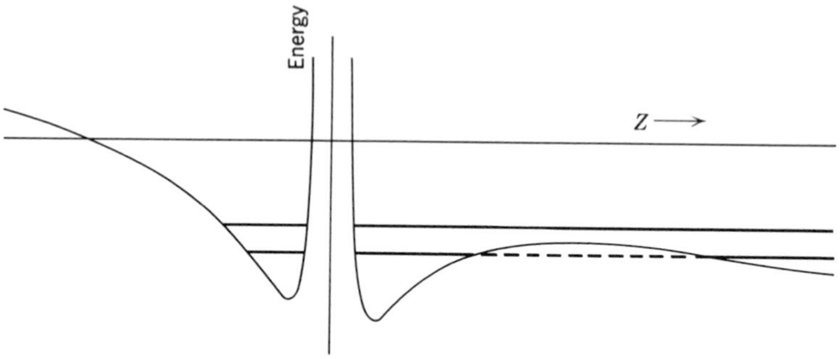

Fig. 11.2 The effective potential of Fig. 11.1 with added electric field. Heavy horizontal lines show region of classically allowed motion for two particular negative energies.

exponentially with increasing $|z|$. For bound states, $E < 0$, there will always be some distance beyond which $E < V$. Hence the electron is confined within the potential-well "atom." The consequent condition that $\psi \rightarrow 0$ as $|z| \rightarrow \infty$ then leads to the familiar quantization of permitted values for E.

Now introduce a uniform electric field of magnitude $|\mathbf{E}|$ directed along the z axis: $\mathcal{V}_{\text{stat}} = -e|\mathbf{E}|r\cos\theta = -e|\mathbf{E}|z$. The effective potential becomes the curve of Fig. 11.2. We see that for sufficiently large positive z, we have $E > V$ for any energy E, and the wavefunction oscillates sinusoidally at large distances. That is, the wavefunction there describes a free particle. Since we can no longer require that as $\psi \rightarrow 0$ as $z = \infty$, we no longer obtain sharply prescribed negative energies.

This result means that if we attempt to localize an electron inside the potential well at some time, say $t = 0$, we must describe the electron by a superposition of eigenstates. As time passes, the initial amplitudes diminish, and the probability grows that the electron is located beyond the potential well. In other words, the electron escapes, and the atom becomes ionized. To completely describe such a process we require time-dependent perturbation theory. However, we can readily note the principal results of such forced ionization, as first pointed out by Oppenheimer [1]. All bound levels become theoretically unstable with respect to ionization. This instability or mode of decay manifests itself as an increased width of spectral lines. The instability increases as one progresses to higher excitation energies, where the potential "barrier" between the atom interior and the exterior becomes lower and narrower. For sufficiently high excitation, the decay probability becomes so large that the widths of spectral lines become comparable to the spacing between levels, and the levels there merge into a continuum. The onset of this continuum occurs below the $E = 0$ level that marks the ionization limit for an isolated atom.

Although even the weakest electric fields introduce this fundamental change in the character of the eigenvalues, if we are concerned with low-lying energy levels and weak fields so that the barrier between interior and exterior is quite thick, then we can obtain an acceptable description of the atom by ignoring the possibility of ionization and applying perturbation theory.

In practice, the Hamiltonian has the form

$$\mathcal{H} = \mathcal{H}^0 + \mathcal{V}_{\text{Coul}} + \mathcal{V}_{\text{spin}} + \mathcal{V}_{\text{stat}} \equiv \mathcal{H}^0 + \mathcal{V}, \tag{1.4}$$

where $\mathcal{H}^0$ is a central-field Hamiltonian, $\mathcal{V}_{\text{Coul}}$ is the interelectron Coulomb repulsion, possibly modified by a central potential, and $\mathcal{V}_{\text{spin}}$ is the spin–orbit interaction. Following the approach of Chapter 6, we employ eigenstates of $\mathcal{H}^0$ as our basis states, and treat $\mathcal{V}$ as a perturbation.

The eigenvalues of $\mathcal{H}^0$ are labeled by sets of principal quantum numbers, $\{n\}$, and azimuthal quantum numbers $\{l\}$, but they are independent of other quantum numbers. (In the Z^{-1} expansion, the eigenvalues depend only on $\{n\}$.) We can therefore choose our basis states in various ways, as discussed in Chapter 6. The simplest choice would be basis functions that are products of single-particle orbitals, bearing the labels

$$\{nlm_l m_s\}.$$

As we have seen in Chapter 6, various linear combinations of these degenerate functions can provide more useful basis functions. For example, functions labeled by

$$\{nl\}\alpha S M_S L M_L$$

or by

$$\{nl\}\alpha SLJM$$

are particularly useful when $\mathcal{V}_{\text{Coul}}$ is the most significant perturbation, because $\mathcal{V}_{\text{Coul}}$ is diagonal in SM_SLM_L or $SLJM$. (Here $\mathbf{S}$ is the total spin, $\mathbf{L}$ is the total orbital angular-momentum, $\mathbf{J}$ is the total angular momentum, $\mathbf{J} = \mathbf{L} + \mathbf{S}$, and M_S, M_L, M, are the corresponding eigenvalues of S_z, L_z, and J_z. Additional quantum numbers α are also needed for atoms with more than one electron.) Although the final results are independent of the choice of basis functions, some functions are more convenient than others for given conditions.

Suppose now that $\mathcal{V}_{\text{stat}}$ is independent of the azimuthal angle ϕ, that is, it is rotationally symmetric about the z axis. Further, suppose that if $\mathcal{V}_{\text{stat}}$ does depend on spin, it only depends on the z component. Thus we consider static fields of the form

$$V(z), \qquad V(z)L_z, \qquad V(z)S_z, \qquad \text{or} \qquad V(z)J_z.$$

The action of uniform electric or magnetic fields are special cases of such interactions. These interaction operators commute with S_z, L_z, and J_z so that eigenstates of S_z and L_z, or J_z, provide convenient basis states. If, as often happens, the relative importance of the perturbations is

$$\mathcal{V}_{\text{Coul}} > \mathcal{V}_{\text{spin}} > \mathcal{V}_{\text{stat}},$$

then we find eigenstates labeled by

$$\alpha SLJM$$

to be convenient: $\mathcal{V}_{\text{Coul}}$ is diagonal in $\alpha SLJM$ and $\mathcal{V}_{\text{spin}}$ is diagonal in JM.

When $\mathcal{V}_{\text{stat}}$ has the form $V(z)$, as it does for the interaction with an electric field, the interaction remains unchanged if we replace J_z or S_z or L_z by $-J_z$ or $-S_z$ or $-L_z$. (That is, the energy does not depend on the direction, clockwise or counterclockwise, in which an electron circulates.) Therefore the energy depends on the magnitude $|M|$ but not on the sign $\pm M$, and the levels have a twofold degeneracy. This *Kramers degeneracy* [2] is absent when $J = 0$. (The Kramers degeneracy occurs with an odd number of electrons.) When $\mathcal{V}_{\text{stat}}$ depends explicitly on the z component of angular momentum, as happens in a magnetic field, this degeneracy no longer occurs. The energy then depends on the sense of circulation of the electron current; that is, whether the magnetic moment is parallel or antiparallel to the magnetic field.

Because the interaction $\mathcal{V}_{\text{Coul}}$ singles out a preferred direction in space, it does not commute with the total angular momentum operator $\mathbf{J}^2$. Therefore $\mathcal{V}_{\text{stat}}$ mixes states having different eigenvalues J (but with the same eigenvalue M). In weak fields, only slight mixing occurs, but in strong fields the mixing may become so great that the label J loses its usefulness. If the field is sufficiently intense so that it overwhelms the spin–orbit interaction, we can consider the hierarchy of interactions

$$\mathcal{V}_{\text{Coul}} > \mathcal{V}_{\text{stat}} > \mathcal{V}_{\text{spin}}.$$

Under these conditions, with the restriction that $\mathcal{V}_{\text{stat}}$ commutes with S_z and L_z, it is convenient to employ basis states labeled by

$$\alpha SM_SLM_L.$$

Such states are appropriate for a description of the *Paschen–Back effect* when an external magnetic field dominates the spin–orbit interaction. In the absence of $\mathcal{V}_{\text{spin}}$, the eigenstates of $\mathcal{H}$ are degenerate: When $\mathcal{V}_{\text{stat}}$ is independent of spin, the degeneracy is $2S + 1$.

Let us see how these general remarks apply to a uniform electric field and a uniform magnetic field.

REFERENCES

[1] J. R. Oppenheimer, *Phys. Rev.* **31**, 66 (1928).
[2] H. A. Kramers, *Proc. Acad. Sci.*, Amsterdam, **33**, 959 (1930).

11.2 UNIFORM MAGNETIC FIELD

The influence of a uniform static magnetic field upon an atom is expressed by the interaction

$$\mathcal{V}_{\text{stat}} = -\boldsymbol{\mu}\cdot\mathbf{H}, \tag{2.1}$$

where $\boldsymbol{\mu}$ is the magnetic moment of the atom. The magnetic moment arises both from the orbital motion of each electron,

$$\boldsymbol{\mu}_{\text{orbital}} = \sum_i \beta\mathbf{l}(i) \equiv \beta\mathbf{L}, \tag{2.2}$$

and from the intrinsic or spin moment of each electron,

$$\boldsymbol{\mu}_{\text{spin}} = \sum_i \beta g_s\mathbf{s}(i) \equiv \beta g_s\mathbf{S} \simeq 2\beta\mathbf{S}, \tag{2.3}$$

where $\beta \equiv e\hbar/2mc$ is the Bohr magneton. Thus we can write

$$\begin{aligned}\mathcal{V}_{\text{stat}} &= -\beta(\mathbf{L} + 2\mathbf{S})\cdot\mathbf{H} \\ &= -\beta(\mathbf{J} + \mathbf{S})\cdot\mathbf{H}.\end{aligned} \tag{2.4}$$

With the z axis as the $\mathbf{H}$ direction, (2.4) reads simply

$$\mathcal{V}_{\text{stat}} = -\beta H_z(L_z + 2S_z) = -\beta H_z(J_z + S_z). \tag{2.5}$$

An energy of one electron volt requires a field of 1.73×10^8 gauss for a magnetic moment of one Bohr magneton. In dealing with wavenumbers we require the *Lorentz splitting factor*

$$\frac{\beta}{hc} \equiv \frac{e}{4\pi mc^2} = 4.66858 \times 10^{-5}\,\text{cm}^{-1}\,\text{G}^{-1}.$$

The quantity $\beta H/hc$ is often referred to as the *Lorentz unit*.

We can readily see that $\mathcal{V}_{\text{stat}}$ commutes with J_z, S_z, and L_z, as well as with $\mathbf{L}^2$ and $\mathbf{S}^2$, so that $\mathcal{H}$ is diagonal in the quantum numbers LSM_SM_L and $M = M_J$. Furthermore $\boldsymbol{\mu}$, which is proportional to the sum of single-particle operators $\mathbf{l}(i)$ and $\mathbf{s}(i)$, is diagonal in the single-particle quantum numbers $\{nl\}$ and the various intermediate spin and orbital angular-momentum quantum numbers. Therefore $\mathcal{V}_{\text{stat}}$ mixes states of different J while preserving the integrity of the labels for configuration, parentage, and spectroscopic term. However, the sublevels of a spectroscopic term are no longer degenerate, since the energy depends explicitly on $M_S M_L$ or M.

Let us consider an atom for which $\mathcal{V}_{\text{Coul}}$ dominates $\mathcal{V}_{\text{spin}}$. When the magnetic field is sufficiently weak, we can rank the interactions as

$$\mathcal{V}_{\text{Coul}} > \mathcal{V}_{\text{spin}} > \mathcal{V}_{\text{stat}},$$

and use eigenstates labeled by the quantum numbers $LSJM$. The interaction has the matrix elements

$$\langle\alpha' S' L' J' M'|\mathcal{V}_{\text{stat}}|\alpha SLJM\rangle = \beta H_z \langle\alpha' S' L' J' M'|J_z + S_z|\alpha SLJM\rangle. \quad (2.6)$$

The first contribution, from J_z, is simply

$$\langle\alpha' S' L' J' M'|J_z|\alpha SLJM\rangle = M\delta_{\alpha\alpha'}\delta_{SS'}\delta_{LL'}\delta_{JJ'}\delta_{LL'}. \quad (2.7)$$

The contribution from S_z follows, with the aid of the Wigner–Eckart theorem and tensor algebra, as

$$\langle\alpha' S' L' J' M'|S_z|\alpha SLJM\rangle = \frac{(JM, 10|J'M')}{\sqrt{2J'+1}}\delta_{MM'}$$
$$\times \sqrt{2J+1}\sqrt{2J'+1}\,(-1)^{S+L+J+1}\begin{Bmatrix} L & S' & J' \\ 1 & J & S \end{Bmatrix}\delta_{LL'}$$
$$\times \sqrt{S(S+1)(2S+1)}\,\delta_{SS'}\delta_{\alpha\alpha'}. \quad (2.8)$$

The nonzero matrix elements of S_z can be written

$$\langle\alpha SLJM|S_z|\alpha SLJM\rangle = \frac{M[S(S+1) + J(J+1) - L(L+1)]}{2J(J+1)} \quad (2.9a)$$

$$\langle\alpha SLJM|S_z|\alpha SLJ \pm 1M\rangle = \frac{\sqrt{J_>^2 - M^2}}{2J_>}$$
$$\times\left[\frac{(L+S+J_> - 1)(S-L+J_>)(L-S+J_>)(L+S-J_>)}{(2J_> + 1)(2J_< + 1)}\right]^{1/2}, \quad (2.9b)$$

where $J_>$ and $J_<$ denote, respectively, the larger and smaller of J and $J \pm 1$.

To first order, perturbation theory gives the disturbed energies as

$$E(\alpha SLJM) = E^1(\alpha SLJ) + \langle\alpha SLJM|\mathcal{V}_{\text{stat}}|\alpha SLJM\rangle, \quad (2.10)$$

where $E^1(\alpha SLJ)$ is an eigenvalue of $(\mathcal{H}^0 + \mathcal{V}_{\text{Coul}} + \mathcal{V}_{\text{spin}})$. When we introduce the Landé g factor,

$$g \equiv \frac{1}{M}\langle\alpha SLJM|J_z + S_z|\alpha SLJM\rangle, \quad (2.11)$$

which, according to (2.8) and (2.9) is given by

$$g = 1 + \frac{S(S+1) + J(J+1) - L(L+1)}{2J(J+1)}$$
$$= \frac{3}{2} + \frac{S(S+1) - L(L+1)}{2J(J+1)}, \tag{2.12}$$

we can write the energy as

$$E(\alpha SLJM) = E^1(\alpha SLJ) + \beta H_z Mg. \tag{2.13}$$

We see the familiar result that a magnetic field splits a level into $2J + 1$ equally spaced sublevels, with spacing equal to $g\beta H_z$. When the field is weak enough for this expression to be applicable, we have the *Zeeman effect* discussed in Chapter 2.

We may note that the g factor depends on the quantum numbers S, L, and J, but not on the parentage or configuration. Therefore configuration mixing will not alter the g value. However, if the spin–orbit interaction is appreciable, S and L cease to be good quantum numbers and the diagonal elements in LS coupling no longer provide useful estimates of energies. It may be more appropriate to use, say, jj-coupling basis states for which we obtain the energy

$$E(\alpha j_1 j_2 JM) = E^1(\alpha j_1 j_2 J) + \langle \alpha j_1 j_2 JM | \mathcal{V}_{\text{stat}} | \alpha j_1 j_2 JM \rangle$$
$$= E^1(\alpha j_1 j_2 J) + \beta H_z Mg. \tag{2.14}$$

The g factor is now

$$g = \frac{1}{M} \langle \alpha j_1 j_2 JM | J_z + S_z | \alpha j_1 j_2 JM \rangle$$
$$= 1 + \frac{\langle \alpha j_1 j_2 J \| \mathbf{s}(1) + \mathbf{s}(2) \| \alpha j_1 j_2 J \rangle}{\sqrt{J(J+1)}}. \tag{2.15}$$

It should be clear that g can be calculated in any coupling scheme. The general formula is

$$g = 1 + \frac{\langle \alpha J \| \mathbf{S} \| \alpha J \rangle}{\sqrt{J(J+1)}}. \tag{2.16}$$

As the field **H** grows more intense the mixing of states with different J increases and perturbation theory becomes less useful. To obtain accurate wavefunctions and energies we must carry out a matrix diagonalization. For example, consider an atom with a single valence electron. Using wavefunctions $\psi(nljm)$, we obtain the following matrix of $\mathcal{H}$ for the mixing of wavefunctions of the same n, l, and m:

	$nll-\frac{1}{2}, m$	$nll+\frac{1}{2}, m$
$nll-\frac{1}{2}, m$	$E_{nl} + \frac{1}{2}l\zeta + \beta H_z m \dfrac{2l+2}{2l+1}$	$\beta H_z \dfrac{\sqrt{(l+\frac{1}{2}-m)(l+\frac{1}{2}+m)}}{2l+1}$
$nll+\frac{1}{2}, m$	$\beta H_z \dfrac{\sqrt{(l+\frac{1}{2}-m)(l+\frac{1}{2}+m)}}{2l+1}$	$E_{nl} - \frac{1}{2}(l+1)\zeta + \beta H_z m \dfrac{2l}{2l+1}$

The eigenvalues obtained from the solution to the secular equation are

$$E(nlm\pm) = E^0(nl) - \tfrac{1}{4}\zeta + m\beta H_z \pm \tfrac{1}{2}\sqrt{(\beta H_z)^2 + 2m\zeta\beta H_z + [\tfrac{1}{2}(2l+1)\zeta]^2}. \tag{2.17}$$

For small fields $[\beta H_z \ll \frac{1}{2}(2l+1)\zeta]$ the eigenvalues are approximately

$$E(nlm\pm) \to E^0(nl) \pm \tfrac{1}{2}\zeta[l + \tfrac{1}{2} \mp \tfrac{1}{2}] + m\beta H_z \left(\frac{2l+1+1}{2l+1}\right), \tag{2.18}$$

whereas for large fields $[\beta H_z \gg \frac{1}{2}(2l+1)\zeta]$ the eigenvalues approach the values

$$E(nlm\pm) \to E^0(nl) + \beta H_z(m \pm \tfrac{1}{2}) \pm \tfrac{1}{2}\zeta(m \pm \tfrac{1}{2}). \tag{2.19}$$

When the interaction $\mathcal{V}_{\text{stat}}$ dominates the spin–orbit interaction, we can again apply perturbation theory. We now use basis states labeled by SM_SLM_L In this scheme the static interaction has the matrix elements

$$\begin{aligned}\langle\alpha' S' M_S' L\, M_L' | \mathcal{V}_{\text{stat}} | \alpha S M_S L M_L\rangle &= \beta H_z \langle \alpha' S' M_S' L' M_L' | L_z + 2S_z | \alpha S M_S L M_L\rangle \\ &= \beta H_z \delta(\alpha, \alpha')\delta(S, S')\delta(M_S, M_S')\delta(L, L')\delta(M_L, M_L')(M_L + 2M_S),\end{aligned} \tag{2.20}$$

and the spin–orbit interaction has the elements

$$\langle\alpha' S' M_S' L' M_L' | \mathcal{V}_{\text{spin}} | \alpha S M_S L M_L\rangle = \sum_i \zeta(i) \langle \alpha' S' M_S' L' M_L' | \mathbf{s}(i)\cdot\mathbf{l}(i) | \alpha S M_S L M_L\rangle. \tag{2.21}$$

The angular part of this expression is

$$\frac{\langle\alpha' S' \| \mathbf{s}(i) \| \alpha S\rangle}{\sqrt{2S'+1}} \frac{\langle \alpha' L' \| \mathbf{l}(i) \| \alpha L\rangle}{\sqrt{2L'+1}} (-1)^q (LM_L, 1q | L'M_L')(SM_S, 1-q | S'M_S'). \tag{2.22}$$

Thus the states labeled by $M_S M_L$ mix with the states $(M_S - 1)(M_L + 1)$ and $(M_S + 1)(M_L - 1)$. The angular matrix elements with $S'L' = SL$ are

$$M_SM_L \rightarrow (M_S - 1)(M_L + 1):$$

$$\tfrac{1}{2}\sqrt{(L + 1 + M_L)(L - M_L)}\,\sqrt{(S + 1 - M_S)(S + M_S)}$$

$$M_SM_L \rightarrow M_SM_L\colon\ M_SM_L \tag{2.23}$$

$$M_SM_L \rightarrow (M_S + 1)(M_L - 1):$$

$$\tfrac{1}{2}\sqrt{(L + 1 - M_L)(L + M_L)}\,\sqrt{(S + 1 + M_S)(S - M_S)},$$

all multiplied by the factor

$$\sum_i \zeta(i)\,\frac{\langle \alpha S \| \mathbf{s}(i) \| \alpha S\rangle}{\sqrt{S(S + 1)(2S + 1)}}\,\frac{\langle \alpha L \| \mathbf{l}(i) \| \alpha L\rangle}{\sqrt{L(L + 1)(2L + 1)}}.$$

With these basis states, perturbation theory gives the energy to first order as

$$\begin{aligned}
E(\alpha SM_SLM_L) &= E^0(\alpha SL) + \langle \alpha SM_SLM_L | \mathcal{V}_{\text{stat}} + \mathcal{V}_{\text{spin}} | \alpha SM_SM_L\rangle \\
&= E^0(\alpha SL) + \beta H_z(M_L + 2M_S) \\
&\quad + M_SM_L \sum_i \zeta(i)\,\frac{\langle \alpha S \| \mathbf{s}(i) \| \alpha S\rangle}{\sqrt{S(S + 1)(2S + 1)}}\,\frac{\langle \alpha L \| \mathbf{l}(i) \| \alpha L\rangle}{\sqrt{L(L + 1)(2L + 1)}}.
\end{aligned} \tag{2.24}$$

When the field is strong enough for this expression to be applicable, we have the *Paschen–Back effect.*

For our example of an atom with one valence electron, the use of wavefunctions $\psi(nlm_lm_s)$ gives the following matrix of $\mathcal{H}$ between wavefunctions having the same value of n, l, and $m = m_l + m_s$:

	$nlm+\frac{1}{2}, -\frac{1}{2}$	$nlm-\frac{1}{2}, +\frac{1}{2}$
$nlm+\frac{1}{2}, -\frac{1}{2}$	$E_{nl} + \beta H_z(m - \frac{1}{2}) - \frac{1}{2}\zeta(m + \frac{1}{2})$	$\frac{1}{2}\zeta\sqrt{(l + \frac{1}{2} - m)(l + \frac{1}{2} + m)}$
$nlm-\frac{1}{2}, +\frac{1}{2}$	$\frac{1}{2}\zeta\sqrt{(l + \frac{1}{2} - m)(l + \frac{1}{2} + m)}$	$E_{nl} + \beta H_z(m + \frac{1}{2}) + \frac{1}{2}\zeta(m - \frac{1}{2})$

The eigenvalues of this matrix are again the values given in (2.17)–(2.19).

If we examine the spectra of atoms placed in increasingly intense magnetic fields, we observe a gradual change in the appearance of the spectral lines. In weak fields we observe lines with the wavenumbers

$$\begin{aligned}\tilde{\nu} &= \frac{E(\alpha SLJM) - E(\alpha' S' L' J' M')}{hc} \\ &= \tilde{\nu}_0 + \frac{\beta}{hc} H_z(Mg - M'g') \\ &= \tilde{\nu}_0 + \frac{\beta H_z}{hc}(M\,\Delta g - g'\,\Delta M),\end{aligned} \tag{2.25}$$

where $\tilde{\nu}_0$ denotes the wavenumber in the absence of a field:

$$\tilde{\nu}_0 = \frac{E^1(\alpha SLJ) - E^1(\alpha' S' L' J')}{hc}, \tag{2.26}$$

and where

$$\Delta g = g - g'; \quad \Delta M = M - M'.$$

With increasing intensity of the static field, the Zeeman components spread further apart and the splitting of levels ceases to vary linearly with field intensity. Furthermore, the relative intensity of the individual components changes because the field introduces mixing of wavefunctions having different J values.

Neither spin nor M_S change during an ordinary ("allowed" or $\mathcal{E}1$) transition. Thus when the field becomes sufficiently strong to dominate the spin–orbit effect we observe the pattern

$$\begin{aligned}\tilde{\nu} &= \frac{E(\alpha SM_SLM_L) - E(\alpha' SM_SL'M_L)}{hc} \\ &= \tilde{\nu}_{00} + \frac{\beta H_z}{hc}\,\Delta M_L,\end{aligned} \tag{2.27}$$

where $\tilde{\nu}_{00}$ denotes the wavenumber separation between the spectroscopic term values,

$$\tilde{\nu}_{00} = \frac{E^0(\alpha SL) - E^0(\alpha SL')}{hc}, \tag{2.28}$$

and where

$$\Delta M_L \equiv M_L - M_L' = +1, 0, -1.$$

This splitting of lines, linearly proportional to the magnetic field, is the Zeeman effect. When $g = g'$, the pattern consists of three lines, known as a Lorentz triplet, spaced at energy intervals of $g\beta H_z$. The Zeeman effect is sometimes categorized as the so-called *normal Zeeman effect* when $g = g' = 1$, and the so-called *anomalous Zeeman effect* when $g \neq 1$ and $g' \neq 1$.

Like the "normal" Zeeman effect, the Paschen–Back effect appears as a splitting of a spectral line into three components. The splitting is proportional to the magnetic field intensity.

The distinction between weak fields (Zeeman effect) and strong fields (Paschen–Back effect) depends upon which levels are disturbed. For example, consider the lowest $^2P^\circ$ levels of sodium and lithium. In sodium, the fine-structure splitting $^2P^\circ_{3/2}$–$^2P^\circ_{1/2}$ is 17.18 cm^{-1}, whereas in lithium this splitting is 0.34 cm^{-1}. The g factor for $^2P_{3/2}$ is $\frac{4}{3}$, so that the splitting factor $\beta g H_z/hc$ is $4.66858 \times \frac{4}{3}$ $cm^{-1} = 6.2$ cm^{-1} for a field of 10^5 G. This is a large effect for lithium, yet a small effect for sodium.

Once we know the g values for two levels, we can immediately calculate the relative spacing of the Zeeman components of the spectral line. According to (2.25) the components are spaced

$$M\,\Delta g - g'\,\Delta M$$

Lorentz units from the undisplaced line. Thus we observe the components $\Delta M = \pm 1$ at a spacing of

$$M\,\Delta g \pm g'$$

and the components $\Delta M = 0$ at

$$M\,\Delta g.$$

The pattern is symmetrical about the position of the undisturbed line. For example, consider the transition $^2S_{1/2} \rightarrow {}^2P^\circ_{3/2}$, for which $J = \frac{1}{2}$, $g = 2$, and $J' = \frac{3}{2}$, $g' = \frac{4}{3}$. The components are spaced at

$$\begin{aligned} \tfrac{3}{3}, \tfrac{5}{3} \quad &\text{for} \quad \Delta M = \pm 1 \\ \tfrac{1}{3}, -\tfrac{1}{3} \quad &\text{for} \quad \Delta M = 0 \\ -\tfrac{3}{3}, -\tfrac{5}{3} \quad &\text{for} \quad \Delta M = -1. \end{aligned}$$

This example is summarized with the *Back–Landé symbol:*

$$\frac{(1)3,\ 5}{3}.$$

This symbol gives the spacing of lines, in Lorentz units $\beta H_z/hc$, away from the undisplaced position $\tilde{\nu}_0$. Parentheses here enclose the $\Delta M = 0$ components. (Further discussion of the Back–Landé symbol occurs in the following paragraphs.)

Although the number of Zeeman components and their relative spacing depend only on the properties of the two levels involved in the transition (the number of components depends only on J and J'; the spacing depends on SLJ and $S'L'J'$), the polarization and relative intensities also depend upon the viewing angle and the type of radiation, that is, the multipole type. Polarization expresses the direction of the electric vector **E** (which is also the direction of the vector potential **A**), whereas intensity is proportional to the magnitude $|\mathbf{E}|^2$. For pure multipole radiation, the electric vector is

$$\begin{aligned}\mathbf{E} &= \sqrt{2\pi\hbar\omega}\,\boldsymbol{\Sigma}_q^{(1)} \quad \text{for} \quad \mathcal{E}1 \\ &= \sqrt{2\pi\hbar\omega}\,\mathbf{\Pi}_q^{(1)} \quad \text{for} \quad \mathcal{M}1 \\ &= \sqrt{2\pi\hbar\omega}\,\boldsymbol{\Sigma}_q^{(2)} \quad \text{for} \quad \mathcal{E}2,\end{aligned}$$

where $q = \Delta M$ is fixed by the particular component considered. Table 11.1 displays these polarization directions for the common multipoles $\mathcal{E}1$, $\mathcal{M}1$, and $\mathcal{E}2$. Conventionally, π *components* are those polarized parallel to the field (the θ direction), and σ *components* are those polarized perpendicular to the field (the ϕ direction). The fields $\boldsymbol{\Sigma}_q^{(l)}$ and $\mathbf{\Pi}_q^{(l)}$ apply to photon absorption, while $\boldsymbol{\Sigma}_q^{(l)*}$ and $\mathbf{\Pi}_q^{(l)*}$ apply to emission.

Table 11.1 shows that, for longitudinal viewing (i.e., along the field), only the $\Delta M = \pm 1$ components appear, and these are always circularly polarized. Thus longitudinal observations do not distinguish multipole type.

Table 11.1 Multipole Zeeman-Component Polarizations

		Transverse ($\theta = 90°$)	Diagonal ($\theta = 45°$)	Longitudinal ($\theta = 0°$)
Electric	$\Delta M = 0$	π	π	—
dipole ($\mathcal{E}1$)	$\Delta M = \pm 1$	σ	r, l elliptical	r, l circular
Magnetic	$\Delta M = 0$	σ	σ	—
dipole ($\mathcal{M}1$)	$\Delta M = \pm 1$	π	r, l elliptical	r, l circular
Electric	$\Delta M = 0$	—	π	—
quadrupole ($\mathcal{E}2$)	$\Delta M = \pm 1$	π	r, l elliptical	r, l circular
	$\Delta M = \pm 2$	σ	r, l elliptical	—

Note: θ is angle from magnetic axis; π components = parallel to field (θ direction); σ components = perpendicular to field (φ direction); r, l refer to right and left elliptical or circular; — denotes zero intensity.

Viewing transversely, we shall see all components of the dipole radiation, but the $\Delta M = 0$ quadrupole components will be missing. The components have opposite polarizations for $\mathcal{E}1$ and $\mathfrak{M}1$ radiation. With $\mathcal{E}1$ transitions, the central components ($\Delta M = 0$) are polarized parallel to the field. With $\mathfrak{M}1$ transitions, the central components are polarized perpendicular to the field. This distinction shows up quite dramatically in polarization photographs of the Zeeman pattern.

The angular distribution of magnetic-dipole radiation is identical with that of electric-dipole radiation, so that the Zeeman pattern for $\mathfrak{M}1$ transitions are given by these same equations. However, because the $\mathbf{\Pi}_q^{(1)}$ and $\Sigma_q^{(1)}$ fields are perpendicular, the $\mathfrak{M}1$ Zeeman components have *opposite polarizations*. For $\mathfrak{M}1$ radiation, the $\Delta M = 0$ transitions are σ components (i.e., polarization in the θ direction), and the $\Delta M = \pm 1$ transitions are π components.

The electric-quadrupole field $\Sigma_{\pm 1}^{(2)}$ vanishes in the transverse direction, so that transverse observations of "forbidden" $\Delta M = \pm 1$ transitions disclose only the magnetic-dipole contribution.

If the radiation arises from spontaneous emission of a pure multipole from an optically thin source, the intensity observed at an angle θ is proportional to the product of the field intensity

$$|\Sigma_q^{(\lambda)}|^2 \qquad \text{or} \qquad |\mathbf{\Pi}_q^{(\lambda)}|^2,$$

the spontaneous emission probability

$$w(\alpha JM \rightarrow \alpha' J' M'),$$

and the density of atoms in the upper sublevels αJM. In typical laboratory sources, the sublevels are populated equally so that only the atomic transition probability and the multipole field intensity need be considered. For dipole transitions ($\mathcal{E}1$ or $\mathfrak{M}1$), the field intensity pattern $I_{\lambda q}(\theta)$ is

$$\begin{aligned} I_{10}(\theta) &= \frac{3}{8\pi} \sin^2 \theta \\ I_{1\pm 1}(\theta) &= \frac{3}{8\pi} \frac{(1 + \cos^2 \theta)}{2}, \end{aligned} \tag{2.29}$$

and for $\mathcal{E}1$ transitions the spontaneous emission probability is

$$\begin{aligned} w_{\mathcal{E}1}(\alpha JM \rightarrow \alpha' J' M') &= \frac{4}{3} \frac{k^3}{\hbar} |\langle \alpha' J' M' | \mathbf{Q}^{(1)} | \alpha JM \rangle|^2 \\ &= \frac{4}{3} \frac{k^3}{\hbar} \mathbf{S}(J, J') \frac{(JM, 1q | J'M')^2}{(2J' + 1)}. \end{aligned} \tag{2.30}$$

Thus the relative intensities of Zeeman components for pure $\mathcal{E}1$ transitions are given by

$$I_{1q}(\theta) \times \frac{(JM, 1q|J'M')^2}{(2J'+1)} \times \mathbf{S}(J, J'). \tag{2.31}$$

For transition $J \rightarrow J$ the pattern is

$$\frac{3}{8\pi}\frac{\mathbf{S}(J, J')}{2J+1} \times \begin{cases} \sin^2\theta \dfrac{M^2}{J(J+1)} & \text{for} \quad \Delta M = 0 \\ \dfrac{(1+\cos^2\theta)}{2}\dfrac{(J \pm M)(J+1 \mp M)}{2J(J+1)} & \text{for} \quad \Delta M = \pm 1, \end{cases} \tag{2.32}$$

and for transition $J \rightarrow J - 1$ it is

$$\frac{3}{8\pi}\frac{\mathbf{S}(J, J-1)}{2J+1} \times \begin{cases} \sin^2\theta\,(J^2 - M^2) & \text{for} \quad \Delta M = 0 \\ \dfrac{(1+\cos^2\theta)}{2}\dfrac{(J \mp M)(J+1 \pm M)}{2J(J+1)} & \text{for} \quad \Delta M = \pm 1. \end{cases} \tag{2.33}$$

[For $J \rightarrow J + 1$ transitions, write $\mathbf{S}(J, J+1)$ and change the signs of $\pm M$.]

Pure $\mathfrak{M}1$ radiation follows this same pattern (but with opposite polarization) with $\mathbf{S}(J, J')$ taken to be the magnetic-dipole transition strength. Pure $\mathcal{E}2$ radiation follows the pattern

$$I_{2q}(\theta) \times \frac{(JM, 2q|J'M')^2}{(2J'+1)} \times \mathbf{S}_Q(J, J') \tag{2.34}$$

The theoretical Zeeman patterns for pure multipole transitions were first worked out by Rubinowitz [2], Huff and Houston [3], and Milianczuk [4] Observations of these effects provided the first confirmation of $\mathcal{E}2$ and $\mathfrak{M}1$ radiation: see Frerichs and Campbell [5], Segré and Bakker [6], Niewodniczanski [7], and Jenkins and Mrozowski [8]. However, many forbidden transitions are mixtures of $\mathfrak{M}1$ and $\mathcal{E}2$ transitions, as noted by Shortley et al. [9]. In such transitions, *amplitudes* rather than intensities must be added. This coherence gives rise to interference between $\mathfrak{M}1$ and $\mathcal{E}2$ radiation. Such interference has been discussed by Gerjouy [10] and observed by Jenkins and Mrozowski [11].

Laboratory Zeeman-effect studies are nearly always confined to transverse observations because (for dipole transition) all the Zeeman components are visible there and they are linearly polarized. The Back–Landé symbol conventionally denotes by parentheses the π-components ($\Delta M = 0$ for $\mathcal{E}1$, and $\Delta M = \pm 1$ for $\mathfrak{M}1$). Thus for the $\mathcal{E}1$ transition $^3P_1 \rightarrow {}^3P_0{}^\circ$ we have the (transverse) pattern

$$\frac{(0)3}{2}.$$

For the pure $\mathfrak{M}1$ transition $^3P_1 \rightarrow {}^3P_0$ (both levels with even parity), the transverse pattern is written

$$\frac{0(3)}{2}.$$

To observe all the components in quadrupole radiation, we must view diagonally. For example, a $^2D_{5/2} \rightarrow {}^2S_{1/2}$ transition has the pattern

$$\frac{(4, 8)10, 14}{5} \qquad \text{transverse}$$

$$\frac{(2)4, 8 \cdot [10, 14]}{5} \qquad \text{diagonal } (45^\circ)$$

where ( ) encloses the π components and [ ] encloses components that are elliptically polarized.

Table 11.2 Basic Zeeman Patterns[a]

J	g	Even Multiplicity	Odd Multiplicity
$J > J'$	$g < g'$		
$J > J'$	$g > g'$	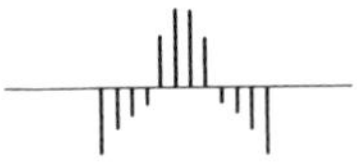	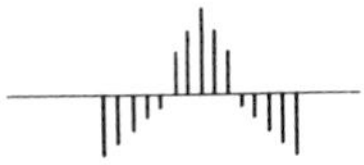
$J = J'$	$g \neq g'$		
{Arbitrary / $J = 0$}	{$g = g'$ / Arbitrary}	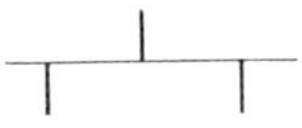	

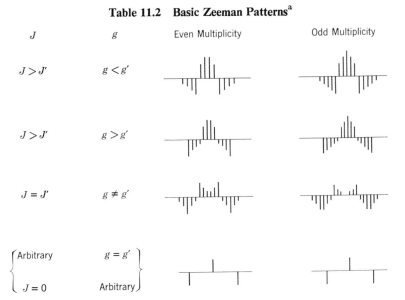

[a] Transverse view of dipole transitions. For $\mathcal{E}1$, central components have π polarization; for $\mathfrak{M}1$, central components have σ polarization.

The theory of the Zeeman effect was widely studied during the 1920's. The book by Back and Landé [12] presents the theory as then formulated. Back and Landé found that the ordinary Zeeman patterns (of $\mathcal{E}1$ radiation viewed transversely) comprised seven basic types. Table 11.2, from Meggers [13], shows these basic patterns. More complete tables were given by Kiess and Meggers [14].

Discussions of the Zeeman effect will be found in the reviews by White [15] and van den Bosch [16], and in standard works on atomic spectra. For more recent work, see Abragam and Van Vleck [17], and Judd and Lindgren [18].

REFERENCES

[1] For example, W. C. Martin and J. L. Tech, *J. Opt. Soc. Am.* **51,** 591 (1961).
[2] A. Rubinowicz, *Z. Physik* **53,** 267 (1929); A. Rubinowicz and J. Blaton, *Ergeb. Exact. Naturw.* **2,** 176 (1932).
[3] L. D. Huff and W. V. Houston, *Phys. Rev.* **36,** 842 (1930).
[4] B. Milianczuk, *Z. Physik* **74,** 825 (1932).
[5] R. Frerichs and J. S. Campbell, *Phys. Rev.* **36,** 151 (1930).
[6] E. Segré and C. J. Bakker, *Z. Physik.* **72,** 724 (1931).
[7] H. Niewodniczanski, *Acta Phys. Polonica* **5,** 111 (1936).
[8] F. A. Jenkins and S. Mrozowski, *Phys. Rev.* **59,** 808 (1941).
[9] G. H. Shortley, L. H. Aller, J. G. Baker, and D. H. Menzel, *Astrophys. J.* **93,** 178 (1941).
[10] E. Gerjouy, *Phys. Rev.* **60,** 233 (1941).
[11] F. A. Jenkins and S. Mrozowski, *Phys. Rev.* **60,** 225 (1941).
[12] E. Back and A. Landé, *Zeeman Effekt und Multipletstruktur der Spektrallinien,* Springer, Berlin (1925).
[13] W. F. Meggers, Zeeman Effect, *Encyclopaedia Brittanica* **23,** 940 (1953).
[14] C. C. Kiess and W. F. Meggers, *J. Res. Natl. Bur. Stds.* **1,** 641 (1928).
[15] H. E. White, *Rept. Progr. Phys.* **6,** 145 (1939).
[16] J. C. van den Bosch, *Handbuch der Physik* **28,** 296 (1957).
[17] A. Abragam and J. H. Van Vleck, *Phys. Rev.* **92,** 1448 (1953).
[18] B. Judd and I. Lindgren, *Phys. Rev.* **122,** 1802 (1961).

11.3 UNIFORM ELECTRIC FIELD

The interaction between a uniform static electric field **E** and an atom is governed by the expression

$$\mathcal{V}_{\text{stat}} = -\sum_i e_i \mathbf{r}(i) \cdot \mathbf{E}, \tag{3.1}$$

where the sum goes over all the particles. Since the dipole moment of the atom is

$$\mathbf{Q}^{(1)} = \sum_i e_i \mathbf{r}(i), \tag{3.2}$$

the interaction may also be written

$$\mathcal{V}_{\text{stat}} = -\mathbf{Q}^{(1)} \cdot \mathbf{E}. \tag{3.3}$$

For convenience, we take the $\mathbf{E}$ direction as the z axis, and write (with atomic units $e = m = \hbar = 1$)

$$\mathcal{V}_{\text{stat}} = -|\mathbf{E}| \sum_i z(i), \tag{3.4}$$

Electric fields are commonly expressed in units of volts per centimeter; an energy of 1 eV requires an electric field of some 1.9×10^8 V/cm for z of one Bohr radius.

The operator $\mathbf{Q}^{(1)}$ has matrix elements only between states of opposite parity. It has no diagonal elements within a configuration. Therefore if states with opposite parity are well separated in energy, we may obtain the effect of a weak electric field from second-order perturbation theory:

$$E(\alpha JM) = E^0(\alpha J) + |\mathbf{E}|^2 \sum_{\bar{\alpha}\bar{J}} \frac{|\langle \bar{\alpha}\bar{J}M | Q_0^{(1)} | \alpha JM \rangle|^2}{E(\alpha J) - E(\bar{\alpha}\bar{J})} \tag{3.5}$$

$$\Psi(\alpha JM) = \psi(\alpha JM) + |\mathbf{E}| \sum_{\bar{\alpha}\bar{J}} \psi(\bar{\alpha}\bar{J}M) \frac{\langle \bar{\alpha}\bar{J}M | Q_0^{(1)} | \alpha JM \rangle}{E(\alpha J) - E(\bar{\alpha}\bar{J})}. \tag{3.6}$$

With the application of the Wigner–Eckart theorem, these expressions may be written

$$E(\alpha JM) = E^0(\alpha J) + |\mathbf{E}|^2 \Bigg\{ [(J+1)a_{J+1} + Ja_{J-1}] - M^2 \left[\frac{Ja_{J+1} - (2J+1)a_J + (J+1)a_{J+1}}{J(J+1)} \right] \Bigg\} \tag{3.7}$$

$$\begin{aligned} \Psi(\alpha JM) = \psi(\alpha JM) + |\mathbf{E}| \sum_{\bar{\alpha}} \Bigg\{ & \psi(\bar{\alpha}\, J+1\ M) \frac{\sqrt{(J+1)^2 - M^2}}{\sqrt{(J+1)(2J+1)}} b_{J+1} \\ & + \psi(\bar{\alpha} JM) \frac{M}{\sqrt{J(J+1)}} b_J \\ & - \psi(\bar{\alpha}\, J-1\ M) \frac{\sqrt{J^2 - M^2}}{\sqrt{J(2J+1)}} b_{J-1} \Bigg\}, \end{aligned} \tag{3.8}$$

where

$$a = \frac{1}{(2J+1)(2\bar{J}+1)} \sum_{\bar{\alpha}} \frac{|\langle \bar{\alpha}\bar{J} \| \mathbf{Q}^{(1)} \| \alpha J \rangle|^2}{E_{\alpha J} - E_{\bar{\alpha}\bar{J}}}, \tag{3.9}$$

$$b_{\bar{J}} = \frac{1}{\sqrt{2\bar{J}+1}} \frac{\langle \bar{\alpha}\bar{J} \| \mathbf{Q}^{(1)} \| \alpha J \rangle}{E_{\alpha J} - E_{\bar{\alpha}\bar{J}}} \tag{3.10}$$

When the field becomes so strong that the Stark splitting greatly exceeds the term separation (or when the terms are degenerate, as they are in the nonrelativistic hydrogen atom) we can no longer use states with well-defined orbital angular momentum (L or l) as the zero-order states. We must either introduce a new operator to replace $\mathbf{L}^2$ or, retaining our eigenstates of $\mathbf{L}^2$, we must diagonalize the matrix of $\mathcal{V}_{\text{stat}}$ between degenerate states. For example, consider the nonrelativistic hydrogen atom and the Hamiltonian

$$\mathcal{H} = \mathcal{H}^0 + \mathcal{V}_{\text{Coul}} + \mathcal{V}_{\text{stat}}. \tag{3.11}$$

Using eigenstates labeled by nlm_lm_s, we require the matrix elements

$$\langle n'l'm_l'm_s' | \mathcal{V}_{\text{stat}} | nlm_lm_s \rangle = \delta(m_l, m_{l'})\delta(m_s, m_{s'}) |\mathbf{E}| \langle n'l'm_l' | z | nlm_l \rangle. \tag{3.12}$$

The elements between states which have the same n are

$$\langle nl'm_l | z | nlm_l \rangle = \frac{(lm_l, 10 | l'm_l)}{\sqrt{2l'+1}} \langle l' \| \mathbf{C}^{(1)} \| l \rangle \int R_{nl} R_{nl'} r^3 \, dr. \tag{3.13}$$

These elements vanish unless $l' = l \pm 1$, when we use

$$\frac{(lm_l, 10 | l'm_l)}{\sqrt{2l'+1}} = (-1)^{l-l_>} \frac{\sqrt{l_>^2 - m_l^2}}{\sqrt{l_>}\sqrt{4l_>^2 - 1}}. \tag{3.14}$$

$$\langle l' \| \mathbf{C}^{(1)} \| l \rangle = (-1)^{l-l_>} \sqrt{l_>}, \tag{3.15}$$

$$\int R_{nl} R_{nl'} r^3 \, dr = -\frac{3}{2} n \sqrt{n - l_>^2} \frac{a_l}{Z}, \tag{3.16}$$

where $l_>$ denotes the larger of l, l'. Thus the required matrix elements are

$$\langle nl'm_lm_s | \mathcal{V}_{\text{stat}} | nlm_lm_s \rangle = -\frac{3}{2} \frac{n}{Z} \sqrt{n^2 - l_>^2} \left(\frac{l_>^2 - m_l^2}{4l_>^2 - 1} \right)^{1/2} |\mathbf{E}|. \tag{3.17}$$

When we diagonalize this matrix, we obtain the appropriate zero-order states for a uniform field along the axis. As an example, the zero-order states for $n = 2$, with their first-order energies, are [with the notation $\psi(nl\, m_l\, m_s)$]

$$\frac{1}{\sqrt{2}} [\psi(2p\, 0\, m_s) + \psi(2s\, 0\, m_s)]: \quad E = -\frac{Z^2}{4} + 3\frac{|\mathbf{E}|}{Z}$$

$$\psi(2p\ 1\ m_s): \qquad E = -\frac{Z^2}{4}$$

$$\psi(2p\ -1\ m_s): \qquad E = -\frac{Z^2}{4}$$

$$\frac{1}{\sqrt{2}}[\psi(2p\ 0\ m_s) - \psi(2s\ 0\ m_s)]: \quad E = -\frac{Z^2}{4} - 3\frac{|\mathbf{E}|}{Z}.$$

This approach was carried through by Schlapp [1] in 1928, who found the general first-order expression

$$E(nk) = -\frac{Z^2}{n^2} + \frac{3}{2}\frac{n}{Z}k|\mathbf{E}| \tag{3.18}$$

where k, the *electric quantum number*, takes the values

$$k = 0, \pm 1, \pm 2, \ldots, \pm(n-1).$$

The *linear Stark effect* found here for hydrogen contrasts with the *quadratic Stark effect* which occurs when there is a large energy difference between spectroscopic terms of opposite parity. In the linear effect the pattern of Stark levels has an energy width of

$$3\frac{n}{Z}(n-1)|\mathbf{E}|. \tag{3.19}$$

The width of the pattern grows as n^2, so that Stark splitting of a spectral line largely reflects the splitting of the upper energy level.

An alternative approach, first used by Schrödinger [2] and by Epstein [3] in 1926, uses parabolic coordinates

$$\xi = r + z, \qquad \eta = r - z, \qquad \phi = \tan^{-1}\left(\frac{y}{x}\right)$$

to write the Schrödinger equation. The hydrogenic wavefunction takes the form

$$\psi(n_1 n_2 m|\xi\eta\phi) = e^{-(\xi+\eta)/2n}\sqrt{\xi^m\eta^m}\,u_{n_1}(\xi)v_{n_2}(\eta)\frac{e^{im\phi}}{\sqrt{2\pi}}, \tag{3.20}$$

where $u_n(x)$ and $v_n(x)$ are polynomials in x, and the principal quantum number is

$$n = n_1 + n_2 + |m| + 1.$$

Application of perturbation theory then yields the energy of a hydrogenic ion in a uniform electric field, to third order, as [4]

$$E(nkm) = -\frac{1}{2}\frac{Z^2}{n^2} + \frac{3}{2}\frac{n}{Z}k|\mathbf{E}| - \frac{1}{16}\left(\frac{n}{Z}\right)^4 [17n^2 - 3k^2 - 9m^2 + 19] \times |\mathbf{E}|^2 + \frac{3}{32}\left(\frac{n}{Z}\right)^7 k[23n^2 - k^2 + 11m^2 + 39] \times |\mathbf{E}|^3 \quad (3.21)$$

where $k = n_1 - n_2$ is, as above, the electric quantum number. The transformation between Stark states and angular-momentum states has been noted by Flamand [5] (see also Stone [6] and Hughes [7]):

$$\psi(nkm) = \sum_l (\lambda m_1, \lambda m_2 | lm)\psi(nlm)$$

where

$$\lambda = \tfrac{1}{2}(n-1), \qquad m_1 = \tfrac{1}{2}(m-k), \qquad m_2 = \tfrac{1}{2}(m+k)$$
$$n = 2\lambda + 1, \qquad k = n_1 - n_2 \qquad m = m_1 + m_2.$$

Because of the degeneracy of states with the same value of $|M|$, the intensities of Stark components of spectral lines are proportional to

$$\frac{3}{8\pi}\sin^2\theta \frac{\mathbf{S}(J, J')}{(2J'+1)} \cdot [(JM, 1\,0|J'M')^2 + (J\,-M, 1\,0|J'\,-M)^2] \quad (3.22)$$

for $\Delta M = 0$, and

$$\frac{3}{8\pi}\frac{(1+\cos^2\theta)}{2}\frac{\mathbf{S}(J, J')}{(2J'+1)} \cdot [(JM, 1\,1|J'M')^2 + (J\,-M, 1\,-1|J'\,-M')^2] \quad (3.23)$$

for $\Delta M = \pm 1$. Specifically, the relative intensities are, for $J \rightarrow J = 1$,

$$\frac{3}{4\pi}\frac{\mathbf{S}(J, J-1)}{(2J+1)}\begin{cases} \dfrac{1+\cos^2\theta}{2}\dfrac{J(J+1)+M^2}{2J(2J+1)} & \text{for} \quad \Delta M = \pm 1 \\ \sin^2\theta \dfrac{[J^2 - M^2]}{J(2J+1)} & \text{for} \quad \Delta M = 0, \end{cases} \quad (3.23)$$

and for transitions $J \rightarrow J$ they are

$$\frac{3}{4\pi}\frac{\mathbf{S}(J, J)}{(2J+1)}\begin{cases} \dfrac{1+\cos^2\theta}{2}\dfrac{J(J+1)-M^2}{2J(J+1)} & \text{for} \quad \Delta M = \pm 1 \\ \sin^2\theta \dfrac{M^2}{J(J+1)} & \text{for} \quad \Delta M = 0. \end{cases} \quad (3.24)$$

The intensity pattern of the $\Delta M = 0$ components is identical with the pattern seen with the Zeeman effect. The pattern for the $\Delta M = \pm 1$ components is the sum of intensities for two opposite polarizations, so the $\Delta M = \pm 1$ components appear linearly polarized at $\theta = 90°$ (transverse) and unpolarized at $\theta = 0$ (longitudinal).

REFERENCES

[1] R. Schlapp, *Proc. Roy. Soc.* (London) **119,** 313 (1928).
[2] E. Schrödinger, *Ann. Phys.* (Leipzig) **80,** 437 (1926).
[3] P. S. Epstein, *Phys. Rev.* **28,** 695 (1926).
[4] H. Bethe and E. E. Salpeter, *Quantum Mechanics of One- and Two- Electron Atoms,* Academic, New York (1957), p. 233.
[5] G. Flamand, *J. Math. Phys.* **7,** 1924 (1966).
[6] A. P. Stone, *Proc. Camb. Phil. Soc.* **52,** 424 (1956).
[7] J. W. B. Hughes, *Proc. Phys. Soc.*, **91,** 810 (1967).

Bibliography

1. TABLES AND ATLASES OF SPECTRAL LINES

Brode, W. R., *Chemical Spectroscopy*, Wiley, New York (1943), 2nd ed.

Eder, J. M., and E. Valenta, *Beitrage zur Photochemie und Spektalanalyse*, Halle (1904).

Eder, J. M., and E. Valenta, *Atlas Typischer Spectren*, Hölder, Wien (1911).

Exner, F., and E. Haschek, *Uber die Ultravioleten Funkenspectra der Elemente*, Sitzungsberichten der kaiserl. Akademie der Wissenschaften in Wien (1895–1901).

Gatterer, A., *Grating Spectrum of Iron*, Specola Vaticana (1951).

Gatterer, A., and J. Junkes, *Atlas der Restlinien*, Specola Vaticana: I Band (1947); II Band (1959); III Band (1949).

Gray, D. (ed.), *American Institute of Physics Handbook*, McGraw-Hill, New York (1963), 2nd ed.

Hagenbach, A., and H. Konen, *Atlas of Emission Spectra of Most of the Elements* (transl. by A. S. King), Wesley, London (1905).

Harrison, G. R. (ed.), *M.I.T. Wavelength Tables*, Wiley, New York (1939).

International Astronomical Union, *Transactions* (triennial) (see especially Commission 14).

Junkes, J., and E. W. Salpeter, *Spectrum of Thorium*, Specola Vaticana (1964).

Junkes, J., and E. W. Salpeter, *Atomic Spectra in the Vacuum Ultraviolet*, Part One, Specola Vaticana (1965).

Kayser, H., *Tabelle der Hauptlinien der Linienspektren aller Elements*, Springer, Berlin (1926); Hilger, London (1939).

Kayser, H., and C. Runge, *Die Spectren der Elemente*, Königl. Akademie der Wissenschaften, Berlin (1888–1894).

Kuba, J., L. Kučera, F. Plzāk, M. Dvořak, and J. Mráz, *Coincidence Tables for Atomic Spectroscopy*, Elsevier, Amsterdam (1965).

Lundegårdh, M., *Die quantitative Spektralanalyse der Elemente*, Gustav Fischer, Jena (1929).

Merrill, P. W., *Lines of the Chemical Elements in Astronomical Spectra*, Carnegie Institution of Washington Publ. 610, Washington, D. C. (1956).

Moore, C. E., *A Multiplet Table of Astrophysical Interest*, U. S. National Bureau of Standards Technical Note 36 (1959).

Moore, C. E., *An Ultraviolet Multiplet Table*, U. S. National Bureau of Standards Circular

488: Section 1, H to V (1950); Section 2, Cr to Nb (1952); Section 3, Mo to La (1961); Section 4, Finding List for Sections 1 and 2 (1961); Section 5, Finding List for Section 3 (1961).

Moore, C. E., M. G. J. Minnaert, and J. Houtgast, *The Solar Spectrum 2935 Å to 8770 Å*, National Bureau of Standards Monograph 61 (1966).

Rowland, H. A., *Preliminary Table of Solar Spectrum Wavelengths*, University of Chicago Press, Chicago (1896).

Stanley, E., *Lines in the Arc Spectra of Elements*, Hilger, London (1911).

Twyman, F., and D. M. Smith, *Wavelength Tables for Spectrum Analysis*, Hilger, London (1931), 2nd ed.

W. L. Wiese, M. W. Smith, and B. M. Glennon, *Atomic Transition Probabilities Volume I: Hydrogen Through Neon*. National Standard Reference Data Series, NSRDS-NBS 4 (1966).

Zaidel', A. N., V. K. Prokof'ev, and S. M. Raiskii, *Tables of Spectrum Lines*, Pergamon, New York (1961) (reprint of Harrison's tables).

2. EXPERIMENTAL SPECTROSCOPY

Ahrens, L. H., and S. R. Taylor, *Spectrochemical Analysis*, Pergamon, New York (1964), 2nd ed.

Baly, E. C. C., *Spectroscopy*, Longmans, Green, London (1924), 2nd ed.

Bauman, R. P., *Absorption Spectroscopy*, Wiley, New York (1962).

Blokhin, N. A., *Methods of X-Ray Spectroscopic Research*, Pergamon, New York (1965).

Brugel, W., *An Introduction to Infrared Spectroscopy*, Wiley, New York (1962).

Burakov, V. S., and A. A. Yankovskii, *Practical Handbook on Spectral Analysis*, Pergamon, New York (1964).

Clark, G. L. (ed.), *The Encyclopedia of Spectroscopy*, Reinhold, New York (1960).

Coblenz, W. W., *Investigations of Infrared Spectra*, Carnegie Institution of Washington Publication 35, Washington, D. C. (1905), Parts I, II; Publication 65 (1906), Parts III, IV.

Dingle, H., *Practical Applications of Spectrum Analysis*, Chapman and Hall, London (1950).

Harrison, G. R., R. C. Lord, and J. R. Loofbourow, *Practical Spectroscopy*, Prentice-Hall, Englewood Cliffs, New Jersey (1948).

Jaffe, H. M., and M. Orchin, *Theory and Applications of Ultraviolet Spectroscopy*, Wiley, New York (1962).

James, R. W., *The Optical Principles of the Diffraction of X-Rays*, Bell, London (1948, 1965).

Kayser, H., and H. Konen, *Handbuch der Spectroscopie*, S. Hirzel, Leipzig: vols. 1–4 (1907); 5 (1910); 6 (1912); 7 (1924).

Landauer, J., *Spectrum Analysis*, Wiley, New York (1898).

Lyman, T., *The Spectroscopy of the Extreme Ultraviolet*, Longmans, Green, New York (1928).

Mavodineanu, R., and H. Boiteux, *L'analyse spectrale quantitative par la flamme*, Masson, Paris (1954).

Roscoe, H., *Spectrum Analysis*, Macmillan, London (1885).

Runge, C., and K. W. Meissner, Spektroskopie, *Handbuch der Astrophysik*, Vol. 1, 214, Springer, Berlin (1933).

Sawyer, R. A., *Experimental Spectroscopy*, Dover, New York (1963), 3rd ed.

Schellen, H., *Spectrum Analysis*, Longmans, Green, London (1872).

Thompson, H. W., *A Course in Chemical Spectroscopy*, Oxford University Press, London (1938).
Townes, C. H., and A. L. Schawlow, *Microwave Spectroscopy*, McGraw-Hill, New York (1955).
Walker, S., and H. Straw, *Spectroscopy*, Macmillan, New York (1962): vol. 1, *Atomic, Microwave, and Radio-Frequency Spectroscopy;* vol. 2, *Ultraviolet, Visible, Infrared, and Raman Spectroscopy.*

3. DESCRIPTIVE SPECTROSCOPY

Brode, W. R., *Chemical Spectroscopy*, Wiley, New York (1943), 2nd ed.
Candler, C., *Atomic Structure and the Vector Model*, Van Nostrand, Princeton, New Jersey (1937, 1964).
Compton, A. H., and S. K. Allison, *X-Rays in Theory and Experiment*, Van Nostrand, New York (1935).
Crawford, M. F., Atomic Spectra, *Reports on Progress in Physics* **3,** 369 (1936).
Dingle, H., *Practical Applications of Spectrum Analysis*, Chapman and Hall, London (1950).
Foster, E. W., Complex Atomic Spectra, *Reports on Progress in Physics* **4,** 319 (1937).
Foote, P., and F. L. Mohler, *Origin of Spectra*, Chemical Catalogue Co., Inc., New York (1922).
Fowler, A., *Report on Series in Line Spectra*, Fleetway, London (1922).
Gibbs, R. C., Line Spectra of the Elements, *Revs. Mod. Phys.* **4,** 278 (1932).
Götze, A. E., Empirical Relations for Energy Levels of Atoms and Ions, *J. Opt. Soc. Am.* **55,** 742 (1965).
Grotrian, W., Gesetzmassigkeit in den Serienspektren, *Handbuch der Astrophysik III*, Springer, Berlin (1930).
Herzberg, G., *Atomic Spectra and Atomic Structure*, Prentice-Hall, Englewood Cliffs, New Jersey (1937); reprinted by Dover, New York (1944).
Hund, F., *Linienspektren und Periodisches System der Elemente*, Springer, Berlin (1927).
Ingram, D. J. E., *Spectroscopy at Radio and Microwave Frequencies*, Butterworth, London (1966).
Kuhn, H. G., *Atomic Spectra*, Academic, New York (1961).
Laporte, O., Theorie der Multiplettspektren, *Handbuch der Astrophysik III*, Springer, Berlin (1930).
Merrill, P. W., *Lines of the Chemical Elements in Astronomical Spectra*, Carnegie Institution of Washington Publication 610, Washington, D. C. (1956).
Paschen, F., and A. Götze, *Seriengesetze der Linienspektren*, Springer, Berlin (1922).
Pauling, L., and S. Goudsmit, *The Structure of Line Spectra*, McGraw-Hill, New York (1930).
Ruark, A. E., and H. C. Urey, *Atoms, Molecules, and Quanta*, Dover, New York (1964), reprint of 1930 edition.
Shenstone, A. G., Atomic Spectra, *Reports on Progress in Physics* **5,** 210 (1938).
Sommerfeld, A., *Atombau und Spectrallinien*, vol. 1, F. Vieweg, Braunschweig (1919, 1924, 1931, 1944, 1949); Ungar (1951).
Sommerfeld, A., *Atomic Structure and Spectral Lines*, vol. 1, Methuen, London (1922, 1929, 1931); Dutton, New York (1934).
Sommerfeld, A., *Atombau und Spectrallinien*, vol. 2, F. Vieweg, Braunschweig (1929, 1939, 1949); Ungar (1951).

Tolansky, S., *Fine Structure in Line Spectra*, Methuen, London (1935).
Varian Associates Staff, *N M R and E P R Spectroscopy*, Pergamon, New York (1960).
Walker, S., and H. Straw, *Spectroscopy*, Macmillan, New York (1962): vol. 1, *Atomic, Microwave, and Radio-Frequency Spectroscopy;* vol. 2, *Ultraviolet, Visible, Infrared, and Raman Spectroscopy.*
White, H. E., *Introduction to Atomic Spectra*, McGraw-Hill, New York (1934).

4. THE BOHR ATOM

d'Abro, A., *The Rise of the New Physics*, Dover, New York (1952).
Bohr, N., *On the Quantum Theory of Line Spectra*, Høst, Copenhagen (1918).
Bohr, N., *The Theory of Spectra and Atomic Constitution*, Cambridge University Press, Cambridge, England (1922).
Born, M., *Atomic Physics*, Blackie and Sons, London (1935, 1937, 1944, 1946, 1951); Hafner, New York (1957, 1962).
Boorse, H. A., and L. Motz, *The World of the Atom*, Basic Books, New York (1966).
Candler, C., *Atomic Spectra and the Vector Model*, Van Nostrand, Princeton, New Jersey (1964).
Darrow, K. K., *The Renaissance of Physics*, Macmillan, New York (1936).
Edlén, B. (ed.), *Proceedings of Rydberg Centennial Conference on Atomic Spectroscopy, Lunds Universitets Arskrift* N. F. Avd. 2, Bd 50, Nr 21, Lund (1955) (cf. especially The Influence of Spectral Series by A. G. Shenstone; Rydberg's Discovery of the Spectral Laws by N. Bohr).
Friedman, F. L., and L. Sartori, *The Classical Atom*, Addison-Wesley, Reading, Mass. (1965).
Hund, F., *Linienspektren und Periodisches System der Elemente*, Springer, Berlin (1927).
Kondratyev, V., *The Structure of Atoms and Molecules*, Dover, New York (1965).
Kramers, H. A., and H. Holst, *The Atom and the Bohr Theory of Its Structure*, Knopf, New York (1923).
Kuhn, H. G., *Atomic Spectra*, Academic, New York (1961).
Pauli, W., Jr. (ed.), *Niels Bohr and the Development of Physics*, McGraw-Hill, New York (1955) (cf. especially The Discovery of Atomic Number by C. G. Darwin; The Development of the Interpretation of the Quantum Theory by W. Heisenberg).
Pauling, L., and S. Goudsmit, *The Structure of Line Spectra*, McGraw-Hill, New York (1930).
Persico, E., *Fundamentals of Quantum Mechanics*, transl. by G. M. Temmer, Prentice-Hall, New York (1950).
Reiche, F., *The Quantum Theory*, Methuen, London (1922).
Richtmyer, F. K., E. H. Kennard, and T. Lauritsen, *Introduction to Modern Physics*, McGraw-Hill, New York (1928, 1934, 1942, 1947, 1955).
Ruark, A. E., and H. C. Urey, *Atoms, Molecules and Quanta*, McGraw-Hill, New York (1930).
Saha, M. N., and N. K. Saha, *A Treatise on Modern Physics*, vol. 1, *Atoms, Molecules and Nuclei*, The Indian Press, Allahabad (1934).
Sommerfeld, A., *Atomic Spectra and Atomic Structure*, Dutton, London (1931, 1934).
Tomonaga, S., *Quantum Mechanics*, vol. I, *Old Quantum Theory*, North-Holland, Amsterdam (1962).
White, H. E., *Introduction to Atomic Spectra*, McGraw-Hill, New York (1934).

5. ATOMIC PHYSICS

Born, M., *Atomic Physics*, Blackie, London (1935, 1937, 1944, 1946, 1951, 1957, 1962).
Darrow, K. K., *The Renaissance of Physics*, Macmillan, New York (1936).
Darrow, K. K., *Introduction to Contemporary Physics*, Van Nostrand, New York (1939).
Eisberg, R. M., *Fundamentals of Modern Physics*, Wiley, New York (1961).
Fano, U., and L. Fano, *Basic Physics of Atoms and Molecules*, Wiley, New York (1959).
Finkelnburg, W., *Structure of Matter*, Springer, Berlin (1964).
Finkelnburg, W., *Atomic Physics*, McGraw-Hill, New York (1950).
French, A. P., *Principles of Modern Physics*, Wiley, New York (1958).
Harnwell, G. P., and J. J. Livingood, *Experimental Atomic Physics*, McGraw-Hill, New York (1933).
Harnwell, G. P., and W. E. Stephens, *Atomic Physics*, McGraw-Hill, New York (1955).
Hochstrasser, R. M., *Behavior of Electrons in Atoms*, Benjamin, New York (1964).
Kondratyev, V., *The Structure of Atoms and Molecules*, Dover, New York (1965).
Kitaigorodsky, A., *Introduction to Physics*, Dover, New York (1965).
Leighton, R. B., *Principles of Modern Physics*, McGraw-Hill, New York (1959).
Melissinos, A. C., *Experiments in Modern Physics*, Academic, New York (1966).
Millikan, R. A., *Electrons (+ and −), Protons, Photons, Neutrons, and Cosmic Rays*, University of Chicago Press, Chicago (1936).
Mitchell, A. C. G., and M. W. Zemansky, *Resonance Radiation and Excited Atoms*, Cambridge University Press, Cambridge, England (1934, 1961).
Oldenberg, O., *Introduction to Atomic Physics*, McGraw-Hill, New York (1949, 1954).
Osgood, T. H., A. E. Ruark, and E. Hutchisson, *Atoms, Radiation, and Nuclei*, Wiley, New York (1964).
Rice, F. O., and E. Teller, *The Structure of Matter*, Wiley, New York (1949).
Richtmyer, F. K., E. H. Kennard, and T. Lauritsen, *Introduction to Modern Physics*, McGraw-Hill New York (1928, 1934, 1942, 1947, 1955).
Rosenfeld, L., *Theory of Electrons*, North Holland, Amsterdam (1951); reprinted by Dover, New York (1965).
Rusk, R. D., *Introduction to Atomic and Nuclear Physics*, Appleton-Century-Crofts, New York (1964).
Slater, J. C., *Introduction to Chemical Physics*, McGraw-Hill, New York (1939).
Slater, J. C., *Modern Physics*, McGraw-Hill, New York (1955).

6. WAVE MECHANICS

Bates, D. (ed.), *Quantum Theory*, Academic, New York (1962).
Bohm, D., *Quantum Theory*, Prentice-Hall, Englewood Cliffs, New Jersey (1952).
Condon, E. U., and P. M. Morse, *Quantum Mechanics*, McGraw-Hill, New York (1929).
Dicke, R. H., and J. P. Wittke, *Introduction to Quantum Mechanics*, Addison-Wesley, Reading, Mass. (1960).
Eyring, H., J. Walter, and G. E. Kimball, *Quantum Chemistry*, Wiley, New York (1944).
Frenkel, J., *Wave Mechanics, Elementary Theory*, Oxford University Press, London (1932); reprinted by Dover, New York (1950).
Frenkel, J., *Wave Mechanics, Advanced General Theory*, Oxford University Press, London (1934).

Heitler, W., *Elementary Wave Mechanics*, Oxford University Press, London (1945, 1956).
Houston, W. V., *Principles of Quantum Mechanics*, McGraw-Hill, New York (1951); reprinted by Dover, New York (1959).
Kauzmann, W., *Quantum Chemistry*, Academic, New York (1957).
Kemble, E. C., *Fundamental Principles of Quantum Mechanics*, McGraw-Hill, New York (1937); reprinted by Dover, New York (1958).
Kramers, H. A., *Quantum Mechanics*, North-Holland, Amsterdam (1957); reprinted by Dover, New York (1964).
Landau, L. D., and E. M. Lifshitz, *Quantum Mechanics*, Addison-Wesley, Reading, Mass. (1958, 1965).
Landé, A., *Quantum Mechanics*, Pitman, London (1951).
Mott, N. F., and H. S. W. Massey, *The Theory of Atomic Collisions*, Oxford University Press, London (1933, 1949, 1965).
Mott, N. F., and I. N. Sneddon, *Wave Mechanics and Its Applications*, Oxford University Press, London (1948); reprinted by Dover, New York (1963).
Pauling, L., and E. B. Wilson, Jr., *Introduction to Quantum Mechanics*, McGraw-Hill, New York (1935).
Persico, E., *Fundamentals of Quantum Mechanics*, translated by G. M. Temmer, Prentice-Hall, New York (1950).
Powell, J. L., and B. Crasemann, *Quantum Mechanics*, Addison-Wesley, Reading, Mass. (1961).
Rice, O. K., *Electronic Structure and Chemical Binding*, McGraw-Hill, New York (1940).
Rojansky, V., *Introductory Quantum Mechanics*, Prentice-Hall, Englewood Cliffs, New Jersey (1938).
Schiff, L. I., *Quantum Mechanics*, McGraw-Hill, New York (1944, 1955), 2nd ed.
Schrödinger, E., *Die Wellenmechanik*, Ernst Battenberg, Stuttgart (1963), vol. 3 of *Dokumente der Naturwissenschaft*, ed. by A. Hermann.
Slater, J. C., *Quantum Theory of Matter*, McGraw-Hill, New York (1951).
Slater, J. C., *Quantum Theory of Atomic Structure*, McGraw-Hill, New York (1960).
Slater, J. C., *Quantum Theory of Molecules and Solids*, McGraw-Hill, New York (1963).
Sommerfeld, A., *Wave Mechanics*, Methuen, London (1930).

7. QUANTUM THEORY

Beard, D. B., *Quantum Mechanics*, Allyn and Bacon, Boston (1966).
Bethe, H. A., *Intermediate Quantum Mechanics*, Benjamin, New York (1964).
Birtwistle, G., *The New Quantum Mechanics*, Cambridge University Press, London (1928).
Blokhintsev, D. I., *Quantum Mechanics*, D. Reidel, Dordrecht, Holland (1964).
Bohm, D., *Quantum Theory*, Prentice-Hall, Englewood Cliffs, New Jersey (1952).
Born, M., W. Heisenberg, and P. Jordan, *Zur Begrundung der Matrizen Mechanik*, Ernst Battenberg, Stuttgart (1962), vol. 2 of *Dokumente der Naturwissenschaft*, ed. by A. Hermann.
Born, M., and P. Jordan, *Elementare Quantenmechanik*, Springer, Berlin (1930).
Davydov, A. S., *Quantum Mechanics*, Pergamon, New York (1966).
Dirac, P. A. M., *The Principles of Quantum Mechanics*, Oxford University Press, New York (1930, 1935, 1947, 1957).
Feynman, R. P., *Lectures on Physics*, vol. 3, *Quantum Mechanics*, Addison-Wesley, Reading, Mass. (1965).

Feynman, R. P., and A. R. Hibbs, *Quantum Mechanics and Path Integrals*, McGraw-Hill, New York (1965).
Gottfried, K., *Quantum Mechanics*, Benjamin, New York (1966).
Heine, V., *Group Theory in Quantum Mechanics*, Pergamon, New York (1960).
Heisenberg, W., *The Physical Principles of the Quantum Theory*, University of Chicago Press, Chicago (1930).
Ikenberry, E., *Quantum Mechanics for Mathematicians and Physicists*, Oxford University Press, New York (1962).
Jackson, J. D., *Mathematics for Quantum Mechanics*, Benjamin, New York (1962).
Kaempffer, F. A., *Concepts in Quantum Mechanics*, Academic, New York (1965).
Kahan, T., *Theory of Groups in Classical and Quantum Physics*, American Elsevier, New York (1966).
Kramers, H. A., *Quantum Mechanics*, North-Holland, Amsterdam (1957); reprinted by Dover, New York (1964).
Kursunoglu, B., *Modern Quantum Theory*, Freeman, San Francisco (1962).
Mackey, G. W., *The Mathematical Foundations of Quantum Mechanics*, Benjamin, New York (1963).
Mandl, F., *Quantum Mechanics*, Academic, New York (1954, 1957).
March, A., *Quantum Mechanics of Particles and Wave Fields*, Wiley, New York (1951).
Merzbacher, E., *Quantum Mechanics*, Wiley, New York (1961).
Messiah, A., *Quantum Mechanics*, Wiley, New York (1962).
Pauli, W., Die Allgemeinen Prinzipien der Wellenmechanik, *Handbuch der Physik*, Vol. V, part 1, Springer, Berlin (1958).
Roman, P., *Advanced Quantum Theory*, Addison-Wesley, Reading, Mass. (1964).
Stehle, P., *Quantum Mechanics*, Holden-Day, San Francisco (1966).
Tomonaga, S. I., *Quantum Mechanics*, vol. 2, Wiley, New York (1966)
Tinkham, M., *Group Theory and Quantum Mechanics*, McGraw-Hill, New York (1964).
von Neumann, J., *Mathematical Foundations of Quantum Mechanics*, translated by R. T. Beyer, Princeton University Press, Princeton, New Jersey (1955).
Weyl, H., *The Theory of Groups and Quantum Mechanics*, translated by H. P. Robertson, Dover, New York (1950).

8. COEFFICIENTS OF FRACTIONAL PARENTAGE

Bacher, R. F., and S. Goudsmit, Atomic Energy Relations, I, *Phys. Rev.* **46,** 948 (1934).
Bayman, B. F., and A. Landé, Tables of Identical-Particle Fractional Parentage Coefficients, *Nucl. Phys.* **77,** 1 (1966).
Chlebowska, D., $\langle p^n p^{n-3} p^3 \rangle$ Fractional Parentage Coefficients, *Acta Physica Polonica* **25,** 513 (1965).
de Shalit, A., and I. Talmi, *Nuclear Shell Theory*, Academic, New York (1963).
Edmonds, A. R., and B. H. Flowers, Studies in *j-j* coupling, II, Fractional Parentage Coefficients and the Central Force Energy Matrix for Equivalent Electrons, *Proc. Roy. Soc.* (*Lond.*) **A214,** 515 (1952).
Edmonds, A. R., and B. H. Flowers, Studies in *j-j* Coupling, III, Nuclear Energy Levels, *Proc. Roy. Soc.* (Lond.) **A215,** 120 (1952).
Eisenstein, J. C., Eigenfunctions of the f^3 Configuration, *J. Res. N.B.S.* **67B,** 169 (1963).
Elliott, J. P., J. Hope, and H. A. Jahn, Theoretical Studies in Nuclear Structure, IV, Wave Function for the Nuclear *p*-shell: Part B, $\langle p^h | p^{h-2} p^2 \rangle$ Fractional Parentage Coefficients, *Phil. Trans. Roy. Soc.* **A246,** 241 (1953).

Elliott, J. P., and B. H. Flowers, The Structure of the Nuclei of Mass 18 and 19, *Proc. Roy. Soc.* (Lond.) **A229,** 536 (1955).

Flowers, B. H., Studies in *j-j* Coupling, I, Classification of Nuclear and Atomic States, *Proc. Roy. Soc.* (Lond.) **A.212,** 248 (1952).

Hassitt, A., Fractional Parentage Coefficients and Their Explicit Evaluation, *Proc. Roy. Soc.* (Lond.) **A.229,** 110 (1954).

Jahn, H. A., Theoretical Studies in Nuclear Structure, II, Nuclear d^2, d^3, and d^4 configurations. Fractional Parentage Coefficients and Central Force Matrix Elements, *Proc. Roy. Soc.* (Lond.) **A.205,** 192 (1951).

Jahn, H. A., and H. van Wieringen, Theoretical Studies in Nuclear Structure, IV, Wave Functions for the Nuclear *p*-Shell: Part A. $\langle p^n | p^{n-1}p \rangle$ Fractional Parentage Coefficients, *Proc. Roy. Soc.* (Lond.) **A.209,** 502 (1951).

Judd, B. R., The Matrix Elements of Tensor Operators for the Electronic Configurations f^N, *Proc. Phys. Soc.* **74,** 330 (1959).

Judd, B. R., The Matrix Elements of Tensor Operators for Configurations of Three Equivalent Electrons, *Proc. Roy. Soc.* (Lond.) A. **250,** 562 (1959).

Judd, B. R., *Operator Techniques in Atomic Spectroscopy*, McGraw-Hill, New York (1963).

Lane, A. M., and D. H. Wilkinson, Concept of Parentage of Nuclear States and Its Importance in Nuclear Reaction Phenomena, *Phys. Rev.* **97,** 1199 (1955).

Layzer, D., Proof of Moszkowski's Formula for the Variance of Term Energies in an Electronic Configuration of the Form l^n, *Phys. Rev.* **132,** 2152 (1963).

Menzel, D. H., and L. Goldberg, Multiplet Strengths for Transitions Involving Equivalent Electrons, *Astrophys. J.* **84,** 1 (1936).

Meshkov, S., Theory of Complex Spectra, *Phys. Rev.* **91,** 871 (1953).

Meshkov, S., and C. W. Ufford, A Complete Bacher and Goudsmit Method, *Phys. Rev.* **94,** 75 (1954).

Racah, G., Theory of Complex Spectra, III, *Phys. Rev.* **63,** 367 (1943).

Racah, G., Theory of Complex Spectra, IV, *Phys. Rev.* **76,** 1352 (1949).

Rajnak, K., and B. G. Wybourne, Configuration Interaction Effects in l^N Configurations, *Phys. Rev.* **132,** 280 (1963).

Redmond, P. J., An Explicit Formula for the Calculation of Fractional Parentage Coefficients, *Proc. Roy. Soc.* (Lond.) **A222,** 84 (1953).

Rohrlich, F., The Classification of the Odd Terms of *Ti I*, *Phys. Rev.* **74,** 1381 (1948).

Rohrlich, F., Theoretical Multiplet Strengths, *Astrophys. J.* **129,** 441 (1959).

Rosenzweig, N., The Configuration Interaction Between the Odd Terms in the Iron Group, *Phys. Rev.* **88,** 580 (1952).

Schwartz, C., and A. de Shalit, Many-Particle Configurations in a Central Field, *Phys. Rev.* **94,** 1257 (1954).

Trees, R. E., Bacher and Goudsmit Theory of Complex Spectra, *J. Res. N.B.S.* **53,** 35 (1954).

9. MULTIPOLE FIELDS

Abragam, A., and R. V. Pound, Influence of Static and Magnetic Fields on Angular Correlations, *Phys. Rev.* **92,** 943 (1953).

Akhiezer, A. I., and V. B. Berestetskii, *Quantum Electrodynamics*, Interscience, New York (1965), Chapter 1, Quantum Mechanics of the Photon.

Biedenharn, L. C., and M. E. Rose, Theory of Angular Correlation of Nuclear Reactions, *Rev. Mod. Phys.* **25,** 729 (1953).
Blatt, J., and V. F. Weiskopf, *Theoretical Nuclear Physics*, Wiley, New York (1952), Appendix B, Multipole Radiation.
Corben, H. C., and J. Schwinger, The Electromagnetic Properties of Mesotrons, *Phys. Rev.* **58,** 953 (1940).
Dancoff, S. M., and P. Morrison, The Calculation of Internal Conversion Coefficients, *Phys. Rev.* **55,** 122 (1939).
de Shalit, A., and I. Talmi, *Nuclear Shell Theory*, Academic, New York (1963), Chapter 16, Multipole Expansion of the Electromagnetic Field.
Debye, P., Der Lichtdruck auf Kugeln vol keliebigen Material, *Ann. Physik* **30,** 57 (1909).
Devons, S., and L. J. B. Goldfarb, Angular Correlations, in *Handbuch der Physik* **42,** 362 Springer, Berlin (1957).
Edmonds, A. R., *Angular Momentum in Quantum Mechanics*, Princeton University Press, Princeton, New Jersey (1957), Chapter 5, Spherical Tensors and Tensor Operations.
Fierz, M., Zur Theorie der Multipolstrahlung, *Helv. Phys. Acta* **22,** 489 (1949).
Fiutak, J., The Multipole Expansion in Quantum Theory, *Can. J. Phys.* **41,** 12 (1963).
Franz, W., Multipolstrahlung als Eigenwertproblem, *Zeits. fur Phys.* **127,** 363 (1950).
French, J. B., and Y. Shimamoto, Theory of Multipole Radiation, *Phys. Rev.* **91,** 898 (1953).
Goertzel, E., Angular Correlation of γ-Rays, *Phys. Rev.* **70,** 897 (1946).
Gottfried, K., Multipole Radiation, in *Preludes in Theoretical Physics*, A. de Shalit, H. Feshbach, and L. van Hove (eds.), North-Holland, Amsterdam (1966).
Hamilton, D. R., On Directional Correlation of Successive Quanta, *Phys. Rev.* **58,** 122 (1940).
Hansen, W. W., A New Type of Expansion in Radiation Problems, *Phys. Rev.* **47,** 139 (1935).
Heitler, W., On the Radiation Emitted by a Multipole and its Angular Momentum, *Proc. Camb. Phil. Soc.* **37,** 112 (1936).
Hill, E. L., The Theory of Vector Spherical Harmonics, *Am. J. Phys.* **22,** 211 (1954).
Jacob, M., and G. C. Wick, On the General Theory of Collisions for Particles with Spin, *Ann. Phys.* **7,** 404 (1959).
Jackson, J. D., *Classical Electrodynamics*, Wiley, New York (1962).
Kramers, H. A., On Multiple Radiation, *Physica* **10,** 261 (1943).
Laporte, O., Electromagnetic Waves in Spherical or Solid-Angular Regions, *Am. J. Phys.* **16,** 206 (1948).
Ling, D. S., and D. L. Falkoff, Interference Effects in Gamma-Gamma Angular Correlations, *Phys. Rev.* **76,** 1639 (1949).
Litherland, A. E., Radiative Transitions Following Nuclear Reactions, in *Nuclear Structure and Electromagnetic Interactions*, N. MacDonald (ed.), Plenum Press, New York (1965), p. 61.
Messiah, A., *Quantum Mechanics*, Wiley, New York (1963), Vol. II, Chapter 21.
Mie, G., Beiträge zur Optik trüber Medien, speziell kolloider Metallosungen, *Ann. Physik* **25,** 377 (1908).
Moszkowski, S. A., Theory of Multipole Radiation, in *Alpha-, Beta-, and Gamma-Ray Spectroscopy*, K. Siegbahn (ed.), North-Holland, Amsterdam (1965).
Racah, G., Directional Correlation of Successive Nuclear Radiations, *Phys. Rev.* **84,** 910 (1951).
Rose, M. E., *Multipole Fields*, Wiley, New York (1955).

Rose, M. E., *Elementary Theory of Angular Momentum*, Wiley, New York (1957), Chapter 7, The Electromagnetic Field.

Spiers, J. A., On the Directional Correlation of Successive Nuclear Reactions, *Phys. Rev.* **80**, 491 (1950).

Stratton, J. A., *Electromagnetic Theory*, McGraw-Hill, New York (1941), Chapter 7, Spherical Waves.

Wallace, P. R., Theory of Multipole Radiation, *Can. J. Phys.* **29**, 393 (1951).

Weisskopf, V. F., Radiative Transition Probabilities in Nuclei, *Phys. Rev.* **83**, 1073 (1951).

Author Index

Subject Index